NUCLEAR PHYSICS

NUCLEAR PHYSICS

Theory and Experiment

R. R. Roy

Professor of Physics
Arizona State University

B. P. Nigam

Professor of Physics
Arizona State University

JOHN WILEY & SONS, INC.   *New York   London   Sydney*

PREFACE

Our aim in writing this book has been to show the mathematical manipulations involved in various theories and the extent to which the theoretical results are substantiated by experiments. Necessarily, then, we have tried to give numerous algebraic details, which are not always easily available, before arriving at a final theoretical expression. Thus we hope that nuclear physics may be studied by the students in a quantitative way. We have kept the speculative discussions to a minimum.

The book is presented as a two-semester graduate-level course. Most of its contents can be understood by students who have had one year of quantum mechanics. Some chapters may also be useful to advanced undergraduate students. Certain parts can also serve as reference material.

The topics selected for discussion reflect our own bias on the subject. Certain standard mathematical expressions, with their derivations, appear in the Appendix.

We should like to express our sincere thanks to the many publishers, editors, and authors who have graciously given us permission to reproduce figures and tables. We are also grateful to the many graduate students for their ever-willing assistance in the preparation of the manuscript, in particular, Messrs. Amrita L. Bhattacharya, Nelson Eddy, Walter Niblack, LeRoy Bessler, and Keh-Lien Chiu.

We are grateful to Mrs. Kathryn Rogers and Mrs. Marcia Croye for their patience in typing the manuscript and Mrs. Eleanor Greene for handling the voluminous correspondence connected with the writing of the book. We also thank Mr. Walter Forbes for his very effective help in the different phases during the production of the manuscript. We are very much indebted to Professor Robert M. Eisberg of the University of California for reading the manuscript carefully and for making valuable suggestions for its improvement.

During the summer of 1965, R. R. Roy was visiting Professor at the University of Strasbourg (France), where he collected certain material for this book. He would like to thank Professor S. Gorodetzky for the hospitality extended during his stay at the University. B. P. Nigam would like to take this opportunity to acknowledge the academic year 1966 to

1967 spent as Professor of Physics at the University of Wisconsin, Milwaukee (on leave of absence from Arizona State University), where he completed a certain amount of the work for this book.

The various errors which may have crept into the text are our responsibility alone, and we express our gratitude to the reader for tolerating them.

R. R. Roy, B. P. Nigam

CONTENTS

Appendix   **541**

Mathematical Preliminaries   **541**

NUCLEAR PHYSICS

1

INTRODUCTION

The atomic nucleus was discovered in 1911 by Rutherford, who demonstrated that the large-angle alpha-particle scattering can be explained only in terms of a positively charged nucleus of radius $\sim 10^{-12}$ cm as compared to a radius $\sim 10^{-8}$ cm for the atom. In addition, the nucleus is massive and contains practically the whole of the mass of the atom.

Before Rutherford, however, there were many other outstanding developments. In 1896, Becquerel identified radioactivity, and the following year J. J. Thomson discovered the electron. A year later, Marie Curie isolated polonium and radium from the ores. The theory of radioactivity was systematized shortly after by the statistical decay law due to Rutherford, Soddy, and Von Schweidler. It was also found that the radiations emitted from radioactive substances could be classified as alpha-, beta-, and gamma-rays by observing the deflection of alpha- and beta-rays in a magnetic field.

Roentgen discovered x-rays in 1895, and Von Laue in 1912 observed their diffraction. From Moseley's study of x-ray spectra in 1913 emerged the concept of atomic number Z which became the basis for the classification of elements in the periodic table. Bohr, in the same year, explained the hydrogen spectrum by assuming a simple model of the atom which incorporated both the atomic number Z and the quantum of radiation first proposed by Planck in 1900. The discovery of the Rutherford-Bohr model of the atom was followed by the advent of quantum mechanics which explained in great detail various atomic phenomena. Quantum mechanics as a tool to understanding atomic phenomena was developed by numerous physicists, among whom are de Broglie, Schrödinger, Heisenberg, Pauli, and Dirac.

Rutherford, in 1919, was the first to demonstrate the phenomenon of nuclear reaction by the disintegration of nitrogen according to the reaction

1

$_7N^{14} + {}_2He^4 \rightarrow {}_8O^{17} + {}_1H^1$. The concept of the structure of the nucleus remained unexplained until 1932 when a neutral particle, the neutron, was discovered by Chadwick, following a series of experiments by Bothe, Joliot, and Chadwick. After this important discovery, it was proposed that the nucleus was composed of neutrons and protons which have almost the same mass. The mass number A of the nucleus is given by the sum of Z protons and $A-Z$ neutrons. This concept of the nucleus which arose in the 1930's is still valid today. Neutrons and protons, commonly referred to as nucleons, are spin-half particles, which obey Fermi-Dirac statistics.

The basic problem in nuclear physics is determining the nature of the force which holds the neutral particles, such as neutrons, and the charged particles, such as protons, together. The force, of course, cannot be electrical in origin since a neutron carries no charge. The interpretation of the scattering experiments indicated that this force must be of short range extending to a distance less than 10^{-11} cm. Yukawa, in 1935, introduced the concept of mesonic force in nuclear interaction. In 1936, Anderson and Neddermeyer discovered μ-meson which was followed by the discovery by Powell in 1946 of still another heavier meson, π-meson. Since then numerous new particles have been discovered. The situation may seem somewhat confusing. However, although the exact nature of the nucleus is still a mystery, much progress has been made towards its understanding.

We shall briefly summarize the various topics presented in this book. We have limited ourselves for the most part to the discussion of low energy phenomena; in Chapter 4, however, we have reviewed the nucleon-nucleon interaction phenomenologically over an energy range extending to about 300 Mev.

Extensive mathematical development is required in understanding and interpreting the problems in nuclear physics. In fact, mathematics has become an integral part of the subject. To emphasize this point, we have included in the Appendix the mathematical formalisms that are essential for developing the various topics throughout the book.

Chapter 2 deals with the nuclear radius and nuclear shapes. Various methods for determining the nuclear radius are examined with special emphasis on the more accurate and recent methods, such as electron scattering. We note particularly that the values obtained in the determination of the nuclear radius are dependent upon the method used. If the nuclear radius found by the alpha scattering method does not agree with that found by the electron scattering, it is because alpha scattering determines the interaction radius, whereas electron scattering gives the density of charge distribution of the nucleus. The structure of a nucleus is explained by the interaction of the nuclear electric charge and magnetic moment distributions with either the external or internal (atomic electrons) electromagnetic field. The electric quadrupole moment measures the deviation of charge distribution from a spherical shape. On the other hand, the magnetic moment of a nucleus interacts with the magnetic field in which the nucleus is located. General expressions for electric and magnetic multipoles are given.

Nuclear forces are complex and thus difficult to understand. Of course, the two-nucleon interaction is comparatively simpler and easier to understand than many-nucleon forces. Chapter 3 covers the two-nucleon interaction in considerable detail by treating its different aspects.

The nuclear mass and the nuclear fission are described by semi-empirical formulas (Chapter 5) which are, in part, related to the liquid drop model of the nucleus. Although many-nucleon forces are not understood completely, the semi-empirical approach in solving these problems helps a great deal in understanding the nuclear mass and the mechanism of nuclear fission.

Nuclear reactions have been studied extensively, both experimentally as well as theoretically. Experimentally, data can be collected with great accuracy by using precise techniques. These data are often analysed in terms of theoretical models such as the compound nucleus, statistical model (Chapter 6), optical model (Chapter 10), direct reaction mechanism (Chapter 11), etc. Such analyses are helpful in understanding the mechanism of nuclear reactions. Theoretical calculations underlying each of these models together with the experimental results are presented.

Considerable progress in the study of nuclear structure has been made by the development of the nuclear shell-model. This model, although basically simple, has led to the explanation of many nuclear properties such as spin, magnetic moment, and nuclear spectra. This model is discussed in Chapter 7.

There are many properties of nuclei, such as large electric quadrupole moments, deviations from the spherical shape, and rotational and vibrational spectra, which cannot be understood in terms of the nuclear shell-model. These properties are a consequence of the collective motion of many nucleons. In Chapter 8 we explore the collective model and its several variations.

The theory of the nuclear many-body problem, basing it on the two-body interaction, is given in Chapter 9. By thus reducing the complex problem into a more workable form, theories make an attempt to describe the properties of nuclear matter.

The study of electromagnetic interaction with nuclei provides much information concerning the nuclear properties. The processes which can be treated are emission of γ-rays, conversion electrons from excited nuclei, γ-γ angular correlations, emission of nucleons with the absorption of photon, and others. Chapter 12 gives a comprehensive discussion of these processes. Experimental data have also been compared with the predictions made by the theory.

Until 1956, Fermi's theory was adequate to explain various aspects of the beta decay process. However, in 1956 its concept was revised to a great extent when Lee and Yang discovered that in weak interaction processes parity is not conserved. Even after this discovery, however, Fermi's theory was not found to be redundant. Chapter 13 describes the beta-decay process, emphasizing this modified theory.

2

NUCLEAR SIZE AND
NUCLEAR SHAPES

The structure of matter has always been an intriguing subject for investigation, but not until Rutherford made his analysis of Geiger and Marsden's experiment was there any real basis for a model of atomic structure. From the fact that charged incident alpha particles follow the Coulomb scattering law of point charges for the energies used, Rutherford deduced that the bulk of the atomic mass and all its positive charge resided in a very small central core of the atom—within a radius of the order of 10^{-12} cm. Since then, various methods have been developed for exploring the nuclear structure and radius.

The most extensive work has been done with probe particles incident on nuclei. If the scattered particle does not enter the nucleus and interacts only via the electromagnetic forces, the scattering is called Coulomb or Rutherford scattering, and the interaction is accounted for by assuming a point-charge Coulomb potential. If the incident particle penetrates into the nuclear charge distribution, the point charge interaction potential no longer holds. Furthermore, if the scattered particle interacts via nuclear forces as well, then the process is further complicated since this interaction is not as well known as the electromagnetic forces. Other methods used to measure the nuclear size are concerned with such factors as the binding energies of mirror nuclei, mesonic atoms, and alpha-decay of nuclei.

In trying to assign a size to the nuclear quantum system, it is necessary to understand exactly what physical quantity is being measured. Indeed, it is not possible to describe the atomic electron cloud with a well-defined radius. However, even if a nuclear radius can be defined, it is not to be expected that this parameter will have the same value regardless of the method used for its determination. For example, high-energy electron scattering determines the density of charge distribution within the nucleus, whereas scattering experiments, such as alpha-particle scattering, determine the interaction radius. In the latter case, the nuclear radius obtained is larger than that of the former.

2.1 Scattering Methods

The determination of the nuclear radius R can be made from the measurement of the elastic differential cross section $d\sigma(\theta)/d\Omega$. In recent years, because of the availability of nearly monoenergetic beams of various particles from accelerators, numerous scattering experiments have been performed. Various kinds of nuclear potential models have been assumed to interpret the data: those with a sharp cutoff of the nuclear potentials and those that introduce a "diffuseness parameter" in the nuclear potential. The most familiar example of the latter is the optical model. The nuclear radius R estimated from these models is not without ambiguity, for R appears in the expression for the potential along with other parameters which are adjustable.

Consider the differential scattering cross section for elastically scattered particles for all values of angular momentum l, given by

$$\frac{d\sigma_{el}}{d\Omega} = |f(\theta)|^2 \tag{1}$$

where the scattering amplitude $f(\theta)$ is given by

$$f(\theta) = \frac{1}{2ik} \sum_{l=0}^{\infty} (\eta_l - 1)(2l + 1)P_l(\cos\theta) \tag{2}$$

and the wave number $k = 1/\lambda$ of the incident alpha particle is in the center-of-mass system. η_l is the coefficient of the lth outgoing spherical partial wave when the coefficient of the incoming spherical wave is taken to be unity. Using classical notions, we define η_l such that for angular momenta larger than l_M the amplitude is set equal to the amplitude that will be obtained for pure Coulomb scattering, whereas for l less than or equal to l_M there is no outgoing wave. Therefore, for $l \leq l_M$ the amplitude of the outgoing wave vanishes and the target nucleus behaves as a perfect absorber; thus l_M is used as a free parameter in fitting the data. We therefore write

$$\eta_l = \begin{cases} 0 & l < l_M \\ \eta_l^{(\text{Coulomb})} = \eta_l^c & l > l_M \end{cases} \tag{3}$$

In analogy with the classical impact parameter and angular momentum, the value of the angular momentum l_M (in units of $\hbar$) can be shown to be given by[1]

$$l_M = kR\left[1 - \frac{V(R)}{E}\right]^{1/2} \tag{4}$$

where E is the energy of the incident particle and $V(R)$ its potential. Using the cutoff condition in Eq. (3), we can write Eq. (2) in the form

$$f(\theta) = \frac{n}{2ik} \frac{1}{\sin^2 (\theta/2)} \exp \left[-in \ln \sin^2 \frac{\theta}{2} + 2i\sigma_o \right]$$
$$- \frac{1}{2k} \sum_{l=0}^{l_M} (2l + 1) \exp (2i\sigma_l) P_l(\cos \theta) \quad (5)$$

where

$$n = \frac{ZZ'e^2}{\hbar v}$$

v is the velocity of the incident particles, and $\exp (2i\sigma_l) = \eta_l^c$ with $\sigma_l = $ arg $\Gamma(l + 1 + in)$; this model of the nucleus is known as the Akhieser-Pomeranchuk[2]-Blair[3] (APB) model. Eisberg and Porter,[1] using the expressions (2) and (3), have analyzed the results[4] of elastically scattered alpha particles from Ag, Ta, Au, Pb, and Th targets between the energies of 13 and 42 Mev. The scattered alpha particles were detected at 60°. The theoretical and experimental results are compared for Au, Pb, and Th in Fig. 2-1.

The value of the differential cross section has been evaluated by numerical methods from Eqs. (2) and (5) and is expressed as $(d\sigma_{el}/d\Omega)$ (Z, E, l_M, θ). The values of Z and θ are fixed by the conditions of the experiment and l_M is found by trial and error to obtain the best fit to the measured energy dependence curves. The values of the nuclear radius R (or more precisely, the interaction radius), which are computed from Eq. (4), are found to vary from 10.58 F (1 Fermi $= 1$ F $= 10^{-13}$ cm) for Au to 11.01 F for Th. It should be emphasized that the values of R obtained are not unique; they only represent the best fit with experimental results.

Kerlee, Blair, and Farwell[5] have studied the elastic scattering of alpha particles between the energies of 12 and 44 Mev in 28 nuclides from Ni to Pu. They analyzed their results using the sharp cutoff model of Blair.[3] They observed that the interaction radius is given by $R_{A_\alpha} = r_0 A^{1/3} + b$ where the nuclear radius parameter $r_0 = (1.414 \pm 0.042)$ F and the alpha-particle radius $b = (2.19 \pm 0.20)$ F. A graph showing the interaction radius as a function of the cube root of the mass number is obtained from the experimental results shown in Fig. 2-2.

In contrast to the sharp cutoff model, the optical model (with its diffuseness parameter in the potential) can be used to analyze the data from elastic alpha-particle scattering. There are many kinds of optical model potentials, which will be discussed in detail in Chapter 10. The

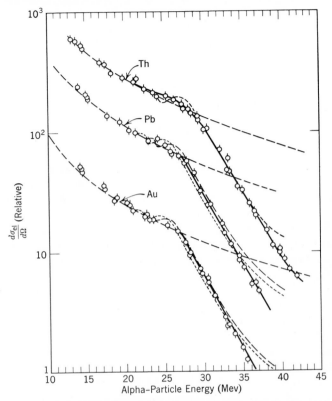

Fig. 2-1 The broad dashed curve gives the Coulomb cross section, and the solid curve represents the experimental data of Farwell and Wegner[4] for Au, Pb, and Th. For Au, the finer theoretical curve corresponds to $R = 10.58 \times 10^{-13}$ cm and the coarser curve to $R = 10.3 \times 10^{-13}$ cm. For Pb, the finer curve corresponds to $R = 10.87 \times 10^{-13}$ cm and the coarser to $R = 10.42 \times 10^{-13}$ cm. For Th, the dashed curve corresponds to $R = 11.01 \times 10^{-13}$ cm (Eisberg and Porter[1]).

optical model potential given by Woods and Saxon[6] is

$$\frac{V + iW}{1 + \exp\left(\dfrac{r - R}{d}\right)} \tag{6}$$

This potential has a real and imaginary part (V and W, respectively). The parameter d is the diffuseness parameter, and R is defined as the radius where the nuclear potential has decreased to half its maximum value. Because the alpha particles (or other projectiles) are both absorbed and scattered, the optical model potential describes these processes and is thus similar to the absorption and reflection of light by a medium with a complex index of refraction. The parameters involved in optical model potentials are not unique. Good fit to a given experimental curve can be

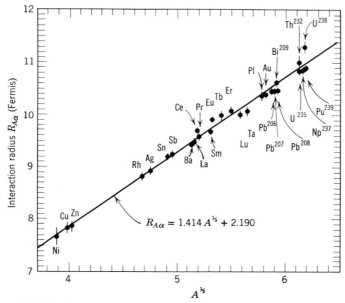

Fig. 2-2 Sharp cutoff radii from elastic scattering of alpha particles. The radii are plotted against the cube root of the mass number. The straight line represents a least-squares best fit (Kerlee et al.[5]).

obtained with different sets of values of V and R. If the potential depth V is increased, it can be compensated for by decreasing the value of R, and good fit is maintained.

The differential scattering cross section can be obtained by solving the radial Schrödinger equation assuming the potential of Eq. (6). Igo and Thaler[7] have analyzed their experimental results of alpha-particle scattering at 40 Mev by various elements and found that the angular dependence of the differential cross section can best be explained by taking $R = (1.35A^{1/3} + 1.3)$ F.

The elastic scattering of protons by nuclei has also been extensively studied both at low and very high energies (Bev). Various forms of the optical model potentials have been used for analyzing experimental data.

The analysis of the results is phenomenological in that the parameters involved in the potentials were varied to obtain a good fit with the experimental results. From studying many experimental results, using the optical model potential, Glassgold[8] suggested a "proton-nuclear" radius $R = (1.25 \pm 0.05)A^{\frac{1}{3}}$ F with a diffuseness parameter $d = (0.65 \pm 0.05)$ F.

At very high proton energy ($E_P \gg V$, the nuclear potential) the interaction is between the incident proton and the individual free nucleons in the target nucleus. At these energies, scattering experiments yield information on the density and distribution of nucleons in the nucleus. The corresponding parameters are about 15% smaller than those previously given.[8] Identical values of $R = (1.25 \pm 0.05)A^{\frac{1}{3}}$ F and $d = 0.65$ F have been suggested by neutron-nuclear scattering data[9] assuming an optical model potential. Spin-orbit coupling terms[8,9] are often added to the optical potentials to obtain a better fit with the results. Their importance diminishes with the increasing energy of incident nucleons since they only describe a surface effect.

In completing this discussion, mention should be made of another method of determining the nuclear radius, the alpha decay method. In the alpha scattering experiments, deviation from the Coulomb scattering law, $ZZ'e^2/r$, occurs when the incident particles begin to feel the nuclear potential. Similarly, in alpha-decay the particle attempting to escape from the nucleus feels a Coulomb barrier—this time from the inside. Because of this barrier, the alpha particle is repeatedly reflected back and forth within the nucleus. According to quantum mechanics, there is a certain probability P, known as the penetration factor, that the alpha particle will "tunnel out" and be emitted from the nucleus. The decay constant λ is simply

$$\lambda = fP \tag{7}$$

where f is the frequency of collision of the alpha particle with the barrier. In order to evaluate f, a specific model is assumed. The value of f has been taken to be 2×10^{21} sec^{-1} by Biswas et al.[11] and 10^{15} sec^{-1} by Bethe.[12] According to the WKB approximation the value of the penetration factor is given by

$$P \simeq \exp\left[-\frac{2}{\hbar}\int_R^{zZe^2/E}\sqrt{2M\left(\frac{zZe^2}{r} - E\right)}\,dr\right] \tag{8}$$

where Z is the charge of the daughter nucleus and z is that of the alpha particle, M is the reduced mass of the system, and E is the energy of the alpha-particle. This value of P can be calculated analytically. The values of R obtained are model dependent; according to the sharp cutoff Coulomb barrier penetration theory, $R = 9.1$ F for the one-body model,[11] and

$R = 12.6$ F for the many-body model.[12] These values compare favorably with those obtained from alpha-scattering experiments.

2.2   Electromagnetic Methods

It has been mentioned that electromagnetic interactions are well known. The simplest type of scattering experiment that can be performed is the Rutherford scattering. In this case, the potential is simply the Coulomb potential, $ZZ'e^2/r$.

Other electromagnetic methods are (1) mirror nuclei, (2) mesonic atoms, and (3) electron scattering. These will now be considered in-dividually.

Nuclear Radii from Mirror Nuclei

The repulsive electrostatic force experienced by positively charged particles like alpha particles and protons, incident on a nucleus, is due to the protons in the nucleus. These protons are responsible for the nuclear Coulomb energy E_c. In 1938, Bethe[13] suggested that the difference of Coulomb energies between two neighboring mirror nuclei (such as $_6C^{11}$ and $_5B^{11}$ in which the proton (neutron) number of one is the neutron (proton) number of the other) could be used to calculate nuclear radii. A quantum mechanical treatment of Coulomb energies, however, involves lengthy calculations and depends upon the nature of the potential. The estimated nuclear radius resulting from such calculations is a few percent[14] smaller than that obtained from classical considerations.

According to the classical method, a nucleus is considered to be ana-logous to a uniformly charged sphere of radius R having charge density

$$\rho = \frac{Ze}{\frac{4}{3}\pi R^3} \tag{9a}$$

The potential due to such a sphere at the surface $r = R$ is

$$V(R) = \tfrac{4}{3}\pi\rho R^2 \tag{9b}$$

The electric field intensity is (for $r < R$)

$$E(r) = -\frac{\partial V}{\partial r} = \frac{1}{r^2}\int_0^r 4\pi r^2 \rho \, dr$$

$$= \tfrac{4}{3}\pi\rho r \tag{9c}$$

Integrating from r to R, we find

$$V(r) - V(R) = \tfrac{2}{3}\pi\rho(R^2 - r^2) \tag{9d}$$

Using $V(R)$ from Eq. (9b) and ρ from Eq. (9a), we obtain

$$V(r) = \frac{Ze}{2R^3}(3R^2 - r^2) \tag{9e}$$

The potential energy of this charge distribution is the Coulomb energy

$$E_c = \frac{1}{2}\int_0^R \rho V(r)4\pi r^2\, dr = \frac{3}{5}\frac{(Ze)^2}{R} \tag{9f}$$

where the factor $\frac{1}{2}$ occurs because the elemental charges must not be counted twice when summed to give the total energy E_c. The difference in Coulomb energies, ΔE_c, between two neighboring mirror nuclei of charges Ze and $(Z + 1)e$ having the same radius R is

$$\Delta E_c = \frac{3}{5R}[(Z + 1)^2 - Z^2]e^2 = \frac{3(2Z + 1)e^2}{5R} \tag{10}$$

We can determine ΔE_c for such mirror nuclei as $(_3\text{Li}^7, {}_4\text{Be}^7)$, $(_5\text{B}^{11}, {}_6\text{C}^{11})$, $(_7\text{N}^{15}, {}_8\text{O}^{15})$, $(_8\text{O}^{17}, {}_9\text{F}^{17})$, and $(_9\text{F}^{19}, {}_{10}\text{Ne}^{19})$. Consider the following energy level diagram for the mirror pair $(_{14}\text{Si}^{29}, {}_{15}\text{P}^{29})$. Except for the fact that there is an upward shift of the $_{15}\text{P}^{29}$ levels with respect to the $_{14}\text{Si}^{29}$ due to the Coulomb energy difference, the level schemes are almost identical when the last neutron in silicon is replaced by a proton to give phosphorous. Assuming the same radius R for both nuclei, and using the experimental value $\Delta E_c = 4.96$ Mev (see Fig. 2-3), Eq. (10) gives $R = 4.94$ F. From $R = r_0 A^{1/3}$, we obtain for the radial parameter $r_0 \simeq 1.5$ F.

A simple consideration such as this obviously yields only a very approximate value for the nuclear radius. Correction terms involving details of nuclear structure reduce the value of R, which should be taken into account. The advantage of this simple model is that there is only one parameter R involved in the expression for ΔE_c. However, the expression for ΔE_c is model dependent and will be very different for a charge distribution that is not uniform. By introducing corrections to this model, Kofoed-Hansen[15] estimated the nuclear radius parameter from mirror nuclei Coulomb energies to be $r_0 = 1.28 \pm 0.05$ F.

A study of the mass difference between the mirror pair H^3 and He^3 can provide information concerning the nature of nuclear forces within these nuclei. As we will explain in more detail in Chapter 3, there is evidence that the nuclear attraction between the pairs (n, p), (n, n), and (p, p) is the same. If this is so, the difference of 764 Kev in the binding energies of H^3 and He^3 must be due to the extra Coulomb energy of the He^3 system resulting from the p-p interaction. If the wave function and at least the nature of the potential are known, the Coulomb energy and radius of the He^3 nucleus can be calculated. This calculation has been done by Pappademos,[16] who assumed the wave function ψ of the following asymptotic form:

$$\psi \simeq F(r) \frac{e^{-2\alpha R}}{R} \tag{11a}$$

where the function $F(r)$ is of the form (r is the separation between the nucleons)

$$F(r) = \frac{1}{\sqrt{r}} [e^{-\alpha(r-d)} - e^{-\beta(r-d)}] \tag{11b}$$

The coefficient α can be expressed in terms of the proton binding energy B_p,

$$\alpha = \tfrac{1}{2}\sqrt{2M_{\mathrm{red}}B_p} \tag{11c}$$

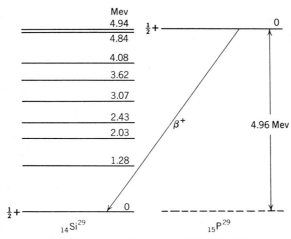

Fig. 2-3   Level schemes of $_{14}\mathrm{Si}^{29}$ and $_{15}\mathrm{P}^{29}$.

The form of the potential between the neutron and proton was taken to be a Yukawa type with a hard core, with d its radius. The parameter β has been estimated by using the form $F(r)$ as a variational trial function for the deuteron problem. The mean square radius for matter distribution in He^3 is given by

$$\langle R^2 \rangle = \tfrac{1}{3}(\psi, r_{12}^2 \psi) \tag{11d}$$

where ψ is symmetric. Carrying out the integration in Eq. (11d) the rms radius is calculated as a function of the hard core radius d. The calculated values of $\langle R^2 \rangle^{1/2}$ for values of d between 0.50 and 0.60 F lie between 1.62 and 1.67 F in agreement with the experimental value[17] 1.65 ± 0.23 F.

Mu-Mesonic Atoms

The μ-meson has a mass value $m_\mu = 207\, m_e$, spin $\tfrac{1}{2}$ and gyromagnetic ratio $g = 2 \times 1.0026$, where m_e is the mass of the electron. The μ-meson behaves like a heavy electron because the main interaction with the nucleus is by means of the electrostatic force; the nonelectromagnetic interaction, if it exists, is very weak. Thus a μ-meson can be captured into the Bohr orbit of a nucleus just as an electron. Because of the large mass of the μ-meson, the radii of the Bohr orbits are m_e/m_μ times smaller than for the electron, and the μ-meson in its lowest atomic state spends a large fraction of its time inside the nucleus (about 50% in the case of lead; the radius of the orbit $n = 1$ is 3.1×10^{-13} cm and that of $n = 2$ is 12×10^{-13} cm). It should therefore be possible to use μ-mesonic atoms to determine the nuclear size.

The first experiment which provided information regarding nuclear sizes using the μ-meson as a probe was performed by Fitch and Rainwater.[18] The μ-mesons were produced from a beam of π-mesons. In passing through the target the μ-mesons are slowed down by loss of kinetic energy to the electrons. At sufficiently small kinetic energy the μ-meson is captured into a Bohr orbit corresponding to a large angular momentum state. From high orbits it cascades to lower orbits first by means of nonradiative transitions (that is, by collisions and by Auger electron emission) and then by radiative transitions, with the emission of gamma rays in the $2p - 1s$ transition. The $2p$ state is generally reached in about 10^{-13} to 10^{-14} sec after capture; the $2p - 1s$ transition has a lifetime of about 10^{-18} sec, and the nuclear capture of the μ-meson occurs with a lifetime of about 10^{-8} sec and greater.

Since the energy of $1s$ state depends sensitively on the nuclear-charge distribution, the $2p - 1s$ transition will enable us to determine the radial parameter corresponding to a given form of charge distribution $\rho(r)$. For light nuclei, the energy-level shift, due to the finite size of the nuclear charge distribution, of a transition is negligible (about 2% for aluminum), since the Bohr radii are inversely proportional to Z, and the nuclear radius is proportional to $A^{1/3}$.

The energy of bound states of a μ^--meson in a nucleus of charge Ze is given by the Dirac theory, treating the meson as a heavy electron. For a point nucleus the binding energy is given by

$$E = \tfrac{1}{2}m_\mu c^2 \left(\frac{Z\alpha}{n}\right)^2 \left[1 + \left(\frac{Z\alpha}{n}\right)^2 \left(\frac{n}{|k|} - \frac{3}{4}\right)\right] \tag{12a}$$

where $|k| = l + 1$ for $j = l + \tfrac{1}{2}$, and $|k| = l$ for $j = l - \tfrac{1}{2}$ and the fine-structure constant $\alpha = e^2/\hbar c$. The change in the Coulomb interaction energy due to the finite nuclear size is, in the first-order perturbation calculation, given by[19]

$$\Delta E_c = \int_0^\infty d^3r\,|\psi|^2 \left(V(r) - \frac{Ze^2}{r}\right) \tag{12b}$$

where $V(r)$ and Ze^2/r are the potentials due to the finite nucleus and the point nucleus, respectively. By assuming a charge distribution $\rho(r)$, such that

$$\int_0^\infty \rho(r)4\pi r^2\,dr = Ze$$

and noting that the radial wave function at small r is

$$\psi = C(Z, n, l)r^{l+1} \tag{12c}$$

where

$$C^2(Z, n, l) = \left[\frac{2Z\mu}{(l+1)a_0 m_\mu}\right]^{2l+3} \frac{1}{(2l+2)!} \tag{12d}$$

and a_0 is the Bohr radius for mesonic hydrogen, from these equations we obtain

$$\Delta E_c = \frac{C^2(Z, n, l)}{(2l+2)(2l+3)} \int_0^\infty \rho(r)r^{2(l+1)}r^2\,dr \tag{13}$$

The foregoing approximation is poor for high Z and $l = 0$ or $l = 1$; a more exact solution of the Dirac equation has been made by Fitch and Rainwater,[18] Ford and Hill,[20] and Cooper and Henley.[21] Corrections due to vacuum polarization have been taken into account by Foldy and Eriksen[22] and by Mickelwait and Corben.[23] An important result from the study of μ-mesonic x-rays was the determination of the smaller effective nuclear radii which has been confirmed by the electron scattering experiments. The value of the nuclear radius parameter as given by μ-mesonic studies is $r_0 \simeq 1.17 \times 10^{-13}$ cm, with the nuclear radius $R = r_0 A^{1/3}$.

The following are results of some very precise measurements of μ-mesonic x-rays from the transition $2p - 1s$. Anderson, Johnson, and Hincks[24] have investigated the nuclear radius for 14 elements from $Z = 12$ to 50 by measuring the μ-mesonic x-rays from $2p - 1s$ transition using a NaI scintillation crystal spectrometer. The results have been expressed in terms of $r_0 = R_{\text{eq}}/A^{1/3}$, where $R_{\text{eq}} = (\frac{5}{3}\langle r^2 \rangle)^{1/2}$ refers to a

Table 2-1 Summary of Results Obtained for r_0 in Various Elements from the Analysis of K_α Lines (Anderson et al.[24])

Element	Mean Energy (Kev)	Mean Width σ(Kev)	$R_{\text{eq}}/A^{1/3}$ (10^{-13} cm)
Mg	295.6 ± 1.6	17.7 ± 1.2	1.45 ± 0.18
Al	346.1 ± 1.4	22.7 ± 1.2	1.37 ± 0.08
	344.5 ± 2.4	18.1 ± 2.4	1.47 ± 0.09
Si	400.4 ± 1.3	22.0 ± 1.8	1.32 ± 0.09
P	458.5 ± 1.3	23.0 ± 1.2	1.25 ± 0.07
S	522.0 ± 1.2	22.7 ± 1.2	1.16 ± 0.04
Cl	582.8 ± 1.3	25.9 ± 1.2	1.24 ± 0.04
Ca	790.8 ± 1.6	32.9 ± 1.4	1.23 ± 0.03
Fe	1261.4 ± 3.3	42.8 ± 2.2	1.25 ± 0.02
	1262.8 ± 3.9	47.7 ± 2.9	1.24 ± 0.02
Ni	1441.6 ± 6.1	51.0 ± 3.9	1.22 ± 0.02
Zn	1614.6 ± 6.2	47.8 ± 4.4	1.23 ± 0.02
As	1874.4 ± 8.2	50.6 ± 4.6	1.24 ± 0.02
Zr	2534.0 ± 5.1	71.9 ± 5.1	1.23 ± 0.01
Mo	2718.5 ± 4.6	66.3 ± 4.8	1.24 ± 0.01
Sn	3446.4 ± 6.4	79.1 ± 6.5	1.24 ± 0.01

uniformly charged sphere of a mean square radius $\langle r^2 \rangle$. The results of the photopeak measurements of K_α lines together with the calculated value of $r_0 = R_{\text{eq}}/A^{1/3}$ for the elements studied are given in Table 2-1.

Recently, another detailed study[25] has been made of the energies of the μ-mesonic x-rays of $2p - 1s$ transitions for 19 elements. A 145 Mev/c muon beam from synchrocyclotron was stopped in the target element; the resulting emitted x-rays from the target were measured by NaI(Tl) scintillation counter. The $2p - 1s$ transition energies have been used to obtain the equivalent nuclear charge radius $R_{\text{eq}} = \sqrt{\frac{5}{3}\langle r^2 \rangle}$. Table 2-2 gives the results of $r_0 = R_{\text{eq}}/A^{1/3}$ for the various elements studied.

The determination of the nuclear radius parameter r_0 is dependent upon the choice of charge distribution which gives the value of the equivalent nuclear charge radius R_{eq}. The value of r_0 obtained from these

Table 2-2 Equivalent Radii of Elements between Rh and Bi. The R_{eq} values are based on the transition energies calculated by Ford and Wills for a "Family II" charge distribution.[26] In column 2 are shown the corrections necessary to apply to the values of Ford and Wills in order to obtain the values of column 3 which agree with the data. For Pb and Bi, some additional calculations of the $2p_{3/2} - 1s_{1/2}$ energies were made. They fall along a straight line within about ± 6 Kev when plotted versus R_{eq}. The errors quoted in the table contain the experimental errors and this contribution. No correction for nuclear polarization is included (Backenstoss et al.[25]).

Element	$\delta R_{eq}/A^{1/3}$ (10^{-16} cm)	$R_{eq}/A^{1/3}$ (F)	Element	$\delta R_{eq}/A^{1/3}$ (10^{-16} cm)	$R_{eq}/A^{1/3}$ (F)
$_{45}$Rh	$+1.9$ ± 12.4	1.242 ± 12	$_{53}$I	$+3.5$ ± 9.9	1.220 ± 10
$_{46}$Pd	$+9.2$ ± 8.8	1.236 ± 9	$_{55}$Cs	$+3.9$ ± 8.4	1.216 ± 8
$_{47}$Ag	$+13.9$ ± 10.8	1.237 ± 11	$_{56}$Ba	-3.7 ± 16	1.206 ± 16
$_{48}$Cd	$+17.0$ ± 10.2	1.232 ± 10	$_{57}$La	-2.2 ± 7.8	1.211 ± 8
$_{49}$In	$+8.6$ ± 9.0	1.226 ± 9	$_{58}$Ce	$+0.6$ ± 12.5	1.217 ± 12
$_{50}$Sn	$+1.3$ ± 10.7	1.220 ± 11	$_{59}$Pr	-1.9 ± 17	1.216 ± 17
$_{51}$Sb	-11.8 ± 10.2	1.215 ± 10	$_{82}$Pb	$+8.6$ ± 7	1.195 ± 7
$_{52}$Te	-12.2 ± 11.1	1.211 ± 11	$_{83}$Bi	-20.6 ± 9	1.200 ± 9

experiments is closer to that estimated from the electron-scattering experiment.

Electron Scattering

In recent years the scattering of electrons from the nucleon and from nuclei at high energies has provided important information about the size of the nucleus. The electron energies are in the region of 100 Mev and higher, so that the de Broglie wavelength associated with the electron is of the order of a few Fermis, which is comparable to the range of the nuclear forces. At these energies the electron acts as a probe for measuring the size of the nucleus which, if not a point, is expected to be of dimensions of the order of a few Fermis. Experiments show that at large angles and high energies, deviations among the observed scattering and those given by theory based on a point nucleus exceed a factor of ten. Since electron scattering occurs through electromagnetic interaction, these experiments determine the so-called electromagnetic structure of the proton, neutron, and nuclei. Because of the present importance of this subject, we shall discuss it in some detail.

Basic Theory

We shall consider, following closely the article by Hofstadter,[27] the scattering of the electron in the first Born approximation, assuming that both the electron and the nucleus (and also the nucleons in the nucleus) are without spin. The target nucleus, containing Z point-protons with coordinates $\mathbf{R}_k(k = 1, 2, \ldots, Z)$, will be described by the wave function $\Phi_i(i = 0, 1, 2, \ldots)$ in the state i; Φ_0 is the wave function in the ground state. The transition probability per unit time for an incident electron of momentum $\mathbf{p}_0$, energy E_0, scattered by the nucleus at rest into a final state $\mathbf{p}$ and E, is given in the time-dependent perturbation theory by

$$w = \frac{2\pi}{\hbar} \rho_f |H'_{fi}|^2 \tag{14a}$$

where H'_{fi} is the matrix element of the Coulomb interaction causing the transition between the initial state i and the final state f, and ρ_f is the density of the final energy states in the continuum. The Coulomb interaction energy is

$$H' = eV = e^2 \sum_{k=1}^{Z} \frac{1}{|\mathbf{r} - \mathbf{R}_k|} \tag{14b}$$

where $\mathbf{r}$ is the position vector of the electron. The matrix element H'_{fi} is therefore given by

$$H'_{fi} = \int \Phi_f^*(\mathbf{R}_k)\psi_f^*(\mathbf{r}) \sum_{k=1}^{Z} \frac{e^2}{|\mathbf{r} - \mathbf{R}_k|} \Phi_0(\mathbf{R}_k)\psi_i(\mathbf{r}) \, d^3r \, d^3R_k \tag{15a}$$

where

$$\psi(\mathbf{r}) = \frac{1}{L^{3/2}} \exp\left(\frac{i\mathbf{p} \cdot \mathbf{r}}{h}\right) \tag{15b}$$

is the plane wave representation of the electron wave function, normalized within a large cubic box of side L. Substituting Eq. (15b) in Eq. (15a), we obtain

$$H'_{fi} = \frac{e^2}{L^3} \int \Phi_f^* \Phi_0 \sum_{k=1}^{Z} \frac{1}{|\mathbf{r} - \mathbf{R}_k|} \exp(i\mathbf{s} \cdot \mathbf{r}) \, d^3r \, d^3R_k \tag{15c}$$

where $\hbar\mathbf{s} = \mathbf{p}_0 - \mathbf{p} = \mathbf{P}$ is the momentum transferred to the nucleus. It is convenient to use a shielded Coulomb potential in order to take into account the shielding due to the atomic electron cloud. Thus we replace

$$\sum_{k=1}^{Z} e^2 \, |\mathbf{r} - \mathbf{R}_k|^{-1}$$

by

$$\sum_{k=1}^{Z} e^2 \, |\mathbf{r} - \mathbf{R}_k|^{-1} \exp\left(-\frac{|\mathbf{r} - \mathbf{R}_k|}{a}\right),$$

where a is a screening parameter of atomic size, $a \gg R$, R being a nuclear dimension. Furthermore, writing $\mathbf{r} = \mathbf{R}_k + (\mathbf{r} - \mathbf{R}_k)$ in Eq. (15c), the integration over the electron coordinates (polar coordinates $\rho'\theta'\phi'$) involves the following integral.

$$e^2 \sum_{k=1}^{Z} \int (\exp i\mathbf{s} \cdot \mathbf{R}_k)[\exp i\mathbf{s} \cdot (\mathbf{r} - \mathbf{R}_k)] \left[\exp - \left(\frac{|\mathbf{r} - \mathbf{R}_k|}{a}\right)\right] \frac{1}{|\mathbf{r} - \mathbf{R}_k|} d^3r \, d^3R_k$$

$$= e^2 \sum_{k=1}^{Z} \int d^3R_k \exp(i\mathbf{s} \cdot \mathbf{R}_k) \int \exp(is\rho' \cos\theta') \frac{\exp(-\rho'/a)}{\rho'} \rho'^2 \sin\theta' \, d\rho' \, d\theta' \, d\phi'$$

$$= e^2 \sum_{k=1}^{Z} \int d^3R_k \exp(i\mathbf{s} \cdot \mathbf{R}_k) \frac{2\pi}{s} \int_0^\infty d\rho' \exp(-\rho'/a) \sin(s\rho')$$

$$= e^2 \sum_{k=1}^{Z} \int d^3R_k \exp(i\mathbf{s} \cdot \mathbf{R}_k) \frac{4\pi}{s^2 + 1/a^2} \simeq \frac{4\pi e^2}{s^2} \sum_{k=1}^{Z} \int d^3R_k \exp(i\mathbf{s} \cdot \mathbf{R}_k) \qquad (16)$$

where in the last step we have used the fact that $1/a \ll s$ for scattering not close to $\theta = 0$. From Eqs. (16), (15c), and (14a) we obtain for the transition probability

$$w = \frac{32\pi^3 e^4 \rho_f}{\hbar L^6 s^4} |M_{fi}|^2 \qquad (17a)$$

where

$$M_{fi} = \int_{\tau_N} \Phi_f^*(\mathbf{R}_k)\Phi_0(\mathbf{R}_k) \left[\sum_{k=1}^{Z} \exp(i\mathbf{s} \cdot \mathbf{R}_k)\right] d^3R_k \qquad (17b)$$

with τ_N standing for integration over the nuclear volume. The density of final states ρ_f is given by (Heitler[28])

$$\rho_f \, dE_f = \frac{L^3 p^2 \, dp \, d\Omega_p}{(2\pi\hbar)^3} = \frac{L^3 pE \, dE \, d\Omega_p}{c^2 (2\pi\hbar)^3} \qquad (18a)$$

where the energy $E = \sqrt{c^2\mathbf{p}^2 + m^2c^4} \simeq cp$ for the extremely relativistic electrons, $d\Omega_p$ is the element of solid angle of the scattered electron, and

$$E_f = E + \sqrt{c^2\mathbf{P}^2 + M^2c^4} = E_0 + Mc^2$$

is the total energy in the final state, so that

$$\frac{dE_f}{dE} = 1 + \frac{c^2(p - p_0 \cos \theta)}{W} \frac{dp}{dE} \tag{18b}$$

with

$$W = \sqrt{c^2 \mathbf{P}^2 + M^2 c^4} \tag{18c}$$

and θ is the angle of scattering $[\cos \theta = (\mathbf{p_0} \cdot \mathbf{p})/p_0 p]$. Therefore we have

$$
\begin{aligned}
\rho_f &= \frac{L^3 pE \, d\Omega_p}{c^2(2\pi\hbar)^3} \frac{W}{W + E(1 - (p_0/p) \cos \theta)} \\
&\simeq \frac{L^3 p^2 \, d\Omega_p}{c(2\pi\hbar)^3} \frac{1}{1 + (2p_0/Mc) \sin^2(\theta/2)}
\end{aligned}
\tag{19}
$$

where in the denominator we have made the approximation that the recoil of the nucleus $P \ll Mc$, so that $W \simeq Mc^2$ and $p \simeq p_0$.

The differential scattering cross section $d\sigma/d\Omega_p$ can be obtained by dividing the transition probability by the probability current in the incident beam, which is $(c^2 p_0/E_0)/L^3 \simeq c/L^3$. From Eqs. (17a) and (19), we obtain for the differential cross section

$$\frac{d\sigma}{d\Omega_p} = \left(\frac{e^2}{2E_0}\right)^2 \frac{1}{\sin^4(\theta/2)} \frac{1}{1 + (2E_0/Mc^2) \sin^2(\theta/2)} |M_{fi}|^2 \tag{20a}$$

where we have used

$$\mathbf{P}^2 = \hbar^2 s^2 = (\mathbf{p} - \mathbf{p_0})^2 \simeq 4p_0^2 \sin^2 \frac{\theta}{2} \simeq \frac{4E_0^2}{c^2} \sin^2 \frac{\theta}{2}$$

and M_{fi} is given by Eq. (17b).

In deriving Eq. (20a), it has been assumed that the electron has zero spin. Actually the electron is a spin-$\frac{1}{2}$ particle and the electron wave function ψ is a spinor and satisfies the Dirac equation. Equation (15b) should therefore be modified to

$$\psi(\mathbf{r}) = L^{-3/2} u(\mathbf{p}, s) \exp\left(\frac{i\mathbf{p} \cdot \mathbf{r}}{\hbar}\right)$$

where $u(\mathbf{p}, s)$ is a spinor, with s indicating the spin state. This modification leads to a multiplying factor of $\frac{1}{2} \sum_{s_i, s_f} |u_f^*(\mathbf{p}, s_f) u_i(\mathbf{p_0}, s_i)|^2$ in Eq. (20a), for an unpolarized incident electron beam, where the factor $\frac{1}{2}$ arises from taking an average over the initial spin state and the summation is over initial and final spin states. Thus by using the Dirac equation for the electron, it can be shown that the following expression for the differential cross section is obtained:

$$\frac{d\sigma}{d\Omega_p} = \left(\frac{e^2}{2E_0}\right)^2 \frac{\cos^2 \theta/2}{\sin^4 \theta/2} \frac{|M_{fi}|^2}{1 + (2E_0/Mc^2) \sin^2 (\theta/2)} \tag{20b}$$

For elastic scattering, $\Phi_f = \Phi_0$ and Eq. (20b) for the differential scattering cross section of a Dirac electron from the nucleus takes the form

$$\frac{d\sigma_{el}}{d\Omega_p} = \left(\frac{e^2}{2E_0}\right)^2 \frac{\cos^2 (\theta/2)}{\sin^4 (\theta/2)} \frac{|F(q)|^2}{1 + (2E_0/Mc^2) \sin^2 (\theta/2)} \tag{20c}$$

where

$$F(q) = \int_{\tau_N} |\Phi_0|^2 \sum_1^Z \exp i\mathbf{q} \cdot \mathbf{R}_k \, d^3R_k \tag{20d}$$

$F(q)$ is called the nuclear "form factor." If we assume that the size of the nucleus is small compared to the de Broglie wavelength of the electrons, then $\mathbf{q} \cdot \mathbf{R}_k \simeq 0$, and if $|\Phi_0|^2$ is normalized to unity over the nucleus, we have $|F(q)|^2 \simeq Z^2$. Thus in the limit of a point nucleus of charge Ze, Eq. (20c) reduces to the well-known Mott-scattering formula

$$\sigma_{\text{Mott}} (\theta) = \left(\frac{d\sigma_{el}}{d\Omega}\right)_{\text{point}} = \left(\frac{Ze^2}{2E_0}\right)^2 \frac{\cos^2 (\theta/2)}{\sin^4 (\theta/2)} \frac{1}{1 + (2E_0/Mc^2) \sin^2 (\theta/2)} \tag{21}$$

In order to consider the scattering from a finite size nucleus, we note that $|\Phi_0|^2$ contains all the proton-configuration coordinates symmetrically, so that

$$|F(q)|^2 = Z^2 \left| \int \phi_0^* \phi_0 \exp i(\mathbf{q} \cdot \mathbf{R}) \, d^3R \right|^2 \tag{22a}$$

where $|\phi_0|^2 \, d^3R$ represents the probability that there is one proton in the volume element d^3R and all other proton positions are arbitrary. Since $\int |\phi_0|^2 \, d^3R = 1$, for normalized wave function ϕ_0, the effective nuclear-charge density $\rho_0(\mathbf{R})$, in the ground state of the nucleus of charge Ze, is

$$\rho_0(\mathbf{R}) = Ze \, |\phi_0|^2 \tag{22b}$$

The nuclear-charge density $\rho(\mathbf{R})$ is usually defined such that

$$\int \rho(\mathbf{R}) \, d^3R = 1 \tag{22c}$$

where $\rho = \rho_0/Ze$ and $\mathbf{R}$ is the position vector of a charged volume element in the nucleus measured from its center of mass. We therefore rewrite

Eq. (20c) in the following form:

$$\frac{d\sigma_{el}}{d\Omega} = \left(\frac{Ze^2}{2E_0}\right)^2 \frac{\cos^2(\theta/2)}{\sin^4(\theta/2)} \frac{|F(q)|^2}{1 + (2E_0/Mc^2)\sin^2(\theta/2)} \tag{23a}$$

$$= \left(\frac{d\sigma_{el}}{d\Omega}\right)_{\text{point}} |F(q)|^2$$

where the electromagnetic form factor $F(q)$ is given by

$$F(q) = \int_{\tau_N} \rho(\mathbf{R}) \exp(i\mathbf{q} \cdot \mathbf{R}) \, d^3R \tag{23b}$$

and $(d\sigma_{el}/d\Omega)_{\text{point}}$ and $\rho(\mathbf{R})$ are defined by Eqs. (21) and (22c) respectively. Equation (23a) defines $|F(q)|^2$ as the ratio of the experimentally observed cross section to the point-charge cross section. For the case of spherically symmetric charge distribution $\rho(\mathbf{R})$, the angular integration in Eq. (23b) can be carried out readily, giving

$$F(q) = \frac{4\pi}{q} \int_0^\infty \rho(r) \sin(qr) r \, dr \tag{23c}$$

with $q \simeq (2p_0/\hbar) \sin(\theta/2)$. If the wavelength of the electron is large compared with the nuclear size, that is $qr \ll 1$, then $\sin(qr)$ can be expanded in powers of qr giving

$$F(q) = \int \rho(r)4\pi r^2 \, dr - \tfrac{1}{6}q^2 \int r^2 \rho(r)4\pi r^2 \, dr + \cdots \tag{23d}$$

$$= 1 - \tfrac{1}{6}(qa)^2 + \cdots$$

where

$$a^2 = \int r^2 \rho(r)4\pi r^2 \, dr \tag{23e}$$

and a is the root-mean-square radius (rms) of the charge distribution. From Eq. (23c) we can also obtain an expression for the charge density by using the Fourier transform. We have

$$\rho(r) = \frac{1}{2\pi^2 r} \int_0^\infty F(q) \sin(qr) q \, dq \tag{24}$$

Thus if $F(q)$ can be determined experimentally with sufficient accuracy, we can obtain the charge density $\rho(r)$ and hence the rms radius a.

As examples, we give curves for the charge density $\rho(r)$ which have been found to agree with experiments. In Fig. 2-4[27] is shown the form factor curve for a charge distribution due to an independent particle shell model of a nucleus for an infinite harmonic-well potential. The corresponding charge density $\rho(r)$ for C^{12} is shown in Fig. 2-5.[27] The

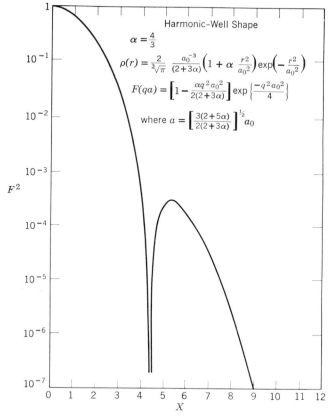

Harmonic–Well Shape

$$\alpha = \frac{4}{3}$$

$$\rho(r) = \frac{2}{\sqrt[3]{\pi}} \frac{a_0^{-3}}{(2+3\alpha)}\left(1 + \alpha\, \frac{r^2}{a_0^2}\right)\exp\left(-\frac{r^2}{a_0^2}\right)$$

$$F(qa) = \left[1 - \frac{\alpha q^2 a_0^2}{2(2+3\alpha)}\right]\exp\left\{\frac{-q^2 a_0^2}{4}\right\}$$

where $a = \left[\frac{3(2+5\alpha)}{2(2+3\alpha)}\right]^{\frac{1}{2}} a_0$

Fig. 2-4 Born approximation for the absolute square of the form factor associated with the harmonic-well shape in the case of $\alpha = \frac{4}{3}$ which is appropriate to carbon $(X = qa)$ (Hofstadter[27]).

comparison of the experimental differential cross section for electron C^{12} scattering at 420 Mev with the first Born approximation calculations, Eq. (23a), using the charge density of Fig. 2-5, is shown in Fig. 2-6.[27] The appearance of zeros at $qa = 4.4$ in Fig. 2-4 in the form factor is characteristic of Born approximation calculations. This is also exhibited in the differential cross section (Fig. 2-6). Actually at these zeros, the experimental curves show diffraction minima, as do also the accurate phase-shift calculations of Ravenhall,[29] shown by the solid line in Fig. 2-6.

Other charge distributions which give fair agreement for spherical nuclei between $Z = 20$ and $Z = 83$ are the Fermi, the modified Gaussian, and the trapezoidal types shown in Fig. 2-7.[27]

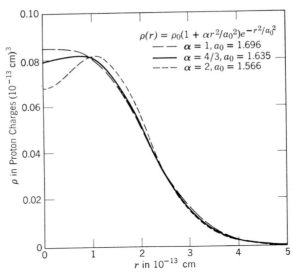

Fig. 2-5 The charge-density distribution for the harmonic-well nuclear model for three different values of α. The abscissa is correct only for carbon, for which $\alpha = \frac{4}{3}$ (Hofstadter[27]).

The Fermi model has the following analytic form:

$$\rho(r) = \frac{\rho_0}{1 + \exp{[(r - c)/a]}} \tag{25}$$

The model is characterized by two parameters, $c = 1.07 A^{1/3} \times 10^{-13}$ cm, which is the "half-density" radius, and $t = 4.4a$ is the skin thickness which is measured between 90 and 10% values of the density. The Fermi charge density distribution has been used for several nuclei: Ca, V, Co, In, Sb, Au, and Bi. For lighter nuclei, better results have been obtained with other distributions. For Be^9, Li^6, and Li^7 the form of the charge distribution used was $\rho(r) = \rho_0(1 + r/a)e^{-r/a}$, for He^4 the function $\rho(r) = \rho_0 e^{-r^2/a^2}$, and for C^{12} the function

$$\rho(r) = \rho_0\left(1 + \frac{\omega r^2}{a^2}\right)e^{-r^2/a^2}$$

was used.

The use of the first Born approximation can be justified only for light nuclei. It is found to give good results for C^{12} and for other light nuclei in the region far from the diffraction zeros. For higher Z values the agreement with experiments is only of a qualitative nature. Dalitz[32] and

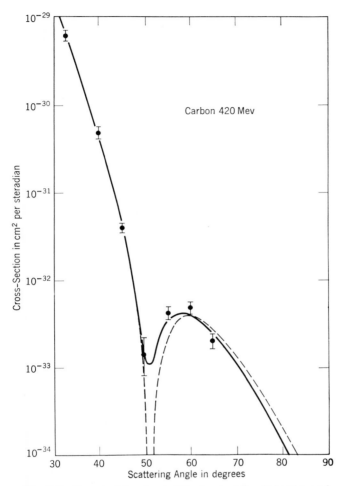

Fig. 2-6 Recent data about C^{12} observed by Sobottka and Hofstadter[30] at an incident electron energy of 420 Mev. Two theoretical curves are presented for comparison. The dashed curve is the Born approximation for a hormonic-well charge distribution corresponding to Fig. 2-5 ($\alpha = \frac{4}{3}$). The solid line is the accurate phase-shift calculation of Ravenhall, which appears to fit the experimental points rather well (Hofstadter[27]).

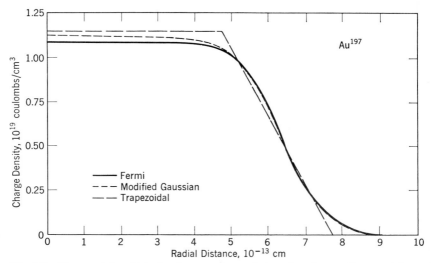

Fig. 2-7 The models which fit the experimental data for the medium and heavy nuclei.[31] A typical set is shown for Au. Present accuracy in the experiments does not permit distinguishing among the three types (Hofstadter[27]).

McKinley and Feshbach[33] have carried out the calculation of the scattering cross section for a point nucleus up to the second order in Born approximation. In the limit of the electron velocity $v \simeq c$, their result is as follows:

$$\left(\frac{d\sigma}{d\Omega}\right) = \left(\frac{Ze^2}{2E_0}\right)^2 \frac{\cos^2(\theta/2)}{\sin^4(\theta/2)}\left[1 + \frac{\pi Z}{137}\frac{\sin(\theta/2)[1 - \sin(\theta/2)]}{\cos^2(\theta/2)}\right] \quad (26)$$

However, for large values of Z, and even for low values where the charge density has sharp edges, the Born approximation is not suitable. At high energies and for various forms of the charge distributions, exact phase-shift calculations have been carried out by Yennie, Ravenhall, and Wilson[34] and other workers. A comparison of these calculations with the Born approximation for point-charge and for uniform-charge models is given in Fig. 2-8.

In the approximation of characterizing the nuclear size by a single parameter r_0, we may assume a uniform charge distribution $\rho = [(4\pi/3)R^3]^{-1}$ for the nucleus of radius $R = r_0 A^{1/3}$. The mean square radius of the charge distribution is

$$a^2 = \int_0^R r^2 \rho 4\pi r^2 \, dr = \tfrac{3}{5}R^2 = \tfrac{3}{5}r_0^2 A^{2/3}$$

so that $r_0 = \sqrt{\frac{5}{3}}\, aA^{-\frac{1}{3}}$. The electron-scattering experiments determine the rms radius a. The value of r_0 consistent with the experimental data ranges from 1.18×10^{-13} cm to 1.40×10^{-13} cm for light nuclei.

High-energy electron scattering experiments provide information on the charge distribution of a nucleus. Usually, the experimental elastic scattering cross sections are compared with values predicted from theory. The theory, on the other hand, has been developed on the basis of a particular model of charge distribution. We have previously discussed

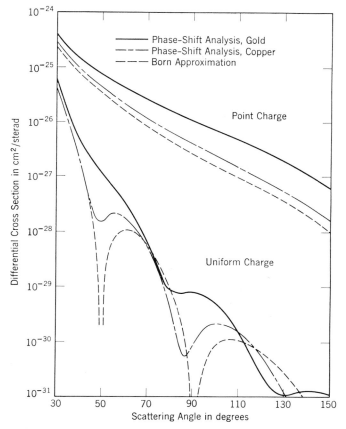

Fig. 2-8 This figure shows the results of exact phase-shift calculations for the point-charge and the uniform-charge models of Au at a value of $kR = 5.4$ (approximately 155 Mev). The Figure also shows similar curves for Cu at about 230 Mev. Comparisons with the Born approximation are also given (Hofstadter[27]).

some results obtained from electron scattering data. To complete our discussion, we shall cite the results of another experiment[35] in which the absolute elastic scattering cross sections for Ca^{40}, V^{51}, Co^{59}, In^{115}, $Sb^{121,123}$, and Bi^{209} have been measured at an electron incident energy of 183 Mev. The experimental results have been compared with the scattering predicted

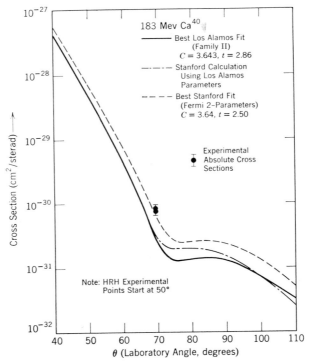

Fig. 2-9 Angular distributions and cross sections for Ca^{40}. The dashed curve is the Hahn, Ravenhall, and Hofstadter[31] (HRH) best-fit curve. The solid curve is the Ford and Hill[20] (Family II) best-fit curve. The two curves have the same relative shape, but the cross sections differ by a factor of two. The experimental points agree well with the HRH (dashed) curve (Crannell et al.[35]).

by the phase shift calculations[34] assuming a nuclear-charge density used by Hahn, Ravenhall, and Hofstadter.[31] This is the Fermi two-parameter model charge distribution given by

$$\rho(r) = \frac{\rho_0}{1 + \exp\left[(r - c)/a\right]}$$

where c is the radius at which the charge density falls to one-half its maximum value, a is the surface thickness parameter, and the radial variable r is measured from the center of the nucleus. Comparison of the experimental results has also been made with the "Family II" nuclear-charge distribution model of Ford and Hill.[20] Some of the experimental

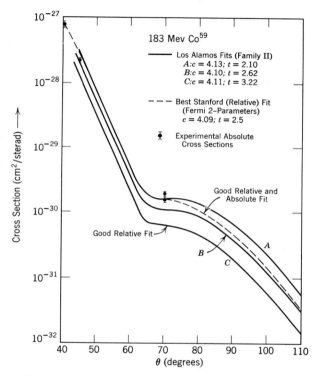

Fig. 2-10 The angular distributions and cross sections for Co[59]. The dashed curve is the HRH best-fit curve. The curve labeled C is the Family II best-fit curve. The two curves have the same relative shape, but the cross sections differ by a factor of two. The experimental results favor the HRH (dashed) curve (Crannell et al.[35]).

results are reproduced in Figs. 2-9 and 2-10. The surface thickness parameter t given in the figures is defined as the distance in which the charge density drops from 90 to 10% of its maximum value. It is related with the Fermi two-parameter model surface thickness parameter a by $t = 4.4a$. The experimental results agree with the HRH model. The values of $c/A^{1/3}$ computed from this model are, respectively, 1.063, 1.073, 1.051, 1.078,

1.073, and 1.090 F for Ca^{40}, V^{51}, Co^{59}, In^{115}, $Sb^{121,123}$, and Bi^{209}. Taking the average value for these elements, we obtain the radial parameter $c = 1.07A^{1/3}$ F, which is considerably smaller than the value obtained from other methods such as alpha scattering, mirror nuclei, and others.

We have discussed the various methods of determining the nuclear radius, and it is now appropriate to summarize the discussion with particular emphasis on what parameters we actually determine from these experiments.

The nuclear radius is found to be given by the formula $R = r_0A^{1/3}$. The nuclear radius parameter r_0, as we have observed, is not constant but is different for different techniques used for its determination. Its value ranges from 1.07 F, in electron scattering experiments, to 1.5 F obtained from mirror nuclei studies. High-energy electron scattering experiments determine the charge distribution, whereas the other methods such as alpha-decay and nuclear-particle scatterings give the interaction radius which is dependent upon the nuclear potential (which includes some intrinsic size of the probe particles). If a particular nuclear potential is assumed there is no certainty that the potential experienced by different incident particles such as neutron, proton, and alpha will be the same. Consequently, it is not surprising to find somewhat varying values of r_0 in different experiments. On the other hand, if we assume that the nuclear charge-distribution is given by $\rho(r)$, then its electrostatic potential is defined. The interaction of fast electrons or μ-mesons with this charge distribution can be calculated. The experiment, however, does not give $\rho(r)$ but some functions of $\rho(r)$ such as different moments of the charge distribution

$$\langle r^n \rangle = \int_\tau \rho(r)r^n \, d^3r$$

The electron scattering experiments determine two parameters, the nuclear radius parameter $\langle r^n \rangle$ and the surface thickness parameter t. The study of μ-mesonic x-rays determines one parameter $\langle r^n \rangle$, which is related to the volume in which the charge is concentrated. In light nuclei these two different kinds of experiments measure the second moment of the charge distribution, that is, $\langle r^2 \rangle$. We have noted that the values of $\langle r^2 \rangle$ are in fair agreement as obtained from these two different techniques.

2.3 Nuclear Shapes

Historically speaking, the shape of the nucleus was first investigated by Schüler and Schmidt[36] by the determination of the nuclear electric quadrupole moment from hyperfine structure in atomic spectra. The nuclear electric quadrupole moment measures the deviation of charge distribution from a spherical shape and hence provides information about nuclear shape. In general, the measurement of quadrupole moments involves interaction of the nuclear-charge distribution with the static charge distributions of the electrons (or of other nuclei) in atomic or molecular systems or with a specified external applied electric field. Similarly, the magnetic moment of the nucleus will interact with the magnetic field in which the nucleus is situated.

We may thus classify the experiments for the determination of nuclear shape into two broad groups which measure (1) the interaction of the nuclear electric charge and magnetic moment distributions with electromagnetic fields and (2) the interaction of nuclei with fast charged particles. The latter are the electron scattering experiments, discussed in Section 2.2, in which measurement of scattering cross sections is interpreted in terms of a charge (and a magnetic moment) distribution over a finite radius. The external fields in (1) should not be so strong that they would appreciably distort the charges and currents in the nucleus.

2.4   Electric Moments

We consider the nucleus to have a charge density $\rho_N(\mathbf{r}_N)$, and if $\rho_e(\mathbf{r}_e)$ is the external charge density due to the charges in the atomic and molecular system, the electrostatic interaction energy is given by

$$W = \iint \frac{\rho_N(\mathbf{r}_N)\rho_e(\mathbf{r}_e)}{|\mathbf{r}_N - \mathbf{r}_e|} \, d^3r_N \, d^3r_e \qquad (27)$$

where d^3r_N and d^3r_e denote volume elements corresponding to the nucleus and the external charges. If the important contribution to the interaction energy W comes from $|\mathbf{r}_e| > |\mathbf{r}_N|$, we can carry out the following well-known expansion for $|\mathbf{r}_N - \mathbf{r}_e|^{-1}$.

$$|\mathbf{r}_N - \mathbf{r}_e|^{-1} = 4\pi \sum_{l=0}^{\infty} \sum_{m=-l}^{l} \frac{1}{2l+1} \frac{1}{r_e} \left(\frac{r_N}{r_e}\right)^l Y_{lm}^*(\hat{r}_N) Y_{lm}(\hat{r}_e) \qquad (28)$$

where Y_{lm} are the usual spherical harmonics and $\hat{r}_N = \mathbf{r}_N/|\mathbf{r}_N| \equiv (\theta_N, \phi_N)$, $\hat{r}_e = \mathbf{r}_e/|\mathbf{r}_e| \equiv (\theta_e, \phi_e)$ are unit vectors specifying the directions of the vectors $\mathbf{r}_N$ and $\mathbf{r}_e$ with respect to an arbitrary coordinate system. Substituting Eq. (28) in Eq. (27), we obtain

$$W = 4\pi \sum_{l,m} \frac{Q_{lm}}{(2l+1)} \int \rho_e(\mathbf{r}_e) r_e^{-l-1} Y_{lm}(\hat{r}_e) \, d^3r_e \qquad (29a)$$

where

$$Q_{lm} = \int \rho_N(\mathbf{r}_N) r_N^l Y_{lm}^*(\hat{r}_N) \, d^3 r_N \tag{29b}$$

are the nuclear electric-multipole moments.

In general, the charge density ρ_e may not be negligible inside the nucleus or in its immediate neighborhood, and thus the expansion [Eq. (28)] is not valid. An alternative procedure, which avoids this difficulty, is to consider the nucleus to be situated in a known electrostatic potential Φ which is the result of all the non-nuclear charges (or the external applied field). Then

$$W = \int \rho_N(\mathbf{r}) \Phi(\mathbf{r}) \, d^3 r \tag{30}$$

where now the subscript N on $\mathbf{r}$ has been dropped. Expanding the potential $\Phi(\mathbf{r})$ in a Taylor's series around the center of the nuclear charge, taken to be the origin, we have

$$\Phi(\mathbf{r}) = \Phi(0) + \mathbf{r} \cdot \nabla\Phi(0) + \tfrac{1}{2} \sum_{i\,j} x_i x_j \left(\frac{\partial^2 \Phi}{\partial x_i \, \partial x_j}\right)_0 + \cdots \tag{31a}$$

$$= \Phi(0) + \mathbf{r} \cdot \nabla\Phi(0) + \tfrac{1}{6} \sum_{i,j} (r^2 \delta_{ij} + q_{ij}) \left(\frac{\partial^2 \Phi}{\partial x_i \, \partial x_j}\right)_0 + \cdots \tag{31b}$$

where

$$q_{ij} = 3 x_i x_j - r^2 \delta_{ij} \tag{31c}$$

In going from Eq. (31a) to Eq. (31b), we have added and subtracted $\tfrac{1}{6} r^2 \delta_{ij} (\partial^2 \Phi / \partial x_i \, \partial x_j)_0$. From Eqs. (30) to (31b) we obtain

$$W = W_{is} + W_e \tag{32}$$

where

$$W_{is} = \tfrac{1}{6} (\nabla^2 \Phi)_0 \int \rho_N r^2 \, d^3 r + \cdots \tag{33a}$$

and

$$W_e = q\Phi(0) - \mathbf{P} \cdot \mathbf{E}(0) - \tfrac{1}{6} \sum_{ij} Q_{ij} \left(\frac{\partial E_j}{\partial x_i}\right)_0 - \cdots \tag{33b}$$

with

$$\mathbf{E} = -\nabla\Phi \tag{34}$$

$$q = \int \rho_N(\mathbf{r}) \, d^3 r = Ze \tag{35}$$

$$\mathbf{P} = \int \mathbf{r} \rho_N(\mathbf{r}) \, d^3 r \tag{36}$$

$$Q_{ij} = \int \rho_N(\mathbf{r})(3 x_i x_j - \delta_{ij} r^2) \, d^3 r \tag{37}$$

The symbols q, **P**, and Q_{ij} stand for the total nuclear charge, electric dipole vector, and electric quadrupole tensor respectively. The energy W_{is} in Eq. (32) is associated with the "isotope shift" of atomic spectra. If the potential $\Phi(\mathbf{r})$ is due only to an external applied electric field, then according to Laplace's Equation $\nabla^2\Phi = 0$, we have $W_{is} = 0$ and $W = W_e$ as given by Eq. (33b).

The quantum mechanical expressions for the operators corresponding to total charge, dipole moment, and quadrupole moment are obtained by substituting the following:

$$\rho_N(\mathbf{r})\, d^3r = Ze\, |\Psi'_N|^2\, d^3r$$

$$= Ze\, |\Psi_N(\mathbf{r}_1, \mathbf{r}_2, \cdots \mathbf{r}_Z; \mathbf{r}_{Z+1}, \cdots \mathbf{r}_A)|^2,\, d^3r_1 \cdots d^3r_A \quad (38)$$

where $\mathbf{r}_1 \cdots \mathbf{r}_A$ are the coordinates of the A nucleons in the nucleus, $\Psi_N(\mathbf{r}_1 \cdots \mathbf{r}_A)$ is the nuclear wave function, and the nuclear volume element $d^3r = d^3r_1 \cdots d^3r_A$. Thus the quantum mechanical equations corresponding to Eqs. (35) to (37) are as follows:

$$q = Ze \int |\Psi_N(\mathbf{r}_1, \cdots \mathbf{r}_A)|^2\, d^3r_1 \cdots d^3r_A = Ze \quad (39)$$

$$\mathbf{P} = \sum_{k=1}^{Z} \int e(\mathbf{r})_k\, |\Psi_N(\mathbf{r}_1, \cdots \mathbf{r}_A)|^2\, d^3r_1 \cdots d^3r_A \quad (40)$$

$$Q_{ij} = \sum_{k=1}^{Z} \int e(3x_i x_j - \delta_{ij} r^2)_k\, |\Psi_N(\mathbf{r}_1, \cdots \mathbf{r}_A)|^2\, d^3r_1 \cdots d^3r_A \quad (41)$$

It is easy to see from Eq. (40) that if the nucleus is in a state of definite parity, that is, $\Psi_N(-\mathbf{r}_1, \cdots -\mathbf{r}_A) = \pm\Psi_N(\mathbf{r}_1, \cdots \mathbf{r}_A)$, the permanent electric dipole moment of the nucleus vanishes. Making the transformation $(\mathbf{r})_k \to (-\mathbf{r})_k$ in Eq. (40), we obtain $\mathbf{P} = -\mathbf{P} = 0$.

We can further show, by making use of the vectorial addition of angular momenta, that a nucleus can have a nonvanishing electric quadrupole moment only if its angular momentum I is equal to or larger than unity. This follows from the observation that the quantity $q_{ij} = 3x_i x_j - \delta_{ij} r^2$ corresponds to angular momentum $l = 2$ so that the state $q_{ij}\Psi_N^I = \sum_J a_{ij}^{IJ} \Psi_N^J$ is a combination of angular momenta $J = |I - 2|$ to $I + 2$ with amplitudes a_{ij}^{IJ}. Therefore from Eq. (41) we have

$$Q_{ij} = \sum_{k=1}^{Z} \sum_{J=|I-2|}^{I+2} \int e(a_{ij}^{IJ})_k \Psi_N^{*I}(\mathbf{r}_1, \cdots \mathbf{r}_A)\Psi_N^J(\mathbf{r}_1, \cdots \mathbf{r}_A)\, d^3r_1 \cdots d^3r_A \,(42)$$

Because of the orthogonality of nuclear states, the only nonzero term in Eq. (42) is when $J = I$. For $I = 0$, since J is equal to 2, the quadrupole moment is zero. For $I = \frac{1}{2}$, $J = \frac{5}{2}$, and $\frac{3}{2}$, and again the quadrupole moment is zero. When $I \geq 1$, one of the J values is equal to I and hence the quadrupole moment exists.

The concept of electric dipole and quadrupole moments can be generalized by introducing the electric multipole moments Q_{lm} as follows:

$$Q_{lm} = \int r^l Y_{lm}^*(\theta, \phi) \rho_N(\mathbf{r}) \, d^3r \tag{43a}$$

which has the quantum-mechanical form

$$Q_{lm} = \sum_{k=1}^{Z} e \int r_k^l Y_{lm}^*(\theta_k, \phi_k) |\Psi_N(\mathbf{r}_1, \mathbf{r}_2, \ldots \mathbf{r}_A)|^2 \, d^3r_1 \cdots d^3r_A \tag{43b}$$

Since $Y_{lm}^*(\hat{r}_k) = (-1)^l Y_{lm}^*(-\hat{r}_k)$, it follows from Eq. (43b) that if the nucleus has a definite state of parity, all electric multipole moments with odd values of l vanish because of invariance under space inversion. Also if the nucleus has a spin I, according to the law of vectorial addition of angular momenta, the electric multipoles of even order l vanish unless the nuclear spin $I \geq l/2$. These are generalizations of the properties obtained for electric dipole and quadrupole moments discussed earlier.

We now discuss the electric quadrupole moment in more detail. From Eq. (41), the quadrupole moment is the expectation value of the operator

$$Q_{ij} = \sum_{k=1}^{Z} e_k (3x_i x_j - \delta_{ij} r^2)_k \tag{44a}$$

The Q_{zz}-component,

$$Q_{zz} = \sum_{k=1}^{Z} e_k (3z_k^2 - r_k^2) \tag{44b}$$

for a spherically symmetric charge distribution is $Q_{zz} = 0$. If the nucleus is elongated along the z-axis, then the mean value of the z-coordinate squared is larger than the mean value of the x- and y-coordinates squared, $Q_{zz} > 0$. Similarly $Q_{zz} < 0$, if the nucleus is compressed along the z-axis.

The properties of the quadrupole moment tensor are (1) it is symmetric $Q_{ij} = Q_{ji}$ and (2) its trace, the sum of the diagonal elements, vanishes; that is, $Q_{xx} + Q_{yy} + Q_{zz} = 0$. From these two properties we can express Q_{ij} in terms of the spin vector $\mathbf{I}$, which specifies the quantized state of the nucleus. It is easy to see from (1) and (2) that

$$Q_{ij} = C(I_i I_j + I_j I_i - \tfrac{2}{3} \mathbf{I}^2 \delta_{ij}) \tag{44c}$$

where C is a constant that can be expressed in terms of the component $Q = Q_{zz}(I_z = I)$ of Q_{ij} in the state in which the projection of the spin along the z-axis is equal to the spin I itself. The value-Q is generally designated as the quadrupole moment. Substituting $I_z = I$ and $\mathbf{I}^2 = I(I+1)$ in Eq. (44c), we obtain

$$Q = \tfrac{2}{3}CI(2I - 1) \tag{44d}$$

$$= 0, \text{ when } I = 0 \text{ or } I = \tfrac{1}{2}.$$

Substituting for C in Eq. (44c), we have

$$Q_{ij} = \frac{3Q}{2I(2I - 1)} [I_i I_j + I_j I_i - \tfrac{2}{3}I(I + 1)\delta_{ij}] \tag{45}$$

Let us consider a rough model for the nucleus. We assume that the charge is uniformly distributed over an ellipsoid of revolution (valid

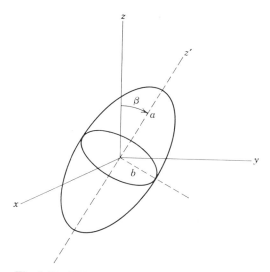

Fig. 2-11 Ellipsoidal charge distribution with z' as the symmetry axis.

for both medium and large A nuclei), with the axis of symmetry along the z'-axis, the semi-major axis of length a, and the other two semi-axes of length b (see Fig. 2-11). The charge density ρ is

$$\rho = \frac{Ze}{\text{volume}} = \frac{Ze}{(4\pi/3)ab^2}$$

The equation of the ellipsoid is

$$\frac{x'^2}{b^2} + \frac{y'^2}{b^2} + \frac{z'^2}{a^2} = 1$$

In cylindrical coordinates (z', s', ϕ') it is $(s'^2/b^2) + (z'^2/a^2) = 1$, where $s'^2 = x'^2 + y'^2$. The quadrupole moment $Q_{z'z'} = Q_B$ in the primed coordinate system (body-fixed axes system), from Eq. (41), is

$$Q_{\text{Body}} = \frac{3Ze}{4\pi a b^2} \int_{-a}^{+a} dz' \int_0^{b\sqrt{1-(z'^2/a^2)}} (2z'^2 - s'^2)s' \, ds' \int_0^{2\pi} d\phi'$$

$$= \tfrac{2}{5} Ze(a^2 - b^2)$$

$$= \tfrac{4}{5} Ze\sigma R^2 \tag{46a}$$

where the eccentricity parameter σ is given by

$$\sigma = \frac{a^2 - b^2}{a^2 + b^2} \tag{46b}$$

and where

$$R^2 = \tfrac{1}{2}(a^2 + b^2) \tag{46c}$$

The quadrupole moment in an arbitrary coordinate system (r, θ, ϕ) fixed in a space whose z-axis makes an angle β with the z'-axis of symmetry is

$$Q_{\text{space}} = \int r^2(3\cos^2\theta - 1)\rho(r) \, d^3r \tag{47a}$$

where

$$\cos\theta = \cos\theta'\cos\beta + \sin\theta'\sin\beta\cos(\phi' - \phi)$$

Substituting in Eq. (47a), we obtain

$$Q_{\text{space}} = \tfrac{1}{2}(3\cos^2\beta - 1)Q_{\text{Body}} \tag{47b}$$

We can associate Q_{Body} with the intrinsic quadrupole moment of the nucleus with respect to its spin axis and Q_{space} as the observed quadrupole moment. The maximum observable quadrupole moment Q is obtained by substituting the maximum value of $\cos\beta$. According to quantum mechanics $\cos\beta = I_z/\sqrt{I(I + 1)}$, and $(\cos\beta)_{\max}$ corresponds to the orientation in which the spin component $I_z = I$. Therefore

$$Q = (Q_{\text{space}})_{\max} = (Q_{\text{space}})_{I_z=I}$$

$$= \frac{2I - 1}{2(I + 1)} Q_B \tag{48a}$$

The quadrupole moment in the state with the z-component of spin I_z, from Eqs. (47a), (47b), and (48a), is given by

$$Q(I_z) = \frac{3I_z^2 - I(I + 1)}{I(2I - 1)} Q \tag{48b}$$

The physical interpretation of Eq. (48a) is that only a fraction of the intrinsic quadrupole moment Q_B can interact with the external field. For $I = \frac{1}{2}$, we again find that $Q = 0$ since the extent of alignment of the vector $\mathbf{I}$ is extremely small. The vanishing of the quadrupole moment for nuclei with $I = 0$ and $\frac{1}{2}$ should not be interpreted to mean that the nucleus is of spherical shape, but rather that the quadrupole moment parameter does not provide a measure of its deviation from spherical charge distribution.

In the shell model the properties of the nucleus are described in terms of the one nucleon or the few nucleons outside the closed shell configuration. The closed shells are assumed to give a spherical shape to the nucleus, and deformations arise because of interaction with the outer nucleons. If there is only one nucleon outside the closed shell, the deformations are small, and the shell model single-particle description of the nucleus is expected to be valid. As the number of nucleons outside the closed shell increases, the collective behavior of the nucleus becomes more important and a large number of nucleons may be involved in collective modes of motion as suggested by Rainwater.[37]

The nuclear electric quadrupole moment due to one proton outside a closed-shell configuration can be obtained from Eq. (41), taking for the nuclear wave function simply the eigenfunction $R(r) Y_{ll}(\theta, \phi)\chi(\frac{1}{2})$ in the angular momentum state l, where R is the radial function, Y_{ll} the spherical harmonic, and $\chi(\frac{1}{2})$ the spin wave function. The spin of the nucleus $I = l \pm \frac{1}{2}$ and the quadrupole moment due to a single proton is therefore given by

$$Q_p = -\frac{2I - 1}{2I + 2} \langle r^2 \rangle \tag{49}$$

where $\langle r^2 \rangle$ is the mean square distance of the proton from the center of the nucleus. This formula gives values of the quadrupole moment which are in reasonable agreement with the observed values for nuclei near a closed shell. However, they are too small, and also have the wrong sign for nuclei in the middle of the shell. A plot of the quadrupole moment against the number of odd nucleons is shown in Fig. 2-12.[38] From the experimental values of the quadrupole moment and Eqs. (45), (48a), and taking $R = r_0 A^{\frac{1}{3}}$, we can calculate the eccentricity parameter σ which is a measure of the aspherical shape of the nucleus. Figure 2-12 shows that nuclei have large positive and negative values of Q as contrasted with Eq. (49) which predicts only small negative Q. Furthermore, nuclei with Z or $N = 8$, 16, 20, 28, 38, 50, 82, and 126 have vanishing quadrupole moment, with Q rising abruptly on either side of these values. These nucleon numbers are associated with magic numbers at which the nuclear shells are completed and the nuclear shape is spherical. The nuclear

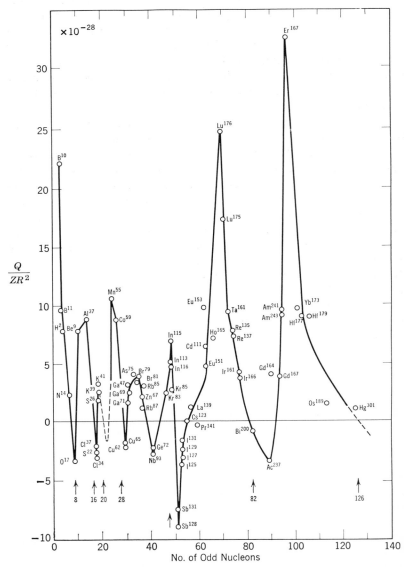

Fig. 2-12 Reduced nuclear quadrupole moments as a function of the number of odd nucleons. The quantity (Q/ZR^2) gives a measure of the nuclear deformation independent of the size of the nucleus (Segrè[38]).

shell theory accounts for the quadrupole moment for nuclei near the magic number. To explain large values of Q, however, it is necessary to consider collective properties of the nucleons (Chapter 8).

2.5 Magnetic Moments

The protons inside the nucleus are in orbital motion and therefore produce electric currents which are then sources of magnetic properties of the nucleus. The vector potential $\mathbf{A}(\mathbf{r})$ at a point $\mathbf{r}$ outside the nucleus due to a localized current density $\mathbf{J}(\mathbf{r}')$ is given by

$$\mathbf{A}(\mathbf{r}) = \frac{1}{c} \int d^3 r' \, \frac{\mathbf{J}(\mathbf{r}')}{|\mathbf{r} - \mathbf{r}'|} \tag{50}$$

Since $|\mathbf{r}| \gg |\mathbf{r}'|$, we can carry out an expansion of $|\mathbf{r} - \mathbf{r}'|^{-1}$ in powers of r'/r. The first term in the expansion involves $\int \mathbf{J}(\mathbf{r}') \, d^3 r'$ which vanishes for a localized steady-state current distribution ($\nabla \cdot \mathbf{J} = 0$), corresponding to the vanishing of the monopole term. We therefore have

$$A_i(\mathbf{r}) = \frac{\mathbf{r}}{c r^3} \cdot \int J_i(\mathbf{r}') \mathbf{r}' \, d^3 r' + \cdots \tag{51a}$$

$$= -\frac{1}{2 c r^3} \mathbf{r} \times \int (\mathbf{r}' \times \mathbf{J}(\mathbf{r}')) \, d^3 r' + \cdots \tag{51b}$$

where we have made use of the following relations:

$$\mathbf{r} \times (\mathbf{r}' \times \mathbf{J}) = (\mathbf{r} \cdot \mathbf{J})\mathbf{r}' - (\mathbf{r} \cdot \mathbf{r}')\mathbf{J} \tag{52a}$$

$$\nabla'_k(x'_j J_k x'_i) = [\delta_{kj} J_k x'_i + x'_j(\nabla'_k J_k)x'_i + \delta_{ij} x'_j J_k]$$
$$= [J_j x'_i + x'_j J_i] \qquad (i, j = 1, 2, 3) \tag{52b}$$

The volume integral of the left-hand side vanishes since the contributions on the surface are zero. By introducing the density of magnetization $\mathcal{M}$ due to the current density $\mathbf{J}$ and the magnetic moment $\boldsymbol{\mu}_0$ as follows,

$$\mathcal{M} = \frac{1}{2c} (\mathbf{r} \times \mathbf{J}) \tag{53a}$$

$$\boldsymbol{\mu}_0 = \int \mathcal{M} \, d^3 r' = \frac{1}{2c} \int \mathbf{r}' \times \mathbf{J}(\mathbf{r}') \, d^3 r' \tag{53b}$$

we obtain

$$\mathbf{A}(\mathbf{r}) = \frac{\boldsymbol{\mu}_0 \times \mathbf{r}}{|\mathbf{r}|^3} \tag{54}$$

If the current is due to the motion of the protons, we have

$$J = \sum_{k=1}^{Z} \frac{e}{M} \mathbf{p}_k \, \delta(\mathbf{r} - \mathbf{r}_k) \tag{55}$$

where $\mathbf{p}_k$ is the momentum of the kth proton and M is the proton mass. Substituting Eq. (55) in Eq. (53b), we obtain for the magnetic moment of the nucleus

$$\boldsymbol{\mu}_0 = \frac{e}{2Mc} \sum_{k=1}^{Z} \mathbf{r}_k \times \mathbf{p}_k$$

$$= \frac{e\hbar}{2Mc} \sum_{k=1}^{Z} \mathbf{l}_k \tag{56}$$

where $\mathbf{l}_k$ is the orbital angular momentum (in units of $\hbar$) of the kth proton.

The nucleons also have intrinsic spin angular momentum in addition to the orbital angular momentum. The contribution to the magnetic moment arising from the spin is

$$\boldsymbol{\mu}_s = \frac{e\hbar}{2Mc} \left[g_p \sum_{k=1}^{Z} \mathbf{s}_k + g_n \sum_{k=Z+1}^{A} \mathbf{s}_k \right] \tag{57}$$

where $\mathbf{s}_k = \frac{1}{2} \boldsymbol{\sigma}_k$ is the spin angular momentum of the proton (or neutron), $\boldsymbol{\sigma}_k$ are the Pauli spin matrices and g_p and g_n are the gyromagnetic ratios of the proton and neutron respectively, with the following values, as determined from the experimental values of the magnetic moments:

$$\mu_p = 2.7934 \frac{e\hbar}{2Mc} \qquad g_p = 5.59 \tag{58a}$$

$$\mu_n = -1.9135 \frac{e\hbar}{2Mc} \qquad g_n = -3.83 \tag{58b}$$

The total magnetic dipole moment $\boldsymbol{\mu}$ is given by the sum of Eqs. (56) and (57):

$$\boldsymbol{\mu} = \boldsymbol{\mu}_0 + \boldsymbol{\mu}_s$$

$$= \frac{e\hbar}{2Mc} \left[\sum_{k=1}^{Z} (\mathbf{l}_k + g_p \mathbf{s}_k) + g_n \sum_{k=Z+1}^{A} \mathbf{s}_k \right] \tag{59}$$

The quantum mechanical expressions corresponding to these equations can be obtained by taking the expectation value in the state

$$\Psi_N^*(\mathbf{r}_1, \mathbf{r}_2, \ldots \mathbf{r}_A).$$

Thus the quantum mechanical expressions for Eqs. (56), (57), and (59) are the following:

$$\mu_0 = \frac{e\hbar}{2Mc} \int \Psi_N^*(\mathbf{r}_1, \cdots \mathbf{r}_A) \sum_{k=1}^{Z} \mathbf{l}_k \Psi_N(\mathbf{r}_1, \cdots \mathbf{r}_A) \, d^3r_1 \cdots d^3r_A \qquad (60a)$$

$$\mu_s = \frac{e\hbar}{2Mc} \int \Psi_N^*(\mathbf{r}_1, \cdots \mathbf{r}_A) \left[g_p \sum_{k=1}^{Z} \mathbf{s}_k + g_n \sum_{k=Z+1}^{A} \mathbf{s}_k \right]$$
$$\times \Psi_N(\mathbf{r}_1, \cdots \mathbf{r}_A) \, d^3r_1 \cdots d^3r_A \qquad (60b)$$

$$\mu = \frac{e\hbar}{2Mc} \int \Psi_N^*(\mathbf{r}_1, \cdots \mathbf{r}_A) \left[\sum_{k=1}^{Z} (\mathbf{l}_k + g_p \mathbf{s}_k) + g_n \sum_{k=Z+1}^{A} \mathbf{s}_k \right]$$
$$\times \Psi_N(\mathbf{r}_1, \cdots \mathbf{r}_A) \, d^3r_1 \cdots d^3r_A \qquad (60c)$$

By continuing a discussion similar to the one following Eq. (42), we find that the magnetic dipole moment vanishes if the nucleus has a total angular momentum (spin) $I = 0$, but not otherwise. Since orbital angular momentum $\mathbf{l} = \mathbf{r} \times \mathbf{p}$ is a pseudo-vector and does not change sign under space reversal $\mathbf{r} \rightarrow -\mathbf{r}$, the magnetic dipole moment of a nucleus in a definite parity state is nonzero in contrast to the vanishing of the electric dipole moment which vanishes in a definite state of parity of the nucleus.

The expression (56) for the magnetic dipole moment can be generalized to define magnetic multipole moments μ_{lm} as follows:

$$\mu_{lm} = \int r^l Y_{lm}^*(\theta, \phi) \rho_m(\mathbf{r}) \, d^3r \qquad (61)$$

where $\rho_m(\mathbf{r})$ is the magnetic charge density

$$\rho_m(\mathbf{r}) = -\operatorname{div} \mathscr{M}(\mathbf{r}) \qquad (62)$$

where $\mathscr{M}(\mathbf{r})$ is the magnetization density defined by Eq. (53a).

The total angular momentum (spin) $\mathbf{l}$ of the nucleus is given by

$$\mathbf{I} = \sum_{k=1}^{A} \mathbf{l}_k + \sum_{k=1}^{A} \mathbf{s}_k \qquad (63)$$

We again define the "magnetic moment" μ as the expectation value, Eq. (60c), in the state $I_z = I$ of the nuclear spin.

$$\mu = \frac{e\hbar}{2Mc} \int \Psi_N^{I,I}{}^*(\mathbf{r}_1, \ldots \mathbf{r}_A) \left[\sum_{k=1}^{Z} (l_{zk} + g_p s_{zk}) + g_n \sum_{k=Z+1}^{A} s_{zk} \right]$$
$$\times \Psi_N^{I,I}(\mathbf{r}_1, \cdots \mathbf{r}_A) \, d^3r_1 \cdots d^3r_A = \frac{e\hbar}{2Mc} gI \qquad (64)$$

where g is the gyromagnetic ratio (g-factor) of the nucleus.

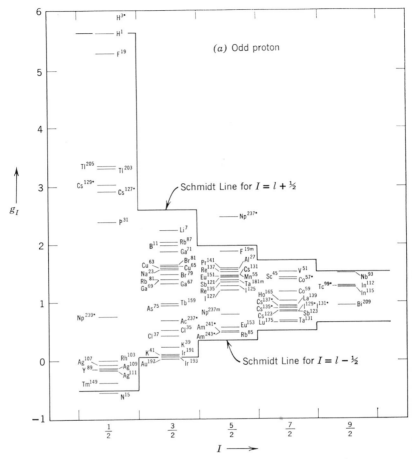

Fig. 2-13 Schmidt lines and experimental nuclear magnetic moments: *, radioactive nuclei; m, metastable states (Segrè[38]).

The magnetic moment of the nucleus is straightforward to calculate in the extreme single-particle model where the magnetic moment is assumed to be entirely due to the odd nucleon, and the orbital and spin angular momenta of all the others cancel in pairs. This is the so-called Schmidt model. Thus from Eqs. (63) and (59) we have

$$\mathbf{I} = \mathbf{l} + \mathbf{s} \tag{65a}$$

$$\boldsymbol{\mu} = \frac{e\hbar}{2Mc}(g_l\mathbf{l} + g_s\mathbf{s}) \tag{65b}$$

where if the odd nucleon is a proton $g_l = 1$, $g_s = g_p$, and if it is a neutron

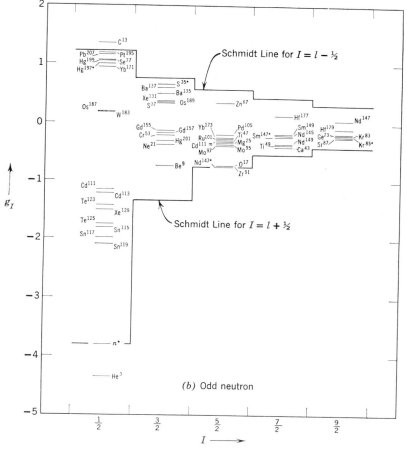

Fig. 2-13 *Continued*

$g_l = 0$, $g_s = g_n$. Since $\mathbf{s} = \frac{1}{2}$, we have $I = l \pm \frac{1}{2}$ or $l = I \mp \frac{1}{2}$. The total angular momentum $\mathbf{I}$ is a constant of the motion, we therefore define the effective magnetic moment $\boldsymbol{\mu}_{\text{eff}}$ as follows:

$$\boldsymbol{\mu}_{\text{eff}} = \frac{1}{I^2} \langle \boldsymbol{\mu} \cdot \mathbf{I} \rangle \mathbf{I} = \frac{e\hbar}{2Mc} \left[g_l \frac{\langle \mathbf{l} \cdot \mathbf{I} \rangle}{I^2} + g_s \frac{\langle \mathbf{s} \cdot \mathbf{I} \rangle}{I^2} \right] \mathbf{I} \tag{66}$$

where

$$\frac{\langle \mathbf{l} \cdot \mathbf{I} \rangle}{I^2} = \frac{I(I+1) + l(l+1) - s(s+1)}{2I(I+1)} \tag{67a}$$

$$\frac{\langle \mathbf{s} \cdot \mathbf{I} \rangle}{I^2} = \frac{I(I+1) - l(l+1) + s(s+1)}{2I(I+1)} \tag{67b}$$

From Eqs. (66), (67a), (67b), and (64), taking the component of $\boldsymbol{\mu}$ with

$I_z = I$, we have

$$g = \frac{1}{I} [\tfrac{1}{2}g_s + (I - \tfrac{1}{2})g_l] \qquad \text{for} \quad l = I - \tfrac{1}{2} \qquad (68a)$$

$$= \frac{1}{I+1} [-\tfrac{1}{2}g_s + (I + \tfrac{3}{2})g_l] \qquad \text{for} \quad l = I + \tfrac{1}{2} \qquad (68b)$$

In Fig. 2-13, the experimental values[38] of the g-factors for odd mass number nuclei are plotted together with the Schmidt lines, Eqs. (68a) and (68b). The experimental values are found mostly to lie between the two Schmidt lines. The extreme single-particle model is an oversimplification; it is thus not surprising that the observed values of the magnetic moments do not correspond to the Schmidt model since the collective behavior of the nucleus would bring about departures from the single-particle approximation.

References

1. Eisberg, R. M., and C. E. Porter, *Rev. Mod. Phys.* **33**, 190, 1961.
2. Akhiezer, A., and I. Pomeranchuk, *J. Phys. (U.S.S.R.)* **9**, 471, 1945.
3. Blair, J. S., *Phys. Rev.* **95**, 1218, 1954.
4. Farwell, G. W., and H. E. Wegner, *Phys. Rev.* **95**, 1212, 1954.
5. Kerlee, D. D., J. S. Blair, and G. W. Farwell, *Phys. Rev.* **107**, 1343, 1957.
6. Woods, R. D., and D. S. Saxon, *Phys. Rev.* **95**, 577, 1954.
7. Igo, G., and R. M. Thaler, *Phys. Rev.* **106**, 126, 1957.
8. Glassgold, A. E., *Rev. Mod. Phys.* **30**, 419, 1958.
9. Fernbach, S., *Rev. Mod. Phys.* **30**, 414, 1958.
10. Perlman, I., and J. O. Rasmussen, in *Handbuch der Physik*, Vol. 42, p. 109, Springer-Verlag, Berlin, 1957.
11. Biswas, S., and A. Patro, *Indian J. Phys.* **22**, 540, 1948.
12. Bethe, H. A., *Rev. Mod. Phys.* **9**, 69, 1937.
13. Bethe, H. A., *Phys. Rev.* **54**, 436, 1938.
14. Hill, D. L., in *Handbuch der Physik* vol. 39, p. 178, Springer-Verlag, Berlin, 1957.
15. Kofoed-Hansen, O., *Rev. Mod. Phys.* **30**, 449, 1958.
16. Pappademos, J. N., *Nucl. Phys.* **42**, 122, 1963.
17. Collard, H., and R. Hofstadter, *Bull. Am. Phys. Soc.* **7**, 489, 1962.
18. Fitch, V. L., and J. Rainwater, *Phys. Rev.* **92**, 789, 1953.
19. Rainwater, J., *Ann. Rev. Nucl. Sci.* **7**, 1, 1957.
20. Ford, K. W., and D. L. Hill, *Ann. Rev. Nucl. Sci.* **5**, 25, 1955.
21. Cooper, L. N., and E. M. Henley, *Phys. Rev.* **92**, 801, 1953.
22. Foldy, L. L., and E. Eriksen, *Phys. Rev.* **95**, 1048, 1954.
23. Mickelwait, A. B., and H. C. Corben, *Phys. Rev.* **96**, 1145, 1954.
24. Anderson, H. L., C. S. Johnson, and E. P. Hincks, *Phys. Rev.* **130**, 2468, 1963.
25. Backenstoss, G., K. Goebel, B. Stadler, U. Hegel, and D. Quitmann, *Nucl. Phys.* **62**, 449, 1965.
26. Ford, K. W., and J. G. Wills, *Nucl. Phys.* **35**, 295, 1962.
27. Hofstadter, R., *Ann. Rev. Nucl. Sci.* **7**, 231, 1957.
28. Heitler, W., *The Quantum Theory of Radiation*, 3rd ed., Chapter 4, p. 430, Oxford University Press, Oxford, 1954.

29. Ravenhall, D. G., see Ref. 27.
30. Sobottka, S., and R. Hofstadter, see Ref. 27.
31. Hahn, B., D. G. Ravenhall, and R. Hofstadter, *Phys. Rev.* **101**, 1131, 1956.
32. Dalitz, R., *Proc. Roy. Soc. London* **206A**, 509, 1951.
33. McKinley, W. A., and H. Feshbach, *Phys. Rev.* **74**, 1759, 1948.
34. Yennie, D. R., D. G. Ravenhall, and R. R. Wilson, *Phys. Rev.* **92**, 1325, 1953; *ibid.*, **95**, 500, 1954.
35. Crannell, H., R. Helm, H. Kendall, J. Oeser, and M. Yearian, *Phys. Rev.* **121**, 283, 1961.
36. Schüler, H., and T. Schmidt, *Z. Physik* **98**, 430, 1935.
37. Rainwater, J., *Phys. Rev.* **79**, 432, 1950.
38. Segrè, E., *Nuclei and Particles*, p. 252, W. A. Benjamin, New York, 1964.

Problems

1. Find the ratio of the magnetic moment μ_0 to the orbital angular momentum l for a particle moving in (a) a circular path and (b) an elliptical path. Comment on the results.

2. Given that $F(q) = \int_{\tau_N} \rho(r) e^{i\mathbf{q}\cdot\mathbf{r}} \, d^3r$, where τ_N is the nuclear volume, $\rho(r)$ the charge distribution in the nucleus, and $\mathbf{q}$ the change in momentum of electron projectile ($\mathbf{q} = \mathbf{k} - \mathbf{k}_0$), show that

$$F(q) = \frac{4\pi}{q} \int_0^{\infty} \rho(r) \sin(qr) r \, dr$$

and that $q = (2p_0/\hbar) \sin(\theta/2)$ where $p_0/\hbar = k_0$ and θ is the scattering angle in the laboratory coordinate system.

3. Assuming a uniform charge density ρ_0 from the center of the nucleus and a linear fall off to zero at the surface over a Compton wavelength of pion, determine an expression for ρ_0.

4. Calculate $F(q)$ for the charge distribution in Problem 3.

5. Using the nuclear wave function $R(r) Y_{1l}(\theta, \phi) \chi_{1/2}$ for the nucleus with one proton outside a closed shell, show that the electric quadrupole moment is given by $Q = -[(2I - 1)/(2I + 2)]\langle r^2 \rangle$, where the nuclear spin $I = l \pm \frac{1}{2}$.

6. Show that the quadrupole moment of the deuteron is

$$Q = \frac{1}{\sqrt{50}} \int_0^{\infty} dr r^2 uw - \frac{1}{20} \int_0^{\infty} dr r^2 w^2$$

where $u(r)$ and $w(r)$ are the radial functions in the S and D states. (For deuteron $J = S = 1$.)

7. Consider a nucleus to be a spherical shell of uniform charge of radius R_0. Neglect relativistic effects as well as the effects of the electrons in the orbits outside the K-shell. Treating the difference in potential energy for point nucleus and the finite size of the nucleus as a small perturbation, calculate the energy correction to the μ-meson in the $1S$-state in a hydrogen-like atom of charge Ze to first order.

3

THE TWO-NUCLEON PROBLEM

3.1 Introduction

To ascertain the many properties of nuclei and to deal with problems such as nuclear structure and binding energies, it is important to understand the nature of the forces existing between nucleons in the nucleus. However, there is not enough known about the internucleon forces, and it is difficult to predict the nuclear properties accurately. In spite of this, theoretical predictions have been made and experiments performed to substantiate these predictions. Consequently, we know a great deal about the nature of nuclear forces despite the fact that the form of the nuclear force law is not known as explicitly as, say, that of the Coulomb law.

The nucleus is complex and is composed of many nucleons; thus even if the internucleon forces were known fully, the nucleus would present a formidable problem for a complete solution. In its simplest form, the two-nucleon potential is considered central and attractive. The following are some of the common potentials used for calculations.

Square-Well Potential

$$V(r) = -V_0 \qquad r \leq r_0$$
$$\quad\;\; = 0 \qquad\quad r > r_0 \qquad\qquad (1a)$$

where r is the relative coordinate of the two nucleons and V_0 is the depth of the potential. The parameter r_0 corresponds to the range.

Exponential Potential

$$V(r) = -V_0 e^{-r/r_0} \qquad\qquad (1b)$$

Gaussian Potential

$$V(r) = -V_0 e^{-r^2/r_0^2} \qquad\qquad (1c)$$

Yukawa Potential

$$V(r) = -V_0 \frac{e^{-r/r_0}}{r/r_0} \qquad\qquad (1d)$$

46

Of all forms, the square well is the least complicated, and it can be solved exactly in quantum mechanics. For this reason, the square-well form of the potential is frequently used in treating several physical problems. This usually provides a reasonable first approximation.

To what extent is the simplified assumption of interaction through such central forces borne out experimentally? Scattering experiments indicate that nuclear forces are short-ranged (although strong) and partly of an "exchange" character. That is, these forces depend not only on r, the separation coordinate, but also on the relative direction of $\mathbf{r}$ and the nucleon spins $\mathbf{s} = \hbar\mathbf{\sigma}/2$. ($\mathbf{\sigma}$ is the Pauli spin matrix.) The potentials $V(r)$ in Eqs. (1) are forms of a purely radial potential called the Wigner potential and have no exchange properties. Three more potentials are the Majorana, Bartlett, and Heisenberg. These are concerned with (1) the exchange of the space coordinates, (2) the exchange of the spin coordinates, and (3) the exchange of both space-spin coordinates.

The Majorana potential is given by

$$V_m(r) = -V_M(r)P_x \tag{2a}$$

where the space-exchange operator P_x has the property

$$P_x\psi(\mathbf{r}_1, \mathbf{r}_2) = \psi(\mathbf{r}_2, \mathbf{r}_1) \tag{2b}$$

and $\mathbf{r}_1$ and $\mathbf{r}_2$ are the position coordinates of nucleons number one and two, and $\psi(\mathbf{r}_1, \mathbf{r}_2)$ is the spatial part of their quantum mechanical wave function. The Bartlett potential

$$V_b(r) = -V_B(r)P_\sigma \tag{3a}$$

contains the spin-exchange operator*

$$P_\sigma = \tfrac{1}{2}(1 + \mathbf{\sigma}_1 \cdot \mathbf{\sigma}_2) \tag{3b}$$

so that

$$P_\sigma\chi(\mathbf{\sigma}_1, \mathbf{\sigma}_2) = \chi(\mathbf{\sigma}_2, \mathbf{\sigma}_1) \tag{3c}$$

where χ is the spin part of the total wave function for nucleons whose Pauli spin matrices are $\mathbf{\sigma}_1$ and $\mathbf{\sigma}_2$. Finally, the Heisenberg potential

$$V_h(r) = -V_H(r)P_H \tag{4a}$$

contains an operator that exchanges both spin and position. This is equivalent to charge exchange or "isotopic spin" exchange (quantum

---

* The spin-exchange operator P_σ acting on the two-nucleon spin singlet state χ_0 (spin antisymmetric state) should change the sign of the spin state, that is, $P_\sigma\chi_0 = -\chi_0$. Similarly, when acting on the spin triplet state χ_1 (spin symmetric state), it should give $P_\sigma\chi_1 = \chi_1$. Noting that the eigenvalues of the operator $\mathbf{\sigma}_1 \cdot \mathbf{\sigma}_2$ are, respectively, -3 and $+1$ for the spin singlet and spin triplet states ($\mathbf{\sigma}_1 \cdot \mathbf{\sigma}_2\chi_0 = -3\chi_0$, $\mathbf{\sigma}_1 \cdot \mathbf{\sigma}_2\chi_1 = \chi_1$), the form, Eq. (3b), of the spin-exchange operator P_σ is readily inferred.

number τ) of the nucleons. This follows from the fact that according to the generalized Pauli exclusion principle the two-nucleon wave function is antisymmetric with respect to exchange of space, spin, and isotopic spin coordinates of the two particles so that $P_H P_\tau = -1$. Thus

$$P_H = P_x P_\sigma = -P_\tau = -\tfrac{1}{2}(1 + \boldsymbol{\tau}_1 \cdot \boldsymbol{\tau}_2) \tag{4b}$$

and

$$P_H \psi(\mathbf{r}_1, \mathbf{r}_2, \boldsymbol{\sigma}_1, \boldsymbol{\sigma}_2) = \psi(\mathbf{r}_2, \mathbf{r}_1, \boldsymbol{\sigma}_2, \boldsymbol{\sigma}_1) \tag{4c}$$

In summary, then, the two-nucleon interaction potential can be written as

$$V(r) = -[V_W(r) + V_M(r)P_x + V_B(r)P_\sigma - V_H(r)P_\tau] \tag{5a}$$

which for the square well becomes

$$V(r) = -V_0(W + MP_x + BP_\sigma - HP_\tau) \tag{5b}$$

where W, M, B, and H are coefficients giving the relative contribution of the various potentials. This potential is still central and it indicates the nature of the nuclear force.*

The exchange nature of nuclear forces is evident from both the scattering experiments and from the binding-energy of the nucleon in the nucleus. If the nuclear force is attractive in all states of the nucleon and is short-ranged, it would seem that in a nucleus consisting of many nucleons the binding energy per nucleon should increase with the increase of the mass number A. In reality, however, evidence is to the contrary, and this binding energy displays a saturation effect. This property of the nuclear force has been explained in terms of the exchange nature of the nuclear force.[3]

The central potential $V(r)$ helps greatly in explaining the two-nucleon interaction, whether in the bound state, such as the deuteron, or in the unbound state, such as nucleon-nucleon scattering. There are two significant discrepancies, however. The algebraic sum of the magnetic moments of the free proton and of the free neutron is not equal to that of the deuteron. Furthermore, a purely radial (central) potential is spherically symmetric, and the quadrupole moment vanishes for a spherically symmetric state. The deuteron, however possesses a (small, positive) quadrupole moment Q which is equal to 2.82×10^{-27} cm². These discrepancies can best be understood in terms of a noncentral tensor force which depends upon the relative orientation of the separation position vector $\mathbf{r}$ and the spins $\mathbf{s}_1$ and $\mathbf{s}_2$ of the two nucleons.

---

* We consider these forces velocity-independent though velocity-dependent forces have been considered by Wheeler[1] and others. Furthermore, they are considered charge-independent after Breit and Feenberg,[2] and Schwinger.[2]

We shall first treat the bound-state deuteron problem quantum mechanically, assuming central forces only. The neutron-proton scattering will next be discussed with a central potential of the square-well type, first ignoring spin and then including it. We shall then consider this problem from the standpoint of the effective range theory, which avoids any assumptions concerning the particular form of the potential. The effective range theory will also be extended to include calculations of the binding energy of the deuteron and the scattering of proton by proton. The experimental results will be presented to substantiate the conclusion reached. Since there is adequate evidence that the force within the the deuteron may not be purely central, we will use tensor interaction in investigating the deuteron problem. This chapter is concerned primarily with the two-nucleon interaction at low energy, namely below 10 Mev. The discussion of the two-nucleon interaction will be completed in chapter 4, with the high energy case approached in a phenomenological manner. The concept of spin-orbit interaction is introduced to account for the experimental results at energies up to 300 Mev.

3.2 The Ground State of the Deuteron

Of the three possible states of the two-nucleon system, di-neutron (nn), di-proton (pp), and deuteron (np), only the deuteron is known to be stable. The deuteron binding energy is[4]

$$W = 2.226 \pm 0.003 \text{ Mev}$$

Other experimentally measured properties of the deuteron are the following:

1. Magnetic moment[5]

$$\mu_d = 0.85735 \pm 0.00003 \text{ nm}$$

where 1 nm = 1 nuclear magneton = $e\hbar/2m_p c$; m_p is the mass of the proton.

2. Electric quadrupole moment[6,25]

$$Q = 2.82 \times 10^{-27} \text{ cm}^2$$

3. Spin $S = 1$ (in units of $\hbar$).

Because the neutron has no charge, the nuclear force binding the deuteron cannot be electrical. Neither can it be a gravitational force, because forces between masses $m_p \approx m_n \approx 1.67 \times 10^{-24}$ gm are far too weak to provide a 2.2 Mev binding energy. Thus the force binding the deuteron is of different origin. Under certain assumptions it is possible to give a simple quantum mechanical description of the deuteron. We proceed with the fact that the force is nuclear in origin and attractive. First, we shall assume that the nuclear force is central; that is, the interaction potential between neutron and proton is some function $V(r)$ where r is the distance separating the two nucleons—the so-called relative coordinate. This assumption somewhat disagrees with the experimentally measured parameters (1) to (3) of the deuteron. Consider the magnetic moment of the proton,[7] $\mu_p = 2.79281 \pm 0.00004$ nm, and of the neutron,[8] $\mu_n = -1.913148 \pm 0.000066$ nm. The fact that $\mu_p + \mu_n - \mu_d$ is not zero (although small) suggests that the deuteron may not be fully described by the spherically symmetric $^3S_1$ state. Moreover, if the nuclear force is due to the exchange of mesons, the magnetic moment of the nucleons when in the free state may not be the same as when in the nucleus. Consequently, a correction to the magnetic moments may arise from mesonic current. In addition, the fact that the electric quadrupole moment of the deuteron is nonzero indicates that the deuteron is not in a purely spherically symmetric state; there is a nonzero probability of finding the deuteron in a higher-l state (see Section 3-11), the ^3D state ($l = 2$).

The D-state contribution to the deuteron ground-state wave function will be treated later by introducing the noncentral tensor force which depends on the orientations of the spin and relative coordinates of nucleons. Thus the forces in the (np) system are spin dependent. At present, however, it will be assumed that the ground state of the deuteron has orbital angular momentum quantum number $l = 0$ and spin quantum number $S = 1$. This means the spins of the neutron and proton are parallel ($\uparrow\uparrow$) and the deuteron is in a triplet-spin state. This approximation is not of great consequence since both $\mu_p + \mu_n - \mu_d$ and the electric quadrupole moment are rather small.

By assuming that the central potential describes the deuteron in its ground state, which is taken to be the $^3S_1$ state, the Schrödinger equation in the center-of-mass system is given by

$$-\frac{\hbar^2}{2\mu} \nabla^2 \psi(\mathbf{r}) + V(r)\psi(\mathbf{r}) = E\psi(\mathbf{r}) \qquad (6a)$$

where the reduced mass

$$\mu = \frac{m_p m_n}{m_p + m_n} \simeq \frac{M}{2} \qquad (6b)$$

and m_p, m_n are the masses of the proton and neutron respectively. The average of these masses is M, and $\mathbf{r}$ is the relative coordinate. Equation (6a) can be written as

$$-\frac{\hbar^2}{M} \frac{d^2 u(r)}{dr^2} + V(r)u(r) = Eu(r) \qquad (6c)$$

where $\psi(r) = u(r)/r$ and $E = -W = -2.226$ Mev equals the binding energy of the deuteron. For the square-well case, Eq. (6c) becomes

$$\frac{d^2u(r)}{dr^2} + \kappa^2 u(r) = 0 \qquad r < r_0 \tag{7a}$$

$$\frac{d^2u(r)}{dr^2} - \gamma^2 u(r) = 0 \qquad r > r_0 \tag{8a}$$

where

$$\kappa = \sqrt{\frac{M}{\hbar^2}(V_0 + E)} = \sqrt{\frac{M}{\hbar^2}(V_0 - W)} \tag{7b}$$

and

$$\gamma = \sqrt{\frac{MW}{\hbar^2}}. \tag{8b}$$

The general solution of Eq. (7a) is

$$u(r) = A \sin \kappa r + B \cos \kappa r \tag{9a}$$

The usual conditions on $\psi(r)$ (finite at $r = 0$ and zero at $r \to \infty$) demand that $u = r\psi$ vanishes at the origin and is square-integrable. The above condition on Eq. (9a) requires that $B = 0$. Thus

$$u(r) = A \sin \kappa r \qquad r < r_0 \tag{9b}$$

The general solution of Eq. (8a) is

$$u(r) = Ce^{-\gamma r} + De^{\gamma r} \tag{10a}$$

and the boundary condition at infinity demands that $D = 0$ so that $u(r)$ remains finite. Thus

$$u(r) = Ce^{-\gamma r} \qquad r > r_0 \tag{10b}$$

Now at $r = r_0$, both $\psi(r)$ [and hence $u(r)$] and its first derivative must be continuous. From Eqs. (9b) and (10b), we have

$$A \sin \kappa r_0 = Ce^{-\gamma r_0} \tag{11a}$$

and

$$A\kappa \cos \kappa r_0 = -\gamma Ce^{-\gamma r_0} \tag{11b}$$

Dividing Eq. (11b) by Eq. (11a), we obtain

$$\kappa \cot \kappa r_0 = -\gamma \tag{12}$$

The value of γ [see Eq. (8b)] is known from the empirical values of W and M. Hence Eq. (12) is a transcendental equation relating the range of the potential r_0 to its depth V_0 [from Eq. (7b)]. Table 3-1 gives the depth V_0 for some representative values of r_0.

Table 3-1 Relationship Between
Range r_0 and Depth V_0 of Potential

Range, r_0 (10^{-13} cm)	Depth of Potential (Mev)
1.0	120
1.5	59
2.0	36
2.5	25
∞	2.83

The results of the approximate calculations are indeed gratifying. From many experimental measurements, it is known that the range of the nuclear force is of the order of 10^{-13} cm. By accepting the approximate value of range $r_0 = 2.0 \times 10^{-13}$ cm, the value of the potential depth is $V_0 = 36$ Mev. From the observed binding energy, the size of the deuteron can be defined by $1/\gamma = 4.3 \times 10^{-13}$ cm, which is about twice that of the range of the potential. This explains the fact that the deuteron is a loosely bound system. (Its binding energy is 1.113 Mev per nucleon compared with the average value of over 8 Mev per nucleon in nuclei.)

Since $V_0 \gg W$, by rewriting Eq. (12) we have

$$\cot \kappa r_0 = -\frac{\gamma}{\kappa} \simeq -\sqrt{\frac{W}{V_0}} \tag{13a}$$

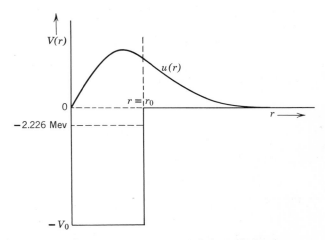

Fig. 3-1 The ground-state wave function of the deuteron, depth of potential and range of nuclear force.

Hence $\cos \kappa r_0 \simeq 0$, and

$$\kappa r_0 \simeq \frac{\pi}{2}, \frac{3\pi}{2}, \ldots \tag{13b}$$

or

$$V_0 r_0^2 \simeq \frac{\hbar^2}{M} \frac{\pi^2}{4}, \frac{\hbar^2}{M}\left(\frac{9\pi^2}{4}\right), \ldots$$

$u(r)$ cannot have a node inside the well, for this would indicate that $u(r)$, and hence $\psi(r)$, is not the lowest (ground) energy level—a contradiction of our hypothesis. Hence only the first term is retained, and

$$V_0 r_0^2 \simeq \frac{\pi^2 \hbar^2}{4M} \tag{13c}$$

The ground-state wave function together with the range and depth of the potential and the ground-state binding energy of the deuteron are shown in Fig. 3-1.

3.3 Excited States of the Deuteron

Experimentally, there is no evidence for the existence of any excited states of the deuteron. Indeed, extending the calculations of the bound state to the cases where the orbital angular momentum quantum number l is greater than zero leads to the result that the deuteron cannot exist in these states. Again it will be assumed that the potential is central and of the square-well type. When we use the separation of variables technique, the radial part of the Schrödinger equation is [again putting $u(r) = r\psi(r)$], for $r \leq r_0$,

$$\frac{d^2 u_l(r)}{dr^2} + \left[\kappa^2 - \frac{l(l+1)}{r^2}\right] u_l(r) = 0 \qquad r \leq r_0 \tag{14a}$$

where κ^2 is given by Eq. (7b). The general solution of this equation involves spherical Bessel functions j_l and spherical Neumann functions n_l. The latter approach $-\infty$ as $r \to 0$ and so the solution to Eq. (14a) is

$$u_l(r) = A j_l(\kappa r) \qquad r \leq r_0 \tag{14b}$$

where

$$j_l(\rho) = \left(\frac{\pi}{2\rho}\right)^{1/2} J_{l+1/2}(\rho) \tag{14c}$$

$J_{l+1/2}$ being the Bessel function of half-odd-integer order. Outside the range of the nuclear force,

$$\frac{d^2 u_l(r)}{dr^2} - \left[\gamma^2 + \frac{l(l+1)}{r^2}\right] u_l(r) = 0 \qquad r > r_0 \tag{15a}$$

where γ^2 is given by Eq. (8b). The solution to this equation is

$$u_l(r) = Bh_l(i\gamma r),\tag{15b}$$

where

$$h_l = j_l + in_l,\tag{15c}$$

the n_l being the spherical Neumann functions given by

$$n_l(\rho) = (-1)^{l+1}\left(\frac{\pi}{2\rho}\right)^{\frac{1}{2}} J_{-l-\frac{1}{2}}(\rho)\tag{15d}$$

The boundary conditions that $u_l(r)$ and its first derivative be continuous at the edge of the well $r = r_0$ may be combined into one condition: the logarithmic derivatives are continuous at $r = r_0$. This gives the relationship between the binding energy and the depth of the potential as

$$\left(\frac{1}{u_l}\frac{du_l(r)}{dr}\right)_i = \left(\frac{1}{u_l}\frac{du_l(r)}{dr}\right)_o \qquad (r = r_0)\tag{16a}$$

(i = inner, o = outer). Using the relation

$$\frac{dj_l(\rho)}{d\rho} = j_{l-1}(\rho) - \frac{l+1}{\rho}j_l(\rho)\tag{16b}$$

we obtain from Eqs. (15a) and (15b)

$$\kappa\left[\frac{j_{l-1}(\kappa r)}{j_l(\kappa r)} - \frac{l+1}{\kappa r}\right]_{r=r_0} = i\gamma\left[\frac{h_{l-1}(i\gamma r)}{h_l(i\gamma r)} - \frac{l+1}{i\gamma r}\right]_{r=r_0}\tag{16c}$$

or

$$\frac{j_{l-1}(\kappa r_0)}{j_l(\kappa r_0)} = \frac{\gamma}{\kappa}\left[\frac{ih_{l-1}(i\gamma r_0)}{h_l(i\gamma r_0)}\right]\tag{16d}$$

Taking $r_0 < 1.43 \times 10^{-13}$ cm, we have $\gamma r_0 < 1$, and since $\gamma \ll \kappa$, the expression in the bracket on the right-hand side is less than 1 and the right-hand side is approximately equal to zero. Therefore, from Eq. (16d),

$$j_{l-1}(\kappa r_0) \approx 0\tag{16e}$$

This condition holds for all angular momenta except $l = 0$.

We have already discussed the case $l = 0$. For $l = 1$ Eq. (16e) gives

$$j_0(\kappa r_0) \approx 0\tag{16f}$$

Using $j_0(\rho) = \sin\rho/\rho$, we obtain from Eq. (16f)

$$\kappa r_0 \simeq \pm\pi, \pm2\pi, \pm3\pi, \ldots\tag{16g}$$

The minimum well depth from Eq. (16g) is thus

$$V_0 \simeq \frac{\pi^2 \hbar^2}{M r_0^2} \tag{16h}$$

where we have made the same assumptions as in Eq. (13c). If we choose $r_0 = 2\text{F} = 2 \times 10^{-13}$ cm (1F = 1 Fermi = 10^{-13} cm), then $V_0 = 144$ Mev. In order to produce a bound state, then, the potential well depth must be considerably larger than that found for the ground state. Repeating this procedure for larger and larger values of l, we find a deeper and deeper well depth is required to produce a bound state. Thus we conclude that no bound state exists for $l \neq 0$.

3.4 Neutron-Proton Scattering at Low Energies

The neutron-proton scattering cross section has been examined extensively, both at low energies and at high energies. The experimental results will be considered in a later section. The scattering cross section depends considerably on the energy of the incident neutrons. At low energies, below 10 Mev, the scattering is essentially due to neutrons with angular momentum $l = 0$. Therefore the angular distribution of the scattered neutrons is isotropic in the center-of-mass system. The chemical binding energy of a proton in a molecule is less than 0.1 ev. Thus to avoid complication from this effect, we consider neutron energies greater than 1 ev, so that the proton is essentially free insofar as the neutrons are concerned.

The Schrödinger equation for a central potential $V(r)$ is given by

$$\left[\nabla^2 + \frac{M}{\hbar^2}(E - V(r)) \right] \psi(\mathbf{r}) = 0$$

where M is the reduced mass of the (np) system. The radial part of the Schrödinger equation is

where

$$\frac{d^2 u_l(r)}{dr^2} + \left[\frac{M}{\hbar^2}(E - V(r)) - \frac{l(l+1)}{r^2} \right] u_l(r) = 0 \tag{17a}$$

$$\psi(\mathbf{r}) = \sum_{l=0}^{\infty} a_l(k) \frac{u_l(r)}{r} P_l(\cos \theta) \tag{17b}$$

$$k = \frac{1}{\lambda} = \sqrt{\frac{ME}{\hbar^2}}$$

and $\cos \theta = \hat{k} \cdot \hat{r}$. The asymptotic form of the solution of Eq. (17a), for large r, is

$$u_l(r) \sim \sin \left(kr - \frac{l\pi}{2} + \delta_l \right) \tag{17c}$$

where δ_l is the scattering phase shift.

The total wave function ψ is composed of the incident plane wave

$$\psi_{\text{inc}} = e^{i\mathbf{k} \cdot \mathbf{r}} = e^{ikr \cos \theta} \tag{17d}$$

and the scattered wave

$$\psi_{\text{sc}} \sim f(\theta) \frac{e^{ikr}}{r} \tag{17e}$$

Hence the complete wave function is

$$\psi = \psi_{\text{inc}} + \psi_{\text{sc}} \sim e^{i\mathbf{k} \cdot \mathbf{r}} + f(\theta) \frac{e^{ikr}}{r} \tag{18a}$$

Expanding this in terms of Legendre polynomials, we may write Eq. (18a) as [Appendix, Eq. (28). Some equations are repeated here for continuity.]

$$\psi(r, \theta) \sim \sum_{l=0}^{\infty} \left[(2l + 1) i^l j_l(kr) + f_l \frac{e^{ikr}}{r} \right] P_l(\cos \theta) \tag{18b}$$

where

$$f(\theta) = \sum_l f_l P_l(\cos \theta) \tag{18c}$$

and

$$j_l(kr) \xrightarrow[r \to \infty]{} \frac{\sin \left(kr - \frac{l\pi}{2} \right)}{kr} \tag{18d}$$

Comparing Eqs. (17b) and (18b) in the asymptotic region $r \to \infty$, we obtain (see Appendix, Section 12)

$$f(\theta) = \frac{1}{k} \sum_{l=0}^{\infty} (2l + 1) e^{i\delta_l} \sin \delta_l P_l(\cos \theta) \tag{19}$$

The differential scattering cross section is defined as the ratio of the number of particles N_s scattered into an element of solid angle $d\Omega$ per second per unit solid angle to the number of incident particles N per unit cross-sectional area per second.

The differential cross section is given by

$$\frac{d\sigma}{d\Omega} = |f(\theta)|^2 \tag{20a}$$

$$= \frac{1}{k^2} \left| \sum_{l=0}^{\infty} (2l + 1) e^{i\delta_l} \sin \delta_l P_l(\cos \theta) \right|^2 \tag{20b}$$

The total cross section is the integral of Eq. (20b) over the entire solid angle

$$\sigma = \int \frac{d\sigma}{d\Omega} d\Omega$$

$$= \frac{4\pi}{k^2} \sum_{l=0}^{\infty} (2l + 1) \sin^2 \delta_l \tag{21a}$$

This is clearly a maximum for

$$\delta_l = (n + \tfrac{1}{2})\pi \qquad n = 0, \pm1, \pm2, \ldots \tag{21b}$$

Consider a low-energy neutron beam (k *very* small) incident on a proton along the z-axis. Then the neutron wave function is given by Eq. (18a). If we assume that the interaction between the neutron and proton is negligibly small, $\delta_l \to 0$ and according to Eq. (19) $f(\theta) \simeq 0$. Hence Eq. (18b) may be written as

$$\psi(\mathbf{r}) \simeq \sum_{l=0}^{\infty} B_l(kr)P_l(\cos\theta) \tag{22a}$$

where

$$B_l(kr) = (2l + 1)i^l j_l(kr) \tag{22b}$$

For $l = 0$

$$B_0(kr) = \frac{\sin(kr)}{kr} \simeq 1 - \frac{(kr)^2}{6} + \cdots \tag{22c}$$

For $l = 1$

$$B_1(kr) = i3\left[\frac{\sin(kr)}{(kr)^2} - \frac{\cos(kr)}{kr}\right]$$

$$\simeq i3\left[\frac{kr}{3} - \frac{(kr)^3}{30} + \cdots\right] \tag{22d}$$

In this treatment, we assume the scattering is elastic and in the center-of-mass system. If the energy of the incident neutron is 1 Mev in the laboratory system, it will be 0.5 Mev in the center-of-mass system. Its momentum is then $p = 1.63 \times 10^{-15}$ gm cm/sec, and its wave number $k = p/\hbar = 1.55 \times 10^{12}$ cm^{-1}. By taking the range of the nuclear force $r_0 = 2 \times 10^{-13}$ cm, we find

$$\left|\frac{B_1}{B_0}\right|^2 \simeq (kr_0)^2 \tag{22e}$$

At this representative energy, then, only about 9% of the scattering is due to neutrons of angular momentum $l = 1$. In fact, if the neutron energy is restricted between the limits 1 ev to 10 Mev, S-wave scattering ($l = 0$) is predominant.

In the absence of a potential, for $l = 0$, Eq. (22a) or Eq. (18b) gives

$$\psi_{l=0}(r) \sim \frac{\sin kr}{kr} = \frac{e^{ikr} - e^{-ikr}}{2ikr} \tag{23a}$$

The first term in the last expression represents an outgoing spherical wave and the second an incoming spherical wave. If a potential is now established, the wave function is given by Eq. (17c) with $l = 0$:

$$\psi_{l=0}(r) = \frac{u_{l=0}(r)}{r} \sim \frac{\sin(kr + \delta_0)}{r} \tag{23b}$$

Since this is a mere proportionality, we may rewrite Eq. (23b) as

$$\psi_{l=0}(r) \sim \frac{e^{i(kr+2\delta_0)} - e^{-ikr}}{2ikr} \tag{23c}$$

From Eqs. (23a) and (23c), we note that the potential affects only the outgoing wave. The difference between (23c) and (23a) is the scattered wave

$$\psi_{sc} \sim \frac{e^{ikr}}{2ikr} (e^{2i\delta_0} - 1) \tag{23d}$$

For elastic scattering, since the phase-shift δ_0 is real,

$$| \text{ outgoing wave } | = | \text{ incoming wave } |$$

where we are neglecting the neutron-proton capture cross section $\sigma_c = 0.33b$[9] (1 b = 1 barn = 10^{-24} cm²) compared with the elastic scattering cross section $\sigma_{sc} = 20.36b$[10]. The total scattering cross section for $l = 0$ is obtained from (21a) and is

$$\sigma_{sc} = 4\pi\lambda^2 \sin^2 \delta_0 \tag{24}$$

For small energy neutrons, their de Broglie wavelength becomes larger than the range r_0 of the nuclear force; consequently, the details of the nuclear potential are not evident at low energy. We note further that from Eqs. (19) and (20b) the differential scattering cross section $d\sigma/d\Omega$ for $l = 0$ is independent of angle, that is, spherically symmetric in the center-of-mass system, a fact that has been verified experimentally at low energy.[11]

3.5 Scattering Length

At low incident neutron energy, the cross section can be expressed in terms of the scattering length a. From Eq. (23c) the asymptotic solution of the wave equation outside the range of the nuclear force can be written as (dropping the subscript on δ_0)

$$u = r\psi = e^{i\delta} \frac{\sin(kr + \delta)}{k} \tag{25a}$$

(This is unnormalized!) Clearly, for very low energy neutrons, in order that u remain finite, δ must approach zero as k does. If we define

$$\lim_{k \to 0} \left(-\frac{\sin \delta}{k} \right) = a \qquad (25b)$$

then Eq. (24) gives

$$\sigma_{sc} = 4\pi \left(\frac{\sin \delta}{k} \right)^2 = 4\pi a^2 \qquad (25c)$$

and a has the geometrical significance of the radius of a hard sphere from which a point neutron is scattered (note: classically $\sigma_{sc} = \pi a^2$).

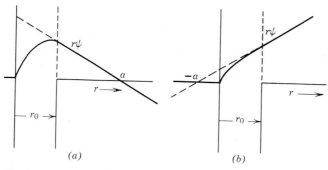

Fig. 3-2 (a) A positive scattering length indicates that a bound state exists. (b) A negative scattering length indicates that there is no bound state of the system.

Since $\delta \to 0$ as k does, and $\delta/k = -a$, using Eq. (25b), we can rewrite Eq. (25a) in the form

$$\lim_{k \to 0} u \sim \frac{kr}{k} + \frac{\delta}{k} = r - a \qquad (25d)$$

which is the equation of a straight line for $u(r)$. The scattering length,[12] a, is the intercept on the r-axis and is obtained by extrapolating the radial wave function inside the well beyond the range of force r_0. Figure 3-2a illustrates the significance of the scattering length. The scattering length a is positive if the scattering state can be a bound state.

3.6   Spin-Dependence of Neutron-Proton Scattering

The theoretical estimate of the value of the scattering cross section σ_{sc} for $l = 0$ is far below the experimentally observed value, as will be seen later. To explain this discrepancy, it is necessary to introduce the spin dependence of the nuclear force.

From Eq. (17a), the radial Schrödinger equation for $l = 0$ inside and outside the square nuclear potential well becomes

$$\frac{d^2u_i}{dr^2} + \kappa^2 u_i = 0 \qquad r \leq r_0 \tag{26a}$$

$$\frac{d^2u_o}{dr^2} + k^2 u_o = 0 \qquad r > r_0 \tag{26b}$$

where

$$\kappa^2 = \frac{M(V_0 + E)}{\hbar^2}, \qquad k^2 = \frac{ME}{\hbar^2} \tag{26c}$$

As in the deuteron problem, using the condition $u \rightarrow 0$ as r does, the solution to Eq. (26a) is given by

$$u_i = D \sin \kappa r \tag{27a}$$

Similarly, the solution for the exterior region is Eq. (23b)

$$u_0 = C \sin (kr + \delta) \tag{27b}$$

The condition that the logarithmic derivatives at $r = r_0$ are continuous gives

$$\frac{1}{u_i} \frac{du_i}{dr}\bigg|_{r=r_0} = \frac{1}{u_0} \frac{du_0}{dr}\bigg|_{r=r_0}$$

or

$$\kappa \cot \kappa r_0 = k \cot (kr_0 + \delta) \tag{27c}$$

The logarithmic derivative $\kappa \cot \kappa r_0$ of the function inside the region can be approximated[19] by the value of the logarithmic derivative $-\gamma$ of the deuteron ground-state wave function. This follows from the Schrödinger Eq. (7a), for the deuteron and Eq. (26a). By subtracting these equations and integrating from 0 to r_0:

$$\left[u \frac{du_d}{dr} - u_d \frac{du}{dr}\right]_0^{r_0} - \frac{M}{\hbar^2}(E + W) \int_0^{r_0} dr \, uu_d = 0 \tag{27d}$$

where u_d represents the deuteron wave function. The contribution of the first term vanishes at $r = 0$ since $u(0) = u_d(0) = 0$. Dividing by $u(r_0)u_d(r_0)$, we obtain

$$\left[\frac{d}{dr} \ln u_d - \frac{d}{dr} \ln u\right]_{r=r_0} = \frac{M}{\hbar^2}(E + W)\eta \tag{27e}$$

with

$$\eta = \frac{\displaystyle\int_0^{r_0} dr \, uu_d}{u(r_0)u_d(r_0)} \simeq \alpha r_0, \qquad 0 < \alpha < 1 \tag{27f}$$

and where we have assumed that $\int_0^{r_0} dr\, uu_d \leq u(r_0)u_d(r_0)r_0$. For a square-well potential, the value of $\alpha \simeq \frac{1}{2}$. From Eqs. (27e) and (27f), we obtain

$$\left[\frac{d}{dr}\ln u\right]_{r=r_0} = -\gamma - \frac{M}{\hbar^2}(E + W)\alpha r_0$$

$$= -\gamma \quad \text{in the limit of zero range } (r_0 = 0). \quad (27\text{g})$$

Thus from Eqs. (27c) and (8b), we have

$$\kappa \cot \kappa r_0 \simeq -\gamma = -\frac{\sqrt{MW}}{\hbar} \quad (28\text{a})$$

and

$$\cot(kr_0 + \delta) \simeq -\frac{\gamma}{k} \quad (28\text{b})$$

If the neutron energy is only a few Kev, then $kr_0 \ll 1$, $\delta \ll 1$, and $k^2 \ll \gamma^2$, and Eq. (28b) is

$$\delta \simeq -\frac{k}{\gamma} - kr_0 \quad (28\text{c})$$

The scattering cross section at low energies from Eq. (24) becomes

$$\sigma_{\text{sc}} \simeq \frac{4\pi}{k^2}\delta^2 = 4\pi\left(\frac{1}{\gamma} + r_0\right)^2 \quad (29\text{a})$$

Using $1/\gamma = 4.3$ F, $r_0 = 2.0$ F, we find that $\sigma_{\text{sc}} = 5.0$ b. Alternatively, if the kr_0 term is neglected in Eq. (28b), we find

$$\sigma_{\text{sc}} \simeq \frac{4\pi}{\gamma^2} = 2.3 \text{ b} \quad \checkmark \quad (29\text{b})$$

Other approximation methods give values somewhere between these two ranges. The experimental value, however, is $\sigma_{\text{sc}} = 20.4$ b. Such a large discrepancy must originate from the assumptions utilized in the derivation of Eqs. (29a) and (29b).

In 1935, Wigner[13] suggested that the internucleon forces are spin-dependent. In the deuteron it was seen that the neutron and proton exist primarily in a triplet spin state ($^3S_1$), that is, with the spins parallel. The spins are said to be correlated. In a general scattering experiment, the neutron beam has its spins randomly oriented and the n-p system is in the triplet and singlet states in proportion to the corresponding weight factors for these states, which are, respectively, $\frac{3}{4}$ and $\frac{1}{4}$. The total scattering cross section consists of two parts

$$\sigma = \tfrac{3}{4}\sigma_t + \tfrac{1}{4}\sigma_s \quad (30)$$

where σ_t and σ_s are the cross sections for scattering in the triplet and singlet states respectively. Experimentally, the weighted average σ as given in Eq. (30) is measured. The triplet cross section σ_t lies between 2.3 and 5.0 b [Eqs. (29a) and (29b)]. In view of the experimental value of 20.4 b, it follows from Eq. (30) that the singlet-state cross section σ_s is between 66.6 and 74.6 b. Thus, although σ_s is operative only one-fourth of the time, it still contributes the most at low energy to the scattering cross section.

3.7 Singlet State in *n-p* System

The ground state of the deuteron is a triplet state. It is of interest to investigate the possibility of a bound deuteron state corresponding to a singlet state.

Let V_t, r_t, and V_s, r_s be the potential depth and range for the triplet and single states respectively. From Eq. (29a), the scattering cross sections in the triplet and singlet states are given by

$$\sigma_t \simeq \frac{4\pi}{k^2} \delta_t^2 = 4\pi \left(\frac{1}{\gamma_t} + r_t\right)^2 \tag{31a}$$

where

$$\delta_t = -k\left(\frac{1}{\gamma_t} + r_t\right) \tag{31b}$$

and

$$\sigma_s \simeq \frac{4\pi}{k^2} \delta_s^2 = 4\pi \left(\frac{1}{\gamma_s} + r_s\right)^2 \tag{32a}$$

where

$$\gamma_t = \sqrt{\frac{MW}{\hbar^2}} \qquad \gamma_s = \sqrt{\frac{MW_s}{\hbar^2}}$$

The total cross section is

$$\sigma = 3\pi \left(\frac{1}{\gamma_t} + r_t\right)^2 + \pi \left(\frac{1}{\gamma_s} + r_s\right)^2 \tag{32b}$$

If we assume $r_t \approx r_s \simeq 2$ F, using $\sigma = 20.4$ b and $1/\gamma_t = 4.3$ F, we find from Eq. (32b) that

$$\left|\frac{1}{\gamma_s}\right| = 2.5 \times 10^{-12} \text{ cm} = 25 \text{ F} \tag{33}$$

which gives $|W_s| = 66$ Kev. Note that Eqs. (32a) and (32b) have not determined the sign of W_s. However, we can find the singlet scattering length a_s [Eq. (25d)], which is negative (for experimental results see Section 3.10). Hence the $W_s = 66$ Kev singlet state is not a bound deuteron state, but a virtual state[14] [see Section 3.9].

3.8   Effective Range Theory in *n-p* Scattering

The energy dependence of the scattering cross section can be expressed in terms of the scattering length a and another parameter which has the dimension of length and is known as the effective range. We denote this parameter by r_0, which is of the same order of magnitude as the range of the nuclear force. Effective range theory predicts the phase shift as a function of energy. Its first calculation was performed by Schwinger[15] and followed by many others.[16] A simpler treatment due to Bethe[17] is given here. We consider S-wave scattering only. The wave equations for two energies, $E = \hbar^2 k^2/M$ and $E = 0$, are

$$u'' + \left(k^2 - \frac{MV}{\hbar^2}\right)u = 0 \tag{34a}$$

$$u_0'' - \frac{MV}{\hbar^2}u_0 = 0 \tag{34b}$$

Multiplying Eqs. (34a) and (34b) by u_0 and u and then subtracting, we obtain

$$\frac{d}{dr}(uu_0' - u_0u') = k^2 uu_0 \tag{34c}$$

We now introduce the auxiliary wave functions v and v_0 which are the solutions to Eqs. (34a) and (34b) for $V = 0$, that is, outside the range of the potential. These are allowed to exist anywhere; however, outside the potential range they coincide with the u and the u_0, respectively. Thus v and v_0 are solutions of

$$v'' + k^2 v = 0 \tag{34d}$$

$$v_0'' = 0 \tag{34e}$$

In a manner similar to Eq. (34c) we obtain from Eqs. (34d) and (34e)

$$\frac{d}{dr}(vv_0' - v_0v') = k^2 v_0 v \tag{34f}$$

By subtracting Eq. (34f) from Eq. (34c),

$$\frac{d}{dr}(uu_0' - u_0u' - vv_0' + v_0v') = k^2(uu_0 - vv_0) \tag{35a}$$

Integrating Eq. (35a) from $r = 0$ to ∞,

$$(uu_0' - u_0u' - vv_0' + v_0v')_{r=0}^{r=\infty} = k^2 \int_0^\infty (uu_0 - vv_0)\, dr \tag{35b}$$

Because $u = v$ and $u_0 = v_0$ outside the potential well, the expression on left-hand side contributes nothing at the upper limit. Furthermore, $u(0) = u_0(0) = 0$. Therefore Eq. (35b) becomes

$$(vv_0' - v_0v')_{r=0} = k^2 \int_0^\infty (uu_0 - vv_0)\, dr \tag{35c}$$

The asymptotic form of v can be written analogously to Eq. (27b). Thus

$$v = C \sin (kr + \delta) \tag{35d}$$

In evaluating the normalization constant C we choose v to be unity at the origin because it is more convenient for later calculations. Thus $C = 1/\sin \delta$ and

$$u(r) \xrightarrow[r \to \infty]{} v(r) \equiv \frac{\sin (kr + \delta)}{\sin \delta} \tag{35e}$$

Equation (34e), $v_0'' = 0$, has a straight line as the solution. Outside the well, $u_0'' = v_0'' = 0$, and recalling Eq. (25d),

$$u_0(r) \xrightarrow[r \to \infty]{} v_0(r) \equiv D(r - a)$$

Since our special normalization gives $v(0) = 1$, we choose D so that

$$v_0(r) \equiv 1 - \frac{r}{a} \tag{35f}$$

Using the relations $v(0) = 1$, $v'(0) = k \cot \delta$, and $v_0'(0) = -(1/a)$ we obtain from Eq. (35c)

$$-\frac{1}{a} - k \cot \delta = k^2 \int_0^\infty (uu_0 - vv_0)\, dr \tag{36a}$$

In the outside region $(r > a)$, the u and v functions approach the same values and the contribution to the integral is negligible. In the inside region we can assume $u \approx u_0$ and $v \approx v_0$. This is because the depth of the potential well V is considerably greater than the energy E, and therefore wave functions u and v depend only slightly on E inside the potential well.[18] In the limit of zero energy neutrons, we define the effective range as

$$r_0 = 2 \int_0^\infty (v_0^2 - u_0^2)\, dr \tag{36b}$$

In this approximation (the so-called shape-independent approximation), Eq. (36a) becomes

$$k \cot \delta = -\frac{1}{a} + r_0 \frac{k^2}{2} \tag{36c}$$

From Eqs. (36c) and (24), the cross section is given by

$$\sigma = \frac{4\pi}{k^2 + \left(\dfrac{1}{a} - \dfrac{r_0 k^2}{2} \right)^2} \tag{37}$$

Besides being a function of $k^2 = ME/\hbar^2$, the cross section is expressed in terms of two parameters, the effective range r_0 and scattering length a. It is clearly independent of the form and shape of the potential. We can determine r_0 and a by measuring cross sections at different low energies of neutrons.

Since the neutron-proton scattering is spin-dependent, actually four parameters are involved: the effective range and scattering length in the triplet and singlet states, r_t, a_t, and r_s, a_s. We have therefore from Eqs. (30) and (37),

$$\sigma = \frac{3\pi}{k^2 + \left(\dfrac{1}{a_t} - \dfrac{r_t k^2}{2}\right)^2} + \frac{\pi}{k^2 + \left(\dfrac{1}{a_s} - \dfrac{r_s k^2}{2}\right)^2} \tag{38}$$

Since the determination of these four parameters is discussed in the section concerning analysis of results, we will only mention that a_t and r_t can be estimated from knowing the ground state of the deuteron, which is a triplet state. The corresponding singlet-state parameters a_s and r_s are determined from neutron-proton scattering experiments.

Effective range calculations for n-p scattering can be extended to obtain the binding energy of the deuteron. Since the method of calculation is similar to that used for n-p scattering, only a brief outline is given here.

We replace v, v_0, u, u_0 by v_B, v_0, u_B, u_0 and k^2 by $-\gamma^2$ (that is E by $-W$) in Eq. (35c). We have

$$[v_B v_0' - v_0 v_B']_{r=0} = -\gamma^2 \int_0^\infty (u_B u_0 - v_B v_0)\, dr \tag{39a}$$

where u_B is the bound-state wave function whose asymptotic form is v_B, and $\gamma = \sqrt{MW}/\hbar$ contains the binding energy W of the deuteron. In view of the large depth of the potential relative to the bound-state energy we can write $v_B \simeq v_0$ and $u_B \simeq u_0$ in the integrand. Equation (39a) is then

$$(v_B v_0' - v_0 v_B')_{r=0} = -\gamma^2 \int_0^\infty (u_0^2 - v_0^2)\, dr = \frac{\gamma^2 r_t}{2} \tag{39b}$$

Proceeding as in Eq. (35c) and using $v_B(0) = v_0(0) = 1$, $v_0'(0) = -1/a_t$, and $v_B'(0) = -\gamma$, from Eq. (39b) we have

$$\gamma = \frac{1}{a_t} + \frac{r_t}{2}\gamma^2 \tag{39c}$$

Thus an experimental determination of r_t and a_t will give γ. In the limit of zero effective range, Eq. (39c) gives $1/\gamma \simeq a_t$. Since $1/\gamma$ is associated with the size of the deuteron, we have that in the limit of zero effective range the scattering is equivalent to scattering on an impenetrable sphere of radius $1/\gamma$.[11]

3.9   Significance of the Sign of the Scattering Length

A positive or negative sign of the scattering length indicates whether the system has a bound or unbound state. Equation (39c) denotes the deuteron system which is in the triplet spin state and is a bound system. In the zero range approximation, or assuming that the second term on the right-hand side is smaller than the first, we note that the sign of both the scattering length and $\gamma = \sqrt{MW}/\hbar$ is positive. Earlier we also interpreted the scattering length a as the cut of the radial wave function $u(r)$ on the r-axis when $u(r)$ is extrapolated outside the range r_0 of the potential. Since the deuteron wave function must incline toward the r-axis (Fig. 3-2a) in order to match the exponentially decaying solution outside the range r_0, the extrapolation of $u(r)$ for $r > r_0$ will make a positive cut on the r axis, therefore implying a positive scattering length. This is precisely the result of Eq. (39c). On the other hand, if the system is unbound, the corresponding radial wave function $u(r)$ (Fig. 3-2b, Section 3.5) will join with an increasing solution outside the range r_0, and then the extrapolation of $u(r)$ will make a negative cut on the r-axis, thus leading to a negative scattering length. In general, a positive scattering length signifies that a bound state of the system exists, whereas a negative scattering length signifies that the system has no bound state.

3.10   Coherent and Incoherent Scattering

The calculations on the scattering of low energy neutrons by a free proton can be extended to the case where the protons are bound in molecules or in crystals. Here, however, it is evident that there will exist a certain amount of coherence in the spins of neighboring protons (for example, the two protons in a hydrogen molecule), and neutrons scattered by such protons can be expected to exhibit interference effects in the scattered beam. One primary condition for this coherent scattering is that the wavelength of the incident neutrons must be greater than the interatomic distances (10^{-8} cm) of the protons. Otherwise the coherence is destroyed by thermal motion.

First, we derive an expression for the coherent scattering cross section for many scattering centers and then discuss some methods of measuring coherent scattering.

Equation (23d) gives the scattered wave function for an S-wave ($l = 0$),

$$\psi_{sc} = \frac{e^{ik|r|}}{2ik\,|\mathbf{r}|}\,(e^{2i\delta} - 1) \tag{40a}$$

Let the different scattering centers be at $\mathbf{r}_1, \mathbf{r}_2, \ldots, \mathbf{r}_N$ and the corresponding phase shifts be $\delta_1, \delta_2, \ldots \delta_N$. If the incident plane wave e^{ikz} falls upon all these scattering centers, then each scatterer contributes its own scattered wave

$$\psi_{sc\,n} = \frac{\exp\left[ik(z_n + |\mathbf{r} - \mathbf{r}_n|)\right]}{2ik\,|\mathbf{r} - \mathbf{r}_n|}(e^{2i\delta_n} - 1) \qquad (40b)$$

where $\mathbf{r}$ is the position vector of the neutron and z_n is the z coordinate of the nth scatterer ($|\mathbf{r}_n| = z_n$) (see Fig. 3-3).

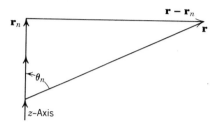

Fig. 3-3 Neutron beam incident along z-axis.

The total scattered wave function is, of course,

$$\psi_{sc} = \sum_n \psi_{sc\,n} \qquad (40c)$$

In general, $r \gg r_n$, and from Fig. 3-3 the law of cosines gives

$$|\mathbf{r} - \mathbf{r}_n| = \sqrt{r^2 + r_n^2 - 2rr_n \cos\theta_n}$$
$$\simeq r\left(1 - \frac{r_n}{r}\cos\theta_n\right) \qquad (40d)$$

We may replace $|\mathbf{r} - \mathbf{r}_n|$ by r in the denominator of Eq. (40b), but in the exponential we use Eq. (40d). Equation (40c) becomes

$$\psi_{sc} = \sum_n \frac{A_n}{2ikr}\,e^{ikz_n}e^{ikr}e^{-ikr_n\cos\theta_n}(e^{2i\delta_n} - 1) \qquad (40e)$$

Assuming the same amplitude A_n for each scatterer, we have

$$\psi_{sc} = \frac{Ae^{ikr}}{kr}\sum_n e^{ik(z_n - r_n\cos\theta_n)}e^{i\delta_n}\sin\delta_n \qquad (40f)$$

The intensity of the scattered beam per unit area is

$$|\psi_{sc}|^2 = \frac{|A|^2}{k^2 r^2}\left|\sum_n e^{i\phi_n}e^{i\delta_n}\sin\delta_n\right|^2 \qquad (40g)$$

where

$$\phi_n = k(z_n - r_n \cos \theta_n) \tag{40h}$$

Equation (40g) can be reformulated as

$$|\psi_{sc}|^2 = \frac{|A|^2}{k^2 r^2} \left\{ \sum_{n=1}^{N} \sin^2 \delta_n + \sum_{n \neq m}^{N} e^{i(\phi_n + \delta_n - \phi_m - \delta_m)} \sin \delta_n \sin \delta_m \right\} \tag{40i}$$

The second term has about as many positive terms as negative for incoherent scattering (that is, for the neutron wavelength smaller than the amplitude of thermal motion of the scattering centers) and can be neglected. On the other hand, the first term is always positive. So in terms of δ_t and δ_s, (40i) reduces to

$$|\psi_{sc}|^2 = \frac{N|A|^2}{k^2 r^2} (\tfrac{3}{4} \sin^2 \delta_t + \tfrac{1}{4} \sin^2 \delta_s) \tag{41a}$$

where N is the number of scattering centers. The number of neutrons scattered per second is

$$N_{sc} = 4\pi r^2 v |\psi_{sc}|^2$$

$$= \frac{4\pi v N |A|^2}{k^2} (\tfrac{3}{4} \sin^2 \delta_t + \tfrac{1}{4} \sin^2 \delta_s) \tag{41b}$$

The scattering cross section is

$$\sigma_{sc} = \frac{N_{sc}}{(\text{incident flux}) \times N} = \frac{N_{sc}}{vN} \tag{41c}$$

$$= \frac{4\pi |A|^2}{k^2} (\tfrac{3}{4} \sin^2 \delta_t + \tfrac{1}{4} \sin^2 \delta_s) \tag{41d}$$

The constant $|A|^2$ involves the "binding factor," a measure of how rigidly the proton scatterer is bound to the molecule or crystal. It is of the order of unity, and is exactly unity for a free proton. For coherent scattering the neutron wavelength $\lambda \gtrsim 10^{-8}$ cm, the interatomic distance, so that its energy $E \lesssim \hbar^2 / 2M\lambda^2 = 0.082$ ev. Certainly, δ_n is small in this very low energy region, and so Eq. (25b) gives

$$\lim_{k \to 0} \left(\frac{\sin \delta_n}{k} \right) = \frac{\delta_n}{k} = -a_n \tag{41e}$$

In this case Eq. (40g) gives

$$|\psi_{sc}|^2 = \frac{|A|^2}{r^2} \left| \sum_n e^{i\phi_n} a_n \right|^2 \tag{41f}$$

Measurement of Coherent Scattering

We shall describe briefly some of the methods used to investigate coherent neutron-proton scattering at low energies. We shall also see how these methods are capable of determining various parameters of scattering.

It is known that diatomic hydrogen gas can exist in two states, ortho- and parahydrogen. In the former molecule, the proton spins are parallel (triplet state), and in the latter, antiparallel (singlet state). Coherent scattering of neutrons from these molecules verifies Wigner's hypothesis that the neutron-proton force is spin-dependent. The calculation of the scattering cross section σ will be similar to the one given by Bethe,[19] which follows the original treatment by Schwinger and Teller.[20] The cross section for ortho- and parahydrogen is expressed in terms of the singlet and triplet scattering lengths a_s and a_t.

The total spin of the neutron-proton system is $\mathbf{S} = \mathbf{s}_n + \mathbf{s}_p$ where the neutron spin is $\mathbf{s}_n = \frac{1}{2}\boldsymbol{\sigma}_n$ and the proton spin is $\mathbf{s}_p = \frac{1}{2}\boldsymbol{\sigma}_p$ (in units of $\hbar$); $\boldsymbol{\sigma}_n$ and $\boldsymbol{\sigma}_p$ are the Pauli spin matrices. $\mathbf{s}_n$ and $\mathbf{s}_p$, being independent, commute. We thus obtain

$$|\mathbf{S}|^2 = |\mathbf{s}_n|^2 + |\mathbf{s}_p|^2 + 2\mathbf{s}_n \cdot \mathbf{s}_p \tag{42a}$$

The eigenvalues of the operator $\mathbf{S}^2$ are $S(S + 1)$; $S = 0$ for the singlet state and $S = 1$ for the triplet. Similarly, $|\mathbf{s}_n|^2 = |\mathbf{s}_p|^2 = \frac{1}{2}(1 + \frac{1}{2}) = \frac{3}{4}$. From Eq. (42a), we therefore have

$$\mathbf{s}_n \cdot \mathbf{s}_p = \frac{1}{2}|\mathbf{S}|^2 - \frac{3}{4} \tag{42b}$$

$$= -\frac{3}{4} \quad \text{for the singlet state}$$

$$= \frac{1}{4} \quad \text{for the triplet state}$$

We can define two "projection operators" which have the following properties:

$$P_t \equiv \frac{3}{4} + \mathbf{s}_n \cdot \mathbf{s}_p = \begin{cases} 0 & \text{for singlet state} \\ 1 & \text{for triplet} \end{cases}$$

$$P_s \equiv \frac{1}{4} - \mathbf{s}_n \cdot \mathbf{s}_p = \begin{cases} 1 & \text{for singlet} \\ 0 & \text{for triplet} \end{cases} \tag{42c}$$

If a_1 and a_2 are the two scattering lengths for scattering of neutron by protons 1 and 2 of the hydrogen molecule, then from Eq. (42c), we obtain for proton number 1

$$a_1 = a_s(\frac{1}{4} - \mathbf{s}_n \cdot \mathbf{s}_{p1}) + a_t(\frac{3}{4} + \mathbf{s}_n \cdot \mathbf{s}_{p1}) \tag{42d}$$

where a_s and a_t are singlet and triplet n-p scattering lengths. A corresponding relation holds for proton 2. If the separation distance between the two protons is less than the neutron wavelength, the scattering length a for scattering by both protons is

$$a = a_1 + a_2 = \frac{a_s + 3a_t}{2} + (a_t - a_s)\mathbf{s}_n \cdot (\mathbf{s}_{p1} + \mathbf{s}_{p2}) \tag{42e}$$

For parahydrogen, the spins are antiparallel and $s_{p1} + s_{p2} = 0$. Using Eq. (42e) and (25c), the scattering cross section per parahydrogen molecule is

$$\sigma_{para/molecule} = 4\pi \left(\frac{3a_t + a_s}{2}\right)^2 \tag{43a}$$

For orthohydrogen the spins are parallel; the total spin of the H_2 molecule is

$$S_H = s_{p1} + s_{p2} \tag{43b}$$

This gives

$$\sigma_{ortho/molecule} = 4\pi \left| \frac{a_s + 3a_t}{2} + (a_t - a_s)s_n \cdot S_H \right|^2 \tag{43c}$$

The neutron spin must be averaged over all possible polarizations of the incident beam. Expanding the scalar product in Cartesian co-ordinates,

$$
\begin{aligned}
|s_n \cdot S_H|^2_{av} = (s_{nx}^2 S_{Hx}^2 &+ s_{ny}^2 S_{Hy}^2 + s_{nz}^2 S_{Hz}^2 \\
&+ s_{nx}s_{ny}S_{Hx}S_{Hy} + s_{nx}s_{nz}S_{Hx}S_{Hz} \\
&+ s_{ny}s_{nx}S_{Hy}S_{Hx} + s_{ny}s_{nz}S_{Hy}S_{Hz} \\
&+ s_{nz}s_{nx}S_{Hz}S_{Hx} + s_{nz}s_{ny}S_{Hz}S_{Hy})_{av}
\end{aligned}
\tag{44a}
$$

From the properties of the Pauli matrices, each of the six cross terms average to zero. Further, $s_n^2 = s_n(s_n + 1) = \frac{3}{4}$, $(s_{nx}^2)_{av} = (s_{ny}^2)_{av} = (s_{nz}^2)_{av} = \frac{1}{4}$. Thus Eq. (44a) becomes

$$|s_n \cdot S_H|^2_{av} = \tfrac{1}{4}(S_{Hx}^2 + S_{Hy}^2 + S_{Hz}^2)_{av} = \tfrac{1}{4}(S_H^2)_{av} = \tfrac{1}{2} \tag{44b}$$

From Eqs. (43c) and (44b), we find

$$\sigma_{ortho/mol} = 4\pi \left[\left(\frac{a_s + 3a_t}{2}\right)^2 + \tfrac{1}{2}(a_t - a_s)^2 \right] \tag{44c}$$

From Eqs. (43a) and (44c), we obtain

$$\sigma_{ortho/mol} = \sigma_{para/mol} + 2\pi(a_t - a_s)^2 \tag{44d}$$

To prove Wigner's hypothesis that the nuclear force is spin-dependent, it is sufficient to show that the orthohydrogen cross section is greater than that of parahydrogen. Such experiments have, in fact, been successfully carried out.[21,22] In some of them[21] the gaseous hydrogen target is enclosed in a tube at the temperature of liquid hydrogen (boiling at a pressure of approximately 60 cm Hg). High-energy neutrons were obtained by bombarding a beryllium target with deuterons from a cyclotron. These neutrons were slowed down in paraffin cooled to liquid air temperature. The range in neutron energies used for scattering varied from $10°$ to $30°$K. The results were $\sigma_{ortho} = 125$ b and $\sigma_{para} = 4$ b. Such a large difference in the values of the cross sections σ_{ortho} and σ_{para} suggests that the singlet n-p scattering length is negative. The most accurate values for the scattering lengths for the triplet and singlet states, determined from the scattering of neutrons by ortho- and parahydrogen and from the (n-p) scattering cross section on free protons are[22] $a_t = 5.37 \pm 0.04 \,\text{F}, a_s = -23.73 \pm 0.07 \,\text{F}$.

Coherent scattering is most accurately measured using the reflection of neutrons from a liquid mirror. The procedure is to measure critical angle of reflection, θ_c, (measured from the normal to the liquid surface) at which the neutrons exhibit the phenomenon of total reflection. The coherent scattering amplitude f_H for hydrogen is negative. The experiment is performed with a liquid containing hydrogen and carbon; the latter has a positive scattering amplitude f_C. The critical angle is given by

$$\theta_c = \lambda_c \sqrt{\frac{N(f_C + 1.5 f_H)}{\pi}} \tag{45}$$

where λ_c is the critical neutron wavelength for a particular θ_c and N is the number of carbon atoms/cm³. In experiments by Hughes, Burgy, and Ringo,[23] the neutrons were reflected from triethylbenzene, because the positive scattering amplitude of carbon f_C is slightly greater than 1.5 times the negative scattering amplitude of hydrogen. The experimental results were $f_C/f_H = -1.753 \pm 0.005$. From the value known for carbon ($f_C = 6.63 \pm 0.03 \,\text{F}$), the value obtained for hydrogen was $f_H = -3.78 \pm 0.02 \,\text{F}$, which compares favorably with $f_H = -3.95 \,\text{F}$.[21]

Another method available for studying coherent scattering depends upon the scattering of slow neutrons by a crystal containing hydrogen. In these experiments diffraction maxima occur at angles determined by the structure of the crystal. From Eq. (41f) the maximum intensity of the diffraction pattern occurs if the scattered waves are all in phase. Then all the ϕ_n in Eq. (41f) differ by integral multiples of 2π. In this case Eq. (41f) gives

$$\left| \sum_{n=1}^{N} e^{i\phi_n} a_n \right|^2 = \left| \sum_{n=1}^{N} a_n \right|^2 = N(\tfrac{3}{4} a_t + \tfrac{1}{4} a_s)^2 \tag{46}$$

and the intensity of the diffraction peak is proportional to $(3a_t/4 + a_s/4)^2$. In the experiment the coherent scattering amplitude was measured in a NaH crystal.[24] A beam of neutrons from a reactor was reflected from a NaCl crystal to produce monoenergetic neutrons. This beam was then reflected from the crystal powder sample of NaH. The neutrons scattered from the powder sample at a certain angle were then detected and counted by a BF₃ counter. A spectrum from the powder was obtained by rotating the sample and the detector through various angles. A plot was then made of counter angle versus counts per minute, from which the crystal structure factor and the coherent scattering amplitude f_H for hydrogen were calculated. The results were $f_H = -3.96$ F and $(\sigma_H)_{coh} = 2.0$ b.

3.11 Tensor Forces and the Deuteron Problem

Both the neutron-proton scattering and the binding energy of the deuteron have been studied previously by assuming that the interaction potential is central and the bound state of the deuteron is a $^3S_1$ state. In other words, a spherically symmetric charge distribution is assumed, suggesting that the electric quadrupole moment is zero. Experimentally, however, a small positive electric quadrupole moment was observed. The most recent value is[25]

$$Q = 2.88 \times 10^{-27} \text{ cm}^2$$

This implies that the interaction potential between a neutron and proton is not purely central and the wave function is not spherically symmetric. Additional support for this conclusion comes from the magnetic moment consideration, $\mu_p + \mu_n - \mu_d \neq 0$. We can surmise the nature of the ground state wave function of the deuteron by using the facts that the total angular momentum J equals 1 and that it is a state of definite parity. The value J equals 1 can be obtained from different combinations of the orbital angular momentum l and spin S, such as

$$l = 0, \qquad S = 1 \rightarrow {}^3S_1$$
$$l = 1, \qquad S = 0 \rightarrow {}^1P_1; \qquad l = 1, \quad S = 1 \rightarrow {}^3P_1$$
$$l = 2, \qquad S = 1 \rightarrow {}^3D_1$$

and no others.* If the wave function of the deuteron is a mixture of some of these states, it can only be $^3S_1$ with $^3D_1$, or $^1P_1$ with $^3P_1$; we can combine states of the same parity (l even or l odd but not l even *and* l odd). Noting that S and D are even parity states, whereas the P state is odd, we now consider which mixture of states is likely to give the ground state wave function of the deuteron with the observed properties. For this we make use of the vector addition of two angular momenta as discussed in the Appendix, Section 7.

The angular momentum wave function $\mathscr{Y}_{lSJ}^M$ for a two-particle system in the orbital angular momentum state l and spin state S, forming the total angular momentum J with z-component M, is given by

$$\mathscr{Y}_{lSJ}^M = \sum_{M_s m_l} \langle lSm_lM_s \mid JM \rangle \chi_S^{M_s} Y_l^{m_l} \tag{47a}$$

* For example, ^3F cannot occur because for $S = 1$, $l = 3$, $J = 2$, 3, or 4 and $J = 1$ is not reached.

where the $Y_l^{m_l}$ are the spherical harmonics, $\chi_S^{M_s}$ are the spin wave functions, and $\langle l S m_l M_s \mid J M \rangle$ are the Clebsch-Gordan coefficients.

The two spin-half particles have the following triplet spin states ($S = 1$):

$$\chi_1^1 = \langle \tfrac{1}{2}\tfrac{1}{2}\tfrac{1}{2}\tfrac{1}{2} \mid 11 \rangle \alpha(1)\alpha(2) = \alpha(1)\alpha(2) \tag{47b}$$

$$\chi_1^0 = \langle \tfrac{1}{2}\tfrac{1}{2} -\tfrac{1}{2}\tfrac{1}{2} \mid 10 \rangle \alpha(1)\beta(2) + \langle \tfrac{1}{2}\tfrac{1}{2}\tfrac{1}{2} -\tfrac{1}{2} \mid 10 \rangle \alpha(2)\beta(1)$$

$$= \frac{1}{\sqrt{2}} [\alpha(1)\beta(2) + \alpha(2)\beta(1)] \tag{47c}$$

and

$$\chi_1^{-1} = \langle \tfrac{1}{2}\tfrac{1}{2} -\tfrac{1}{2} -\tfrac{1}{2} \mid 1 - 1 \rangle \beta(1)\beta(2) = \beta(1)\beta(2) \tag{47d}$$

The singlet state is

$$\chi_0^0 = \langle \tfrac{1}{2}\tfrac{1}{2}\tfrac{1}{2} -\tfrac{1}{2} \mid 00 \rangle \alpha(1)\beta(2) + \langle \tfrac{1}{2}\tfrac{1}{2} -\tfrac{1}{2}\tfrac{1}{2} \mid 00 \rangle \beta(1)\alpha(2)$$

$$= \frac{1}{\sqrt{2}} [\alpha(1)\beta(2) - \beta(1)\alpha(2)] \tag{47e}$$

where $\alpha = \begin{pmatrix} 1 \\ 0 \end{pmatrix}$ and $\beta = \begin{pmatrix} 0 \\ 1 \end{pmatrix}$ are "spin up" and "spin down" states of the nucleon. The arguments of the α's and β's stand for particle number one or two. The angular momentum wave functions $\mathscr{Y}_{lSJ}^M$ for the four states corresponding to $J = 1$ are the following:

$^3S_1$: $J = 1$, $M = 1$, $l = 0$, $S = 1$

$$\mathscr{Y}_{011}^1 = \langle 0101 \mid 11 \rangle Y_0^0 \alpha(1)\alpha(2)$$

$$= Y_0^0 \alpha(1)\alpha(2) \tag{47f}$$

$^3D_1$: $J = 1$, $M = 1$, $l = 2$, $S = 1$

$$\mathscr{Y}_{211}^1 = \sum_{M_s} \langle 21(1 - M_s)M_s \mid 11 \rangle Y_2^{1-M_s} \chi_1^{M_s}$$

$$= \sqrt{\frac{3}{5}} \, Y_2^2 \beta(1)\beta(2) - \sqrt{\frac{3}{10}} \, Y_2^1 \frac{1}{\sqrt{2}} [\alpha(1)\beta(2) + \beta(1)\alpha(2)]$$

$$+ \sqrt{\frac{1}{10}} \, Y_2^0 \alpha(1)\alpha(2) \tag{47g}$$

$^1P_1$: $l = 1$, $S = 0$, $J = M = 1$

$$\mathscr{Y}_{101}^1 = \langle 1010 \mid 11 \rangle Y_1^1 \chi_0^0$$

$$= Y_1^1 \frac{1}{\sqrt{2}} [\alpha(1)\beta(2) - \beta(1)\alpha(2)] \tag{47h}$$

$^3P_1$: $l = S = J = M = 1$

$$\mathscr{Y}_{111}^1 = \sum_{M_s} \langle 11(1 - M_s)M_s \mid 11 \rangle Y_1^{1-M_s} \chi_1^{M_s}$$

$$= \frac{1}{\sqrt{2}} \, Y_1^1 \frac{1}{\sqrt{2}} [\alpha(1)\beta(2) + \beta(1)\alpha(2)] - \frac{1}{\sqrt{2}} \, Y_1^0 \alpha(1)\alpha(2) \tag{47i}$$

We now have the angular momentum wave functions for the four states possible. We shall use these wave functions to study some known properties such as the magnetic dipole and electric quadrupole moments of the deuteron.

The Magnetic Moment of the Deuteron

The magnetic moments of the neutron[8] (μ_n), the proton[7] (μ_p), and the deuteron[6,25] (μ_d) have been very accurately measured. The difference, $(\mu_p + \mu_n) - \mu_d = 0.0222$ nm, is small, but definitely not zero. This suggests that the deuteron is mostly in a $^3S_1$ state, but spends a small amount of time in some other state.

We wish to find which mixture of states can explain the magnetic moment of the deuteron. Introducing the spin wave function for the neutron and proton as in Eqs. (47b) to (47e)

$$\chi_1^1 = \alpha(p)\alpha(n)$$

$$\chi_1^0 = \frac{1}{\sqrt{2}}[\alpha(p)\beta(n) + \beta(p)\alpha(n)]$$

$$\chi_1^{-1} = \beta(p)\beta(n) \tag{48a}$$

and

$$\chi_0^0 = \frac{1}{\sqrt{2}}[\alpha(p)\beta(n) - \beta(p)\alpha(n)],$$

we can write the wave function $\phi_{lSJ}(\mathbf{r})$ for the four cases discussed, in terms of three radial wave functions $u_l(r)$, $v_l(r)$ and $w_l(r)$, where the subscript l is the orbital angular momentum quantum number.

$$^3S_1: \quad \phi_{011}^1(\mathbf{r}) = \frac{u_0(r)}{r}\mathscr{Y}_{011}^1 = \frac{u_0(r)}{r}Y_0^0\chi_1^1$$

$$^3D_1: \quad \phi_{211}^1(\mathbf{r}) = \frac{u_2(r)}{r}\mathscr{Y}_{211}^1$$

$$= \frac{u_2(r)}{r}\left[\sqrt{\frac{3}{5}}Y_2^2\chi_1^{-1} - \sqrt{\frac{3}{10}}Y_2^1\chi_1^0 + \sqrt{\frac{1}{10}}Y_2^0\chi_1^1\right] \tag{48b}$$

$$^1P_1: \quad \phi_{101}^1(\mathbf{r}) = \frac{v_1(r)}{r}\mathscr{Y}_{101}^1 = \frac{v_1(r)}{r}Y_1^1\chi_0^0$$

$$^3P_1: \quad \phi_{111}^1(\mathbf{r}) = \frac{w_1(r)}{r}\mathscr{Y}_{111}^1$$

$$= \frac{w_1(r)}{r}\left[\frac{1}{\sqrt{2}}Y_1^1\chi_1^0 - \frac{1}{\sqrt{2}}Y_1^0\chi_1^1\right]$$

The nuclear magnetic moments have been already defined in Chapter 2. Taking the magnetic moment projection along the z-axis and noting that in the center-of-mass system the orbital angular momentum associated with the proton is half of the relative orbital angular momentum ($\mathbf{l}_p = \frac{1}{2}\mathbf{l}$), the z-component of the deuteron magnetic moment is

$$\mu_z = \tfrac{1}{2}l_z + g_p s_{pz} + g_n s_{nz} \tag{48c}$$

where g_p and g_n are the gyromagnetic ratios for the proton and neutron, and s_{pz} and s_{nz} are the z-components of their respective spins. Quantum mechanically, Eq. (48c) is an operator and the magnetic moment in the state ϕ_{lSJ}^M is found by taking the expectation value

$$\langle \mu_z \rangle = \int d^3 r \, \phi_{lSJ}^{*\,M} \mu_z \phi_{lSJ}^M \tag{48d}$$

This may be written in Dirac notation as

$$\langle \phi_{lSJ}^M | \mu_z | \phi_{lSJ}^M \rangle = \left\langle \frac{u_l}{r} \mathcal{Y}_{lSJ}^M \middle| \mu_z \middle| \frac{u_l}{r} \mathcal{Y}_{lSJ}^M \right\rangle \tag{48e}$$

We shall compute these expectation values for the states $^3S_1$, $^3D_1$, $^1P_1$, $^3P_1$. We note that†

and that
$$l_z Y_l^m = m Y_l^m; \qquad g_{p,n} = 2\mu_{p,n}; \qquad (s_{p,n})_z = \tfrac{1}{2}(\sigma_{p,n})_z$$

$$\begin{array}{ll}
s_{pz}\chi_1^1 = \tfrac{1}{2}\chi_1^1 & s_{nz}\chi_1^1 = \tfrac{1}{2}\chi_1^1 \\
s_{pz}\chi_1^0 = \tfrac{1}{2}\chi_0^0 & s_{nz}\chi_1^0 = -\tfrac{1}{2}\chi_0^0 \\
s_{pz}\chi_1^{-1} = -\tfrac{1}{2}\chi_1^{-1} & s_{nz}\chi_1^{-1} = -\tfrac{1}{2}\chi_1^{-1} \\
s_{pz}\chi_0^0 = \tfrac{1}{2}\chi_1^0 & s_{nz}\chi_0^0 = -\tfrac{1}{2}\chi_1^0
\end{array} \tag{48f}$$

By making use of the relations in Eqs. (48b), (48c), (48d), and (48f), we have the following expressions:

$$\mu_z \mathcal{Y}_{011}^1 = \tfrac{1}{2}(g_p + g_n)\mathcal{Y}_{011}^1 = \frac{g_p + g_n}{2} Y_0^0 \chi_1^1$$

$$\mu_z \mathcal{Y}_{211}^1 = \sqrt{\frac{3}{5}}\left(1 - \frac{g_p + g_n}{2}\right) Y_2^2 \chi_1^{-1} - \frac{1}{2}\sqrt{\frac{3}{10}} Y_2^1[\chi_1^0 + (g_p - g_n)\chi_0^0]$$

$$+ \sqrt{\frac{1}{10}} \frac{g_p + g_n}{2} Y_2^0 \chi_1^1 \tag{48g}$$

$$\mu_z \mathcal{Y}_{101}^1 = \tfrac{1}{2} Y_1^1[\chi_0^0 + (g_p - g_n)\chi_1^0]$$

$$\mu_z \mathcal{Y}_{111}^1 = \frac{1}{2\sqrt{2}}\Big[Y_1^1 \chi_1^0 + g_p(Y_1^1 \chi_0^0 - Y_1^0 \chi_1^1) - g_n(Y_1^1 \chi_0^0 + Y_1^0 \chi_1^1) \Big]$$

† We shall use the values[7,8] $\mu_p = 2.7928$ nm, $\mu_n = -1.9131$ nm.

By using the orthonormality of the Y_l^m's when integrated over the solid angle and that of the $\chi_S^{m_s}$, and Eqs. (48b), (48e), and (48g), we obtain the expectation values:

$$^3S_1: \quad \langle \phi_{011}^1 | \mu_z | \phi_{011}^1 \rangle = \frac{g_p + g_n}{2} \int_0^\infty u_0^2(r) \, dr = \frac{g_p + g_n}{2} = 0.8797 \text{ nm}$$

$$^3D_1: \quad \langle \phi_{211}^1 | \mu_z | \phi_{211}^1 \rangle = \left[\frac{3}{4} - \frac{1}{4} (g_p + g_n) \right] \int_0^\infty u_2^2(r) \, dr$$

$$= [\tfrac{3}{4} - \tfrac{1}{4}(g_p + g_n)] = 0.3101 \text{ nm}$$

$$^1P_1: \quad \langle \phi_{101}^1 | \mu_z | \phi_{101}^1 \rangle = \frac{1}{2} \int_0^\infty v_1^2(r) \, dr = 0.5000 \text{ nm}$$

$$^3P_1: \quad \langle \phi_{111}^1 | \mu_z | \phi_{111}^1 \rangle = [\tfrac{1}{4} + \tfrac{1}{4}(g_p + g_n)] \int_0^\infty w_1^2(r) \, dr$$

$$= [\tfrac{1}{4} + \tfrac{1}{4}(g_p + g_n)] = 0.6899 \text{ nm}$$

(48h)

In stating that the radial functions integrate to unity over the range $0 \le r \le \infty$, we have tacitly assumed that the deuteron is entirely in one of the four states. However, the experimental value of the magnetic moment of the deuteron has been very accurately determined[5] as 0.8573 nm, which is not equal to any one of the values in Eq. (48h). We are therefore forced to consider a mixture of states to attain this experimental value.

As mentioned earlier, in constructing the ground-state wave function of the deuteron, only states of the same parity can be mixed, that is, $^3S_1$ with $^3D_1$, and $^1P_1$ with $^3P_1$. For an S and D mixture, the wave function is

$$\phi = \phi_S + \phi_D$$
$$= \phi_{011}^1 + \phi_{211}^1 \qquad (49a)$$

The normalization condition gives

$$\langle \phi | \phi \rangle = P_S + P_D = 1 \qquad (49b)$$

where $P_S = \int_0^\infty u_0^2 \, dr$ and $P_D = \int_0^\infty u_2^2 \, dr$ are the probabilities of finding the deuteron in the S and D states respectively. Using Eq. (48h) we find the magnetic moment for an even parity mixture, Eq. (49a), is

$$\mu(^3S_1 + {}^3D_1) = \tfrac{1}{2}(g_p + g_n)P_S + [\tfrac{3}{4} - \tfrac{1}{4}(g_p + g_n)]P_D \qquad (49c)$$

Equations (49b) and (49c) are two equations for the two unknowns P_S and P_D. By inserting the experimental values for $\mu(^3S_1 + {}^3D_1) = \mu_d$, and g_p and g_n, we obtain $P_D = 0.04$. Thus, if the deuteron remains about 4% of time in the $^3D_1$ state, the experimental value of μ_d is obtained. When relativistic effects, meson currents, etc. are taken into account, however, it would seem that this value should be about 10%.[26] A similar calculation indicates that the magnetic moment found from a mixture of $^1P_1$ and $^3P_1$ states is below the value for a pure $^3P_1$ state—0.6899 nm which itself is 24% smaller than the experimental result. Relativistic, mesonic, and any other corrections thus far considered[27,28] are too small to account for the discrepancy.

In conclusion, a study of the magnetic moment of the deuteron makes it clear that the ground-state wave function is predominantly in the $^3S_1$ state with a small admixture of $^3D_1$. However, the uncertain nature of some of the corrections, especially relativistic, makes it difficult to say precisely the percentage composition of the two states. We can, therefore, write the ground-state wave function of the deuteron as

$$\psi_d = \frac{u_0}{r}\mathscr{Y}_{011}^1 + \frac{u_2}{r}\mathscr{Y}_{211}^1 \tag{49d}$$

The Quadrupole Moment of the Deuteron

Having established that the ground state of the deuteron is primarily a $^3S_1$ state with a small admixture of $^3D_1$, it is interesting to see what more information can be learned from the electric quadrupole moment Q. The value of Q can be found in a straightforward manner. From Chapter 2, Eq. (44), we have

$$Q = \int \psi_{\text{nucl}}^*(3z^2 - r^2)\psi_{\text{nucl}}\, d^3r \tag{50a}$$

$$= \int \psi_{\text{nucl}}^*(3\cos^2\theta - 1)\psi_{\text{nucl}}\, r^2\, d^3r \tag{50b}$$

In the center-of-mass system, the distance of the neutron and proton from the center of mass is $r/2$, and only the proton contributes to Q, the neutron being uncharged. Using the ground-state wave function of the deuteron ψ_d, the quadrupole moment is

$$Q = \frac{1}{4}\int \psi_d^*(3\cos^2\theta - 1)\psi_d\, r^2\, d^3r \tag{50c}$$

In terms of spherical harmonics, this becomes

$$Q = \frac{1}{4}\sqrt{\frac{16\pi}{5}}\int \psi_d^*(r^2 Y_2^0)\psi_d\, d^3r \tag{50d}$$

Using Eq. (49d) for ψ_d, we obtain

$$Q = \frac{1}{4}\sqrt{\frac{16\pi}{5}}\int [u_0^2\mathscr{Y}_{011}^{*1}Y_2^0\mathscr{Y}_{011}^1 + u_0 u_2(\mathscr{Y}_{011}^{*1}Y_2^0\mathscr{Y}_{211}^1 + \mathscr{Y}_{011}^1 Y_2^0\mathscr{Y}_{211}^{*1})$$
$$+ u_2^2\mathscr{Y}_{211}^{*1}Y_2^0\mathscr{Y}_{211}^1]\, d^3r \tag{50e}$$

The first term represents the pure $^3S_1$ contribution, and when integrated over the solid angle it is zero because of spherical symmetry. In the second term, we note the two terms in the parentheses are Hermitian conjugates of each other (the only imaginary contribution comes from $e^{im\phi}$ in the Y_l^m's). Hence the second term can be written as

$$\frac{2}{4}\sqrt{\frac{16\pi}{5}} \int u_0 u_2 \mathscr{Y}_{011}^{*1} Y_2^0 \mathscr{Y}_{211}^1 \, d^3r \tag{51a}$$

which, after angular integration, gives

$$\frac{1}{\sqrt{50}} \int_0^\infty u_0 u_2 r^2 \, dr \tag{51b}$$

The third term, the contribution from the $^3D_1$ state, gives

$$-\frac{1}{20} \int_0^\infty u_2^2 r^2 \, dr \tag{51c}$$

Using Eqs. (51c) and (51c) in Eq. (50e) gives

$$Q = \frac{\sqrt{2}}{10} \int_0^\infty u_0 u_2 r^2 \, dr - \frac{1}{20} \int_0^\infty u_2^2 r^2 \, dr \tag{52}$$

It is necessary to know the radial wave functions to proceed further; but these depend upon the nature of the nuclear force. We therefore digress briefly and consider the nuclear force in some detail.

From the presence of a quadrupole moment Q and the nonadditivity of the magnetic moments ($\mu_p + \mu_n \neq \mu_d$), we have concluded that the nature of the nuclear force is at least partially noncentral, that is, it contains partly a "tensor" force. We surmise that the potential must be symmetric in the coordinates of the two nucleons and invariant under rotations and reflections of their space coordinates. This means the potential is a scalar. The only quantities available for constructing scalars are the separation vector $\mathbf{r}$ of the neutron and proton and their spins $\mathbf{s}_1 = \frac{1}{2}\hbar\boldsymbol{\sigma}_1$ and $\mathbf{s}_2 = \frac{1}{2}\hbar\boldsymbol{\sigma}_2$. The various scalars that can be constructed out of $\mathbf{r}$, $\boldsymbol{\sigma}_1$, and $\boldsymbol{\sigma}_2$ have been discussed in the Appendix, Section 16, together with the properties of the tensor operator

$$S_{12} = 3(\boldsymbol{\sigma}_1 \cdot \hat{r})(\boldsymbol{\sigma}_2 \cdot \hat{r}) - (\boldsymbol{\sigma}_1 \cdot \boldsymbol{\sigma}_2) \tag{53a}$$

where $\hat{r} = \mathbf{r}/r$ is a unit vector. The tensor force is due to the following potential

$$V = V_T(r)S_{12} \tag{53b}$$

In order to generalize the potential, we include a pure central term and a pure spin term along with Eq. (53b)

$$V = V_d(r) + V_\sigma(r)(\boldsymbol{\sigma}_1 \cdot \boldsymbol{\sigma}_2) + V_T(r)S_{12} \tag{53c}$$

The Schrödinger equation is therefore (center-of-mass system)

$$\left\{-\frac{\hbar^2}{M}\nabla^2 + V_c + V_T S_{12}\right\}\psi_d = E\psi_d \tag{53d}$$

where

$$V_c(r) = V_d(r) + V_a(r) \tag{53e}$$

is the central potential in the triplet state and ψ_d is given by Eq. (49d). By using Eq. (49d) and rearranging Eq. (53d),

$$\left\{-\frac{\hbar^2}{M}\nabla^2 + V_c - E\right\}\left(\frac{u_0}{r}\mathscr{Y}_{011}^1 + \frac{u_2}{r}\mathscr{Y}_{211}^1\right)$$

$$+ V_T\left\{\frac{u_0}{r}\sqrt{8}\,\mathscr{Y}_{211}^1 + \frac{u_2}{r}(\sqrt{8}\,\mathscr{Y}_{011}^1 - 2\mathscr{Y}_{211}^1)\right\} = 0 \tag{54a}$$

In writing Eq. (54a) we have used the following properties of S_{12} (Appendix, Table A-3):

$$S_{12}\mathscr{Y}_{011}^1 = \sqrt{8}\,\mathscr{Y}_{211}^1$$
$$S_{12}\mathscr{Y}_{211}^1 = \sqrt{8}\,\mathscr{Y}_{011}^1 - 2\mathscr{Y}_{211}^1 \tag{54b}$$

We note that

$$\nabla^2 = \frac{1}{r^2}\frac{\partial}{\partial r}\left(r^2\frac{\partial}{\partial r}\right) - \frac{L^2}{\hbar^2 r^2} \tag{54c}$$

where

$$L^2 = -\frac{\hbar^2}{\sin^2\theta}\left[\sin\theta\frac{\partial}{\partial\theta}\left(\sin\theta\frac{\partial}{\partial\theta}\right) + \frac{\partial^2}{\partial\phi^2}\right] \tag{54d}$$

and

$$L^2 Y_l^m(\theta, \phi) = l(l+1)\hbar^2 Y_l^m(\theta, \phi) \tag{54e}$$

We therefore find

$$\nabla^2\left(\frac{u_0}{r}\mathscr{Y}_{011}^1\right) = \frac{1}{r}\frac{d^2 u_0}{dr^2}\mathscr{Y}_{011}^1 \tag{54f}$$

and

$$\nabla^2\left(\frac{u_2}{r}\mathscr{Y}_{211}^1\right) = \left(\frac{1}{r}\frac{d^2 u_2}{dr^2} - \frac{1}{r}\frac{2(2+1)}{r^2}u_2\right)\mathscr{Y}_{211}^1 \tag{54g}$$

If we multiply Eq. (54a) by $\mathscr{Y}_{011}^{*1}$, integrate over the solid angle, and make use of the orthonormality property of the $\mathscr{Y}_{lSJ}^M$'s,

$$-\frac{\hbar^2}{M}\frac{d^2 u_0}{dr^2} + (V_c - E)u_0 = -\sqrt{8}\,V_T u_2 \tag{55a}$$

Similarly, multiplying Eq. (54a) by $\mathscr{Y}_{211}^{*1}$ and integrating, we obtain

$$-\frac{\hbar^2}{M}\left(\frac{d^2 u_2}{dr^2} - 6\frac{u_2}{r^2}\right) + (V_c - 2V_T - E)u_2 = -\sqrt{8}\,V_T u_0 \tag{55b}$$

These equations were first obtained by Rarita and Schwinger.[49] Equations (55a) and (55b) are coupled differential equations. If one postulates a reasonable form for V_c and V_T, the radial wave functions can be computed numerically. The electric quadrupole moment can be calculated from Eq. (52). There are four variable parameters: range and depth of the potentials V_c and V_T. This problem has been discussed and results derived for various potential forms.[29] The binding energy and quadrupole moment of the deuteron are known and provide two relations, thus effectively leaving two free parameters. The experimental values of the magnetic moment and the triplet effective range for *n-p* scattering are usually used for the determination of the two remaining parameters. However, these do not lead to a unique determination of the four parameters. Generally, several sets of values of the parameters fit the experimental quantities almost equally well.

We shall return to this problem toward the end of this chapter and in Chapter 4 where there will be further discussion of the specification of the two-nucleon interaction from the study of the so-called double and triple scattering parameters.

3.12 Proton-Proton Scattering at Low Energy

In many ways, proton-proton scattering experiments are easier to perform than neutron-proton scattering experiments. First it is possible to obtain highly monoenergetic beams of protons from different types of accelerators. Also, because of its ionization ability, it is easier to detect a proton and measure its energy. The proton-proton interaction differs from a neutron-proton because of the Coulomb repulsion. In fact, below 100 Kev, the Coulomb force prevents close contact between two protons. The nuclear potential still exists but its effect is small. As the energy increases above this value, however, the interaction potential becomes a mixture of Coulomb and nuclear potentials. In addition, identical particles must have antisymmetric wave functions in accordance with the Pauli exclusion principle. Therefore, the symmetric spatial wave function combines with an antisymmetric spin wave function and vice versa.

In this section we shall use some of the formulas derived in the Appendix, Section 14, in order to deduce results for proton-proton scattering, using the effective range theory.

Effective Range Calculations for Proton-Proton Scattering

Effective range calculations for *p-p* scattering are essentially similar to those for *n-p* scattering. The one complication is the inclusion of the Coulomb effect in the calculations. But we can still describe *p-p* scattering in terms of a scattering length a_p and an effective range r_{0p}.

We shall begin by considering S-waves ($l = 0$) scattering for the p-p system. We consider the Coulomb forces (center-of-mass system) at two different energies, E_1 and E_2 within the range of nuclear force. Thus for these two relative (center-of-mass) energies, the Schrödinger equations are

$$-\frac{\hbar^2}{2\mu} u_1'' + \left[\frac{e^2}{r} + V(r)\right] u_1 = E_1 u_1 \tag{56a}$$

$$-\frac{\hbar^2}{2\mu} u_2'' + \left[\frac{e^2}{r} + V(r)\right] u_2 = E_2 u_2 \tag{56b}$$

where $V(r)$ and e^2/r are the nuclear and Coulomb potentials, respectively, and μ is the reduced mass. Introducing

$$k_1^2 = \frac{2\mu E_1}{\hbar^2}, \qquad k_2^2 = \frac{2\mu E_2}{\hbar^2}, \qquad \text{and} \quad R = \frac{\hbar^2}{2\mu e^2}$$

Eqs. (56a) and (56b) can be rewritten as follows:

$$u_1'' + \left[k_1^2 - \frac{1}{Rr} - \frac{\hbar^2 V(r)}{2\mu}\right] u_1 = 0 \tag{56c}$$

$$u_2'' + \left[k_2^2 - \frac{1}{Rr} - \frac{\hbar^2 V(r)}{2\mu}\right] u_2 = 0 \tag{56d}$$

Multiplying these two equations by u_2 and u_1, respectively, and subtracting, we obtain

$$u_1'' u_2 - u_2'' u_1 = (k_2^2 - k_1^2) u_1 u_2 \tag{57a}$$

At large r, $V(r) = 0$, and we introduce the two Coulomb wave functions $v_1(r)$ and $v_2(r)$ which are asymptotic forms of $u_1(r)$ and $u_2(r)$ outside the range of the nuclear force. They satisfy the differential equations

$$v_1'' + \left(k_1^2 - \frac{1}{Rr}\right) v_1 = 0 \tag{57b}$$

$$v_2'' + \left(k_2^2 - \frac{1}{Rr}\right) v_2 = 0 \tag{57c}$$

Multiplying Eqs. (57b) and (57c) by v_2 and v_1, respectively, and subtracting, we have

$$v_1'' v_2 - v_2'' v_1 = (k_2^2 - k_1^2) v_1 v_2 \tag{57d}$$

Subtracting Eq. (57a) from Eq. (57d),

$$v_1'' v_2 - v_2'' v_1 - u_1'' u_2 + u_2'' u_1 = (k_2^2 - k_1^2)(v_1 v_2 - u_1 u_2) \tag{57e}$$

or

$$\frac{d}{dr}\left(v_1' v_2 - v_2' v_1 - u_1' u_2 + u_2' u_1\right) = (k_2^2 - k_1^2)(v_1 v_2 - u_1 u_2) \tag{57f}$$

Integrating Eq. (57f) from $r = 0$ to ∞, we obtain

$$(v_1'v_2 - v_2'v_1 - u_1'u_2 + u_2'u_1)_0^\infty = (k_2^2 - k_1^2) \int_0^\infty (v_1v_2 - u_1u_2) \, dr \quad (57\text{g})$$

As $r \to \infty$, u's and v's become identical. At $r = 0$, the u's must vanish to keep $\psi = u/r$ finite, leaving

$$[v_1'v_2 - v_2'v_1]_{r=0} = (k_2^2 - k_1^2) \int_0^\infty (v_1v_2 - u_1u_2) \, dr \quad (57\text{h})$$

Because of the Coulomb interaction, the asymptotic functions $v(r)$ cannot be treated in precisely the same way as in the n-p case. As seen in the Appendix, the solution of the Coulomb equation is made up of a linear combination of sine and cosine terms having the argument $[kr - \eta \ln (2kr) + \text{constant}]$, where* $\eta = \mu e^2/\hbar^2 k = e^2/\hbar v$. The constant is chosen so that $\sin [kr - \eta \ln (2kr) + \text{const.}]$ becomes the asymptotic form and is zero at $r = 0$. This then is the regular solution. The cosine part is the irregular solution because it does not vanish at $r = 0$ as the sine does. For the Coulomb case the regular and irregular solutions are obtained from the properties of the confluent hypergeometric function or a series expansion.

The regular solution is

$$F_l(kr) \sim \sin \left[kr - \eta \ln (2kr) - \frac{l\pi}{2} + \sigma_l \right] \quad (58\text{a})$$

For $l = 0$, this reduces to

$$F_0(kr) = C_0 kr(1 + \eta kr + \cdots) \quad (58\text{b})$$

where

$$C_0 = \frac{2\pi\eta}{e^{2\pi\eta} - 1} \quad (58\text{c})$$

C_0 is the Coulomb penetration factor. At small energies less than 100 Kev, the Coulomb field prevents the protons from approaching close enough for the nuclear potential to have any effect. At higher energies (small η), however, $C_0 \to 1$, and the scattering is due primarily to the nuclear potential except at small scattering angles.

The irregular solution is

$$G_l(kr) \sim \cos \left[kr - \eta \ln (2kr) - \frac{l\pi}{2} + \sigma_l \right] \quad (59\text{a})$$

For $l = 0$ this becomes

$$G_0(kr) = \frac{1}{C_0} [1 + 2\eta kr\{\ln (2\eta kr) + 2\gamma - 1 + h(\eta)\} + \cdots] \quad (59\text{b})$$

* The symbol η is used here instead of ε used in the Appendix.

where γ = Euler's constant = $0.57722 \cdots$ and

$$h(\eta) = \eta^2 \sum_{n=1}^{\infty} \frac{1}{n(n^2 + \eta^2)} - \ln \eta - \gamma \tag{59c}$$

The series expansions of $F_0(kr)$ and $G_0(kr)$ are made around $kr = 0$. If $\eta = 0$ (one particle uncharged), F_0 and G_0 reduce to the asymptotic form which corresponds to the wave function for the n-p system

$$v_{np}(r) = \frac{\sin(kr + \delta)}{\sin \delta} = \cos kr + \cot \delta \sin kr \tag{59d}$$

By analogy, the asymptotic form for the wave function of the p-p system is

$$v_{pp}(r) = C_0[G_0(kr) + \cot \delta F_0(kr)] \tag{59e}$$

using the same C_0 as in Eq. (58c). The next step is to eliminate $v_1'(0)$ and $v_2'(0)$ from Eq. (57h). Using the series forms for $F_0(kr)$ and $G_0(kr)$, differentiation of Eq. (59e) gives

$$\frac{dv}{dr} = C_0 \frac{dG_0}{dr} + C_0 \cot \delta \frac{dF_0}{dr} \tag{60a}$$

At $r = 0$,

$$\frac{dF_0}{dr}\bigg|_{r=0} = C_0 k$$

and

$$C_0 \frac{dG_0}{dr}\bigg|_{r=0} = \frac{1}{R} \ln \frac{r}{R} + \frac{2\gamma}{R} + \frac{1}{R} h(\eta) \tag{60b}$$

where we note $\eta = 1/2Rk$. Substituting Eqs. (60b) in Eq. (60a), we obtain

$$v'(0) = \frac{1}{R} \ln \frac{r}{R} + \frac{2\gamma}{R} + \frac{1}{R} h(\eta) + C_0^2 k \cot \delta \tag{60c}$$

The term $(1/R) \ln (r/R)$ is logarithmically divergent as $r \to 0$. However, since in Eq. (57h) the difference $v_1'(0) - v_2'(0)$ [letting $v_1(0) = v_2(0) = 1$] is involved, this term cancels out. Thus from Eqs. (57h) and (60c) we obtain

$$\frac{1}{R} h(\eta_2) + C_{02}^2 k_2 \cot \delta_2 - \frac{1}{R} h(\eta_1) - C_{01}^2 k_1 \cot \delta_1$$

$$= (k_2^2 - k_1^2) \int_0^{\infty} (v_1 v_2 - u_1 u_2)\, dr \tag{60d}$$

Applying the definition of scattering length near zero energy as in Eq. (25b), where $k_1 \to 0$, we have

$$\lim_{k_1 \to 0} \left[C_{01}^2 k_1 \cot \delta_1 + \frac{1}{R} h(\eta_1) \right] = -\frac{1}{a_p} \tag{60e}$$

Equations (60d) and (60e) combine to give

$$C_0^2 k \cot \delta + \frac{1}{R} h(\eta) = -\frac{1}{a_p} + k^2 \int_0^\infty (v_0 v - u_0 u)\, dr \qquad (60f)$$

where k_2 has been replaced by k. At low energies we make the same approximations as for the n-p system, namely $v \approx v_0$ and $u \approx u_0$. We define the effective range r_{0p} at zero energy of incident protons to be

$$r_{0p} \equiv 2 \int_0^\infty (v_0^2 - u_0^2)\, dr \qquad (60g)$$

Equation (60f) now becomes

$$C_0^2 k \cot \delta + \frac{1}{R} h(\eta) = -\frac{1}{a_p} + \frac{k^2}{2} r_{0p} \qquad (61)$$

Equation (61) expresses the p-p scattering in terms of the effective range, scattering length, and the Coulomb interaction $(1/R)\, h(\eta)$. It will be recalled that it was possible to discuss n-p scattering at very low energies. For p-p scattering, however, at very low energies, the nuclear interaction between the two protons is completely overshadowed by the Coulomb effect (η becomes very large as the energy diminishes). In spite of this, extrapolation procedures yield a value for the effective range $r_{0p} = 2.65 \times 10^{-13}$ cm $= 2.65$ F.[30] This singlet-state value compares well with the singlet-state n-p effective range $r_{0p} = 2.4 \pm 0.3$ F.[24] It appears, then, that the nuclear force is charge independent. Thus, for low energies at least, the same nuclear potential can describe the singlet state scattering of both the n-p and p-p systems.

3.13   Analysis of n-p and p-p Scattering

In this section we shall compare our theoretical predictions with experimental observations. High-energy scattering results will also be included for completeness.

n-p Scattering at Low Energy

The common meeting ground between theory and experiment lies in the determination of the phase shifts which are introduced by a partial wave analysis. For n-p scattering at low energy the total cross section for a free proton is given by Eq. (24):

$$\sigma_{sc} = 4\pi \left(\frac{\sin \delta}{k} \right)^2$$

where δ is the phase shift due to the nuclear force and k is the wave number of the incident neutron. At the zero energy limit the cross section is expressed in terms of the scattering length a and is given by Eq. (25c),

$\sigma_{sc} = 4\pi a^2$. The effective range theory gave us four parameters related to the phase shift, the singlet and triplet effective ranges and scattering lengths r_s, r_t, a_s, and a_t. The total cross section σ was expressed in terms of these in Eq. (38). By determining cross sections in coherent scattering experiments, these parameters have been determined. Table 3-2 gives several results.

Table 3-2 Scattering Parameters and Cross Sections Obtained from Low-Energy *n-p* Scattering Experiments and the Analysis of Data

References	σ (barns)	f_H(F)	a_s(F)	a_t(F)	r_t(F)	r_s(F)
Melkonian[10]	20.36 (free proton)					
Squires et al.[22]	20.41 (free proton)					
Noyes[45]			−23.678	5.396	1.726	2.51
Hughes et al.[23]		−3.75	−23.67	5.40	1.74	
		−3.78	−23.69	5.37	1.70	
Shull et al.[24]	2.0 (coherent)	−3.96	−23.5	5.20	1.6	2.7
Sutton et al.[21]	125 (para) 4 (ortho)	−3.95	−23.71	5.38	1.6	

In conclusion we can make the following assertions:

1. The *n-p* scattering is spin dependent.
2. Most of the neutron scattering is due to the singlet state.
3. The singlet state is not bound, as is indicated by the negative value of a_s.

Proton-proton Scattering at Low Energy

For *p-p* scattering the effective range expression is very similar to the one for *n-p* scattering, except for the addition of the Coulomb effect [Eq. (61)]. For comparison with experimental results, it is expedient to introduce a "nuclear well shape" parameter[31] T in Eq. (61). Thus

$$C_0^2 k \cot \delta + \frac{h(\eta)}{R} = -\frac{1}{a_p} + \frac{k^2}{2} r_{0p} - T k^4 r_{0p}^3 \tag{62}$$

For *n-p* scattering, T is usually small and is neglected. The determination of phase shifts through the scattering length a_p and the effective range

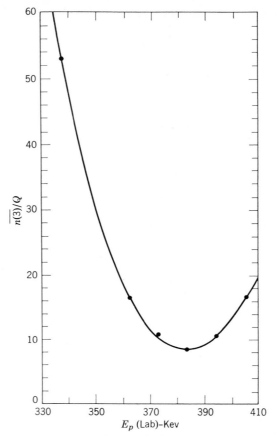

Fig. 3-4 Comparison of relative counting rate as a function of proton energy E_p near the interference minimum with best theoretical fit (omitting point at 373 Kev) in which the theoretical cross section has been folded with the finite geometrical resolution. Fit shown gives $E_{min} = 383.43 \pm 0.13$ Kev, with $a = -7.80$ F and $r_0 = 2.65$ F. Best fit with all six points gives a curve indistinguishable from the other with the linewidth employed (Brolley et al.[30]).

r_{0p} links theory and experiment for the *p-p* system. In the $l = 0$ state, the system exists only in the $^1S_0$ state and hence the only parameters to be determined are a_p and r_{0p} for the singlet state.

In the *p-p* scattering experiments the Coulomb force is repulsive and the nuclear force attractive, and there will be interference between the effect of these forces. This interference results in a low cross section at a particular energy. The observed energy minimum is very near 383 Kev. Recent experiment[30] gives $T = 0.028$, $a_p = -7.80$ F, and $r_{0p} = 2.65$ F. The energy for the minimum occurs at 383.4 Kev. The experimental results, Fig. 3-4, indicate that the *p-p* system is in the $^1S_0$ state, which is virtual as is evidenced from the negative value of a_p.

High-energy n-p and p-p Scattering

Neutron-proton scattering.   At high energy, the wavelength λ of the incident particle is sufficiently short to permit observation of the finer details of the nuclear interaction potential. At high energy, the presence of higher angular momentum states results in a large number of parameters, making the data much more difficult to interpret and relate to theory. The analysis is still more complicated for neutrons since a monoenergetic neutron beam is not available. For proton-proton scattering, however, a monoenergetic beam can be obtained relatively easily. Because of the Pauli exclusion principle, there are only half as many states over a given energy range, and therefore half as many phase shifts as in neutron-proton scattering. The analysis is, however, not simple.

Figure 3-5 gives a graphical summary of the experimental results for the *n-p* scattering cross section σ_{np} as compiled by Wilson.[32] We recall that near zero energy $\sigma_{np} = 20.36$ b. As the energy of the incident neutron increases, the scattering cross section σ_{np} diminishes rapidly. From about 10 Mev up to around 200 Mev, $\sigma_{np} \sim 1/E_n$. Between 200 Mev and 400 Mev, σ_{np} varies only slightly. Below 300 Mev, the scattering is elastic. The threshold for meson production is about 300 Mev. Above this energy, $\sigma_{np} = \sigma_{elas} + \sigma_{inelas}$. The cross section rises to 42 mb at about 1400 Mev and falls back to 38 mb at about 2500 Mev.

Some differential cross sections $d\sigma/d\Omega$ are presented in Fig. 3-6[32] as a function of the angle θ_{cm} in the center-of-mass system for energies up to 580 Mev. The most striking fact about these distributions is the forward ($\theta_{cm} = 0°$) and backward ($\theta_{cm} = 180°$) maxima (see Chen et al.).

The peak at 0° can be understood in terms of absorption and diffraction of neutrons in the scattering medium. The "backward peaking" at 180° is the result of the exchange force which interchanges the neutron and proton position coordinates, the Majorana force. Serber[33] suggested a potential which is a mixture of the ordinary central and Majorana potentials in order to explain the forward and backward peaking. The Serber potential is attractive for states of even *l* and vanishes for states of odd *l*; it is given by

$$V(r) = -V_0[1 - \tfrac{1}{4}(1 + \boldsymbol{\sigma}_1 \cdot \boldsymbol{\sigma}_2)(1 + \boldsymbol{\tau}_1 \cdot \boldsymbol{\tau}_2)] \tag{63}$$

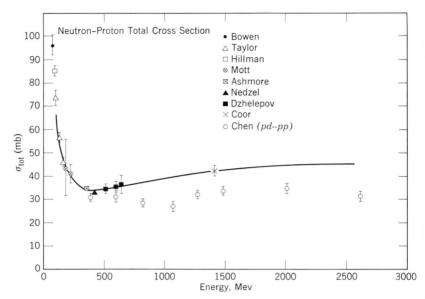

Fig. 3-5 Plot of σ versus E for total n-p cross section (Wilson[32]).

Bowen, P. H., G. C. Cox, G. B. Huxtable, A. H. Langsford, J. P. Scanlon, and J. J. Thresher, *Phys. Rev. Letters*, **7**, 248, 1961.

Taylor, A. E., and E. Wood, *Phil. Mag.* **44**, 95, 1952.

Hillman, P., R. H. Stahl, and N. F. Ramsey, *Phys. Rev.* **96**, 115, 1954.

Mott, G. R., G. L. Guernsey, and B. K. Nelson, *Phys. Rev.* **88**, 9, 1952.

Ashmore, A., R. G. Jarvis, D. S. Mather, and S. K. Sen, *Proc. Phys. Soc.* (*London*) **A70,** 745, 1957.

Nedzel, V. A., *Phys. Rev.* **94**, 174, 1959.

Dzhelepov, V. P., U. B. Moskalev, and S. B. Medvedev, *Dokl. Akad. Nauk SSSR*, **104**, 380, 1955.

Coor, T., D. A. Hill, W. F. Hornyak, L. H. Smith, and G. Snow, *Phys. Rev.* **98,** 1369, 1955.

Chen, F. F., C. P. Leavitt, and A. M. Shapiro, *Phys. Rev.* **103**, 211, 1956.

where τ_1 and τ_2 are the isospins. By using this potential, the scattering amplitude and hence the cross section are predicted to be even functions of θ. This turns out to be the case (approximately) to about 200 Mev. However, at higher energies, this is not true and it is apparent that the odd l terms cannot be neglected entirely.

Proton-proton scattering. The proton-proton scattering cross sections have been measured from low to very high energies: up to the Bev (billion electron volt) range. At high energy the scattering cross section σ_{pp} is measured using polyethylene and liquid H_2 as both an attenuator of the

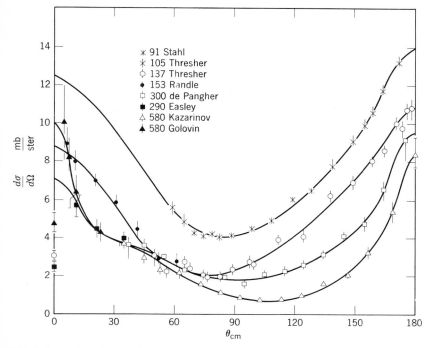

Fig. 3-6 *np* Angular distribution from 90 to 580 Mev. The lines are merely to guide the eye (Wilson[32]).

Stahl, R. H., and N. F. Ramsey, *Phys. Rev.* **96**, 1310, 1954.
Thresher, J. J., R. G. P. Voss, and R. Wilson *Proc. Roy. Soc. London*, **A229**, 492, 1955.
Randle, value quoted by Wilson.[32]
de Pangher, J., *Phys. Rev.* **99**, 1447, 1955.
Easley, J. W., UCRL Rept. No. 2693, 1954.
Kazarinov, Yu. M., and Yu. N. Simonov. *Soviet Phys. JETP*, **4**, 161, 1957.
Golovin, B. M., V. P. Dzhelepov, Yu. Katyshev, A. D. Konin, and S. B. Medvedev. Joint Institute for Nuclear Research p. 243, 1958.

incident beam and as a target. The total cross section (except for Coulomb) σ_{pp} in the region below 300 Mev, where the scattering is elastic, is calculated from the differential cross section. The total cross section, together with the elastic cross section, for *p-p* scattering is given in Fig. 3-7.[34] (Low energy data are not given in this graph.) The total cross section σ_{pp} falls rapidly from 72 mb at 40 Mev to 23 mb at 140 Mev. This value remains roughly the same up to about 350 Mev, beyond which the meson production plays a part. The total cross section rises to 48 mb at 850 Mev and stays approximately constant to about 1500 Mev. After this the cross section more or less steadily diminishes. The differential cross section of

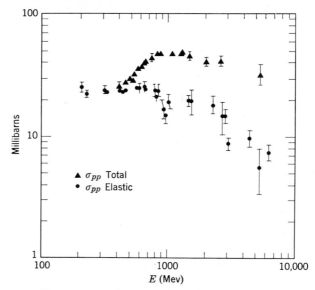

Fig. 3-7 Experimental values of the total and elastic proton-proton cross sections up to Bev-energy range (Hess[34]).

proton-proton scattering is presented in Fig. 3-8[35] based on data collected by Hess.[34] The total cross section above 400 Mev is $\sigma_{tot} = \sigma_{elas} + \sigma_{inel}$. At small angles in the center-of-mass system, there is interference between Coulomb and nuclear scattering. In the range slightly over 100 to 400 Mev, the differential cross section is found to be nearly isotropic, the value being 3.6 mb/sterad. The deviation above 400 Mev is a result of meson production.

The explanation of the isotropy of the p-p differential cross section was first given by Jastrow[48] in terms of a hard (repulsive) core potential interaction.

The differential cross section is[48]

$$\frac{d\sigma_{pp}(\theta)}{d\Omega} = \tfrac{1}{4}\,|f_s(\theta) + f_s(\pi - \theta)|^2 + \tfrac{3}{4}\,|f_t(\theta) - f_t(\pi - \theta)|^2$$
$$= \lambda^2 \sum_{l,l'=\text{even}} (2l + 1)(2l' + 1)\sin\delta_l^s \sin\delta_{l'}^s \cos\delta_{ll'}^s P_l P_{l'}$$
$$+ 3\lambda^2 \sum_{l,l'=\text{odd}} (2l + 1)(2l' + 1)\sin\delta_l^t \sin\delta_{l'}^t \cos\delta_{ll'}^t P_l P_{l'}$$
$$\delta_{ll'} = \delta_l - \delta_{l'}$$

where s and t stand for spin singlet and spin triplet states of the p-p system. In this expression the squared (direct) terms are positive while the interference terms can have both positive and negative signs. Since, at $\pi/2$, the successive even Legendre polynomials alternate in sign, the interference terms such as the *S-D* terms etc. are negative at $\pi/2$ and positive at $0°$, provided the interaction potential is of the same sign everywhere so that the phase shifts are of the same sign. The odd angular momenta contribute zero at $\pi/2$ and maximum at $0°$. Thus a potential of the same sign everywhere would give an angular distribution which

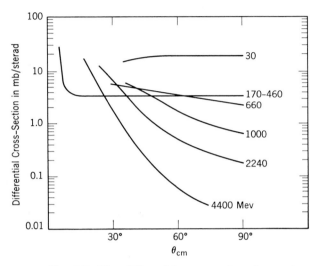

Fig. 3-8 The differential cross section for proton-proton scattering at different energies between 30 and 4400 Mev (Lock[35]).

is predominantly forward. However, if, in addition to the attractive potential, a short-range strongly repulsive potential (hard core) is introduced in the *p-p* interaction, it can lead to isotropy in the angular distribution. This follows from the fact that as the energy increases, the *S*-wave will be affected more by the repulsive hard core and less by the outer attractive potential so that the *S* phase shift will change from positive to negative as the energy increases. Since the impact parameter is larger for higher angular momentum states, these are affected largely by the attractive potential, and the higher phase shifts will remain positive with increasing energy until energies are reached at which they change sign. Thus in this energy region the *S-D* interference term will be positive at $\pi/2$ and negative at $0°$, thereby tending to reduce the scattering in the forward direction and increasing it at $\pi/2$ resulting in the isotropy of the scattering cross section.

Neutron-neutron Scattering

If we assume nuclear forces are charge independent, then neutron-neutron scattering should be equal to proton-proton scattering except at small energies, where Coulomb effects are also present. This type of experiment has been carried out[36] by bombarding D_2O and H_2O with neutrons and noting the difference between the two types of scattering. The differential cross section $(d\sigma/d\Omega \equiv \sigma(\theta))$ for neutron-deuteron scattering, $\sigma_{nd}(\theta)$, is

$$\sigma_{nd}(\theta) = \sigma_{nn}(\theta) + \sigma_{np}(\theta) + I(\theta) \tag{64}$$

where $I(\theta)$ represents the interference term. The experimental results[36] indicate that at 300 Mev

$$\sigma_{nn}(\theta) = 3.7 \pm 0.6 \text{ mb/sterad}$$
$$(\sigma_{nn})_{\text{tot}} = 22 \pm 5 \text{ mb}$$
$$\sigma_{pp}(\theta) = 3.6 \text{ mb/sterad}$$
$$(\sigma_{pp})_{\text{tot}} = 23 \text{ mb}$$

The close agreement between the total scattering cross sections σ_{nn} and σ_{pp} supports the hypothesis of charge independence of nuclear forces.

3.14 Interpretation of *p-p* and *n-n* Scattering

We first reiterate some pertinent facts. At small scattering angles in the center-of-mass system the differential cross section for scattering shows the effect of a long-range Coulomb potential. At higher angles the cross section becomes nearly constant at 3.6 mb/sterad. Above 400 Mev the increase in the cross section is explained adequately by the inelastic scattering leading to the production of π-mesons. Below this energy the scattering is elastic.

Furthermore, by comparing the cross sections for *p-p* and *n-n* scattering, we see the values are nearly the same. This is explained by the assumption that nuclear scattering is charge independent. The *n-p* system has both singlet and triplet states corresponding to the isotopic spin (isospin) states $T = 1$ and 0. On the other hand, in the *p-p* system only the triplet isotopic spin state exists (symmetric isotopic spin state $T = 1$). It follows from Pauli's principle that the space-spin states should be antisymmetric. This involves combining even orbital angular momentum states with the spin singlet state, and combining the odd angular momentum states with the spin triplet state. Thus the *p-p* and *n-n* systems will be only in the configurations $^1S_0$, $^3P_{0,1,2}$, $^1D_2$, $^3F_{2,3,4}$, $\cdots$. The *n-p* system has $T_z = 0$ and therefore is a mixture of $T = 0$ and $T = 1$ states. The $T = 1$ state combines with the space-spin states as in the *p-p* system. The $T = 0$ state being isospin antisymmetric will now have even l combine with the spin triplet state, and odd l combine with the spin singlet state.

Finally, we note that the method of partial wave analysis is fairly simple for low-energy scattering ($l = 0$), but it becomes very involved at higher energies because of the higher angular momentum states which give nonnegligible contributions. There is a phase shift for each angular momentum and spin state and a large number of parameters have to be determined to obtain a fit with experimental data.[37]

The question now arises from the preceding, "What is the nature of the nuclear potential which encompasses all these effects?" As we saw, Wigner's purely central potential was inadequate; it failed to explain the saturation properties of the nuclear forces. However, these saturation effects could be treated by introducing a potential which has exchange characteristics and by a potential which is repulsive at short distances. The latter potential, the so-called hard core* potential, occurred from considerations of the differential cross section for *p-p* scattering. The scattering would be isotropic if only S-waves were involved. In that case, the maximum differential cross section at 400 Mev, say, would be

$$\frac{d\sigma}{d\Omega}\bigg|_{max} = \frac{4\pi}{k^2} \sin^2 \delta_0 \bigg|_{max} \simeq 2 \text{ mb/sterad}$$

for $\sin^2 \delta_0 = 1$. The observed value is 3.7 mb/sterad. The contributions from higher-l are not negligible. The observed isotropic distribution is due to a certain combination of higher-l angular momentum states. The phenomenon of isotropy itself rules out potentials for which higher-l values of the δ_l's have the same sign. Isotropy can be obtained only from alternately positive and negative phase shifts. This sign change is interpreted as being related to attractive and repulsive potential wells. The S-waves will, of course, interact strongly with the hard core, and a negative δ_0 will correspond to a positive (repulsive) potential. Higher-l waves will contribute to the attractive potential and δ_l will be positive. This type of potential could explain the observed effect in *n-p* scattering where σ decreases faster than $1/E$. It seems that the repulsive hard core potential has merit.

The potentials which incorporate the hard core and exchange properties, and which have compared favorably with experiment, have been given by Signell and Marshak, by Gammel and Thaler, and by other authors.[38] The form of the potentials used is

$$V(r) = V_c(r) + V_T(r)S_{12} + V_{LS}(r)\boldsymbol{\sigma} \cdot \mathbf{L} \tag{65}$$

---

* The repulsive core was first introduced by Jastrow (*Phys. Rev.* **81**, 165, 1951) in an attempt to describe the *n-p* and *p-p* scattering by a common interaction.

where V_c is the purely central potential, V_T is the tensor potential, and V_{LS} is the spin-orbit potential. $V(r)$ has a repulsive core inside the region $r < r_0$ and a Yukawa shape outside.

3.15 Polarization

The spin orientations of particles in a beam from an accelerator are normally randomly distributed. If somehow the spins are oriented in some preferred direction, the beam is then said to be polarized in that direction. There are many ways to produce such a situation. For example, in the *d-d* reaction, even at the low deuteron incident energy of $\sim$300 Kev, polarization has been observed[39] in the emitted protons when scattered by helium. Numerous experiments have been performed with polarized nucleons. In these experiments one first polarizes the beam by scattering and then determines the effect of polarization in a second scattering experiment. This is the so-called double scattering experiment.

In high-energy nucleon-nucleon scattering, experiments with a polarized beam provide valuable information concerning the spin dependence of nuclear forces. With a purely central interaction potential and an unpolarized target nucleus, the scattered particles would not show any left-right asymmetry (the direction left-right is taken to be perpendicular to the plane of scattering), even with a polarized incident beam. However, if the interaction has a tensor or noncentral character with the coupling of the spin and orbital angular momentum, then a polarized beam may show asymmetry when scattered.[40] The asymmetry is large if the orbital angular momentum involved in the scattering is large. Consequently, polarization experiments become important at high energy, where many partial waves corresponding to high values of *l* contribute to the phase shift. The first successful experiment performed to produce polarized protons at high energy was done by Oxley, Cartwright, and Rouvina.[41] Polarized neutrons were first used by Wouters.[42]

The polarization is denoted by P and is defined as

$$P(\theta) = \frac{N_+(\theta) - N_-(\theta)}{N_+(\theta) + N_-(\theta)} \tag{66}$$

where N_+ and N_- are respectively the number of particles with spin up and spin down for spin-$\frac{1}{2}$ particles when an unpolarized beam is scattered at the angle θ. P depends upon the scattering angle θ, the energy of the beam, and the nature of the particles. The angular dependence of the differential cross section $d\sigma/d\Omega$ of a polarized beam will depend upon the polarization P, provided the interaction potential is spin dependent.

If $d\sigma/d\Omega$ is plotted as a function of the scattering angle θ, the distribution will show asymmetry in a plane normal to the direction of incidence.

Consider a double scattering experiment of spin-$\frac{1}{2}$ particles. Let there be n particles in the beam, which is initially unpolarized. The first scattering takes place by an unpolarized target T_1. Since the beam is unpolarized, there are $n/2$ particles with spins of each sign ($+$ or $-$). After scattering once to the left by T_1, the number of particles reaching the second unpolarized target T_2 with polarization P_1 and spin up is $(n/2)f_1(1 + P_1)$, where f_1 is the fraction of all particles reaching T_2. The number $(n/2) \times f_1(1 - P_1)$ will reach T_2 with spin down. Similarly, those particles scattered once to the right by T_1, $(n/2)f_1(1 - P_1)$ will reach T_2 with spin up, and $(n/2)f_1(1 + P_1)$ will arrive there with spin down. Let P_2 and f_2 be respectively the polarization with spin up and the fraction of all particles scattered by the second target into a detector; thus the number scattered twice to the left (LL) with spin up is $(n/2)f_1f_2(1 + P_1)(1 + P_2)$, and with spin down is $(n/2)f_1f_2(1 - P_1)(1 - P_2)$. The number of particles scattered twice, first to the left by T_1 and then to the right by T_2 (LR) with spin up, is

$$(n/2)f_1f_2(1 + P_1)(1 - P_2),$$

and with spin down is $(n/2)f_1f_2(1 - P_1)(1 + P_2)$. Hence the number of particles scattered twice to the left (LL) is $(n/2)f_1f_2(2 + 2P_1P_2)$, and is greater than the number scattered twice, first to the left and second to the right (LR), namely $(n/2)f_1f_2(2 - 2P_1P_2)$. The left-right asymmetry for the second scattering is given by the ratio

$$e = \frac{(LL) - (LR)}{(LL) + (LR)} = P_1 P_2 \tag{67a}$$

If the second scattering is identical to the first, then $P_1 = P_2 = P$ and Eq. (67a) becomes

$$e = P^2 \tag{67b}$$

The magnitude of the polarization, $|P|$, can be determined from actual experiment. Figure 3-9 gives the dependence of polarization as a function of the scattering angle θ in the center-of-mass system for p-p elastic scattering at 315 Mev.[43] The sign (positive) of the polarization P can be determined from low-energy p-p scattering experiments near the interference minimum caused by the combination of Coulomb and nuclear scattering.[30] The other method of determining the sign of polarization is from the phase-shift analysis of scattering data below 10 Mev.[44]

There are a number of parameters associated with the polarization P which can be determined from experiments; these are the Wolfenstein parameters.[40] Depolarization D is obtained from a triple scattering experiment. If e_{3n} is the asymmetry after the third scattering, and P_3 is the

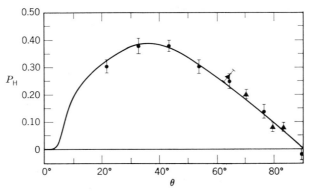

Fig. 3-9 Polarization in *p-p* elastic scattering at 315 Mev. The triangle points represent the polarization observed in *p-p* scattering from deuterium (Chamberlain et al.[43]).

polarization following the scattering at the target T_3 normal to the scattering plane, then, when all three planes of scattering are parallel, the depolarization D is

$$e_{3n} = \frac{P_2 \pm DP_1}{1 \pm P_1 P_2} P_3 \tag{67c}$$

where plus and minus signs refer respectively to the left and right after the second scattering. In terms of the experimentally measurable quantities e_{3n}, $e_3 = P_1 P_3$, $e_2 = P_1 P_2$, and $e_1 = P_1^2$, the depolarization from Eq. (67c) can be written as

$$D = \frac{e_{3n}}{e_3} (e_2 \pm 1) \mp \frac{e_2}{e_1} \tag{67d}$$

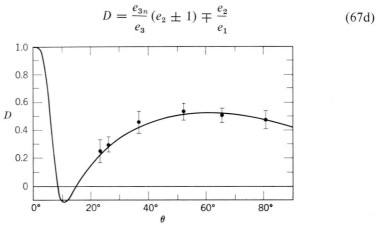

Fig. 3-10 Depolarization in *p-p* elastic scattering at 310 Mev (Chamberlain et al.[43]).

Figure 3-10 gives the depolarization parameter D of Eq. (67d) plotted as a function of the scattering angle θ in the center-of-mass system, as obtained from experiment.[43]

In high-energy nucleon-nucleon scattering, the angular dependence of the differential cross section $d\sigma/d\Omega$ is analyzed in terms of the phase shifts. However, the large number of phase shifts and associated parameters make such an analysis extremely complicated and often ambiguous. Since polarization parameters can be expressed in terms of phase shifts, polarization experiments in the form of double and triple scattering have been satisfactorily explained by the phase-shift analysis. We shall return to this problem in Chapter 4.

3.16 Photodisintegration of the Deuteron

The process of photodisintegration arises when the energy of the incident γ-rays is greater than the binding energy $W = 2.226$ Mev of the deuteron. The deuteron breaks up into a proton and a neutron. Actually the center-of-mass threshold energy of the γ-rays which disintegrate the deuteron provides an accurate measurement of its binding energy.

To discuss the photodisintegration process and derive expressions for the cross section, it is necessary to develop the theory of interaction of the electromagnetic field with particles. The electromagnetic field is described by the four-potential A_μ, $(\mathbf{A}, i\phi)$. It is convenient to choose the gauge such that $\phi = 0$. The vector potential $\mathbf{A}$, which is real can be expanded as follows:

$$\mathbf{A}(\mathbf{x}) = \sum_{\mathbf{k},\lambda} \mathbf{A}_{\mathbf{k}\lambda} = \sum_{\mathbf{k},\lambda}(q_\lambda \mathbf{a}_{\mathbf{k}\lambda} + q_\lambda^* \mathbf{a}_{\mathbf{k}\lambda}^*) \tag{68a}$$

where

$$\mathbf{a}_{\mathbf{k}\lambda} = |\mathbf{a}_{\mathbf{k}\lambda}|\, \hat{\epsilon}_\lambda e^{i\mathbf{k}\cdot\mathbf{x}} \tag{68b}$$

and q_λ and q_λ^* are the annihilation and creation operators for a photon with wave vector $\mathbf{k}$ and whose polarization direction is along the unit vector $\hat{\epsilon}_\lambda$; λ denotes the direction of polarization. In order to determine $|\mathbf{a}_{\mathbf{k}\lambda}|$, we make use of the fact that for n_λ photons per unit volume, the average energy density $\langle u_\lambda \rangle$ of the radiation field is given by

$$\langle u_\lambda \rangle = \frac{1}{8\pi}[\langle \mathbf{E}_\lambda^2 \rangle + \langle \mathbf{H}_\lambda^2 \rangle] = n_\lambda \hbar\omega, \qquad \omega = ck \tag{69a}$$

where the electric and magnetic fields are obtainable from the four-potential

$$\mathbf{H} = \text{curl } \mathbf{A} \tag{69b}$$

$$\mathbf{E} = -\text{grad } \phi - \frac{1}{c}\frac{\partial \mathbf{A}}{\partial t} \tag{69c}$$

From Eqs. (69) and with $\phi = 0$, we have

$$\langle u_\lambda \rangle = \frac{1}{8\pi} \left\langle \frac{1}{c^2} \left(\frac{\partial A_{k\lambda}}{\partial t} \right)^2 + (\text{curl } A_{k\lambda})^2 \right\rangle; \qquad A_{k\lambda} = \hat{\epsilon}_\lambda |a_{k\lambda}| \, 2 \cos (\mathbf{k} \cdot \mathbf{x} - \omega t)$$

$$= \frac{1}{4\pi c^2} \langle (2 |a_{k\lambda}| \, \omega)^2 \sin^2 (\mathbf{k} \cdot \mathbf{x} - \omega t) \rangle$$

$$= \frac{|a_{k\lambda}| \, \omega^2}{2\pi c^2} = n_\lambda \hbar \omega$$

which gives

$$|a_{k\lambda}| = \sqrt{\frac{2\pi \hbar c^2 n_\lambda}{\omega}} \tag{69d}$$

The plane-wave expansion of the vector potential is therefore

$$\mathbf{A}(\mathbf{x}) = \sum_{k,\lambda} \sqrt{\frac{2\pi \hbar c^2 n_\lambda}{\omega}} \, \hat{\epsilon}_\lambda [q_\lambda e^{i\mathbf{k} \cdot \mathbf{x}} + q_\lambda^* e^{-i\mathbf{k} \cdot \mathbf{x}}] \tag{70a}$$

which for a continuous spectrum of $\mathbf{k}$ becomes

$$\mathbf{A}(\mathbf{x}) = \frac{1}{(2\pi)^{3/2}} \sum_\lambda \int d^3 k \sqrt{\frac{2\pi \hbar c}{k}} \sqrt{n_\lambda} \, \hat{\epsilon}_\lambda [q_\lambda e^{i\mathbf{k} \cdot \mathbf{x}} + q_\lambda^* e^{-i\mathbf{k} \cdot \mathbf{x}}] \tag{70b}$$

For the absorption or emission of a photon of wave vector $\mathbf{k}$ and polarization λ, the vector potential $\mathbf{A}(\mathbf{x})$ can be replaced by

$$\frac{1}{(2\pi)^{3/2}} \sqrt{\frac{2\pi \hbar c}{k}} \, \hat{\epsilon}_\lambda e^{i\mathbf{k} \cdot \mathbf{x}} \qquad \text{(absorption)} \tag{70c}$$

$$\frac{1}{(2\pi)^{3/2}} \sqrt{\frac{2\pi \hbar c}{k}} \, \hat{\epsilon}_\lambda e^{-i\mathbf{k} \cdot \mathbf{x}} \qquad \text{(emission)} \tag{70d}$$

Interaction of the Electromagnetic Field with Particles

The classical interaction Hamiltonian of a charged particle of current $\mathbf{j}$ and having a magnetic moment $\mathbf{\mu}$ is given by

$$H' = -\frac{1}{c} \mathbf{j} \cdot \mathbf{A} - \mathbf{\mu} \cdot \mathbf{H}$$

$$= -\left[\frac{e}{mc} \mathbf{p} \cdot \mathbf{A} + \mathbf{\mu} \cdot \text{curl } \mathbf{A} \right] \tag{71a}$$

The first term is also easily obtained by the usual process of including interaction of a charged particle with the electromagnetic field, namely, of replacing the momentum $\mathbf{p}$ by $\mathbf{p} - (e/c)\mathbf{A}$ in the kinetic energy term

$\mathbf{p}^2/2m$; the $\mathbf{A}^2$ term is not included in Eq. (71a) since it involves interaction with two photons simultaneously. The second term $-\boldsymbol{\mu} \cdot \mathbf{H}$ is the conventional interaction of the magnetic moment $\boldsymbol{\mu}$ with the magnetic field. The quantum mechanical interaction Hamiltonian analogue of Eq. (71a) can be written in a straightforward manner. From Eqs. (71a) and (70b), we obtain

$$
H' = \frac{1}{(2\pi)^{3/2}} \sum_{\lambda} \int d^3k \sqrt{\frac{2\pi\hbar c}{k}} \sqrt{n_{\lambda}} \left[-\frac{e}{mc} (\hat{\epsilon}_{\lambda} \cdot \mathbf{p})[q_{\lambda}e^{i\mathbf{k}\cdot\mathbf{x}} + q_{\lambda}^*e^{-i\mathbf{k}\cdot\mathbf{x}}] \right.
$$
$$
\left. - i\hat{\epsilon}_{\lambda} \cdot (\boldsymbol{\mu} \times \mathbf{k})[q_{\lambda}e^{i\mathbf{k}\cdot\mathbf{x}} - q_{\lambda}^*e^{-i\mathbf{k}\cdot\mathbf{x}}] \right] \quad (71b)
$$

In considering the absorption of a photon of wave vector $\mathbf{k}$, the matrix element for the transition of the particle from an initial state $\psi_i(\mathbf{x})$ to a final state $\psi_f(\mathbf{x})$ is given by

$$
\langle f | H' | i \rangle = \sqrt{\frac{\hbar c}{4\pi^2 k}} \sum_{\lambda} \int d^3x \, \psi_f^*(\mathbf{x}) \left[-\frac{e}{mc} (\hat{\epsilon}_{\lambda} \cdot \mathbf{p}) - i\hat{\epsilon}_{\lambda} \cdot (\boldsymbol{\mu} \times \mathbf{k}) \right] e^{i\mathbf{k}\cdot\mathbf{x}} \psi_i(\mathbf{x})
$$

$$
\text{(absorption)} \quad (71c)
$$

The results of Eqs. (71b) and (71c) can easily be generalized for the case of interaction with n particles. We have

$$
H' = \frac{1}{(2\pi)^{3/2}} \sum_{j=1}^{n} \sum_{\lambda} \int d^3k \sqrt{\frac{2\pi\hbar c}{k}} \sqrt{n_{\lambda}} \left\{ -\frac{e_j}{m_j c} (\hat{\epsilon}_{\lambda} \cdot \mathbf{p}_j)[q_{\lambda}e^{i\mathbf{k}\cdot\mathbf{x}_j} + q_{\lambda}^*e^{-i\mathbf{k}\cdot\mathbf{x}_j}] \right.
$$
$$
\left. - i\hat{\epsilon}_{\lambda} \cdot (\boldsymbol{\mu}_j \times \mathbf{k})[q_{\lambda}e^{i\mathbf{k}\cdot\mathbf{x}_j} - q_{\lambda}^*e^{-i\mathbf{k}\cdot\mathbf{x}_j}] \right\} \quad (72a)
$$

and the matrix element for the absorption of a photon of wave vector $\mathbf{k}$ is

$$
\langle f | H' | i \rangle = \sqrt{\frac{\hbar c}{4\pi^2 k}} \int d^3x_1 \, d^3x_2 \cdots d^3x_n \psi_f^*(\mathbf{x}_1, \mathbf{x}_2, \ldots, \mathbf{x}_n)
$$

$$
\times \sum_{j=1}^{n} \sum_{\lambda} \left[-\frac{e_j}{m_j c} (\hat{\epsilon}_{\lambda} \cdot \mathbf{p}_j) - i\hat{\epsilon}_{\lambda} \cdot (\boldsymbol{\mu}_j \times \mathbf{k}) \right] e^{i\mathbf{k}\cdot\mathbf{x}_j} \psi_i(\mathbf{x}_1, \mathbf{x}_2, \ldots, \mathbf{x}_n)
$$

$$
(72b)
$$

Equation (72b) can be applied to the photodisintegration of the deuteron by using

$$
m_j = M \quad \text{for} \quad j = 1 \text{ and } 2 \quad (73a)
$$

$$
\boldsymbol{\mu}_1 = \boldsymbol{\mu}_p = g_p \left(\frac{e\hbar}{2Mc} \right) \tfrac{1}{2} \boldsymbol{\sigma}_p = \mu_p \boldsymbol{\sigma}_p \quad (73b)
$$

$$
\boldsymbol{\mu}_2 = \boldsymbol{\mu}_n = g_n \left(\frac{e\hbar}{2Mc} \right) \tfrac{1}{2} \boldsymbol{\sigma}_n = \mu_n \boldsymbol{\sigma}_n \quad (73c)
$$

where

$$g_p = 5.59 \quad \text{and} \quad g_n = -3.83 \tag{73d}$$

are the gyromagnetic ratios for the proton and neutron, respectively. Furthermore, by introducing the center-of-mass coordinate $\mathbf{X}$ and the relative coordinate $\mathbf{x}$ by the relations

$$\mathbf{X} = \tfrac{1}{2}(\mathbf{x}_1 + \mathbf{x}_2), \qquad \mathbf{x} = \mathbf{x}_1 - \mathbf{x}_2 \tag{74a}$$

and assuming that in the initial state the center-of-mass is at rest, whereas in the final state it has a momentum $\hbar\mathbf{K}$, the initial and final state particle wave functions are

$$\psi_i(\mathbf{x}_1, \mathbf{x}_2) = \frac{1}{(2\pi)^{3/2}} \, \psi_i(\mathbf{x}) \tag{74b}$$

$$\psi_f(\mathbf{x}_1, \mathbf{x}_2) = \frac{1}{(2\pi)^{3/2}} \, e^{i\mathbf{K}\cdot\mathbf{X}} \psi_f(\mathbf{x}) \tag{74c}$$

From Eqs. (72b) to (74c), the matrix element for the photodisintegration of the deuteron is given by

$$\langle f|\, H'\,|i\rangle = \delta(\mathbf{K} - \mathbf{k}_q)\sqrt{\frac{\hbar c}{4\pi^2 k}}\sum_\lambda \int d^3x\, \psi_f^*(\mathbf{x})\left[-\frac{e}{Mc}(\hat{\epsilon}_\lambda \cdot \mathbf{p}_p)e^{i\mathbf{k}_q\cdot\mathbf{x}/2} \right.$$
$$\left. - i(\mathbf{k}_q \times \hat{\epsilon}_\lambda)\cdot[\boldsymbol{\mu}_p e^{i\mathbf{k}_q\cdot\mathbf{x}/2} + \boldsymbol{\mu}_n e^{-i\mathbf{k}_q\cdot\mathbf{x}/2}]\right]\psi_i(\mathbf{x}) \tag{75a}$$

where the subscript q on the vector $\mathbf{k}_q(|\mathbf{k}_q| = k)$ has been inserted to emphasize that it refers to the incident photon (quantum). The δ-function $\delta(\mathbf{K} - \mathbf{k}_q)$ implies the over-all conservation of total momentum and can be dropped (formally it can be retained and included in the calculations).

Dipole Approximation

The wavelength of the incident photon corresponding to the threshold energy is $\lambda_{\text{th}} \sim 1.24 \times 10^{-10}$ cm, which is very large compared to the size of the deuteron $r_d \sim \hbar/\sqrt{MW} = 4.32 \times 10^{-13}$ cm. Since the deuteron wave function vanishes exponentially outside the deuteron radius, we have $\mathbf{k}_q \cdot \mathbf{x} \ll 1$ and it is a very good approximation to take

$$\exp(\pm i\mathbf{k}_q \cdot \mathbf{x}/2) \simeq 1$$

in Eq. (75a). This is referred to as the dipole approximation. Equation (75a) can therefore be rewritten as follows:

$$\langle f|\, H'\,|i\rangle \simeq \sqrt{\frac{\hbar c}{4\pi^2 k}}\sum_\lambda \int d^3x\, \psi_f^*(\mathbf{x})\left[-\frac{e}{Mc}(\hat{\epsilon}_\lambda \cdot \mathbf{p}_p) \right.$$
$$\left. - i(\mathbf{k}_q \times \hat{\epsilon}_\lambda)\cdot(\boldsymbol{\mu}_p + \boldsymbol{\mu}_n)\right]\psi_i(\mathbf{x}) \tag{75b}$$

Equation (75b) can be rendered into a form to exhibit more explicitly the dipole nature of the electric interaction (first term). Quantum mechanically, we have†

$$\mathbf{p}_p = \frac{M\dot{\mathbf{x}}}{2} = \frac{M}{2}\frac{1}{i\hbar}[\mathbf{x}, H_p] \qquad \left(\text{reduced mass} = \frac{M}{2}\right) \tag{76a}$$

where

$$[\mathbf{x}, H_p] = \mathbf{x}H_p - H_p\mathbf{x} \tag{76b}$$

and H_p is the Hamiltonian for the particle. By operating on Eq. (76a) on the left by $\psi_f^*(\mathbf{x})$ and on the right by $\psi_i(\mathbf{x})$, we obtain

$$\psi_f^*(\mathbf{x})\mathbf{p}\psi_i(\mathbf{x}) = \frac{M}{2i\hbar}(E_i - E_f)\psi_f^*(\mathbf{x})\mathbf{x}\psi_i(\mathbf{x}) \tag{76c}$$

where E_i and E_f are the initial and final relative energies of the two-particle system given by

$$E_f - E_i = \hbar c k - \frac{\hbar^2\left(\dfrac{k}{2}\right)^2}{M} \tag{76d}$$

Substituting Eq. (76c) in Eq. (75b), we obtain

$$\langle f| H'|i\rangle = \langle f| H_e'|i\rangle + \langle f| H_m'|i\rangle \tag{77a}$$

where $\langle f| H_e'|i\rangle$ and $\langle f| H_m'|i\rangle$ are the matrix elements of the electric and magnetic dipole transitions given by

$$\langle f| H_e'|i\rangle = -\sqrt{\frac{\hbar c}{4\pi^2 k}}\sum_\lambda\int d^3 x\,\psi_f^*(\mathbf{x})\frac{e}{Mc}(\hat{\epsilon}_\lambda \cdot \mathbf{p}_p)\psi_i(\mathbf{x})$$

$$= \frac{i}{\hbar c}(E_i - E_f)\sqrt{\frac{\hbar c}{4\pi^2 k}}\sum_\lambda\int d^3 x\,\psi_f^*(\mathbf{x})\hat{\epsilon}_\lambda \cdot \left(\frac{e\mathbf{x}}{2}\right)\psi_i(\mathbf{x}) \tag{77b}$$

$$\langle f| H_m'|i\rangle = -i\sqrt{\frac{\hbar c}{4\pi^2 k}}\sum_\lambda\int d^3 x\,\psi_f^*(\mathbf{x})(\mathbf{k}_q \times \hat{\epsilon}_\lambda) \cdot (\boldsymbol{\mu}_p + \boldsymbol{\mu}_n)\psi_i(\mathbf{x}) \tag{77c}$$

The essential parts of Eqs. (77b) and (77c) can be written quite readily. Since only the proton has charge, the center of charge is at $\mathbf{x}/2$, and therefore the electric dipole operator for the deuteron is $\hat{\epsilon}_\lambda \cdot (e\mathbf{x}/2)$. Similarly, since the magnetic moment interaction is $-\boldsymbol{\mu} \cdot \mathbf{H} = -\boldsymbol{\mu} \cdot \text{curl } \mathbf{A}$, the corresponding operator is $(\boldsymbol{\mu}_p + \boldsymbol{\mu}_n) \cdot (\hat{\epsilon}_\lambda \times \mathbf{k}_q)$.

† Equation (76a) is incorrect when the nucleon-nucleon potential is momentum dependent. Also, then the second line of Eq. (71a) is incorrect because momentum dependent terms will give extra terms in the interaction Hamiltonian H'. However, the result of the second line of Eq. (77b) is correct for low energy γ-rays, because of Siegert theorem (A. J. F. Siegert, *Phys. Rev.* **52**, 787, 1937).

Cross Section for Photodisintegration

The differential cross section for the photodisintegration of the deuteron can be obtained by using Eqs. (77) and the well-known formula from time-dependent perturbation theory, namely, that the differential cross section per unit solid angle is given by

$$\frac{d\sigma}{d\Omega_k} = \frac{2\pi}{\hbar} \frac{\rho_f}{j_{\text{inc}}} \frac{1}{6} \sum_{\lambda,m,m'} |\langle f| H' |i\rangle|^2 \tag{78a}$$

where j_{inc} is the incident flux (of photons), ρ_f the density of final states per unit energy range; the summations λ, m, m' are over polarization directions of the photon and the spin states of the initial deuteron and final particles; and the factor $\frac{1}{6} = 1/(2 \times 3)$ results from averaging over the two polarization directions of the photon and three spin states (triplet state) of the deuteron in the initial system. The final system consists of the neutron and proton with relative momentum $\hbar k$ and reduced mass $M/2$. Therefore we have

$$\rho_f \, dE_f = \frac{\hbar^3 \, d\mathbf{k}}{(2\pi\hbar)^3}, \qquad E_f = \frac{(\hbar k)^2}{2(M/2)}$$

which yields

$$\rho_f = \frac{Mk \, d\Omega}{2(2\pi)^3 \hbar^2} \tag{78b}$$

From Eq. (70b), it is easy to find that

$$|\mathbf{j}_{\text{inc}}| = \frac{c}{(2\pi)^3} \tag{78c}$$

The calculation of the differential cross section in Eq. (78a) can be performed by evaluating the matrix element $\langle f| H' |i\rangle$ [Eqs. (77)]. To do this, it is necessary to specify the wave functions ψ_i and ψ_f of the particles in the initial and final system. The wave function ψ_i is the deuteron ground state given by

$$\psi_i(\mathbf{x}) = \frac{N_g}{\sqrt{4\pi}} \left[\frac{1}{r} u_g(r) + \frac{1}{\sqrt{8}} S_{12} \frac{1}{r} w_g(r) \right] \chi_1^m \tag{79a}$$

where $u_g(r)$ and $w_g(r)$ are S and D radial wave functions of the deuteron, $\chi_1^m (m = +1, 0 \text{ or } -1)$ is the initial spin state, and N_g is the normalization constant given by

$$N_g^{-2} = \int_0^\infty dr [u_g^2(r) + w_g^2(r)] \tag{79b}$$

Asymptotically

$$u_g(r) \xrightarrow[r \to \infty]{} \cos \epsilon_g e^{-\gamma r}, \qquad \gamma = \sqrt{\frac{MW}{\hbar^2}} \tag{79c}$$

$$w_g(r) \xrightarrow[r \to \infty]{} \sin \epsilon_g e^{-\gamma r} \left[1 + \frac{3}{\gamma r} + \frac{3}{(\gamma r)^2} \right] \tag{79d}$$

where ϵ_g specifies the mixing of S and D states in the deuteron ground state. In the following, we shall simplify the calculations by considering the deuteron to be a pure S-state, that is, $\epsilon_g = 0$. For the general case, the reader is referred to the article by Hulthen and Sugawara[46] (on which largely the discussion here is based). We shall write

$$u_g(r) \simeq \sqrt{2\gamma}\, e^{-\gamma r}, \qquad \psi_i(r) \simeq \sqrt{\frac{\gamma}{2\pi}}\, \frac{e^{-\gamma r}}{r}\, \chi_1^m \tag{79e}$$

We remark that the use of Eq. (79e) for the S-state radial function is not completely correct since it does not satisfy the boundary condition $u_g(0) = 0$. This can be taken into account by using the Hulthen function $u_g(r) = N_g(e^{-\gamma r} - e^{-\eta r})$, but we shall not include this refinement here.

The final state wave function $\psi_f(\mathbf{x})$ pertains to the neutron and proton in a free state, which can be either a triplet or a singlet spin state. Expanding it in Legendre polynomials, we have

$$\psi_{ft}(\mathbf{x}) = \left[\sum_{l=0}^{\infty} (2l+1) i^l e^{i\delta_{lt}} \frac{1}{kr} u_{lt}(r) P_l(\hat{k} \cdot \hat{x})\right] \chi_1^{m'} \tag{80a}$$

or

$$\psi_{fs}(\mathbf{x}) = \left[\sum_{l=0}^{\infty} (2l+1) i^l e^{i\delta_{ls}} \frac{1}{kr} u_{ls}(r) P_l(\hat{k} \cdot \hat{x})\right] \chi_0^0 \tag{80b}$$

where $\hbar\mathbf{k}$ is the relative momentum in the center-of-mass system, and

$$u_l(r) \xrightarrow[r \to \infty]{} \sin\left(kr - \frac{l\pi}{2} + \delta_l\right) \tag{80c}$$

Photoelectric Disintegration Cross Section

The electric dipole operator $ex/2$ responsible for the photoelectric disintegration of the deuteron changes the parity of the initial state, and therefore a nonzero value of the matrix element Eq. (77b) will be obtained only when the final state wave function ψ_f is in a P state. Since the electric dipole operator does not affect the spin wave function, we also require that $\chi_1^{m'} = \chi_1^m$. The form of the triplet P-wave function $u_{1t}(r)$, which outside the range of nuclear potential tends asymptotically to

$$\sin[kr - (\pi/2) + \delta_1],$$

is suggested by the spherical Bessel function $j_1(kr)$. In the zero-range approximation, we take

$$u_{1t}(r) = \frac{\sin(kr + \delta_{1t})}{kr} - \cos(kr + \delta_{1t})$$

$$= \mathrm{Re}\left[e^{i(kr+\delta_{1t})} \frac{(1 - ikr)}{ikr}\right] \tag{81a}$$

where Re stands for the real part. From Eqs. (81a) and (80a), we have

$$\psi_{ft}(\mathbf{x}) = 3ie^{i\delta_{1t}}\frac{1}{kr}\operatorname{Re}\left[e^{i(kr+\delta_{1t})}\frac{(1-ikr)}{kr}\right]P_1(\hat{k}\cdot\hat{x})\chi_1^m \qquad (81b)$$

From Eqs. (77b), (78a), (79e), and (81b), we find that the angular integration involved in the calculation of the matrix element $\langle f|H_e'|i\rangle$ is

$$\int d\hat{x}P_1(\hat{k}\cdot\hat{x})(\hat{\epsilon}_\lambda\cdot\hat{x}) \qquad (82a)$$

The integral in Eq. (82a) can be evaluated as follows. Take the polarization unit vector $\hat{\epsilon}_\lambda$ of the incident photon along the z-axis, the relative momentum vector $\hbar\mathbf{k}$ of the final neutron-proton in the x-z plane with polar coordinates $(\theta_1, 0)$, and the unit vector $\hat{x}$ with polar coordinates (θ, φ). Then

$$\hat{\epsilon}_\lambda = \hat{k}, \qquad \hat{k} = \hat{i}\sin\theta_1 + \hat{k}\cos\theta_1$$
$$\hat{x} = \hat{i}\sin\theta\cos\phi + \hat{j}\sin\theta\sin\phi + \hat{k}\cos\theta \qquad (82b)$$

Substituting Eq. (82b) in Eq. (82a), we obtain

$$\int d\hat{x}P_1(\hat{k}\cdot\hat{x})(\hat{\epsilon}_\lambda\cdot\hat{x}) = \int_0^{2\pi}d\phi\int_0^\pi d\theta(\sin\theta_1\sin\theta\cos\phi + \cos\theta_1\cos\theta)\cos\theta$$
$$= \frac{4\pi}{3}\cos\theta_1 = \frac{4\pi}{3}(\hat{\epsilon}_\lambda\cdot\hat{k}) \qquad (82c)$$

where $(\hat{\epsilon}_\lambda \cdot \hat{k})$ is the cosine of the angle between the polarization direction of the incident γ-ray and the direction of relative motion of the outgoing neutron and proton. If the incident beam is unpolarized, the average over both directions of polarizations gives

$$\langle(\hat{\epsilon}_\lambda\cdot\hat{k})^2\rangle = \tfrac{1}{2}\sum_\lambda(\hat{\epsilon}_\lambda\cdot\hat{k})^2 = \tfrac{1}{2}\sin^2\theta \qquad (83a)$$

where θ is the angle of the emitted neutron or proton with respect to the incident photon direction in the two-nucleon center-of-mass system. If, however, the direction of polarization is held fixed and the average is carried out over all proton (or neutron) directions, we have

$$\int d\Omega_k(\hat{\epsilon}_\lambda\cdot\hat{k})^2 = \frac{4\pi}{3} \qquad (83b)$$

The differential cross section $d\sigma_e$ for the photoelectric disintegration of the deuteron is obtained from combining Eqs. (77b), (78a), (79e), (81b),

(82c), and (83a).

$$d\sigma_e = \frac{\pi e^2}{\hbar c} \frac{(E_f - E_i)^2}{h\nu W} \frac{2\gamma^3}{k} \frac{d\Omega_k}{4\pi} \tfrac{1}{2} \sin^2 \theta \, I_{sp}^2 \tag{84a}$$

where $h\nu$ is the energy of the γ-ray in the laboratory system and

$$\begin{aligned} I_{sp} &= \int_0^\infty dr r u_g u_{1t} \\ &= \frac{2k^2}{(\gamma^2 + k^2)^2}\left[1 + \delta_{1t} \frac{\gamma(\gamma^2 + 3k^2)}{2k^3}\right] \end{aligned} \tag{84b}$$

The total cross section neglecting the δ_{1t} term is given by

$$\sigma_e = \frac{8\pi}{3} \frac{e^2}{\hbar c} \frac{\gamma k^3}{(\gamma^2 + k^2)^3} \tag{84c}$$

Photomagnetic Disintegration Cross Section

The cross section for the photomagnetic disintegration of the deuteron can be obtained using matrix element $\langle f| H'_m |i\rangle$, Eq. (77c), for the magnetic dipole transition. Since the operator $(\boldsymbol{\mu}_p + \boldsymbol{\mu}_n) \cdot (\hat{\epsilon}_\lambda \times \mathbf{k}_q)$ does not contain any orbital operators, it cannot change the orbital state of the initial wave function. Therefore the spin state must change, for the matrix element will vanish between states that have the same spin and orbital states and pertain to different energies. The deuteron is in a spin triplet state, and the two magnetic moments are antiparallel. The field tends to align the magnetic moments, thereby inducing transitions from the triplet to the singlet state which is unbound, and it therefore disintegrates into a neutron and proton. Thus the interaction with the magnetic dipole induces the transition $^3S_1 \rightarrow {}^1S_0$.

The spin matrix elements required for the magnetic moment transition are as follows:

$$\langle \chi_0^0| \mu_p \sigma_{pz} + \mu_n \sigma_{nz} |\chi_1^1\rangle = 0 \tag{85a}$$

$$\langle \chi_0^0| \mu_p \sigma_{pz} + \mu_n \sigma_{nz} |\chi_1^0\rangle = \mu_n - \mu_p \tag{85b}$$

$$\langle \chi_0^0| \mu_p \sigma_{pz} + \mu_n \sigma_{nz} |\chi_1^{-1}\rangle = 0 \tag{85c}$$

The result of Eqs. (85) can be anticipated by writing

$$\mu_p\boldsymbol{\sigma}_p + \mu_n\boldsymbol{\sigma}_n = \tfrac{1}{2}(\mu_p + \mu_n)(\boldsymbol{\sigma}_p + \boldsymbol{\sigma}_n) + \tfrac{1}{2}(\mu_p - \mu_n)(\boldsymbol{\sigma}_p - \boldsymbol{\sigma}_n) \tag{85d}$$

It is to be noted that the total spin operator $\mathbf{S} = \tfrac{1}{2}(\boldsymbol{\sigma}_p + \boldsymbol{\sigma}_n)\hbar$ does not change the spin state of the deuteron and therefore transforms the triplet state χ_1^m to itself (apart from a multiplicative constant). However, the operator $(\boldsymbol{\sigma}_p - \boldsymbol{\sigma}_n)$ changes the spin states.

The differential cross section for the photomagnetic disintegration $^3S_1 \to {}^1S_0$ is given by

$$d\sigma_m = \frac{e^2}{\hbar c}(\mu_p - \mu_n)^2 \frac{khv}{4Mc^2} \frac{d\Omega_k}{4\pi} \frac{1}{6} \sum_{\lambda,m}$$

$$\times \left| \int d^3x \psi_f^*(\mathbf{x})(\hat{k}_q \times \hat{\epsilon}_\lambda)\left(\frac{\boldsymbol{\sigma}_p - \boldsymbol{\sigma}_n}{2}\right) \psi_i(\mathbf{x}) \right|^2$$

$$= \frac{\pi}{3} \frac{e^2}{\hbar c}(\mu_p - \mu_n)^2 \frac{hv}{Mc^2} \frac{2\gamma}{k} \frac{d\Omega_k}{4\pi} I_{ss}^2 \qquad (86a)$$

where

$$I_{ss} = \int_0^\infty dr u_g u_{0s} \qquad (86b)$$

The total cross section can readily be obtained by integrating over the solid angle $d\Omega_k$ and is given by

$$\sigma_m = \frac{\pi}{3} \frac{e^2}{\hbar c}(\mu_p - \mu_n)^2 \frac{hv}{Mc^2} \frac{2\gamma}{k} I_{ss}^2 \qquad (86c)$$

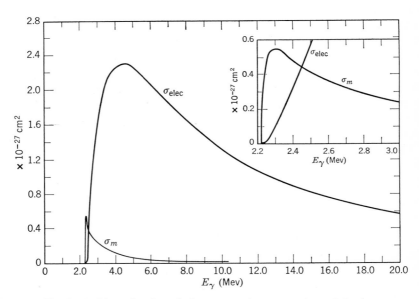

Fig. 3-11 Photoelectric and photomagnetic cross sections of the deuteron. The inset shows the region near threshold energy much magnified (Bethe and Morrison[47]).

The integral I_{ss} can be calculated by substituting in Eq. (86b) the expression Eq. (79e) for u_g, and from Eqs. (80b) and (80c) taking

$$u_{0s} = \sin (kr + \delta_{0s}) \tag{87a}$$

The final result for the total cross section for photomagnetic disintegration of the deuteron is

$$\sigma_m = \frac{2\pi}{3}\left(\frac{e^2}{\hbar c}\right)(\mu_p - \mu_n)^2 \frac{h\nu}{Mc^2}\frac{\gamma}{k}\frac{\gamma^2}{(\gamma^2 + k^2)^2}\sin^2 \delta_{0s}\left(1 + \frac{k}{\gamma}\cot \delta_{0s}\right)^2 \tag{87b}$$

where the singlet S phase shift δ_{0s} can be expressed in terms of the singlet scattering length and effective range parameters, a_s and r_{0s}, by the relation

$$k \cot \delta_{0s} = -\frac{1}{a_s} + \tfrac{1}{2}k^2 r_{0s} - P_s k^4 r_{0s}^3 \tag{87c}$$

A plot of the photoelectric and photomagnetic cross sections as a function of the incident γ-energy is given in Fig. 3.11.[47]

Angular Distribution

From Eqs. (84a) and (86a), the angular distribution for the photoelectric disintegration is $d\sigma_e/d\Omega_k \sim \sin^2 \theta$, where θ is the angle between the emitted proton (or neutron) and the incident photon direction in the center-of-mass system of the two nucleons, whereas the angular distribution $d\sigma_m/d\Omega_k$ for the photomagnetic process is isotropic. This result is to be expected since $a \sin^2 \theta$ distribution is characteristic of the electric dipole transition which involves a $^3S_1 \rightarrow {}^3P$ transition. In the photomagnetic process, the initial orbital S-state, which is isotropic, remains unchanged in the transition, and therefore the differential cross section is isotropic. The combined angular distribution due to the two effects is given by

$$\frac{d\sigma}{d\Omega_k} = a + b \sin^2 \theta \tag{88a}$$

where the coefficients a and b can be determined from Eqs. (84a) and (86a). If the D-component of the deuteron ground-state wave function is included in the calculation, the angular distribution can be shown to be

$$\frac{d\sigma}{d\Omega_k} = \begin{cases} a + (b + c \cos \theta) \sin^2 \theta \\ \text{or} \quad (a + b \sin^2 \theta)(1 + c \cos \theta) \end{cases} \tag{88b}$$

which is a slight modification of Eq. (88a). At low energies the pure $\sin^2 \theta$ coefficient is dominant. But at high energies (larger than 130 Mev) the coefficient b is very small, whereas the coefficient of the $\cos \theta$ term is large, resulting in the predominance of the forward emission. Also, the more general form of the angular distribution

$$\frac{d\sigma}{d\Omega_k} = a(1 + \beta_1 \cos \theta) + b \sin^2 \theta(1 + \beta_2 \cos \theta) \qquad (88c)$$

has been proposed.[26]

References

1. Wheeler, J. A., *Phys. Rev.* **50**, 643, 1936.
2. Breit, G., and E. Feenberg, *Phys. Rev.* **50**, 825, 1936; Schwinger, J. S., *Phys. Rev.* **78**, 135, 1950.
3. Blatt, J. M., and V. F. Weisskopf, *Theoretical Nuclear Physics*, p. 140, John Wiley and Sons, New York, 1952.
4. Mobley, R. C., and R. A. Laubenstein, *Phys. Rev.* **80**, 309, 1950.
5. Ramsey, N. F., *Nuclear Moments*, John Wiley and Sons, New York, 1953.
6. Auffray, J. P., *Phys. Rev. Letters* **6**, 120, 1961.
7. Sanders, J. H. *Nuovo Cimento, Suppl.* **6**, No. 1, 242, 1957.
8. Cohen, V. W., N. R. Corngold, and N. F. Ramsey, *Phys. Rev.* **104**, 283, 1956.
9. Meads, R. E., C. J. England, C. H. Collie, and G. C. Weeks, *Proc. Phys. Soc.* (*London*) **A69**, 469, 1956.
10. Melkonian, E., *Phys. Rev.* **76**, 1744, 1750, 1949.
11. Dee, P., and C. Gilbert, *Proc. Roy. Soc.* (*London*) **A163**, 265, 1937; Barschall, H., and M. Kanner, *Phys. Rev.* **58**, 590, 1940.
12. Fermi, E., and L. Marshall, *Phys. Rev.* **71**, 666, 1947.
13. Wigner, E. P., (unpublished); Bethe, H. A., and R. F. Bacher., *Rev. Mod. Phys.* **8**, 193, 1936.
14. Ma, S. T., *Rev. Mod. Phys.* **25**, 853, 1953.
15. Schwinger, J. S., *Phys. Rev.* **72**, 742, 1947.
16. Blatt, J. M., *Phys. Rev.* **74**, 92, 1948; Blatt, J. M., and J. Jackson, *Phys. Rev.* **76**, 18, 1949; Chew, G., and M. Goldberger, *Phys. Rev.* **75**, 1637, 1949.
17. Bethe, H. A., *Phys. Rev.* **76**, 38, 1949.
18. Blatt, J. M., and V. F. Weisskopf, *Theoretical Nuclear Physics*, p. 62, John Wiley and Sons, New York, 1952.
19. Bethe, H. A., *Elementary Nuclear Theory*, John Wiley and Sons, New York, 1947.
20. Schwinger, J., and E. Teller, *Phys. Rev.* **52**, 286, 1937.
21. Sutton, R. B., T. Hall, E. E. Anderson, H. S. Bridge, J. W. DeWire, L. S. Lavatelli, E. A. Long, T. Snyder, and R. W. Williams, *Phys. Rev.* **72**, 1147, 1947.
22. Squires, G. L., and A. T. Stewart, *Proc. Roy. Soc.* (*London*) **A230**, 19, 1955.
23. Hughes, D. J., M. T. Burgy, and G. R. Ringo, *Phys. Rev.* **77**, 291 1950; Ringo, G. R., M. T. Burgy, and D. J. Hughes, *Phys. Rev.* **84**, 1160, 1951.
24. Shull, C. G., E. O. Wollan, G. A. Morton, and W. L. Davidson, *Phys. Rev.* **73**, 842, 1948.
25. Glendening, N. K., and G. Kramer, *Phys. Rev.* **126**, 2159, 1962.
26. De Swart, J., and R. Marshak, *Physica* **25**, 1001, 1959.
27. Young, H. D., and R. E. Cutkosky, *Phys. Rev.* **117**, 595, 1960.
28. Sugawara, M., *Phys. Rev.* **117**, 614, 1960.
29. Feshbach, H., and V. F. Weisskopf, *Phys. Rev.* **76**, 1550, 1949; Biedenharn, L. C., Thesis, MIT, 1950; Gartenhaus, S., *Phys. Rev.* **100**, 903, 1955.

30. Brolley, J. E., J. D. Seagrave, and J. G. Berry, *Phys. Rev.* **135B**, 1119, 1964.
31. Jackson, J. D., and J. M. Blatt, *Rev. Mod. Phys.* **22**, 77, 1950.
32. Wilson, R., *The Nucleon-Nucleon Interaction*, Interscience Publishers, New York, 1962.
33. Serber, R., *Phys. Rev.* **72**, 1114, 1947.
34. Hess, W. N., *Rev. Mod. Phys.* **30**, 368, 1958.
35. Lock, W. O., *High Energy Nuclear Physics*, p. 146, Methuen and Co., London, 1960.
36. Dzhelepov, V. P., Yu. M. Kazarinov, B. M. Golovin, V. B. Flyagin, and V. I. Satarov, *Nuovo Cimento III Supplement*, No. 1, **61**, 1956.
37. Stapp, H. P., T. Ypsilantis, and N. Metropolis, *Phys. Rev.* **105**, 302, 1957; Signell, P., and D. G. Marker, *Phys. Rev.* **134B**, 365, 1964; Signell, P., N. R. Yoder, and J. E. Matos, *Phys. Rev.* **135B**, 1128, 1964.
38. Signell, P., and R. Marshak, *Phys. Rev.* **106**, 832, 1957; *ibid.*, **109**, 1229, 1958; Gammel, J. L., and R. M. Thaler, *Progr. Cosmic Ray Phys.* **5**, 99, 1960; Bryan, R. A., *Nuovo Cimento* **16**, 895, 1960; Saylor, D. P., R. A. Bryan, and R. E. Marshak, *Phys. Rev. Letters* **5**, 266, 1960; Hamada, T., *Progr. Theoret. Phys.* (*Kyoto*) **24**, 1033, 1960; *ibid.*, **25**, 247, 1961; Hamada, T., and I. D. Johnston, *Nucl. Phys.* **34**, 382, 1962.
39. Bishop, G. R., J. M. Westhead, G. Preston, and H. H. Halban, *Nature*, **170**, 113, 1952.
40. Wolfenstein, L., *Ann. Rev. Nucl. Sci.* **6**, 43, 1956.
41. Oxley, C. L., W. F. Cartwright, and J. Rouvina, *Phys. Rev.* **93**, 806, 1954.
42. Wouters, L. F., *Phys. Rev.* **84**, 1069, 1951.
43. Chamberlain, O., E. Segré, R. D. Trip, C. Wiegand, and T. Ypsilantis, *Phys. Rev.* **105**, 288, 1957.
44. Johnson, M. H., and E. Teller, *Phys. Rev.* **98**, 783, 1955.
45. Noyes, H. P., *Phys. Rev.* **130**, 2025, 1963.
46. Hulthen, L., and M. Sugawara, "The Two-Nucleon Problem," in *Handbuch der Physik*, vol. **39**, p. 1, Springer-Verlag, Berlin, 1957.
47. Bethe, H. A., and P. Morrison, *Elementary Nuclear Theory*, 2nd ed., p. 80, John Wiley and Sons, New York, 1956.
48. Jastrow, R., *Phys. Rev.* **81**, 165, 1951.
49. Rarita, W., and J. Schwinger, *Phys. Rev.* **59**, 436, 1941.

Problems

1. The *n-p* scattering at low energy can be described by the *s*-wave scattering amplitude f_0. Assuming conservation of angular momentum and parity, f_0 is diagonal in the total spin S of the two nucleons and $\langle \chi_i | f_0 | \chi_j \rangle = \delta_{ij} f_{0i}$ where $i, j = 1$ or 0. Show that the matrix f_0 is not diagonal in the two-particle spin states $\alpha_1\alpha_2, \alpha_1\beta_2, \beta_1\alpha_2, \beta_1\beta_2$. Determine all the sixteen matrix elements in terms of f_{00} and f_{01}.

2. Show that the cross section for *s*-wave *n-p* scattering for spin-flip and without spin-flip are given by

$$\sigma_{\text{flip}} = 4\pi \tfrac{1}{2}\{|f_{01}|^2 + \tfrac{1}{4}|f_{00}|^2\} \quad \text{and} \quad \sigma_{\text{no flip}} = 4\pi \tfrac{1}{2}\tfrac{1}{4}|f_{01} - f_{00}|^2.$$

Hence what is the cross section for scattering of unpolarized beam? (Use the results of Problem 1.)

3. Show that $\sigma_1 \cdot \sigma_2 = 1$ and -3 respectively for the spin-triplet and spin-singlet states of the two-nucleon system.

4. Assuming a two-nucleon potential of the form

$$V_{ij}^c = [c_0 + c_\sigma(\sigma_i \cdot \sigma_j) + c_\tau(\tau_i \cdot \tau_j) + c_{\sigma\tau}(\sigma_i \cdot \sigma_j)(\tau_i \cdot \tau_j)]v^c(r_{ij}),$$

determine the potential V_{ij}^c for triplet-even, triplet-odd, singlet-even and singlet-odd states.

5. Assume the interaction potential between the neutron and proton to be exponential, namely, $V = V_0 e^{-r/r_n}$ where V_0 and r_n are respectively the well depth and range of the nuclear potential.

(a) Write down the Schrödinger equation (in center-of-mass system) for the ground state of the deuteron for the case in which the angular momentum $l = 0$.

(b) Let $x = e^{-r/2r_n}$ and $\psi(r) = u(r)/r$. Show that the Schrödinger equation gives a Bessel equation. Write down the general solution of this equation.

(c) Applying the boundary conditions (ψ = finite at $r = 0$ and ∞), determine the relation between V_0 and r_n.

6. For proton-proton scattering, show that the differential scattering cross section in the laboratory system is given by

$$\left(\frac{d\sigma}{d\Omega}\right)_{\text{lab}} = \left(\frac{d\sigma}{d\Omega}\right)_{\text{cm}} \left[2^{3/2}(1 + \cos\theta_{\text{cm}})^{1/2}\right]$$

7. Show that
$$S_{12}\mathscr{Y}_{011}^1 = \sqrt{8}\,\mathscr{Y}_{211}^1$$

and
$$S_{12}\mathscr{Y}_{211}^1 = \sqrt{8}\,\mathscr{Y}_{011}^1 - 2\mathscr{Y}_{211}^1$$

where
$$S_{12} = 3(\sigma_1 \cdot \hat{r})(\sigma_2 \cdot \hat{r}) - \sigma_1 \cdot \sigma_2$$

and
$$\mathscr{Y}_{LSJ}^M = \sum_{M_L + M_s = M} \langle LSM_L M_s | JM\rangle Y_L^{M_L}\chi_S^{M_s}$$

8. Show that

(a) $$\sqrt{\frac{16\pi}{5}}\frac{1}{2}\int d^3r u_0 u_2 \mathscr{Y}_{011}^{1*} Y_2^0 \mathscr{Y}_{211}^1 = \frac{1}{\sqrt{50}}\int_0^\infty dr r^2 u_0 u_2$$

(b) $$\sqrt{\frac{16\pi}{5}}\frac{1}{4}\int d^3r u_2^2 \mathscr{Y}_{211}^{1*} Y_2^0 \mathscr{Y}_{211}^1 = -\frac{1}{2}\int_0^\infty dr r^2 u_2^2$$

9. In order that the 66-Kev singlet bound state may exist in the (n-p) system what should be the depth of the potential V_s? (See Ref. 14.)

10. For $C_{12}H_{18}$, typical values for $\theta_C = 5.6'$, $\lambda_C = 8$ Å, $f_H = -3.75$ F, and $f_C = 6.66$ F. Calculate the index of refraction of this mirror to produce the above θ_C and λ_C. (See Ref. 23.)

11. Given $J_d = 1$ and $s_p = \frac{1}{2}$, the neutron spin s_n can have values $\frac{1}{2}, \frac{3}{2}, \frac{5}{2}, \cdots$. Show that the cross section for coherent scattering of neutrons by parahydrogen gives too large a value with $s_n = \frac{3}{2}, \frac{5}{2}, \cdots$ and that the neutron spin $s_n = \frac{1}{2}$ gives closer agreement with experimental values.

4

PHENOMENOLOGY OF THE
TWO-NUCLEON INTERACTION

4.1   Introduction

In recent years a considerable amount of progress has been achieved in the study of the two-nucleon interaction. The experimental investigation of polarization and the triple scattering parameters of p-p scattering at high energies has made it possible to examine several features of the two-nucleon interaction which did not appear in the data on cross sections at lower energies.

The first set of triple scattering experiments was performed by Chamberlain, Segrè, Tripp, Wiegand, and Ypsilantis,[1] who measured five scattering parameters: cross section σ, polarization P, depolarization D, rotation parameters R and A, for p-p scattering at 310 Mev. Similar experiments have since been performed at 150 Mev,[2,3] 210 Mev,[4] and other energies. The theoretical investigation of the experimental data has followed two main procedures: (1) phase-shift analysis of the experimental data and (2) phenomenological potential models. In the first approach several sets of phase-shift solutions are obtained which fit the experimental data; then the problem is that of discriminating among the various sets of solutions on the basis of other experimental evidence. Stapp, Ypsilantis, and Metropolis[5] have carried out the phase-shift analysis of the experiment of Chamberlain et al., obtaining several phase-shift solutions from which only four were finally acceptable.

A later, modified analysis of the p-p scattering data at 310 Mev was performed by Cziffra, MacGregor, Moravcsik, and Stapp[6] in which the partial waves G and higher were calculated from the one-pion-exchange contribution to the scattering amplitude; that is, the higher phase shifts were obtained by carrying out a partial wave analysis of the scattering amplitude calculated in the Born approximation, taking into account

111

one-pion-exchange between the two nucleons. This procedure left only two distinguishable solutions.

The second approach followed by Signell and Marshak,[7] Gammel and Thaler,[8] Otsuki,[9] Watari,[10] and Tamagaki,[11] starts with a phenomenological potential, and a set of phase shifts is calculated that makes possible the calculation of the experimental scattering parameters. Both Signell and Marshak (SM)[7] and Gammel and Thaler (GT)[8] found it necessary to add a strong spin-orbit short-range potential to the central and tensor potential in order to explain the polarization and the triple scattering data at 150 and 310 Mev. The introduction of the spin-orbit potential was criticized earlier by the Japanese group.[9-12] Now its presence, however, is rather widely accepted.[13] The more recent phenomenological potentials are due to Bryan,[14] Saylor, Bryan, and Marshak,[15] Hamada,[16] and Hamada and Johnston.[17] These differ from the SM and GT potentials in explicitly realizing that the two-nucleon interaction in the asymptotic region where the nucleon-nucleon separation becomes large ($\sim$ a few pion wavelengths), is obtained from the one-pion-exchange contribution, which can be determined unambiguously.

The use of meson theory to obtain the spin-orbit interaction of the requisite strength has not had much success. The two-pion-exchange interaction predicts a spin-orbit term,[18] but the strength is too small. Moreover, the various workers differ in the results because of the ambiguities involved in the calculations and the treatment of the effects of nucleon recoil. However, the use of dispersion theory[19] (Mandelstam representation[20]) is expected to be more promising. In this, the covariant S-matrix for the scattering process is obtained from the general requirements of field theory, that is, analyticity and unitarity, and from the mass spectrum of the strongly interacting particles.

The recent review articles on the nucleon-nucleon system have been written by Phillips,[21] Gammel and Thaler,[22] Marshak,[23] MacGregor, Moravcsik, and Stapp,[24] Moravcsik and Noyes,[25] Breit,[26] and Nigam.[27] In this chapter we do not go into specific details of the problems involved. It is intended mainly to provide a broad background of the various approaches used in the study of nucleon-nucleon interaction, and the discussion here is largely based on and reproduced, in parts, from Ref. 27.

4.2 Phase-Shift Analysis

The wave function which describes the scattering of a two-nucleon system can asymptotically be written as[5,28]

$$\psi \simeq e^{i\mathbf{k}\cdot\mathbf{r}}\chi_s^{m_s} + \frac{e^{ikr}}{r} \sum_{m'_s} M^{m_s m'_s}(\theta, \phi)\chi_s^{m'_s} \tag{1}$$

where $\chi_s^{m_s}$ is the singlet ($s = 0$, $m_s = 0$) and the triplet ($s = 1$, $m_s = 0$, ± 1) spin states of the two-nucleon system, and $M^{m_s m'_s}(\theta, \phi)$ is the matrix in spin space which describes the scattering of an incident spin state $\chi_s^{m'_s}$ into the final spin state $\chi_s^{m_s}$. The total spin s is conserved for interactions conserving parity. $\mathbf{k}$ and (θ, ϕ) are the momentum and the scattering angles in the center-of-mass system. The asymptotic expressions ($r \to \infty$) for the incoming and the scattered waves, in the $lsm_l m_s$ ($= \lambda$) representation, are given by

$$\psi_{s,m'_s}^{\text{inc}}(\theta', \phi', r) \simeq -\frac{1}{r} \sum_{l', m_{l'}} e^{-i(kr - \pi l'/2)} g(\lambda') Y_{l'}^{m_{l'}}(\theta', \phi') \chi_s^{m'_s} \tag{2}$$

$$\psi_{s,m_s}^{\text{sc}}(\theta, \phi, r) \simeq \frac{1}{r} \sum_{l, m_l} e^{i(kr - \pi l/2)} f(\lambda) Y_l^{m_l}(\theta, \phi) \chi_s^{m_s}$$

$$= \frac{e^{ikr}}{r} \sum_{m_s} M^{m_s m'_s}(\theta, \phi) \chi_s^{m'_s} \tag{3}$$

where $Y_l^{m_l}(\theta, \phi)$ is the spherical harmonic for angular momentum l with z component m_l, s the spin with the z component m_s, and the amplitude g as given by a plane-wave expansion of a wave proceeding along the direction $\mathbf{k}/|\mathbf{k}| = \hat{k}$ is

$$g = \frac{4\pi}{2ik} e^{il'\pi/2} Y_{l'}^{m_{l'}*}(\hat{k})$$

The amplitudes f and g are connected by the R matrix ($R = S - I$) by the relation

$$f(\lambda) = \sum_{\lambda'} \langle \lambda | R | \lambda' \rangle g(\lambda') \tag{4}$$

Substituting Eq. (4) in Eq. (3), we obtain

$$\sum_{m'_s} \chi_s^{m_s*} M^{m_s m'_s}(\theta, \phi) \chi_s^{m'_s} = \sum Y_l^{m_l}(\theta, \phi) M(lsm_l m_s; sm'_s) \tag{5}$$

where

$$M(lsm_l m_s; sm'_s) = \frac{4\pi}{2ik} e^{-il\pi/2} \sum_{l', m_{l'}} \langle \lambda | R | \lambda' \rangle e^{i\pi l'/2} Y_{l'}^{m_{l'}*}(\hat{k}') \tag{6}$$

We can choose the z-axis along the direction of the incident beam so that $m_{l'} = 0$ and $\hat{k}' = (\theta' = 0, \phi' = 0)$. Since the total angular momentum j, its z component m_j, and the spin s are conserved, the R-matrix is diagonal in these quantum numbers, and thus it is convenient to express it in the $lsjm_j$ representation by using the relation

$$|lsm_l m_s\rangle = \sum_{j, m_j} \langle lsm_l m_s | jm_j \rangle |lsjm_j\rangle \tag{7}$$

where $\langle lsm_l m_s | jm_j \rangle$ are the usual Clebsch-Gordan coefficients. The matrix elements of R in the $lsjm_j$ representation are then directly related to the phase shifts through the S matrix. By denoting the matrix elements of the R matrix by α_l for scattering in the spin-singlet state, and the diagonal and the nondiagonal (in l) scattering matrix elements of R in the spin triplet state by α_{lj} and α^j, respectively, we have

$$\langle l0lm_j| \, R \, |l0lm_j\rangle = \alpha_l$$

$$\langle l1jm_j| \, R \, |l1jm_j\rangle = \alpha_{lj} \tag{8}$$

$$\langle j \pm 1, 1, j, m_j| \, R \, |j \mp 1, 1, j, m_j\rangle = \alpha^j$$

where the α's can be expressed in terms of the phase shifts δ's and the coupling parameters ε_j, which couple the states of angular momenta $j - 1$ and $j + 1$ with a given j, as follows:

$$
\begin{aligned}
\alpha_l &= e^{2i\delta_l} - 1 \\
\alpha_{lj} &= e^{2i\delta_l} - 1, \quad \text{for} \quad l = j \\
\alpha_{j\pm1,j} &= \cos^2 \varepsilon_j e^{2i\delta_{j\pm1,j}} + \sin^2 \varepsilon_j e^{2i\delta_{j\mp1,j}} - 1 \\
\alpha^j &= \tfrac{1}{2} \sin 2\varepsilon_j (e^{2i\delta_{j\mp1,j}} - e^{2i\delta_{j\pm1,j}})
\end{aligned}
\tag{8a}
$$

If we wish to include the effects of Coulomb interaction for p-p scattering in a nonrelativistic manner, then in the asymptotic expressions for ψ^{inc} and ψ^{sc} we must replace kr by $kr - \eta \ln 2kr$, where $\eta = e^2/\hbar v$, v being the velocity in the laboratory system. Furthermore, $R = S - 1 \equiv (S - S_c) + (S_c - 1)$, where S_c is the Coulomb scattering matrix. In $S - S_c$, S_c is expressed in terms of Coulomb phase shifts

$$\phi_l = \sum_{n=1}^{l} \arctan \frac{\eta}{n}$$

and thereby the unity on the right-hand side of the equations for α's [Eq. (8a)] is replaced by $e^{2i\phi_l}$. The term $S_c - 1$ gives rise to the Coulomb scattering amplitude

$$f_c(\theta) = -[\eta/k(1 - \cos \theta)] \{\exp [-i\eta \ln \tfrac{1}{2}(1 - \cos \theta)]\} \tag{8b}$$

Substituting Eqs. (8) and (7) in Eq. (5), we obtain

$$
\begin{aligned}
M^{m_s m's}(\theta, \phi) = f_c^{m_s m's}(\theta) + \sum_j [\{a_{j-1j}^{m_s m's}(\theta, \phi)\alpha_{j-1j} \\
+ a_{jj}^{m_s m's}\alpha_{jj} + a_{j+1j}^{m_s m's}\alpha_{j+1j}\} + a^{jm_s m's}\alpha^j] + \sum_l a_l^{m_s m's}\alpha_l
\end{aligned}
\tag{9}
$$

where the singlet state $f_c^{ss}(\theta) = f_c(\theta) + f_c(\pi - \theta)$, the triplet state $f_c^{11} = f_c^{00} = f_c(\theta) - f_c(\pi - \theta)$, and all others are equal to zero. Because of

Pauli exclusion principle the first summation over j is over values corresponding to odd (even) l and the second summation over l is over even (odd) values for the nucleons in the isotopic spin state $T = 1(0)$. The coefficients $a^{m_s m's}$ are given in Table III of Stapp et al.[5] From Eqs. (8a) and (9), it is easy to obtain the following expression for the M matrix in terms of phase shifts[13]

$$
\begin{aligned}
M^{m_s m's}(\theta, \phi) = f_c^{m_s m's}(\theta) + \sum_j \Big\{ \sum_{mn} a_{mn}^{m_s m's}(\theta, \phi) \langle m'n, \phi_m | \\
+ f(\varepsilon_j, a_{j+1j}^{m_s m's}, a_{j+1j}^{m_s m's}, \tfrac{1}{2} a^{jm_s m's}) \langle j-1j, j+1j| \Big\}
\end{aligned}
\tag{9a}
$$

where mn take values $jj, j-1j, j+1j$ and j and $m' = m$ except when $m = j - 1, m' = j + 1$, and

$$
\langle A, B| = 2i e^{i(\delta_A + \delta_B)} \sin (\delta_A - \delta_B)
$$
$$
f(\varepsilon_j, a, b, c) = a \cos^2 \varepsilon_j + b \sin^2 \varepsilon_j + c \sin 2\varepsilon_j
\tag{9b}
$$

4.3 *S*-Matrix Approach

The scattering matrix for nucleon-nucleon scattering can also be obtained from the general considerations of charge symmetry and invariance with respect to rotation, parity, and time reversal. The variables which characterize the scattering problem are $\mathbf{k}_i$, the initial momentum in the center-of-mass-system; $\mathbf{k}_f$, the final momentum; and $\boldsymbol{\sigma}_1$ and $\boldsymbol{\sigma}_2$, spins of nucleons 1 and 2. From the momentum vectors, it is convenient to construct three orthogonal unit vectors

$$
\mathbf{P} = \frac{\mathbf{k}_i + \mathbf{k}_f}{|\mathbf{k}_i + \mathbf{k}_f|} \qquad \mathbf{K} = \frac{\mathbf{k}_f - \mathbf{k}_i}{|\mathbf{k}_f - \mathbf{k}_i|}
$$

and

$$
n = \frac{\mathbf{k}_i \times \mathbf{k}_f}{|\mathbf{k}_i \times \mathbf{k}_f|}
$$

where the first two are polar vectors, whereas the third is an axial (pseudo-) vector; the spin vectors are pseudovectors. The scattering matrix can be constructed from these variables by forming scalar combinations which would also be invariant under time reversals; the pseudoscalar combinations are not allowed because of parity conservation. It therefore follows that the $\boldsymbol{\sigma}$'s appear either bilinearly or linearly in conjunction with a pseudovector. By taking into account the symmetry between nucleons 1 and 2, we can form the following independent products of scalar functions

$$1, \sigma_{1n} + \sigma_{2n}, \quad \sigma_{1n}\sigma_{2n}, \quad \sigma_{1K}\sigma_{2K}, \quad \sigma_{1P}\sigma_{2P},$$

$$\sigma_{1P}\sigma_{2K}, \quad \sigma_{1K}\sigma_{2P}, \quad (\boldsymbol{\sigma}_1 \times \boldsymbol{\sigma}_2) \cdot \mathbf{n} \quad (10a)$$

where $\sigma_{1n} = \boldsymbol{\sigma}_1 \cdot \mathbf{n}$, etc. We also have to test whether each of the terms in Eq. (10a) is invariant under time reversal. The time reversal transformation has the following effect:

$$\mathbf{k}_i \rightarrow -\mathbf{k}_f, \mathbf{k}_f \rightarrow -\mathbf{k}_i, \boldsymbol{\sigma} \rightarrow -\boldsymbol{\sigma} \quad (10b)$$

so that

$$\mathbf{n} \rightarrow -\mathbf{n}, \quad \mathbf{P} \rightarrow -\mathbf{P}, \quad \mathbf{K} \rightarrow \mathbf{K} \quad (10c)$$

Taking Eqs. (10b) and (10c) into account, we find that the last three terms in Eq. (10a) are not permitted by invariance under time reversal.

The scattering matrix for each isotopic spin state $T = 1, 0$ is given by[28]

$$M(\theta) = A + C(\sigma_{1n} + \sigma_{2n}) + B\sigma_{1n}\sigma_{2n}$$

$$+ \tfrac{1}{2}G(\sigma_{1K}\sigma_{2K} + \sigma_{1P}\sigma_{2P}) + \tfrac{1}{2}H(\sigma_{1K}\sigma_{2K} - \sigma_{1P}\sigma_{2P}) \quad (11)$$

where the coefficients A, C, B, G, and H are complex and are functions of energy and angle. We can express the coefficients of the M matrix in terms of elements $M^{m_s m'_s}$ in the spin space of the two nucleons by multiplying Eq. (11) on the left by $\chi_s^{m_s*}$ and by $\chi_s^{m'_s}$ on the right. It is then easy to obtain from Eq. (11) the following relations:

$$A = \tfrac{1}{4}(2M^{11} + M^{00} + M^{ss})$$

$$C = \tfrac{1}{4}i\sqrt{2}(M^{10} - M^{01})$$

$$B = \tfrac{1}{4}(-2M^{1-1} + M^{00} - M^{ss})$$

$$G = \tfrac{1}{2}(M^{11} + M^{1-1} - M^{ss})$$

$$H = (\tfrac{1}{2}\cos\theta)(M^{00} + M^{1-1} - M^{11})$$

$$= -\frac{1}{2}\frac{\sqrt{2}}{\sin\theta}(M^{10} + M^{01}) \quad (12)$$

with

$$M^{11} = M^{-1-1}, \quad M^{-11} = M^{1-1},$$

$$M^{01} = -M^{0-1}, \quad M^{10} = -M^{-10} \quad (13)$$

The M matrix for p-p, n-n, and n-p scattering can be expressed in terms of the M matrices M_1 and M_0 for the total isotopic spin states $T = 1$ and $T = 0$, respectively, by transforming from the $\tau_1\tau_2\tau_{1z}\tau_{2z}$ representation to that of the $\tau_1\tau_2 T T_z$, making use of Eq. (7) and the rotational invariance of the M matrix in isospin space. We then obtain (neglecting Coulomb corrections)

$$\langle pp| M |pp\rangle = \langle nn| M |nn\rangle = M_1$$
$$\langle np| M |np\rangle = \tfrac{1}{2}(M_1 + M_0) \qquad (14)$$
$$\langle np| M |pn\rangle = \tfrac{1}{2}(M_1 - M_0)$$

We can rewrite Eq. (11) as

$$M(\theta) = bS + c(\sigma_{1n} + \sigma_{2n}) + \tfrac{1}{2}g(\sigma_{1K}\sigma_{2K} + \sigma_{1P}\sigma_{2P})T$$
$$+ \tfrac{1}{2}h(\sigma_{1K}\sigma_{2K} - \sigma_{1P}\sigma_{2P})T + n\sigma_{1n}\sigma_{2n}T \qquad (15)$$

where

$$S = \tfrac{1}{4}(1 - \boldsymbol{\sigma}_1 \cdot \boldsymbol{\sigma}_2), \qquad T = \tfrac{1}{4}(B + \boldsymbol{\sigma}_1 \cdot \boldsymbol{\sigma}_2)$$
$$n = A + B, \qquad g = 2A + G,$$
$$b = A - B - G, \qquad c = C, \qquad h = H$$

and use has been made of the relations

$$\sigma_{1n}\sigma_{2n}T = \sigma_{1n}\sigma_{2n} + S$$

and

$$\sigma_{1P}\sigma_{2P} + \sigma_{1K}\sigma_{2K} + \sigma_{1n}\sigma_{2n} = \boldsymbol{\sigma}_1 \cdot \boldsymbol{\sigma}_2$$

It is now easy to see[29] from the requirement of antisymmetry of the two-nucleon system with respect to interchange of space (implying $\mathbf{k}_f \to -\mathbf{k}_f$), spin, and isotopic spin coordinates, that the coefficients $b_1(\theta)$, $h_1(\theta)$, $c_1(\theta)$, $g_0(\theta)$, and $n_0(\theta)$ remain unchanged for $\theta \to \pi - \theta$, whereas $b_0(\theta)$, $h_0(\theta)$, $c_0(\theta)$, $g_1(\theta)$, and $n_1(\theta)$ change sign, where the suffixes 1 and 0 refer to the value of the isotopic spin T. Thus it is necessary to know the coefficients only over the range 0 to $\pi/2$.

In addition, Puzikov, Ryndin, and Smorodinski[30] showed that the unitarity of the S matrix leads to five integral equations of constraints on the coefficients of the M matrix. The unitarity of the S matrix implies

$$SS^\dagger = 1 = (R + 1)(R^\dagger + 1)$$

that is,

$$\langle \Omega| R + R^\dagger |\Omega'\rangle = - \sum_{\Omega''} \langle \Omega| R |\Omega''\rangle\langle \Omega''| R^\dagger |\Omega'\rangle \qquad (16)$$

where $\Omega = (\theta, \phi) \equiv \hat{k}$. From Eqs. (2) to (4) it is easy to obtain

$$M(\mathbf{k}, \mathbf{k}') = \frac{4\pi}{2ik} \langle \Omega| R |\Omega'\rangle \qquad (17)$$

so that Eq. (16) becomes

$$-\frac{i}{2}(M - M^\dagger) = \operatorname{Im} M(\mathbf{k}, \mathbf{k}')$$
$$= \frac{k}{4\pi} \int d\Omega'' M(\mathbf{k}, \mathbf{k}'')M^\dagger(\mathbf{k}'', \mathbf{k}') \qquad (18)$$

From Eqs. (11) and (18), the following integral equations can be obtained:

$$4\pi \text{ Im } A(\theta) = \frac{k}{4} \int d\Omega'' \text{ Tr } [M(\mathbf{k}, \mathbf{k}'')M^\dagger(\mathbf{k}'', \mathbf{k}')]$$

$$4\pi \text{ Im } B(\theta) = \frac{k}{4} \int d\Omega'' \text{ Tr } [M(\mathbf{k}, \mathbf{k}'')M^\dagger(\mathbf{k}'', \mathbf{k}')\sigma_{1n}\sigma_{2n}]$$

$$4\pi \text{ Re } C(\theta) = \frac{ik}{8} \int d\Omega'' \text{ Tr } [M(\mathbf{k}, \mathbf{k}'')M^\dagger(\mathbf{k}'', \mathbf{k}')(\sigma_{1n} + \sigma_{2n})] \tag{19}$$

$$4\pi \text{ Im } [G(\theta) + H(\theta)] = \frac{k}{2} \int d\Omega'' \text{ Tr } [M(\mathbf{k}, \mathbf{k}'')M^\dagger(\mathbf{k}'', \mathbf{k}')\sigma_{1K}\sigma_{2K}]$$

$$4\pi \text{ Im } [G(\theta) - H(\theta)] = \frac{k}{2} \int d\Omega'' \text{ Tr } [M(\mathbf{k}, \mathbf{k}'')M^\dagger(\mathbf{k}'', \mathbf{k}')\sigma_{1P}\sigma_{2P}]$$

It therefore follows from Eq. (19) that, as a consequence of the unitarity of the S-matrix, the ten complex (or 20 real) coefficients A_T, B_T, C_T, G_T, and H_T ($T = 0, 1$) are not completely independent. For each isotopic spin state T, there are five integral equations of constraints whose solutions determine five parts (real or imaginary) of the five complex coefficients provided the remaining five parts are known over the angular range 0 to $\pi/2$ at the energy under consideration. Thus the M matrix for p-p (n-p) scattering at a given angle and energy requires a knowledge of 10 (20) real coefficients (phase factor being determined as well) at this angle and energy or, alternatively, 5 (10) real coefficients over the angular range 0 to $\pi/2$ at this energy.

The number of elements of the matrix $M^{m_s m'_s}$ ($m_s, m'_s = 0, \pm 1$, and s) is also 10 (20) for p-p (n-p) scattering. It has been pointed out by Golovin, Dzhelepov, Nadezhdin, and Satarov[31] that the performance of each pair of experiments to determine the same characteristics of the p-p system for $0 \le \theta \le \pi/2$ and the n-p system for the angular range 0 to π provides information about three real functions which describe scattering. Therefore, in order to determine all the ten complex coefficients (except for the common phase factor), it is necessary to perform six pairs of identical experiments on p-p and n-p scattering, giving information regarding 18 real functions and one more p-p or n-p scattering experiment.

Schumacher and Bethe[32] pointed out that, because of the bilinear form of the expressions of scattering parameters, ambiguities arise in constructing the nucleon-nucleon scattering matrix from data at one angle and energy. They showed that these ambiguities can be eliminated by a knowledge of the polarization transfer tensor K_{ik} which measures the polarization of the recoil (scattered) nucleon in the scattering of a polarized (unpolarized) beam from an unpolarized (polarized) target. Since their method does not utilize the condition of unitarity, it is also applicable at energies at which inelastic processes occur.

4.4 Experimental Scattering Parameters

The scattering parameters describing nucleon-nucleon scattering are called single, double, and triple scattering parameters. The cross section for the unpolarized beam is the single scattering parameter, and the polarization P of the beam once scattered by the target is the double scattering parameter. The triple scattering parameters, depolarization D, rotation parameters R, A, R', and A', describe how the second scatterer changes the direction or magnitude, or both, of the polarization; the first scatterer acts as a polarizer and the final scatterer as an analyzer. These coefficients can be defined by expressing the final-state polarization $\langle \sigma_f \rangle$ in terms of the initial-state polarization $\langle \sigma_i \rangle$. If $\mathbf{k}_i$ is the initial momentum of the nucleon and $\mathbf{k}_f$ its final momentum, then it is convenient to express $\langle \sigma_i \rangle$ in terms of the three mutually perpendicular unit vectors $\hat{k}_i$, $\hat{k}_i \times \hat{k}_f$, and $\hat{k}_i \times (\hat{k}_i \times \hat{k}_f)$ and similarly express $\langle \sigma_f \rangle$ in terms of the vectors $\hat{k}_f$, $\hat{k}_i \times \hat{k}_f$ and $\hat{k}_f \times (\hat{k}_i \times \hat{k}_f)$. Assuming that $\langle \sigma_f \rangle$ depends linearly on $\langle \sigma_i \rangle$ and observing that σ is a pseudovector, provided parity is conserved, we can express $\langle \sigma_f \rangle$ in terms of the components of $\langle \sigma_i \rangle$ along the three mutually perpendicular directions $\hat{k}_i$, $\hat{k}_i \times \hat{k}_f$, and $\hat{k}_i \times (\hat{k}_i \times \hat{k}_f)$ as follows.[28]

$$
\begin{aligned}
I_f \langle \sigma_f \rangle = I_i \{ &[P + D\langle \sigma_i \rangle \cdot (\hat{k}_i \times \hat{k}_f)](\hat{k}_i \times \hat{k}_f) \\
&+ [A\langle \sigma_i \rangle \cdot \hat{k}_i + R\langle \sigma_i \rangle \cdot \hat{k}_i \times (\hat{k}_i \times \hat{k}_f)]\hat{k}_f \times (\hat{k}_i \times \hat{k}_f) \\
&+ [A'\langle \sigma_i \rangle \cdot \hat{k}_i + R'\langle \sigma_i \rangle \cdot \hat{k}_i \times (\hat{k}_i \times \hat{k}_f)]\hat{k}_f \}
\end{aligned}
\tag{20}
$$

where I_f is the cross section for all cases, I_i is the cross section for an unpolarized beam, and only those terms occur on the right-hand side which transform like a pseudovector. From Eq. (20), it is now easy to understand the significance of each of the scattering parameters P, D, A, A', R, and R' in the transformation of the initial polarization $\langle \sigma_i \rangle$ to the final polarization $\langle \sigma_f \rangle$. These are illustrated in Fig. 4-1.

The polarization P involves the determination of the amount of the unpolarized incident beam rendered into a polarized beam after the first scattering, with the direction of polarization perpendicular to the scattering plane, that is, the plane containing the incident and scattered beams. This direction of polarization is denoted by ○. The depolarization D determines the amount of polarization perpendicular to the scattering plane converted into the same after the second scattering. The triple-scattering parameter A describes the process in which the polarization

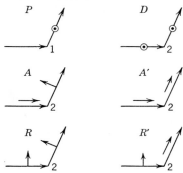

along the direction of the first scattered beam (longitudinal polarization) is converted into polarization perpendicular to the scattered beam (with the polarization vector lying in the scattering plane) after the second scattering. The polarization direction in the plane of the scattering is denoted by arrows. The interpretation of the triple-scattering parameters A', R, and R' can be similarly inferred from Fig. 4-1.

Fig. 4-1 Diagrammatic representation of the scattering parameters; 1 and 2 denote the first and second scattering. The horizontal line describes the beam before the first or the second scattering and the inclined line describes it after scattering. The arrows indicate the direction of the polarization vector, the circle $\odot$ indicating polarization direction normal to the page (Nigam[27]).

In order to obtain expressions for the scattering parameters, we quote a result, due to Wolfenstein,[28] which relates the final state spin operator to the initial state spin operator by means of the M matrix which transforms from the spin space of the initial channel to the spin space of the final channel. If the incident and the target particles have spins s and s_t, respectively, and S^μ denotes the base matrices, where the index μ runs from 1 to $(2s + 1)^2(2s_t + 1)^2$, then

$$I_0\langle S^\mu\rangle_f = \frac{1}{(2s + 1)(2s_t + 1)} \sum_v \langle S^v\rangle_i \, \mathrm{Tr}\,(MS^vM^\dagger S^\mu) \tag{21}$$

where I_0 is the differential scattering cross section. Comparing the various coefficients of Eqs. (20) and (21), we obtain

$$I_0P = \tfrac{1}{4}\,\mathrm{Tr}\,[MM^\dagger(\boldsymbol{\sigma}, \mathbf{k}_i \times \mathbf{k}_f)]$$

$$I_0D = \tfrac{1}{4}\,\mathrm{Tr}\,[M(\boldsymbol{\sigma}, \mathbf{k}_i \times \mathbf{k}_f)M^\dagger(\boldsymbol{\sigma}, \mathbf{k}_i \times \mathbf{k}_f)]$$

$$I_0A = \tfrac{1}{4}\,\mathrm{Tr}\,[M(\boldsymbol{\sigma}, \mathbf{k}_i)M^\dagger(\boldsymbol{\sigma}, \mathbf{k}_f \times (\mathbf{k}_i \times \mathbf{k}_f))]$$

$$I_0A' = \tfrac{1}{4}\,\mathrm{Tr}\,[M(\boldsymbol{\sigma}, \mathbf{k}_i)M^\dagger(\boldsymbol{\sigma}, \mathbf{k}_f)]$$

$$I_0R = \tfrac{1}{4}\,\mathrm{Tr}\,[M(\boldsymbol{\sigma}, \mathbf{k}_i \times (\mathbf{k}_i \times \mathbf{k}_f))M^\dagger(\boldsymbol{\sigma}, \mathbf{k}_f \times (\mathbf{k}_i \times \mathbf{k}_f))]$$

$$I_0R' = \tfrac{1}{4}\,\mathrm{Tr}\,[M(\boldsymbol{\sigma}, \mathbf{k}_i \times (\mathbf{k}_i \times \mathbf{k}_f))M^\dagger(\boldsymbol{\sigma}, \mathbf{k}_f)] \tag{22}$$

Using $\alpha\alpha$, $\alpha\beta$, $\beta\alpha$, and $\beta\beta$ as the basis spin states for the two nucleons, the matrices $\boldsymbol{\sigma}$ can be explicitly expressed. By further expressing the elements of the M matrix in the representation

$$\langle s_1s_2\, m_1m_2|\, M\, |s_1s_2\, m_1'm_2'\rangle$$

in terms of elements

$$\langle s_1 s_2 s m_s | M | s_1 s_2 s m'_s \rangle = M_{m_s m'_s}$$

in the triplet-singlet representation, by means of Eq. (7) we obtain the following expressions for the scattering parameters:

$$I_0 P = \left(\frac{\sqrt{2}}{4}\right) \text{Re} \{i(M_{10} - M_{01})(M_{11} - M_{1-1} + M_{00})^*\}$$

$$I_0 D = \tfrac{1}{2} \text{Re} \{(M_{11} + M_{1-1})M_{ss}^* + (M_{11} - M_{1-1})M_{00}^*\} - \text{Re} \, M_{10} M_{01}^*$$

$$\frac{I_0 R}{\cos \theta/2} = \tfrac{1}{2} \text{Re} \left\{ \left[M_{00} + (\cos \theta - 1) \frac{\sqrt{2} M_{10}}{\sin \theta} \right] (M_{11} + M_{1-1})^* \right.$$

$$\left. + \left[M_{00} + \cos \theta \, \frac{\sqrt{2} M_{10}}{\sin \theta} \right] M_{ss}^* \right\}$$

$$\frac{I_0 A}{\sin \theta/2} = -\tfrac{1}{2} \text{Re} \left\{ \left[M_{00} + \cos \theta \, \frac{\sqrt{2} M_{10}}{\sin \theta} - \frac{\sqrt{2} M_{01}}{\sin \theta} \right] (M_{11} + M_{1-1})^* \right.$$

$$\left. + \left[M_{00} + (\cos \theta + 1) \frac{\sqrt{2} M_{10}}{\sin \theta} \right] M_{ss}^* \right\}$$

$$\frac{I_0 R'}{\sin \theta/2} = \tfrac{1}{2} \text{Re} \left\{ \left[M_{00} + (\cos \theta + 1) \frac{\sqrt{2} M_{10}}{\sin \theta} \right] (M_{11} + M_{1-1})^* \right.$$

$$\left. + \left[M_{00} + \cos \theta \, \frac{\sqrt{2} M_{10}}{\sin \theta} - \frac{\sqrt{2} M_{01}}{\sin \theta} \right] M_{ss}^* \right\}$$

$$\frac{I_0 A'}{\cos \theta/2} = \tfrac{1}{2} \text{Re} \left\{ \left[M_{00} + \cos \theta \, \frac{\sqrt{2} M_{10}}{\sin \theta} + \frac{\sqrt{2} M_{10}}{\sin \theta} \right] (M_{11} + M_{1-1})^* \right.$$

$$\left. + \left[M_{00} + (\cos \theta - 1) \frac{\sqrt{2} M_{10}}{\sin \theta} \right] M_{ss}^* \right\}$$

$$I_0 = \tfrac{1}{2} |M_{11}|^2 + \tfrac{1}{4} |M_{00}|^2 + \tfrac{1}{4} |M_{ss}|^2 + \tfrac{1}{2} |M_{10}|^2 + \tfrac{1}{2} |M_{01}|^2 + \tfrac{1}{2} |M_{1-1}|^2$$

$$(23)$$

where the expressions for $M_{m_s m'_s}(\theta, \varphi)$ in terms of the phase shifts are given by Eq. (9).

The other experimental parameters are the spin correlation coefficients C_{nn}, C_{KP}, C_{PP}, and C_{KK}. In these experiments an unpolarized nucleon beam is scattered by nucleons and components of the polarization of the scattered nucleon and the recoil nucleon along the directions indicated by the indices are measured in coincidence. Thus $C_{nn} = \langle \sigma_{1n}\sigma_{2n} \rangle$, etc., and the following are the expressions for these coefficients:

$$\tfrac{1}{2}I_0 C_{nn} = \operatorname{Re} A^*B + |C|^2 - \tfrac{1}{4}|G|^2 + \tfrac{1}{4}|H|^2$$

$$I_0 C_{KP} = -2 \operatorname{Im} C^*H,$$

$$\tfrac{1}{2}I_0(C_{PP} + C_{KK}) = \operatorname{Re} G^*(A - B)$$

$$\tfrac{1}{2}I_0(C_{PP} - C_{KK}) = -\operatorname{Re} H^*(A + B) \tag{24}$$

4.5 Phase-Shift Analysis of Experimental Parameters

A complete set of experiments on proton-proton scattering at 310 MeV was performed by Chamberlain, Segré, Tripp, Wiegand, and Ypsilantis.[1] The experiment consisted of the measurement of five scattering parameters I_0, P, D, R, and A. As Puzikov, Ryndin, and Smorodinsky[30] have shown, because of the identity of particles it is only necessary to measure in the angular range from 0 to $\pi/2$ and if the unitarity of the S matrix is used, only five scattering parameters need be measured at a given energy. It has been further pointed out by Marshak[23] that the S matrix will be uniquely determined only if at least one of the experiments involves scatterings that are not in the same plane.

The phase-shift analysis of the 310 Mev proton-proton scattering experiment of Chamberlain et al.[1] was carried out by Stapp, Ypsilantis, and Metropolis[5] and led to eight possible sets of phase-shift solutions because of inaccuracies of the experiments. Three of the solutions (solutions number 5, 7, and 8) were excluded because they did not fit the production of pions in the process $p + p \to d + \pi^+$. Solution number 6 can be discarded because of the measurement[33] of C_{KP} at $\pi/2$ at 382 Mev, thus leaving four sets of solutions.

A modified phase-shift analysis of the p-p scattering data of the experiment at 310 Mev has been carried out by Moravcsik et al.[6] which makes it almost possible to obtain a unique phase-shift solution. Their procedure is based on the contention of the Japanese group, led by Taketani, that the nucleon-nucleon interaction at great distances is adequately described by the one-pion-exchange potential. They therefore evaluate the partial waves G and higher from the one-pion-exchange pole in the scattering amplitude and calculate the remaining lower partial waves from the experimental data. Moravcsik et al.[6] arrive at the conclusion that the modified solutions 1 and 2 converge, respectively, to solutions 3 and 4; thus, essentially only two solutions remain.

Experiments similar to those of Chamberlain et al.[1] have been done at Harvard[2] and Harwell[3] at an energy of 150 Mev. The group at Rochester[4] has measured the proton-proton scattering cross section σ, polarization P, and the triple-scattering parameters A, R, and D at 210 Mev. MacGregor and Moravcsik[34] have applied their modified phase-shift analysis to the Rochester data,[4] and obtained four sets of phase-shift solutions. Of these, two have been excluded primarily because they do not have the behavior corresponding to one of the two acceptable phase-shift solutions at 310 Mev.

4.6 Phenomenological Two-Nucleon Potential

The scattering matrix approach, although very general, has its limitations. In order to determine the wave functions of the two-nucleon system, its bound states, and off-the-energy-shell matrix elements, it is necessary to know the Hamiltonian for the system. If the two-nucleon potential can be specified, it is possible to determine the phase shifts uniquely, and hence all the scattering parameters. An unambiguous derivation of the complete potential from meson theory would solve this problem, but as yet this does not seem possible; only the second-order one-pion-exchange potential is unambiguously known. We shall therefore confine ourselves to the phenomenological and the semiphenomenological potentials based on concepts of meson theory.

Wigner[35] proposed the first general form of the phenomenological nucleon-nucleon potential under the restrictions that: (1) the potential depends on the spins σ_1 and σ_2, the relative separation $\mathbf{r}$, and the relative momentum $\mathbf{p}$ of the two nucleons so that the center-of-mass motion is separable and the total momentum is conserved; (2) the potential has rotational invariance so that the total angular momentum is conserved; and (3) the potential depends, at the most, linearly on the relative momentum $\mathbf{p}$. Okubo and Marshak[36] have given the most general velocity-dependent proton-proton potential by dropping restriction (3). They determine the potential under the restrictions of (1) translational invariance, (2) rotational invariance, (3) Galilean invariance, (4) space reflection invariance, (5) time reversal invariance, (6) charge independence, (7) permutation symmetry, and (8) hermiticity, and arrive at the following expression:

$$V = V_0 + (\sigma_1 \cdot \sigma_2)V_1 + S_{12}V_2 + (\mathbf{L} \cdot \mathbf{S})V_3$$
$$+ \tfrac{1}{2}[(\sigma_1 \cdot \mathbf{L})(\sigma_2 \cdot \mathbf{L}) + (\sigma_2 \cdot \mathbf{L})(\sigma_1 \cdot \mathbf{L})]V_4$$
$$+ (\sigma_1 \cdot \mathbf{p})(\sigma_2 \cdot \mathbf{p})V_5 + \text{hermitian conjugate} \qquad (25)$$

where $S_{12} = 3(\sigma_1 \cdot \mathbf{r})(\sigma_2 \cdot \mathbf{r})/r^2 - (\sigma_1 \cdot \sigma_2)$ and the functions $V_i = V_i(r^2, p^2, L^2)$. In the case of the n-p system, the potential is the sum of the isospin $T = 1$ and $T = 0$ potentials, each one of which is of the form of

Eq. (25). For elastic scattering (on the energy shell), it can be shown that the V_5 term can be dropped out and $V_i = V_i(r^2, L^2)$.

Equation (25) describes the form of the most general potential. Since the phenomenological potentials have been obtained by fitting the experimental data over a certain energy range, it is general practice to require the determination of as few parameters in the potential as possible, unless, in order to fit the experiments, it is necessary to include more terms in the potential. A very thorough effort was made by Gammel, Christian, and Thaler[37] to fit the nucleon-nucleon scattering data at 170 and 310 Mev by central and tensor potentials of the Yukawa type outside the hard core; the radius of the hard core was assumed to be independent of the parity. Their analysis led them to the following results:

(1) The calculated n-p polarizations agree with the experimental n-p polarization even at the highest energies so that the potential describes the triplet even-parity interaction correctly.

(2) There is qualitative discrepancy between the calculated and the experimental values of the high-energy p-p polarization because the polarization predicted by the potential is opposite in sign to that experimentally observed.

(3) For a singlet range $^1r_0 = 0.4 \times 10^{-13}$ cm, the $^1S_0$, $^1D_2$ and $^1G_4$ phase shifts are of the type of Stapp's solution,[5] 1 and 3, so that the potential describes the singlet even-parity interaction correctly.

The essential main conclusion of the analysis of Gammel, Christian, and Thaler[37] was that the triplet odd-parity interaction is not capable of being described by central and tensor potentials (and hard cores) alone. Gammel and Thaler,[8] noting the fact that central and tensor potentials, although successful in many respects, fail to predict the p-p polarization data at 170 and 310 Mev correctly, observed that Stapp's[5] phase-shift analysis of the 310 Mev p-p scattering indicates that the triplet p-wave phase shifts $^3P_{0,1,2}$ are split in a manner inconsistent with the tensor force. They therefore looked for a potential which will fit the low-energy scattering experiments and the phase-shift solution 1 of Stapp et al.[5] To achieve this, it was found that the potential should have the qualitative features: (1) the tensor force is long range and attractive in the $^3P_0$ state; and (2) a strong short-range spin-orbit force which is repulsive in the $^3P_0$ state. Thus the general form of the potential taken was

$$V = +\infty, \quad \text{for} \quad r < r_0$$

$$= V_c(r) + S_{12}V_T(r) + \mathbf{L} \cdot \mathbf{S}V_{LS}(r), \quad \text{for} \quad r > r_0$$

where $\quad V(r) = \dfrac{Ve^{-\mu r}}{\mu r}$ \hfill (26)

Assuming charge independence of nuclear forces, a spin-orbit term in the triplet-even-parity potential of the same short range (but lesser depth) as the triplet-odd-parity spin-orbit term was also introduced. In the following we list the parameters of their triplet-odd and singlet-even potentials (the p-p system):

$$^3r_0^- = 0.4125 \times 10^{-13} \text{ cm,} \qquad ^1r_0^+ = 0.4 \times 10^{-13} \text{ cm}$$
$$^3V_c^- = 0$$
$$^3V_T^- = -22 \text{ Mev,} \qquad\qquad ^3\mu_T^- = 0.8 \times 10^{13} \text{ cm}^{-1}$$
$$^3V_{LS}^- = 7317.5 \text{ Mev,} \qquad\quad ^3\mu_{LS}^- = 3.7 \times 10^{13} \text{ cm}^{-1}$$
$$^1V_c^+ = 425.5 \text{ Mev,} \qquad\qquad ^1\mu_c^+ = 1.45 \times 10^{13} \text{ cm}^{-1} \qquad (27)$$

The p-p scattering data fit well with the potential, Eqs. (26) and (27), except that the differential cross section was slightly low in the forward direction at 90 and 156 Mev.

An alternative potential which also included a spin-orbit interaction besides the central and the tensor interactions was independently proposed by Signell and Marshak[7] at about the same time that Gammel and Thaler[8] had proposed their potential. It was noted by Signell and Marshak[7] that although several meson-theoretic two-nucleon potentials give a reasonable fit of the data at low energies, yet all of these, Lèvy[38] and Gartenhaus[39] potentials, fail to fit the 100 and 150 Mev p-p scattering data. The phase shift analysis by Ohnuma and Feldman[40] of the experimental cross sections at 150 Mev favored the inclusion of a spin-orbit potential. Signell and Marshak (SM)[7] therefore decided to add a spin-orbit term to the Gartenhaus[39] potential.

The Gartenhaus potential was derived by applying Chew and Low's static nucleon extended source (cutoff) p-wave pion $PS(pv)$ interaction Hamiltonian to the two-nucleon problem in the second- and the fourth-order nonrelativistic perturbation theory, omitting the so-called ladder corrections, using coupling constant (renormalized) $f_0^2 = 0.089$ and cutoff $\omega_m = 6\mu$, where μ is the pion mass. Gartenhaus potential was chosen by Signell and Marshak[7] because it appeared to have the most plausible meson-theoretic basis and it fitted the low-energy data very well. The following is the form of the SM potential:[7]

$$V = V_G + \mathbf{L} \cdot \mathbf{S} \frac{V_0}{x_c} \frac{d}{dx}\left(\frac{e^{-x}}{x}\right)\Big|_{r=r_c} \qquad \text{for} \quad r \leq r_c$$

$$V = V_G + \mathbf{L} \cdot \mathbf{S} \frac{V_0}{x} \frac{d}{dx}\left(\frac{e^{-x}}{x}\right) \qquad \text{for} \quad r > r_c \qquad (28)$$

where V_G is the Gartenhaus potential,[39] which has central parts plus tensor parts, and $x = r/r_0$, $x_c = r_c/r_0$, $r_c = 1/M = 0.21 \times 10^{-13}$ cm,

$r_0 = 1.07 \times 10^{-13}$ cm, $V_0 = +30$ Mev; the sign of V_0 is chosen as that needed for the shell model. This potential was found to be in very good agreement with experimental scattering data up to 150 Mev. Later, recognizing the fact that Klein[18] and Greene[18] found evidence of the short-range spin-orbit potential in the fourth-order $PS(ps)$ field theory, provided nucleon recoil is considered, Signell, Zinn, and Marshak[41] modified the spin-orbit part of the SM potential so that the spin-orbit potential has a range of $(2\mu)^{-1}$ corresponding to the exchange of two mesons by the nucleons. This is called the SM1 potential[41] given by

$$V_{LS} = \frac{V_0}{x} \frac{d}{dx}\left(\frac{e^{-2x}}{x}\right) \qquad (29)$$

where $x = \mu r$, $V_0 = 21$ Mev, and the Gartenhaus triplet-odd potential is modified to include an infinitely repulsive core out to $x_0 = 0.37$ in order to avoid the bound $^3P_2$ state. The SM1 potential improved the fit of the data up to 150 Mev.

A separate effort to solve the two-nucleon problem was in progress in Japan. The Japanese group led by Taketani[42] attempted to solve the two-nucleon problem with much stronger faith in the meson-theoretic calculations. Their approach was discussed in detail by Iwadare, Otsuki, Tamagaki, and Watari.[12] One of their essential steps consisted of the division of the internucleon distance into three regions.

(1) *Region I.*   This is the outer region $x \geqslant 1.5$ (in units of $\hbar/\mu c$) in which the potential due to one-pion exchange is dominant and corrections to it can be neglected. The asymptotic form of the one-pion-exchange potential does not depend on the detailed form of the coupling or on the approximations, so that the potential in this region can be specified unambiguously.

(2) *Region II.*   This is the intermediate region $0.7 < x < 1.5$, where the two-pion-exchange potential is important and starts dominating over the one-pion-exchange potential. The nucleon recoil effects contribute appreciably to the two-pion-exchange potential, and since they depend very much on the coupling (p wave or other), the high-energy pion field cutoff procedure, and the shape of the source function, the many derivations of it are not free from ambiguities.

(3) *Region III.*   This is the inner region $x < 0.7$, where because of effects such as many-pion-exchange and heavy-meson-exchange, it is beyond the scope of theoretical investigation, and it therefore can be treated only phenomenologically by means of hard cores or by specifying the value of the logarithmic derivative of the wave function determined by fitting the experimental parameters.

In addition to these divisions of the internucleon distance, wide use was made of the "impact parameter" considerations. By an extensive calculation Matsumoto and Watari[43] showed that the partial wave with angular momentum L is hardly affected by the nuclear potential inside about $b/2$, where the impact parameter $b = [L(L + 1)]^{1/2}\hbar/p$; p is the momentum of the nucleon in the laboratory system. The Japanese group hoped to explain the two-nucleon scattering experiments by means of hard cores and central and tensor potentials arising out of one- and two-pion-exchange processes, and strongly criticized the use of spin-orbit interaction by Gammel and Thaler[8] at 310 Mev and by Signell and Marshak[7] at 150 Mev as unwarranted.

Otsuki,[9] Watari,[10] and Tamagaki[11] had reasonable success in fitting the cross section and polarization at 90 and 150 Mev by purely central and tensor potentials. However, it was pointed out by Nigam[13] that if the Harvard data on depolarization parameter D at 150 Mev (in contrast to the Harwell data) are correct, that is, that D goes to positive values at $75°$ in the center-of-mass system, it is very unlikely that pure central and tensor potentials can achieve this result in spite of the fact that polarization can be fitted.

It was found by Nigam that D is a very sensitive function of the $^3P_0$ phase shift and a positive depolarization requires a small or even negative $^3P_0$ phase shift, a result which can be obtained by introducing spin-orbit interactions as done by Gammel and Thaler,[8] and Signell and Marshak.[7] With purely central and tensor forces the depolarization at 150 Mev was predicted to be too negative, as was also found out later by Otsuki et al.[12] It was also suggested by Nigam that to fit the Harvard data on depolarization, the spin-orbit interaction should be strengthened compared to its value in the SM1 potential.[41] A considerably improved fit to the high-energy p-p scattering data from the 40- to 310-Mev range was obtained by Bryan[14] by choosing the static potentials (central, tensor, and spin-orbit) of the general form

$$V = \sum_{n=2}^{5} A_n x^{-n} e^{-2x} + V_2(\text{OPEP}) \tag{30}$$

together with infinite repulsive cores for the central potentials where x is the distance in units of $\hbar/\mu c$, $V_2(\text{OPEP})$ stands for the one-pion-exchange potential, and A_n are constants to be fitted from the scattering data. The curves obtained by Bryan[14] are illustrated in Figs. 4-2 to 4-4.

An approach similar to that of Bryan[14] was also carried out successfully by Hamada.[16] Since the linear spin-orbit potential vanishes in the singlet states, a quadratic spin-orbit potential was added to fit the singlet-even-parity states. The various potentials included terms corresponding to

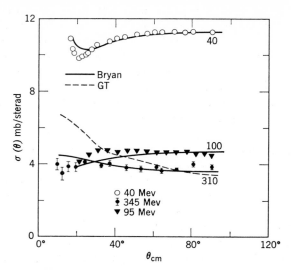

Fig. 4-2 Comparison of 40-, 100-, and 310-Mev
p-p differential cross-section predictions with
experiment (Bryan[14]).

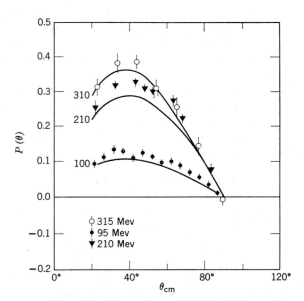

Fig. 4-3 Comparison of 100-, 210-, and
310-Mev *p-p* polarization predictions with experiment (Bryan[14]).

ranges of one-, two-, and three-pion Compton wavelengths. A two-nucleon potential for the isotopic spin state $T = 0$ was also determined which, when added to the $T = 1$ potential, was found to reproduce the n-p experimental data below 300 Mev. The triplet-even-parity potential was not strictly energy independent; the energy dependence is rather small and mainly confined to the core region. The $T = 0$ quadratic spin-orbit potential is stronger than required in the $T = 1$ state. Since the first

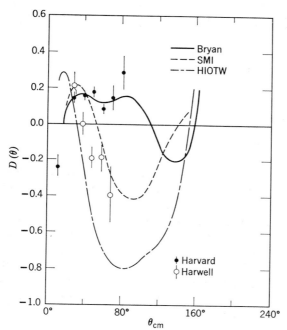

Fig. 4-4 Comparison of 150-Mev p-p depolarization $D(\theta)$ predictions with experiments (Bryan[14]).

triplet-even state affected by the linear spin-orbit potential is the D state, whereas the first triplet-odd state affected is the P state, the linear spin-orbit potential is not as important in the $T = 0$ state as in $T = 1$ state. On the other hand, the quadratic spin-orbit potential plays an important role in the $T = 0$ state. In the following, we give the Hamada-Johnston[17] potential:

$$V(r) = +\infty \quad \text{for } x \leq 0.343$$
$$= V_c(r) + V_T(r)S_{12} + V_{LS}(r)(\mathbf{L} \cdot \mathbf{S}) + V_{LL}(r)L_{12}, \quad \text{for } x > 0.343$$

$$(31a)$$

where

$$L_{12} = (\boldsymbol{\sigma}_1 \cdot \boldsymbol{\sigma}_2)\mathbf{L}^2 - \tfrac{1}{2}[(\boldsymbol{\sigma}_1 \cdot \mathbf{L})(\boldsymbol{\sigma}_2 \cdot \mathbf{L}) + (\boldsymbol{\sigma}_2 \cdot \mathbf{L})(\boldsymbol{\sigma}_1 \cdot \mathbf{L})]$$
$$= \{\delta_{LJ} + (\boldsymbol{\sigma}_1 \cdot \boldsymbol{\sigma}_2)\}\mathbf{L}^2 - (\mathbf{L} \cdot \mathbf{S})^2 \tag{31b}$$

with

$$V_c = 0.08 \frac{\mu}{3}(\boldsymbol{\tau}_1 \cdot \boldsymbol{\tau}_2)(\boldsymbol{\sigma}_1 \cdot \boldsymbol{\sigma}_2)\frac{e^{-x}}{x}\left(1 + a_c \frac{e^{-x}}{x} + b_c \frac{e^{-2x}}{x^2}\right) \tag{32a}$$

$$V_T = 0.08 \frac{\mu}{3}(\boldsymbol{\tau}_1 \cdot \boldsymbol{\tau}_2)(\boldsymbol{\sigma}_1 \cdot \boldsymbol{\sigma}_2)\left(1 + \frac{3}{x} + \frac{3}{x^2}\right)\frac{e^{-x}}{x}\left(1 + a_T \frac{e^{-x}}{x} + b_T \frac{e^{-2x}}{x^2}\right) \tag{32b}$$

$$V_{LS} = \mu G_{LS} \frac{e^{-2x}}{x^2}\left(1 + b_{LS} \frac{e^{-x}}{x}\right) \tag{32c}$$

$$V_{LL} = \mu G_{LL}\left(1 + \frac{3}{x} + \frac{3}{x^2}\right)\frac{e^{-x}}{x^3}\left(1 + a_{LL} \frac{e^{-x}}{x} + b_{LL} \frac{e^{-2x}}{x^2}\right) \tag{32d}$$

$$x = r\frac{\mu c}{\hbar}, \qquad \mu = \text{pion mass} \tag{32e}$$

The parameters a, b are different in singlet-even and odd states as well as in triplet-even and odd states. The values of the parameters are listed in Table 4-1. The potential is not claimed to be unique, although it was found necessary to include all the four parts, V_C, V_T, V_{LS}, and V_{LL}. The p-p and n-p experimental differential cross section and polarization as fitted by the model[17] are shown in Figs. 4-5 to 4-8 (from Hamada and Johnston[17]). Other scattering parameters are also well fitted by the model.

The boundary condition model which was first suggested by Breit and Bouricius[44] and used to describe S-wave scattering was extended to higher waves by Feshbach and Lomon,[45] who, however, predicted phase shifts

Table 4-1   Parameters for the Hamada-Johnston[17] Potential

Parameter \ State	Singlet Even	Triplet Even	Singlet Odd	Triplet Odd
a_c	+8.7	+6.0	−8.0	−9.07
b_c	+10.6	−1.0	+12.0	+3.48
a_T		−0.5		−1.29
b_T		+0.2		+0.55
G_{LS}		+0.0743		+0.1961
b_{LS}		−0.1		−7.12
G_{LL}	−0.00089	+0.00267	−0.00267	−0.000891
a_{LL}	+0.2	+1.8	+2.0	−7.26
b_{LL}	−0.2	−0.4	+6.0	+6.92

of the type of solution 6 of Stapp et al.,[5] which solution was found to be in disagreement with the measurement of C_{KP} at 380 Mev. Saylor, Bryan, and Marshak,[15] noting that the Bryan potential model[14] for p-p scattering defines in the triplet states a region of great strength between

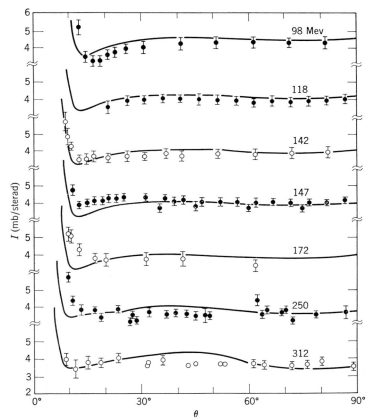

Fig. 4-5 The p-p differential cross sections at 98, 118, 142, 147, 172, 250, and 312 Mev. Experimental points shown as at 312 Mev are taken from Chamberlain et al.,[1] and Ref. 5 (Hamada and Johnston[17]).

$0.6/\mu$ and the radius of the infinite core $0.38/\mu$, and that in the outside region the potential is weak, developed a boundary condition model with potential tails outside with considerable success. Both the Taketani-Machide-Ohnuma[46] potential and the one-pion-exchange potential in the outside region with suitable energy-independent boundary conditions for each partial wave (at $r_0 = 0.53/\mu$ for singlet states and at $r_0 = 0.56/\mu$ for triplet states) were found to fit the p-p scattering data from 40 to

310 Mev very well, predicting a phase-shift set consistent with solution 1 of MacGregor, Moravcsik, and Stapp.[6] The predicted cross section was found to be a little low in the forward direction.

A study of the two-nucleon phenomenological phase shifts with energy has been extensively pursued by Breit, Hull, Pyatt, Fischer, Lassila, and

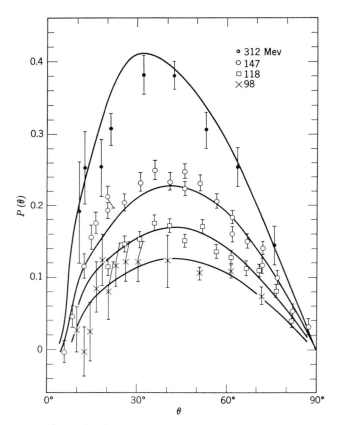

Fig. 4-6 The *p-p* polarization at 98, 118, 147, and 312 Mev (Hamada and Johnston[17]).

Degges[47] at Yale by expressing the phase shifts as some function of energy-containing parameters which can be varied so as to obtain a fit of the data at several energies. They have fitted the data over the whole energy range up to 345 Mev. Starting with one of the phase-shift solutions, say the Signell-Marshak[7] (or Gammel-Thaler[8]), corrections were suitably introduced into the preliminary phase-parameters so that the mean weighted sum of the squares of deviations from experimental values was minimized.

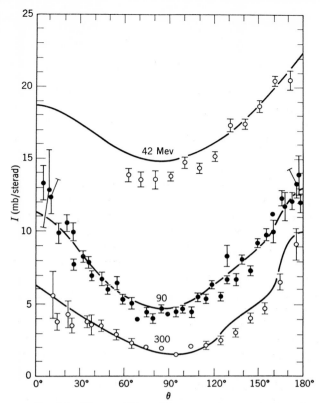

Fig. 4-7 The *n-p* differential cross sections at 42, 90, and 300 Mev (Hamada and Johnston[17]).

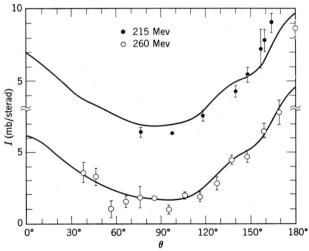

Fig. 4-8 The *n-p* differential cross sections at 215 (upper scale) and 260 Mev (lower scale) (Hamada and Johnston[17]).

The quality of the fits to angular distribution curves for the scattering parameters was also used in deciding on the correction functions to be tried. A similarity of results was observed whether one started with SM or the GT potentials. This was interpreted as indicating the existence of a region in phase-parameter space favored by experiment. Also by adding the one-pion-exchange phase shifts for the higher orbital angular momenta to the phase-shift expression in the low angular momentum states, the quality of the fit was found to improve.

Studies of nucleon-nucleon bremsstrahlung such as $p + p \rightarrow p + p + \gamma$ provide knowledge about the p-p interaction off the energy shell. Some preliminary results[64,65] are now available. The importance of the proton-proton bremsstrahlung experiments in discriminating among the various nucleon-nucleon potentials has been emphasized by Sobel and Cromer.[65] The cross section for this process depends strongly on the off-energy-shell behavior of the T-matrix. Sobel and Cromer have calculated the cross section for p-p bremsstrahlung at 160 Mev incident energy using the Yale and the Brueckner-Gammel-Thaler phenomenological nucleon-nucleon potentials and have found that the results for these potentials differ by a factor of two to three. The measurement of this cross section can provide information concerning the off-energy-shell behavior of the p-p interaction and may also enable us to distinguish between the various potentials. However, the work of Sobel and Cromer has been criticized by Yennie[66] that their treatment possibly violates charge conservation. Recent calculation[66] on nucleon-nucleon bremsstrahlung assuming one-pion-exchange appears to agree better with the experimental data.

4.7 Meson Theoretic Potential

The theoretical derivation of the two-nucleon potential from meson theory involves the calculation of the interaction between the two nucleons arising from the exchange of one pion (second-order calculation), two pions (fourth-order calculation), and a higher number of pions between the two nucleons. The calculations have been carried out with both the pseudoscalar (pseudoscalar) [$PS(ps)$] and the pseudoscalar (pseudovector) [$PS(pv)$] interactions between the meson field and the nucleon. The second-order one-pion-exchange potential in the static limit (lowest-order terms in μ/M) is given by

$$V^{(1)}(x) = \frac{1}{3}\left(\frac{g^2}{4\pi}\right)\mu c^2(\boldsymbol{\tau}_1 \cdot \boldsymbol{\tau}_2)\left\{(\boldsymbol{\sigma}_1 \cdot \boldsymbol{\sigma}_2) + S_{12}\left(1 + \frac{3}{x} + \frac{3}{x^2}\right)\right\}\frac{e^{-x}}{x} \quad (33)$$

and all authors agree on the form of this part of the interaction. Also, the correctness of the one-pion-exchange potential is now well established in view of the detailed analysis of the nucleon-nucleon scattering data.

The fourth-order contribution to the static two-nucleon potential has, among the various authors, probably been best derived by Gartenhaus[39] who used the nonrelativistic p-wave extended source (cut-off) model of Chew and Low and carried out a nonrelativistic perturbation calculation. Gartenhaus was successful in obtaining a good fit of the low-energy nucleon-nucleon scattering data with his potential. However, Gartenhaus' method is incapable of yielding a spin-orbit interaction since the interaction Hamiltonian used is completely static. Klein and Greene[18] have found that short-range spin-orbit potential originated in the fourth-order field theory provided that nucleon recoil is taken into account. The static limit consists in taking the lowest order in μ/M, and the so-called "adiabatic approximation" involves the limit $\mathbf{p}/M \to 0$, where $\mathbf{p}$ is the nucleon momentum. Since both μ/M and $\mathbf{p}/M$ are not very small, the nonstatic and the nonadiabatic corrections which will take into account the nucleon recoil may be important at high energies.

Several authors[19,20] have calculated the two-pion-exchange contribution to the two-nucleon potential and considered the nucleon recoil. In general, all of them have reported a spin-orbit $(\mathbf{L} \cdot \mathbf{S})$ interaction term, although there is general lack of agreement on its sign and magnitude. The most favorable $\mathbf{L} \cdot \mathbf{S}$ interaction obtained, meson-theoretically, is due to Tzoar, Raphael, and Klein[18] who adopted the procedure used by Klein and McCormick[48] to construct the potential for pion-nucleon scattering. The $\mathbf{L} \cdot \mathbf{S}$ term of Tzoar et al.[18] is quite similar to the one introduced phenomenologically by Signell and Marshak.[7] Taketani and Machida,[49] Hoshizaki and Machida,[50] and Otsuki, Tamagaki, and Watari[51] have recently carried out a detailed investigation of the two-nucleon potential with full recoil.

It has been pointed out by Charap and Fubini[52] and by Gupta[53] that the calculation of the nonstatic corrections is not an unambiguous procedure. For instance, for the static potential, the μ/M limit must be taken at the beginning of the calculations, for otherwise it leads to ambiguities. Furthermore, the adiabatic limit $\mathbf{p}/M \to 0$ is unambiguous only if $\mathbf{p}$ is the initial and the final nucleon momentum. Also the nonadiabatic corrections cannot be separated unambiguously from the higher-order adiabatic corrections. All these factors make the derivation of the two-pion-exchange contribution to the two-nucleon potential highly dependent on the approximations used in the calculation.

It is worth mentioning regarding the three-pion-exchange potential that not only will it be a prohibitive job to calculate it, but also that with the present status of meson theory it is quite unnecessary to do so. The range of the three-pion-exchange potential is $\hbar/3m_\pi c \sim 0.47 \times 10^{-13}$ cm, where the region is very much masked by the repulsive core introduced phenomenologically and not yet understood in terms of meson theory.

With the recent discovery of several heavier mesons and resonances, it is of interest to determine the explicit contribution of these to the nucleon-nucleon interaction. Actually it was suggested earlier by Breit[54] (1935, 1959) and by Sakurai[55] (1959) that a meson of spin 1 could explain both the repulsive core and the spin-orbit interaction in the nucleon-nucleon potentials. The ρ-meson ($T = 1$) and the ω-meson ($T = 0$) have $J = 1$ and decay into two and three π-mesons, respectively. The electron-nucleon scattering and the pion-nucleon scattering are substantially influenced by these mesons. A third meson, the η-meson, has $T = 0, J = 0$. Several of these mesons, heavier than π-meson, may dominate the short-range part of the nucleon-nucleon interaction since the range is inversely proportional to the mass μ of the meson exchanged (range $\sim \hbar/\mu c$). Amati, Leader, and Vitale,[56] and McKean[57] have explicitly taken into account the contribution of the meson exchange to the nucleon-nucleon interaction. The contribution of two π-meson exchange corresponds to two uncorrelated π-mesons, whereas that from ρ, ω, η, etc., correspond to bound pion state contributions. These authors suggest that the latter dominate the former.

Measurements of the elastic differential cross section for p-p scattering have recently been carried out from 7 to 20 Bev/c incident proton momentum at Brookhaven by Diddens, Lillethun, Manning, Taylor, Walker, and Wetherell,[58] by Foley, Lindenbaum, Love, Ozaki, Russell, and Yuan,[59] and by Baker, Jenkins, Read, Cocconi, Cocconi, Krish, Orear, Rubinstein, Scarl, and Ulrich.[60] The basic purpose of these experiments has been to investigate the nature of strong interactions at high energies since the behavior of the cross section at high energies is predicted by the Regge pole theory. Chew and Frautschi and others[61] have shown that if the vacuum pole or Pomeranchuk-Regge trajectory dominates, then at high energies the differential cross section for any incident particle is given by

$$\frac{d\sigma}{dt} = \left[\frac{d\sigma}{dt}\right]_{t=0} F(t) \left[\frac{s}{2m_p^2}\right]^{-2+2\alpha_p(t)} \tag{34}$$

where t is the negative square of the four-momentum transfer, $[d\sigma/dt]_{t=0}$ is the forward $(d\sigma/dt)$ predicted from the optical theorem,* and s is the Lorentz-invariant square of the total center-of-mass energy.

---

* According to the optical theorem the imaginary part of the forward scattering amplitude $f(\theta = 0)$ is directly proportional to the total cross section σ_{tot}, that is, $\sigma_{tot} = (4\pi/k) \operatorname{Im} f(0)$. A more generalized form of the optical theorem is

$$\int d\Omega_{k''} f(\theta_{kk''}) f^*(\theta_{k'k''}) = \frac{4\pi}{k} \operatorname{Im} f(\theta_{kk'})$$

where $\theta_{kk'}$ denotes the angle between the wave vectors $\mathbf{k}$ and $\mathbf{k}'$, etc. For $\mathbf{k} = \mathbf{k}'$, this result reduces to the previous form.

The results of Foley et al.[59] are shown in Fig. 4-9 in which the experimental values of $\alpha(t)$ are plotted against t. The figure indicates that $\alpha(t)$ varies linearly with t and the extrapolated straight line goes through $\alpha_p(0) = 1.07 \pm 0.03$, and for the data above 10 Bev/c only, through

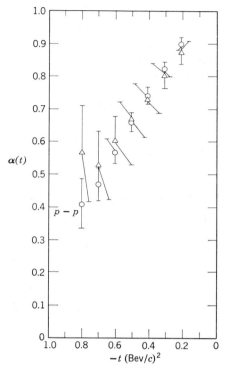

Fig. 4-9 Plot of $\alpha(t)$ versus t. The open circles are the results for all the $p + p$ data. The open triangles are the results using only the $p + p$ data above 10 Bev/c incident momentum (Foley et al.[59]).

$\alpha_p(0) = 1.0 \pm 0.05$. The experiment of Diddens et al.[58] indicates that $\langle \alpha_p \rangle \simeq 0$ for $t < -1$. With reference to Eq. (34), we note that this behavior of $\alpha_p(t)$ at low t gives a shrinkage of $d\sigma/dt$ which in a semiclassical way corresponds to a growth of the radius of interaction.

A simple theory of scattering with large momentum transfer for p-p scattering has been given by Serber.[62] This theory is based on an optical model in which the medium is taken to be purely absorptive and spatially distributed according to a Yukawa function. Other papers[63] which have discussed the shrinkage are due to Orear, Narayan and Sharma, Krisch and others.

4.8   Conclusion

It seems fair to say that in recent years the understanding of the two-nucleon interaction has improved considerably. The phenomenological study of nucleon-nucleon scattering and its comparison with the experimental data are definitely in favor of the existence of a strong spin-orbit interaction. There is also evidence that the two-body spin-orbit interaction is capable of explaining spin-orbit interaction in complex nuclei as desired by the shell theory. Meson theoretic verification of the spin-orbit interaction has not yet been satisfactorily accomplished because an unambiguous treatment of the two-pion-exchange interaction without neglecting nucleon recoil contributions is still lacking. However, the validity of the one-pion-exchange potential in the outer region has been well demonstrated through the work of Iwadare et al.,[12,55] the modified phase-shift analysis by Moravcsik et al.,[6] Breit et al.,[47,60] and Saylor-Bryan-Marshak.[15] The application[25] of dispersion-relation theory to nucleon-nucleon scattering perhaps offers the possibility of carrying out an unambiguous calculation in terms of one-pion- and two-pion-exchange contributions. The two-pion-exchange calculations are highly involved and require first the solution of the pion-pion and the pion-nucleon scattering amplitude problems. It is hoped that a satisfactory solution of the nucleon-nucleon scattering problem within the framework of dispersion theory will be available in the near future.

References

1. Chamberlain, O., E. Segrè, R. D. Tripp, C. Wiegand, and T. J. Ypsilantis, *Phys. Rev.* **105**, 288, 1957.
2. Palmieri, J. N., A. M. Cormack, N. F. Ramsey, and R. Wilson, *Ann. Phys. N.Y.*, **5**, 299, 1958; Ophel, T. R., E. H. Thorndike, R. Wilson, and N. F. Ramsey, *Phys. Rev. Letters* **2**, 310, 1959; Hwang, C. F., T. R. Ophel, E. H. Thorndike, and R. Wilson, *Phys. Rev.* **119**, 325, 1960; Thorndike, E. H., J. Lefrancois, and R. Wilson, *Phys. Rev.* **120**, 1819, 1960.
3. Taylor, A. E., and E. Wood, *Proc. of the Sixth and Seventh Annual International Conf. on High Energy Physics*, Interscience, New York, 1956 and 1957.
4. Gotow, K., and E. Heer, *Phys. Rev. Letters* **5**, 111, 1960; England, A., W. Gibson K. Gotow, E. Heer, and J. Tinlot, *Phys. Rev.* **124**, 561, 1961; Tinlot, J., and R. Warner, *Phys. Rev.* **124**, 890, 1961.
5. Stapp, H. P., T. J. Ypsilantis, and N. Metropolis, *Phys. Rev.* **105**, 302, 1957.
6. Cziffra, P., M. H. MacGregor, M. J. Moravcsik, and H. P. Stapp, *Phys. Rev.* **114**, 880, 1959; MacGregor, M. H., M. J. Moravcsik, and H. P. Stapp, *Phys. Rev.* **116**, 1248, 1959.
7. Signell, P. S., and R. E. Marshak, *Phys. Rev.* **106**, 832, 1957; **109**, 1229, 1958.

8. Gammel, J., and R. Thaler, *Phys. Rev.* **107**, 291, 1957.
9. Otsuki, S., *Progr. Theoret. Phys.* (*Kyoto*), **20**, 171, 1958.
10. Watari, W., *Progr. Theoret. Phys.* (*Kyoto*) **20**, 181, 1958.
11. Tamagaki, R., *Progr. Theoret. Phys.* (*Kyoto*) **20**, 505, 1958.
12. Iwadare, J., R. Tamagaki, and W. Watari, *Progr. Theoret. Phys.* (*Kyoto*), Suppl. **1**, 32, 1956; Hamada, T., J. Iwadare, S. Otsuki, R. Tamagaki, and W. Watari, *Progr. Theoret. Phys.* (*Kyoto*) **22**, 566, 1959; **23**, 366, 1960.
13. Nigam, B. P., *Progr. Theoret. Phys.* (*Kyoto*) **23**, 61, 1960.
14. Bryan, R. A., *Nuovo Cimento* **16**, 895, 1960.
15. Saylor, D. P., R. A. Bryan, and R. E. Marshak, *Phys. Rev. Letters* **5**, 266, 1960.
16. Hamada, T., *Progr. Theoret. Phys.* (*Kyoto*) **24**, 1033, 1960; **25**, 247, 1961.
17. Hamada, T., and I. D. Johnston, *Nucl. Phys.* **34**, 382, 1962.
18. Klein, A., *Phys. Rev.* **91**, 740, 1953; **92**, 1017, 1953; Greene, J. M., and D. Feldman, U.S. Atomic Energy Commission Report NYO—7540, 1956 (unpublished); Shindo, M., and K. Nishijima, *Progr. Theoret. Phys.* (*Kyoto*) **13**, 103, 1955; Nakabayasi, K., and I. Sato, *Phys. Rev.* **88**, 144, 1952; Sato, I., *Progr. Theoret. Phys.* (*Kyoto*) **10**, 323, 1953; Sugawara, M., and S. Okubo, *Phys. Rev.* **117**, 605, 611, 1960; Gupta, S. N., *Phys. Rev. Letters* **2**, 124, 1959; Tzoar, N., and T. Raphael, and A. Klein, *Phys. Rev. Letters* **2**, 433, 1959 (Erratum: **3**, 145, 1959).
19. Karplus, R., and M. A. Ruderman, *Phys. Rev.* **98**, 771, 1955; Goldberger, M. L., *Phys. Rev.* **97**, 508. 1955; **99**, 979, 1955; Bogoliubov, N. N., *Rept. Intern. Conf. Theoret. Phys.*, Seattle, 1956 (unpublished); Symanzik, K., *Phys. Rev.* **105**, 743, 1957; Goldberger, M. L., Y. Nambu, and R. Oehme, *Ann. Phys. N. Y.* **2**, 226, 1957.
20. Mandelstam, S., *Phys. Rev.* **115**, 1741, 1752, 1959.
21. Phillips, R. J. N., *Rept. Progr. Phys.* **22**, 562, 1959.
22. Gammel, J. L., and R. M. Thaler, *Progr. Cosmic Ray Phys.* **5**, 99, 1960.
23. Marshak, R. E., *Proc. Intern. Conf. Nucl. Forces and the Few-Nucleon Problem*, p. 5, Pergamon Press, New York, 1959.
24. MacGregor, M. H., M. J. Moravcsik, and H. P. Stapp, *Ann. Rev. Nucl. Sci.* **10**, 291, 1960.
25. Moravcsik, M. J., and H. P. Noyes, *Ann. Rev. Nucl. Sci.* **11**, 95, 1961.
26. Breit, G., *Rev. Mod. Phys.* **34**, 766, 1962.
27. Nigam, B. P., *Rev. Mod. Phys.* **35**, 177, 1963.
28. Wolfenstein, L., *Phys. Rev.* **96**, 1654, 1954; *Ann. Rev. Nucl. Sci.* **6**, 43, 1956.
29. Wolfenstein, L., *Phys. Rev.* **101**, 427, 1956.
30. Puzikov, L. D., R. M. Ryndin, and J. Smorodinsky, *Soviet Phys.—JETP* **5**, 489, 1957.
31. Golovin, B., V. Dzhelepov, V. Nadezhdin, and V. I. Satarov, *Soviet Phys.—JETP* **9**, 302, 1959.
32. Schumacher, C. R., and H. A. Bethe, *Phys. Rev.* **121**, 1543, 1961.
33. Ashmore, A., A. N. Diddens, and G. B. Huxtable, *Proc. Phys. Soc.* (*London*) **73**, 957, 1959.
34. MacGregor, M. H., and M. J. Moravcsik, *Phys. Rev. Letters* **4**, 524, 1960.
35. Eisenbud, L., and E. Wigner, *Proc. Natl. Acad. Sci. U.S.* **27**, 281, 1941.
36. Okubo, S., and R. E. Marshak, *Ann. Phys. N.Y.*, **4**, 166, 1958.
37. Gammel, J. L., R. Christian, and R. M. Thaler, *Phys. Rev.* **105**, 311, 1957.
38. Lèvy, M. M., *Phys. Rev.* **88**, 725, 1952.
39. Gartenhaus, S., *Phys. Rev.* **100**, 900, 1955.
40. Ohnuma, S., and D. Feldman, *Phys. Rev.* **102**, 1641, 1956.
41. Signell, P. S., R. Zinn, and R. E. Marshak, *Phys. Rev. Letters* **1**, 416, 1958.
42. Taketani, M., S. Nakamura, and M. Sasaki, *Progr. Theoret. Phys.* (*Kyoto*) **6**, 581, 1951.

43. Matsumoto, M., and W. Watari, *Progr. Theoret. Phys. (Kyoto)* **12**, 503, 1954.
44. Breit, G., and W. G. Bouricius, *Phys. Rev.* **79**, 1029, 1949; Saperstein, A. M., and L. Durand, *Phys. Rev.* **104**, 1102, 1956.
45. Feshbach, H., and E. L. Lomon, *Phys. Rev.* **102**, 891, 1956.
46. Taketani, M., S. Machida, and S. Ohnuma, *Progr. Theoret. Phys. (Kyoto)* **6**, 638, 1951.
47. Breit, G., *Proc. Intern. Conf. Nucl. Forces and the Few-Nucleon Problem*, p. 23, Pergamon Press, New York, 1959; Breit, G., M. H. Hull, K. E. Lassila, and K. D. Pyatt, Jr., *Phys. Rev.* **120**, 2227, 1960.
48. Klein, A., and B. H. McCormick, *Phys. Rev.* **104**, 1747, 1956.
49. Taketani, M., and S. Machida, *Progr. Theoret. Phys. (Kyoto)* **24**, 1317, 1960.
50. Hoshizaki, N., and S. Machida, *Progr. Theoret. Phys. (Kyoto)* **24**, 1325, 1960.
51. Otsuki, S., R. Tamagaki, and W. Watari, *Progr. Theoret. Phys.(Kyoto)* **27**,315,1962.
52. Charap, J. M., and S. P. Fubini, *Nuovo Cimento* **14**, 540, 1959.
53. Gupta, S. N., *Phys. Rev.* **117**, 1146, 1960.
54. Breit, G., from R. Wilson, "The Nucleon-Nucleon Interaction," *Interscience Tracts on Physics and Astronomy*, John Wiley and Sons, New York, 1962.
55. J. J. Sakurai, same as Ref. 54.
56. Amati, D., E. Leader, and B. Vitale, *Nuovo Cimento* **17**, 68, 1959; **18**, 402, and 458, 1960.
57. McKean, R. S., *Phys. Rev.* **125**, 1399, 1962.
58. Diddens, A. N., E. Lillanthun, G. Manning, A. E. Taylor, T. G. Walker, and A. M. Wetherell, *Phys. Rev. Letters* **9**, 108, and 111, 1962.
59. Foley, K. J., S. J. Lindenbaum, W. A. Love, S. Ozaki, J. J. Russell, and L. C. L. Yuan, *Phys. Rev. Letters* **10**, 376, 1963; **11**, 425, 1963.
60. Baker, W. F., E. W. Jenkins, A. L. Read, C. Cocconi, V. T. Cocconi, A. D. Krisch, J. Orear, R. Rubinstein, D. B. Scarl, and B. T. Ulrich, *Phys. Rev. Letters* **12**, 132, 1964.
61. Chew, G. F., and S. C. Frautschi, *Phys. Rev. Letters* **7**, 394, 1961; Frautschi, S. C., M. Gell-Mann, and F. Zachariasen, *Phys. Rev.* **126**, 2204, 1962; Chew, G. F., S. C. Frautschi, and S. Mandelstam, *Phys. Rev.* **126**, 1202, 1962; Blackenbecler, R., and M. L. Goldberger, *Phys. Rev.* **126**, 766, 1962.
62. Serber, R., *Phys. Rev. Letters* **10**, 357, 1963.
63. Orear, J., *Phys. Rev. Letters* **12**, 112, 1964; Narayan, D. S., and K. V. L. Sharma, *Phys. Rev. Letters* **5**, 365, 1963; Krisch, A. D., *Phys. Rev. Letters* **11**, 217, 1963.
64. Gottschalk, B., W. J. Shlaer, and K. H. Wang, *Phys. Letters* **16**, 294, 1965. Rothe, K. W., P. F. M. Koehler, and E. H. Thorndike, University of Rochester Report, 1965 (unpublished).
65. Sobel, M. I. and A. H. Cromer, *Phys. Rev.* **132**, 2698, 1963.
66. Ueda, Yoshiaki, *Phys. Rev.* **145**, 1214, 1966.

Problems

1. Obtain the results of Eqs. (9), (9a), and (9b).
2. Obtain the results of Eq. (12).
3. Derive Eq. (14).
4. Show explicitly that the other terms which could have been included in Eq. (20) drop out because of parity conservation.
5. Using Eq. (22), obtain the results of Eq. (23).

5

SEMI-EMPIRICAL MASS FORMULAS AND NUCLEAR FISSION

PART I. SEMI-EMPIRICAL MASS FORMULAS

There is no formal theory which predicts the binding energy of a nucleus except for that of very light nuclei. The nucleus consisting of many nucleons is complex and is not properly understood. To calculate the binding energy, it is essential to know the many-nucleon forces, a task which has yet to be accomplished. However, considerable progress has been made by Brueckner and his collaborators in understanding the properties of nuclear matter (infinite nucleus). Extension of these calculations has also been performed for finite nucleus, and predictions have been made regarding many nuclear properties including binding energies. These are given in Chapter 9. In this section we shall discuss various semi-empirical formulas developed on the basis of specific model (liquid drop) to account for the mass and binding energy of a nucleus. We shall first discuss certain properties of the nucleus which will help us to understand the semi-empirical mass formula.

The binding energy B of the nucleus of mass number A and atomic number Z is defined by

$$B(A, Z) = c^2[ZM_H + NM_N - M(A, Z)] \tag{1}$$

where M_H is the mass of a hydrogen atom, M_N is the mass of a neutron, and $M(A, Z)$ is the actual mass of the atom.

Equation (1) includes both the electronic and nuclear binding energies, although the former is negligible since for H^2, $B_{atom}/B_{nucl.} \simeq 6 \times 10^{-6}$ and for U^{238}, taking into account all the electrons in different shells, $B_{atom}/B_{nucl} \simeq 3 \times 10^{-4}$.

The binding energy per nucleon as a function of A shows remarkable constancy, as is evident from Fig. 5-1.[1] After an initial fluctuation below $A = 16$, the binding energy per nucleon varies only from 7.4 to 8.8 Mev, reaching a maximum at around $A = 60$. The acceptability of a semi-empirical mass formula is partially determined by its ability to reproduce the curve of Fig. 5-1.

The nearly constant value of B/A for A greater than 16 indicates that the binding energy is proportional to the mass number A. On the other hand, if it is assumed that the interaction forces are the same between all the pairs of nucleons, then it should be expected that the binding energy is proportional to the number of pairs of nucleons, that is, $A(A-1)/2$,

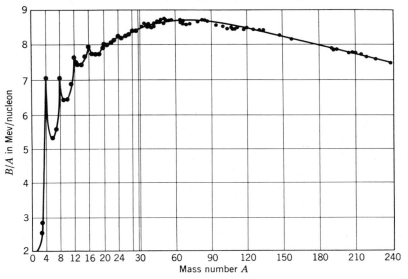

Fig. 5-1 Average binding energy B/A in Mev per nucleon for the naturally occurring nuclides (and Be^8), as a function of mass number A. Note the change of magnification in the A scale at $A = 30$. For $A \geqslant 16$, B/A is roughly constant (Evans[1]).

in the nucleus. It appears[2] then that a nucleon interacts with only a few neighboring nucleons. In other words, the nuclear forces are saturated.

It is appropriate at this stage to inquire what kind of nuclear force can produce saturation. Heisenberg originally suggested that the nuclear force might be of an exchange nature. Evidence for this comes from high-energy neutron-proton experiments, as noted in Chapter 3. It should be remarked that the exchange potential alone is not enough to account for the saturation of the nuclear forces. In addition the hard-core potential must be considered (see Chapter 9). Of the several types of known exchange forces, we shall discuss the Majorana type which is concerned with the exchange of space coordinates. We consider the binding energy of He^4. According to the Pauli principle we can put two neutrons and two protons of opposite spins in an s-state. Thus a system of two neutrons and two protons can exist with all four particles in the lowest energy state, and we say that the Majorana forces of attraction give a high binding energy for He⁴. The addition of one more nucleon gives He⁵ or Li⁵. The last nucleon must enter a p-state. It is as if the Pauli principle results in a repulsive force for the fifth nucleon in the s-state. The saturation of the Majorana forces is also evident in He⁴ from its very high binding energy in comparison with that of the neighboring nuclei such as H³ and He³. The exchange force is evident from Fig. 3-6 which indicates two peaks at 0° and 180°. The forward peak at 0° is a diffraction peak due to the ordinary Wigner potential, whereas the peak at 180° has been interpreted as resulting from exchange force.

5.1 Potential Energy

The following calculation of the binding energy by introducing an exchange term into the potential energy operator is based on the treatment given by Blatt and Weisskopf.[2]

Let us consider the case of a nucleus with number N of neutrons which is larger than the number Z of protons ($N > Z$). Then, according to the Pauli principle, in the lowest state the protons and neutrons will fill up the levels as shown in Fig. 5-2. The number of levels filled with four particles

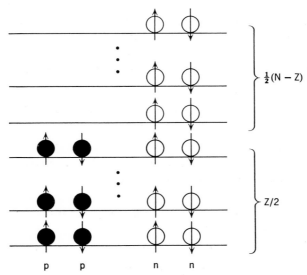

Fig. 5-2 A schematic picture of arrangements of nucleons in different levels.

($2p$ and $2n$) in each level is $Z/2$. The number of levels filled with two particles ($2n$) is $\frac{1}{2}(N - Z)$. The potential energy between two particles labeled by i and j is given by

$$V_{ij}(\mathbf{r}_{ij}) = V_{ij}^{W}(\mathbf{r}_{ij}) + V_{ij}^{M}(\mathbf{r}_{ij})P_{ij}^{M} \tag{2}$$

where the superscripts W and M stand for the Wigner and Majorana forces and P^{M} is the space-exchange operator. $P^{M} = +1$ for a pair of particles which are space symmetric, and $P^{M} = -1$ for a pair with anti-symmetric space wave function. The total potential energy V is obtained by summing over all pairs.

$$V = \sum_{i<j}^{A} V_{ij}(\mathbf{r}_{ij}) \tag{3}$$

If the wave function of the nucleus is $\Psi(\mathbf{r}_1, \mathbf{r}_2, \ldots, \mathbf{r}_A)$, then the expectation value of the potential energy is given by

$$\langle V \rangle = \sum_{i<j}^{A} \int \Psi^{*}(\mathbf{r}_1, \mathbf{r}_2, \ldots, \mathbf{r}_A) V_{ij}(\mathbf{r}_{ij}) \Psi(\mathbf{r}_1, \mathbf{r}_2, \ldots, \mathbf{r}_A) \, d^3\tau_N \tag{4}$$

where $A = N + Z$, and $d^3\tau_N = d^3\mathbf{r}_1 \, d^3\mathbf{r}_2 \cdots d^3\mathbf{r}_A$ is an element of the nuclear volume. We note that

$$\sum_{i<j}^{A} \int \Psi^{*} V_{ij}^{W}(\mathbf{r}_{ij}) \Psi \, d^3\tau_N = \frac{1}{2}A(A - 1)pV_{W} \tag{5}$$

where $\frac{1}{2}A(A - 1)$ is the total number of pair interactions and V_{W} is a space-averaged Wigner potential. Also

$$\int \Psi^{*} P_{ij}^{M} \Psi \, d^3\tau_N = 1 \qquad \text{for } i \text{ and } j \text{ in the same level} \tag{6a}$$

$$= -1 \qquad \text{for } i \text{ and } j \text{ in different levels with} \tag{6b}$$
particles i and j being of the same kind and same spin state

$$= 0 \qquad \text{otherwise} \tag{6c}$$

p is the average probability of finding a pair of nucleons closer than the range b of nuclear force and is given by[2]

$$p = \frac{1}{(\frac{4}{3}\pi R^3)^2} \iint e(b - r_{12}) \, d^3r_1 \, d^3r_2 \tag{6d}$$

where the function $e(x)$ is defined by

$$e(x) = 1 \qquad \text{if } x > 0$$
$$= 0 \qquad \text{if } x < 0, \tag{6e}$$

r_{12} is the distance between the two nucleons, and R the radius of the nucleus. The result of integrations, which go over the interior of the nucleus, gives

$$p = \left(\frac{b}{R}\right)^3 \left[1 - \frac{9}{16}\left(\frac{b}{R}\right) + \frac{1}{32}\left(\frac{b}{R}\right)^3\right] \quad \text{for} \quad R > \frac{b}{2}$$
$$= 1 \qquad\qquad\qquad\qquad\qquad\qquad \text{for} \quad R < \frac{b}{2} \tag{6f}$$

This equation has the correct asymptotic behavior; i.e., for the large nuclear radius, the probability of finding two nucleons within the nuclear force range b is $(b/R)^3$, and for $R < b/2$, corresponding to the collapsed state of the nucleus, the probability is unity. In the collapsed state the binding energy of a nucleus is extremely high because each nucleon lies within the range of the interaction of every other nucleon, and consequently the binding energy should be proportional to $\frac{1}{2}A(A-1)$. Thus the collapsed state represents a system with unsaturated forces, which is contrary to the observed binding energy per nucleon for $A > 16$. Equations (6a), (6b), and (6c) follow from the requirement imposed by the Pauli principle that the wave function be totally antisymmetric with respect to the exchange of space, spin, and isotopic spin states of any two particles. The space wave function of two protons or two neutrons with spins antiparallel is symmetric and with spins parallel is antisymmetric. The exchange of two particles in different levels with opposite spin states [case (6c)] leads to a nuclear state which violates the Pauli principle, and hence is not allowed. The number of space symmetric pairs is determined by the total number of ways of pairing particles within each level, which is $6(Z/2)$ for the first $Z/2$ levels, and $\frac{1}{2}(N-Z)$ for the remaining $\frac{1}{2}(N-Z)$ levels. Thus the total number n_+ of symmetric pairs is

$$n_+ = 6\left(\frac{Z}{2}\right) + \frac{1}{2}(N-Z) \tag{7}$$

Similarly, the total number n_- of antisymmetric pairs is

$$n_- = 2\left[\frac{1}{2}\frac{Z}{2}\left(\frac{Z}{2}-1\right) + \frac{1}{2}\frac{N}{2}\left(\frac{N}{2}-1\right)\right] \tag{8}$$

where the factor 2 appears for the two types of protons and neutrons.

We therefore obtain the Majorana contribution to the average potential energy $\langle V \rangle$,

$$\sum_{i<j=2}^{A} \int \Psi^* V_{ij}^M(\mathbf{r}_{ij}) P_{ij}^M \Psi \, d^3\tau_N$$
$$= V_M\left\{\left[6\left(\frac{Z}{2}\right) + \frac{1}{2}(N-Z)\right] - \left[\frac{Z}{2}\left(\frac{Z}{2}-1\right) + \frac{N}{2}\left(\frac{N}{2}-1\right)\right]\right\}p \tag{9}$$

where V_M is a space-averaged Majorana potential. Combining Eqs. (4), (5), and (9) we obtain

$$\langle V \rangle = \tfrac{1}{2}A(A-1)V_W p + V_M \left\{ \left[6\left(\frac{Z}{2}\right) + \tfrac{1}{2}(N-Z) \right] \right.$$

$$\left. - \left[\frac{Z}{2}\left(\frac{Z}{2}-1\right) + \frac{N}{2}\left(\frac{N}{2}-1\right) \right] \right\} p$$

$$= \tfrac{1}{2}A(A-1)V_W p - \left(\frac{A^2}{8} - 2A + \frac{T^2}{2} + 2T \right) V_M p$$

$$= \tfrac{1}{2}A\left[(A-1)V_W - \left(\frac{A}{4}-4\right)V_M \right] p - \left(\frac{T^2}{2} + 2T \right) V_M p \quad (10a)$$

where $T = \tfrac{1}{2}(N-Z)$. $\qquad\qquad\qquad\qquad\qquad\qquad\qquad\qquad (10b)$

Since $A \ll A^2$ and $T \ll T^2$, we may write

$$\langle V \rangle \simeq \left[\frac{A^2}{2}\left(V_W - \frac{V_M}{4} \right) - \frac{T^2}{2} V_M \right] p$$

$$= \left[\frac{A}{2}\left(V_W - \frac{V_M}{4} \right) - \frac{T^2}{2A} V_M \right] \left(\frac{b}{r_0}\right)^3 \left(1 - \frac{9}{16}\frac{b}{r_0 A^{1/3}} + \frac{1}{32}\frac{b^3}{r_0^3 A} \right) \quad (10c)$$

where we have used $R = r_0 A^{1/3}$. Neglecting small terms, we obtain

$$\langle V \rangle \simeq -a_V A + a_s A^{2/3} + c_1 \frac{T^2}{A} \quad (10d)$$

where a_V, a_s, c_1 can be defined from Eq. (10c). The first term is negative because both the Wigner potential, V_W, and the Majorana potential, V_M, are negative. For a_V to be positive it is necessary that $|V_M| \leq 4 |V_W|$. This is the condition for saturation of binding energy for all A. This also implies that the Majorana force must contribute at least four-fifths of the attraction and the Wigner force in comparison is rather small, contributing no more than one-fifth.

5.2   Kinetic Energy

We next calculate the contribution to the binding energy from the kinetic energy of N neutrons and Z protons obeying the Pauli exclusion principle. We assume the Fermi gas model in which the particles move without interaction in a sphere of radius R and volume V as the particles in an ideal gas do. According to the theory of the Fermi gas, the number of states of protons with momentum between momenta p and $p + dp$ in a volume V is $2V4\pi p^2 \, dp/(2\pi\hbar)^3$. The spin-weight factor 2 originates from the two spin states of the proton (and neutron). The ground state of the system will correspond to zero temperature, with momentum spread of zero to a maximum p_{FP}, so that the number of protons in this lowest energy state is given by

$$Z = \int_0^{p_{FP}} \frac{2V 4\pi p^2 \, dp}{(2\pi\hbar)^3} = \frac{V 8\pi}{h^3} \frac{(p_{FP})^3}{3}$$

Therefore the Fermi momentum for the protons is

$$p_{FP} = \hbar k_{FP} = h \left(\frac{3}{8\pi} \frac{Z}{V} \right)^{1/3} = h \left(\frac{3}{8\pi} \rho_P \right)^{1/3} \tag{11a}$$

where $\rho_P = Z/V$ is the proton density. Similarly for the neutrons, we have

$$p_{FN} = \hbar k_{FN} = h \left(\frac{3}{8\pi} \frac{N}{V} \right)^{1/3} = h \left(\frac{3}{8\pi} \rho_N \right)^{1/3} \tag{11b}$$

where $\rho_N = N/V$ is the neutron density. If we define the total nuclear density $\rho_A = A/V = (N + Z)/V$, and assume that there are four particles in each state with equal numbers of neutrons and protons, the Fermi momentum is given by

$$p_{FA} = \hbar k_{FA} = h \left(\frac{3}{16\pi} \frac{A}{V} \right)^{1/3} = h \left(\frac{3}{16\pi} \rho_A \right)^{1/3} \tag{11c}$$

The total kinetic energy of the protons in the ground state is

$$T_P = \int_0^{p_{FP}} \left(2V \frac{4\pi p^2 \, dp}{h^3} \frac{p^2}{2M} \right)$$

$$= \frac{8\pi V}{2Mh^3} \frac{(p_{FP})^5}{5} \tag{12}$$

$$= \frac{4\pi}{5M} \left(\frac{3}{8\pi} \right)^{5/3} \frac{h^2}{V^{2/3}} Z^{5/3} \tag{13}$$

Equation (13) is obtained by substituting in Eq. (12) the value of p_{FP} from Eq. (11a).

Similarly, the total kinetic energy for neutrons is

$$T_N = \frac{4\pi}{5M} \left(\frac{3}{8\pi} \right)^{5/3} \frac{h^2}{V^{2/3}} N^{5/3} \tag{14}$$

The total kinetic energy of N neutrons and Z protons is then

$$\text{K.E.} = \frac{4\pi}{5M} \left(\frac{3}{8\pi} \right)^{5/3} \frac{h^2}{V^{2/3}} (Z^{5/3} + N^{5/3}) \tag{15a}$$

We introduce the mass number $A = N + Z$, and $T = \frac{1}{2}(N - Z)$; hence $N = A/2 + T$ and $Z = A/2 - T$. Since the volume of the nucleus $V \propto R^3$ and $R \propto A^{1/3}$, we may write

$$\frac{1}{A^{2/3}}(Z^{5/3} + N^{5/3}) = \frac{1}{A^{2/3}}\left(\frac{A}{2}\right)^{5/3}\left[\left(1 - \frac{2T}{A}\right)^{5/3} + \left(1 + \frac{2T}{A}\right)^{5/3}\right] \quad (15b)$$

Hence the total kinetic energy, for $T \ll A$, can be written

$$\text{K.E.} \propto 2\frac{A}{2^{5/3}}\left[1 + \frac{20}{9}\frac{T^2}{A^2}\right]$$

and

$$\langle \text{K.E.} \rangle \simeq bA + c_2\frac{T^2}{A} \quad (16)$$

where

$$b = \frac{4\pi}{5M}\left(\frac{3}{8\pi}\right)^{5/3}\frac{h^2}{(\frac{4}{3}\pi r_0^3)^{2/3}}\frac{2}{2^{5/3}}$$

$$c_2 = \frac{4\pi}{5M}\left(\frac{3}{8\pi}\right)^{5/3}\frac{h^2}{(\frac{4}{3}\pi r_0^3)^{2/3}}\frac{2}{2^{5/3}}\frac{20}{9}$$

and r_0 is the nuclear radius constant.

By combining the terms in Eqs. (10d) and (16), the binding energy of a nucleus becomes

$$B(A, Z) = -a_V A + bA + C\frac{T^2}{A} + a_s A^{2/3} \quad (17)$$

where C is a new constant $= c_1 + c_2$.

In Eq. (17), the first term is known as the volume energy and has been obtained from the saturation of exchange forces. It indicates that the binding energy is proportional to the mass number. The force which holds the nucleus together (that is, the short-range exchange force together with the saturation property) is analogous to that holding a drop of liquid together. That is why the semiempirical binding energy formula is associated with the liquid drop model. The molecules composing the liquid correspond to the nucleons in the nucleus. Since the density of the liquid can be considered to be independent of its size, the radius of a liquid drop is proportional to the cube root of the number of the molecules. The binding energy of a nucleus can be compared to the energy needed to evaporate the drop of liquid into separate molecules, and hence the energy is proportional to the number of molecules.

The second term of Eq. (17) arises from the consideration of the kinetic energy of N neutrons and Z protons. The third term is due to the symmetry effect which resulted from the Majorana exchange forces and kinetic energy. From Fig. 5-3, we note[1] that for $N = Z$ the nucleus is very stable

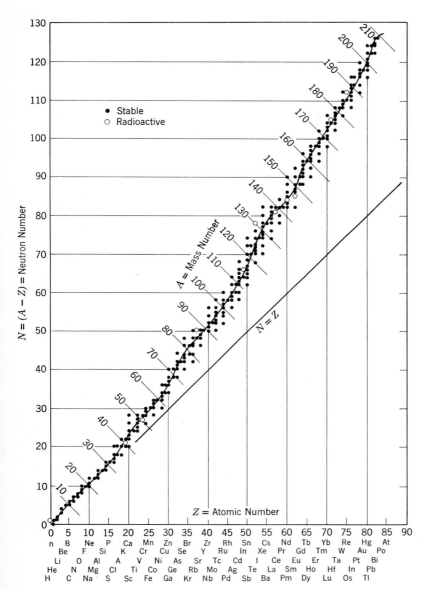

Fig. 5-3 The naturally occurring nuclides for $Z \leq 83$. Open circles show the radioactive nuclides. The chemical elements are identified by their symbols along the Z axis (Evans[1]).

at low A. Departure from this condition occurs in heavy elements, where $N > Z$, and the nuclei tend to be unstable. The instability also occurs if $N < Z$. Since the Majorana space exchange forces are attractive between particles in the same level, the nuclei with $N = Z$ which provide the highest number of symmetric pairs will result in greater stability. When $N \neq Z$, the larger number of antisymmetric pairs and their associated antisymmetric wave functions (for which the exchange force is repulsive for particles in different levels) result in a small binding energy, or, in other words, as $|N - Z|$ increases, nuclei become increasingly unstable.

The term $a_s A^{2/3}$ can be identified as the surface effect because the surface area of the nucleus is $4\pi R^2 = 4\pi (r_0 A^{1/3})^2$. In the derivation of the term corresponding to volume energy, it was assumed that a nucleon interacts equally with all other nucleons. This leads to an overestimation of the volume energy since the nucleons at the surface are not completely surrounded. The surface term appears as a correction to the volume energy. The surface term is repulsive and diminishes the energy. It can be compared with the surface tension effect in a liquid. This term is important for light nuclei since the ratio of the surface area to the volume of the nucleus diminishes with the increase in the mass number A.

5.3 Coulomb Energy

The effect of the Coulomb repulsion between protons is to lower the binding energy. The Coulomb energy term, which has already been calculated in Section 2.2, in the consideration of mirror nuclei, must therefore be added to the binding energy formula.

$$\text{Coulomb energy} = a_c \frac{Z(Z - 1)}{A^{1/3}} \tag{18a}$$

5.4 Pairing Energy

The last term in the binding energy formula which will be considered is that of pairing energy. It can be understood by considering the stability of the nucleus in terms of the various combinations of Z and N. It is known that the even-even nuclei are most stable, whereas the odd-odd nuclei are the least stable. The stability of even-odd or odd-even nuclei lies between these two extremes. This becomes more evident when we consider the stability of isobars* as a function of Z. If the mass $M(A, Z)$ is plotted versus Z, we obtain a parabola. Figure 5-4a corresponds to the mass

---

* Those nuclei which have the same mass number A but different atomic number Z are called isobars.

number $A = 135$ and Fig. 5-4b to 102. The most stable element of the group $A = 135$ lies at the apex of the parabola where it has the highest binding energy in comparison with other isobars.[1] In Fig. 5-4b, we obtain two parabolas corresponding to odd-odd nuclei which lie in the upper curve and even-even nuclei which lie in the lower curve. The odd-odd nuclei which have greater masses and less binding energy than even-even nuclei decay, giving the stable even-even nuclei of the same isobaric group.

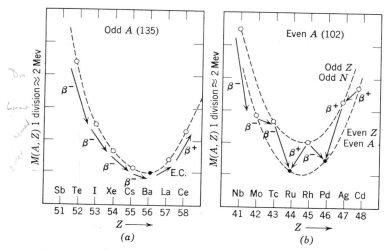

Fig. 5-4 (a) and (b). Stability of isobars, showing atomic mass M plotted against atomic number Z. Open circles represent unstable, and full circles stable nuclei (Evans[1]).

A function δ which is to be added to the binding energy formula takes into account the odd-even effect. In the liquid drop model which we have used in the derivation of the binding energy formula, the intrinsic spins of the nucleons have been ignored and the nuclear forces have been taken to be spin-independent. The empirical fact that there is a shift in the apex of the parabolas (Fig. 5-4b) for even-even and odd-odd nuclei involves the introduction of the pairing energy parameter δ into the empirical mass formula. It will be seen in Chapter 7 (shell model) that nucleons in even-even nuclei (characterized by highest binding energy) pair in such a way as to give zero spin. In odd nuclei, the spin is determined by the unpaired nucleon and in odd-odd nuclei (characterized by the least binding energy) by the unpaired proton and neutron. The pairing energy term, δ, in a way compensates for the lack of spin consideration in the mass formula. A good fit to the data is obtained by relating δ with A

in the following manner:

$$\delta = -0.036A^{-\frac{3}{4}} \text{ amu} = -33A^{-\frac{3}{4}} \text{ Mev} \qquad \text{for even-even nuclei}$$

$$\delta = 0 \qquad \qquad \qquad \text{for even-odd, or odd-even nuclei}$$

$$\delta = +0.036A^{-\frac{3}{4}} \text{ amu} = +33A^{-\frac{3}{4}} \text{ Mev} \qquad \text{for odd-odd nuclei}$$

(18b)

The complete semi-empirical binding energy formula then becomes [from Eqs. (17), (18a), and (18b)]

$$B(A, Z) = (-a_V + b)A + C\frac{T^2}{A} + a_c\frac{Z(Z-1)}{A^{\frac{1}{3}}} + a_s A^{\frac{2}{3}} + \delta \quad (19)$$

The binding energy formula contains a term proportional to T^2. For an odd A, from Eq. (18b) $\delta = 0$, and if we plot the binding energy for a group of isobars, we will obtain a parabola. The most stable nucleus, characterized by the highest binding energy, will be at the apex of the parabola. All other elements, which are unstable, will lie on the two arms of the parabola, as already noted in Fig. 5-4a. For even A, when δ is taken into account, we obtain two parabolas as in Fig. 5-4b.

The formula for mass is obtained by substituting the binding energy expression $B(A, Z)$ from Eq. (19) into Eq. (1) and is given by

$$M(A, Z) = \left\{ ZM_H + NM_N - (a_V - b)A + C\frac{T^2}{A} \right.$$
$$\left. + a_c\frac{Z(Z-1)}{A^{\frac{1}{3}}} + a_s A^{\frac{2}{3}} + \delta \right\} \quad (20)$$

This is known as the Weizsäcker mass formula.[3] Various corrections have been proposed to modify: the symmetry term[2,4]; the surface effect term, in order to take into account the composition of the surface[5]; the Coulomb energy term,[6] which is dependent upon the nature of the charge distribution; and the exchange effects.

Equation (20) contains five coefficients, which can be evaluated from five known masses. In theory the formula can then be used to predict accurately the masses of nuclei which range from light to heavy. In reality, however, the situation is complicated. If these five masses are not accurately known, the masses obtained by the use of Eq. (20) will be in error. In addition, there might be local variation of masses due to effects such as the shell effect. Extensive calculations have been performed by Green[7] to evaluate the coefficients.

The value of the Coulomb coefficient $a_c = 3e^2/5r_0$ can easily be found. From high-energy electron-scattering experiments the value of the nuclear charge radius constant r_0 is known to be 1.07 F,[8] so that $a_c = 0.807$ Mev.

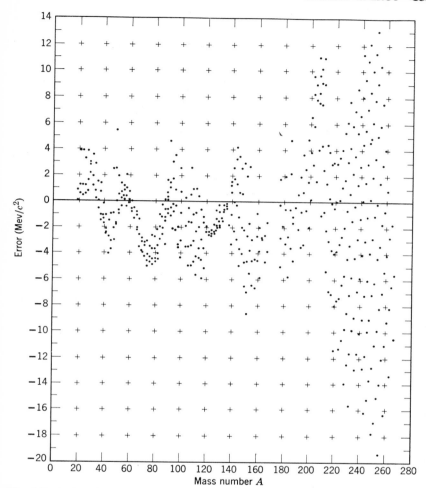

Fig. 5-5 Errors δ_i of 488 mass excesses for odd-mass atoms calculated from Eq. (21a) with coefficients of Eq. (21b) plotted versus atomic mass number A. The large systematic shell effects are clearly in evidence (Seeger[9]).

The coefficients involved in the mass formula can be evaluated by fitting all the known masses into a least-square adjustment of the coefficients.

The formula obtained by substituting the coefficients enables us to predict in general the masses or the binding energy per particle, B/A. Detailed analysis shows that there is a systematic departure of the masses from the semi-empirical mass law. This deviation has been attributed to the deformation of the nucleus and also to the shell structure effect; the latter effect is shown in Fig. 5-5 (Seeger[9]). In plotting Fig. 5-5, Seeger used the following more refined mass excess formula for odd-A nuclei.

$$\Delta M(Z, A) = 8.3674N + 7.5848Z - \alpha A + \left(\beta - \frac{\eta}{A^{1/3}}\right)\left(\frac{I^2 + 2|I|}{A}\right)$$

$$+ \gamma A^{2/3} + 0.8076 \frac{Z^2}{A^{1/3}}\left(1 - \frac{0.7636}{Z^{2/3}} - \frac{2.29}{A^{2/3}}\right) \quad (21a)$$

where the coefficients, as determined by the least-square fit, are

$$\alpha = 16.11 \text{ Mev}/c^2 \qquad \gamma = 20.21 \text{ Mev}/c^2$$
$$\beta = 20.65 \text{ Mev}/c^2 \qquad \eta = 48.00 \text{ Mev}/c^2 \qquad (21b)$$

and where $I = N - Z$, ΔM (the mass excess) $= M - A$, M being the atomic mass and A the mass number.

In Eq. (21a) no account was taken of the shell effect. The values of the coefficients in Eq. (21b) change when the nuclear deformation and the shell effect are considered. The refinement in Eq. (21a) is due to the fact that several additional effects have been considered. The symmetry term is modified to include $|I|$ as well as I^2. The surface effect term takes into account the composition of the surface and is reflected in the coefficient β. The Coulomb term is modified to trapezoidal charge distribution and exchange effects.

5.5   Shell Effect

Levy[10] has developed a semi-empirical mass formula which is capable of giving good results, particularly in the shell region. The basis for Levy's formula is that when the atomic masses or mass differences are plotted against Z, N, A, or I, a systematic and simple relationship can be seen. For example, when the atomic mass is plotted against Z with constant A, a parabolic relationship is obtained. Beta-decay energy plotted against the neutron number N for constant Z gives a straight line. An acceptable semi-empirical mass formula should be able to reproduce these relationships. The mass equation of Levy has the form

$$\Delta M(A, Z) = \alpha_0 + \alpha_1 A + \alpha_2 Z + \alpha_3 AZ + \alpha_4 Z^2 + \alpha_5 A^2 + \delta \quad (22)$$

where $\Delta M = M - A$ and M, A are, respectively, the atomic mass and the mass number. The alphas are constant for a given shell and are evaluated from the experimental masses in each shell region. They differ for different shell regions because there are discontinuities in nuclear binding energies at the magic numbers of protons or neutrons and because the slope of the straight-line relationship changes from one shell region to another. The pairing term δ depends upon odd-odd, odd-even, even-odd, or even-even nuclides. Since Eq. (22) must give the parabolic relationship when M is plotted against Z for constant A, we can express Eq. (22) in the form

$$\Delta M(A, Z) = \Delta M(A, Z_A) + K(Z_A - Z)^2 + \delta \qquad (23a)$$

where Z_A is the most stable Z for a given A, and where Z_A and $\Delta M(A, Z_A)$ are functions only of A. Comparing the coefficients of Z^2 terms in Eqs. (22) and (23a) we find that $K = \alpha_4$. Hence Eq. (23a) can be rewritten in the form

$$\Delta M(A, Z) = \Delta M(A, Z_A) + \alpha_4(Z_A - Z)^2 + \delta \qquad (23b)$$

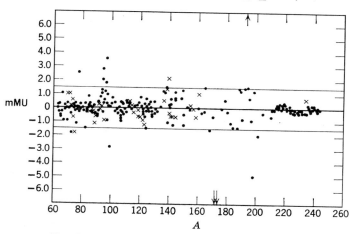

Fig. 5-6 The values in mMU of $\rho = \Delta M$ (meas.) $- \Delta M$ (calc.) for the new empirical mass equation plotted versus mass number, A. An $\times$ represents a "closed shell" nuclide. Lines at $+1.5$ and -1.5 mMU represent the range within which fall 95% of the ρ's (Levy[10]).

The relation of Z_A to A can be found by taking the partial derivative of Eq. (22) with respect to Z and setting this derivative equal to zero. We then obtain

$$Z_A = - \left(\frac{\alpha_3}{2\alpha_4} A + \frac{\alpha_2}{2\alpha_4} \right) \qquad (23c)$$

Comparing Eq. (23b) with Eq. (22) and using Eq. (23c), we find

$$\Delta M(A, Z_A) = \left(\alpha_0 - \frac{\alpha_2^2}{4\alpha_4} \right) + \left(\alpha_1 - \frac{\alpha_2 \alpha_3}{2\alpha_4} \right) A + \left(\alpha_5 - \frac{\alpha_3^2}{4\alpha_4} \right) A^2 \qquad (23d)$$

Equation (23d) gives $\Delta M(A, Z_A)$ as a function of A.

Levy calculated the atomic masses of nuclides with Z and N greater than 28. In Fig. 5-6 are the results of the 340 nuclides including several nuclides with closed neutron or proton shells. The empirical formula is able to reproduce the experimental masses with good accuracy. Levy's semi-empirical formula has been deduced theoretically from the shell model by Zeldes.[11] The calculations are very involved and will not be attempted here.

5.6 Atomic Masses

Information about atomic masses is obtained by various methods such as the total energies of disintegration in β-decay, Q-values of nuclear reactions, and the mass differences of mass-spectroscopic doublets.

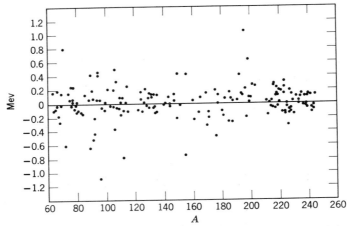

Fig. 5-7 The values in Mev of Q_β (meas.) $-$ Q_β (calc.) plotted versus mass number, A, using the new empirical mass equation to calculate Q_β (Levy[10]).

The beta-decay energy Q_β for positron emission, electron capture, or electron emission can be calculated by using Levy's formula:

$$Q_{\beta+} = 2\alpha_4(Z - Z_A - 0.5) + (\delta_1 - \delta_2) \qquad \text{for positron emission}$$
$$Q_{\beta-} = 2\alpha_4(Z_A - Z - 0.5) + (\delta_1 - \delta_2) \qquad \text{for electron emission}$$

Figure 5-7 gives[10] a plot of the differences between the experimental Q_β and the theoretical Q_β obtained by using the above formulas as a function of the mass number A. The agreement between the predicted value and the experimental value is excellent. About 95% of the points agree to within ± 0.50 Mev.

The total beta-decay energy, for example $Q_{\beta-}$ for electron emission, can be obtained by measuring the maximum energy of the beta particle emitted during the decay process and is given by the mass difference between the parent and daughter nuclei in the ground states. However, the situation is complicated because in addition to the neutrino emission during the decay process, the daughter nucleus may remain in an excited state, which may de-excite by the emission of various γ-rays and conversion electrons. Therefore, in order to measure the total beta-decay energy it is necessary to measure the energy of the different radiations. Although the energy of the neutrino cannot be measured directly, it can be estimated from the shape of the beta spectrum. The energy of the γ-rays can be measured with a scintillation counter or by means of a spectrometer. In the latter, γ-rays are allowed to bombard a target placed in front of the γ-ray source within the spectrometer. The momentum of the emitted photoelectrons or pair-production electrons can be determined from the spectrometer measurements, and we can thus estimate the energy of the γ-rays. Similarly, the energy of the conversion electron or beta-rays can be accurately ascertained by means of either a magnetic or an electric spectrometer.

The atomic masses can also be accurately estimated from the measurement of Q-values of nuclear reactions. Consider a target nucleus of mass M_T at rest, bombarded by a particle of mass m with kinetic energy E. A final nucleus of mass M_f with kinetic energy E_f and a light particle of mass m' with kinetic energy E' are produced as a result of nuclear reactions. Then from conservation of energy we have

$$(M_T + m)c^2 + E = (M_f + m')c^2 + E_f + E' \tag{25a}$$

or rearranging,

$$(M_T + m - M_f - m')c^2 = Q = E_f + E' - E \tag{25b}$$

where Q is the energy released due to the reaction. The kinetic energy of the final nucleus E_f is usually small, due to its large mass, and is difficult to measure. However, we can eliminate E_f by applying conservation of linear momentum and thus obtain

$$Q = E'\left(1 + \frac{m'}{M_f}\right) - E\left(1 - \frac{m}{M_f}\right) - \frac{2}{M_f}(EE'mm')^{\frac{1}{2}}\cos\theta \tag{25c}$$

where θ is the angle between the directions of the incident and the outgoing light particle. The value of Q is now expressed in terms of measurable quantities. The incident particle is accelerated, usually with the aid of an electrostatic generator which in conjunction with a beam-analyzing magnet can give an accurate measurement of the bombarding energy E. The energy of the light outgoing particle can also be determined with equal precision by means of an analyzer, either magnetic or electrostatic. By knowing the Q-values for a set of nuclear reactions and by the repeated

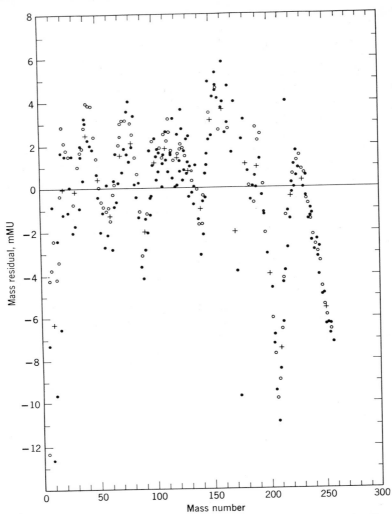

Fig. 5-8 Experimental mass residuals of beta-stable nuclei. The circles correspond to even-A nuclei, the dots to odd-A nuclei. The crosses represent the "normal points" (Green[12]).

application of Eq. (25c) it is possible to estimate atomic masses with great accuracy.

The other precise method of determining the atomic masses is from the mass difference of mass-spectrographic doublets, measured after the mass spectrograph is calibrated at one point by using a standard atomic mass, formerly O^{16}. Since 1960, however, C^{12} has been used as the standard.

The difference of masses for ions whose A/n ratios are the same is measured, e.g., $H_2^1 - H^2$ ($A/n = 2$), $N_2O - CO_2$ ($A/n = 44$), $C_6H_6 - Kr$ ($A/n = 78$), where the value $n = 1, 2, 3, \ldots$, depending upon whether the ionization is single, double, etc. The measured mass differences are then applied to the approximate mass value to obtain very accurate atomic masses with a precision of one part in 10^6. The masses determined by the Q-value method compare very favorably with those obtained by the spectrometer method.

5.7 Significance of Atomic Mass

Detailed studies of atomic masses provide information about a great many nuclear properties. We have already noted the influence of shell structure upon the masses. Actually, more accurate values of the masses are predicted when the shell effect is considered. The shell-structure effect can be seen in the short-range fluctuations of the nuclear masses[12] from Fig. 5-5 as well as in those shown in Fig. 5-8. The ordinate is the mass residual which is defined as $R = \Delta_x - \Delta_e$, where $\Delta_e = 0.01(A - 100)^2 - 64$ and $\Delta_x = M - A$ is the mass defect. The normal points are obtained from linear averages of residuals at equally spaced intervals centered about mass numbers $10, 20, \ldots, 250$.

The semi-empirical mass formula includes a Coulomb energy term which contains the nuclear radius parameter r_0. Green[12] obtained a best fit of mass values with the semi-empirical mass formula by assuming $r_0 = 1.216 \times 10^{-13}$ cm, which is comparable with the value calculated from the electron-scattering data.[8] Such an agreement may possibly be accidental since the nuclear masses show fluctuations in the shell region. The strength of the nuclear forces is evident when we study the binding energy per particle, $\epsilon = E/A$, where the nuclear energy $E = M - ZM_H - NM_N$; M_H and M_N represent respectively the mass of the hydrogen atom and neutron. The variation of nuclear energy as a function of the mass number A is given in Fig. 5-9. It can be seen that nuclear energy increases almost linearly with mass number. The smooth curve corresponds to an empirical expression for mass decrement $\Delta_e = 0.01(A - 100)^2 - 64$. The binding energy per particle varies slowly after $A = 50$, indicating saturation of the nuclear energy. The two parallel lines represent the nuclear energies of the last neutron and proton. The departure of the average neutron energy E_n and proton energy E_p from E give the degree of saturation.

In addition to the several properties mentioned, other properties such as surface thickness, compressibility, and surface composition can be studied with the aid of appropriate nuclear models.

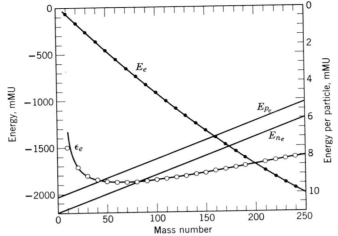

Fig. 5-9 Nuclear energies (E_e), nuclear energies per particle (ϵ_e) and nuclear energies of the last proton and neutron (E_{p_e}) and (E_{n_e}) for beta-stable nuclei. The dots and circles represent averages of the experimental values in the neighborhoods of $A = 10$, 20, . . . , etc. The smooth curves are all based upon an empirical expression for mass decrements (Green[12]).

PART II. NUCLEAR FISSION

Nuclear fission is a process by which a nucleus splits into two or more lighter nuclides either spontaneously or after the original nucleus absorbs various particles or γ-rays. The fission process was discovered by Hahn and Strassman[13] in 1939. Since then numerous papers and review articles have been published which describe the nature of the process. In this section we first describe some characteristics of the fission process and then discuss some of the theories of nuclear fission.

5.8 Cross Section

Fission can be induced in some nuclides by certain incident particles of appropriate energy. For example, U^{235} undergoes fission when bombarded by thermal neutrons ($v = 2200$ m/sec), whereas U^{238} does not. U^{238} will undergo fission, however, when bombarded by fast neutrons (>1 Mev energy), as will U^{235}. Slow-neutron fission occurs quite often in nuclei containing an odd number of neutrons, such as U^{235}. This can be interpreted as due to a large excitation produced in the compound nucleus because of the energy released in the pairing of neutrons when the incident neutron is absorbed. The slow-neutron fission cross section for U^{235} varies with energy in a complicated way. In the region of about 0.28 ev, the fission cross section σ_f varies as the reciprocal of the neutron velocity v. From 0.28 to about 1000 ev, there are many closely spaced resonances. These resonances correspond to the capture of a neutron with kinetic energy such that the binding energy of the neutron (approximately 6 Mev) plus the kinetic energy of motion equal some quantum level. In general, the fission cross section for U^{235} decreases with increasing energy until around 2 Mev, where it levels off near 1.5 barns. The resonance peaks observed in fission are often analyzed by using the Breit-Wigner single isolated-level formula discussed in Chapter 6 (see Eqs. 14b and 26c). We shall quote the formula as applied to fission. The fission cross section for all values of angular momentum l is

$$\sigma_f^{(l)} = (2l + 1)\frac{\pi}{k^2}\frac{\Gamma_n \Gamma_f}{4(E - E_{\text{res}}^l) + (\Gamma/2)^2}$$

The quantities E and E_{res}^l refer to the incident energy of neutrons and neutron energy at resonance; Γ is the total width of the level, the sum of neutron width Γ_n, the radiation width Γ_γ, and fission width Γ_f; k is the wave number of neutrons. The quantity k^2 can be expressed as $1/\lambda\lambda_0$ where λ is the wavelength of neutrons and λ_0 is the wavelength at resonance. If the values of these parameters are known, then the fission cross section can be computed accurately. The formula indicates that the shape of the resonance curve is symmetric with a maximum at the resonance

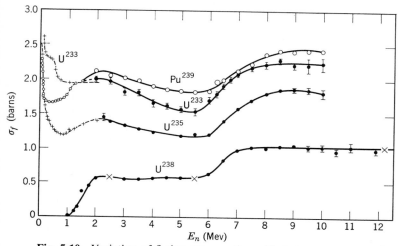

Fig. 5-10 Variation of fission cross section with fast-neutron energy for U^{238}, U^{233}, U^{235} and Pu^{239}. Data from Smith, Nobles, and Henkel[14] (Hyde[15]).

energy. The experimental shape is quite often asymmetric and deviates from the prediction of the Breit-Wigner formula. These deviations may be due either to unresolved levels or to interference from the neighboring resonance level.

Some heavy nuclides like U^{234}, U^{236}, and U^{238} undergo fission only with fast neutrons. For these nuclides one can think of fission in terms of a threshold reaction and the cross section varies similarly to that of other nuclear reactions. At a neutron energy of about 1 Mev, U^{238} will start to undergo fission, and from there on, the cross section increases as the incident energy increases. Figure 5-10 illustrates the behavior of some heavy

Table 5-1 Measured Fission Thresholds (Halpern[16])

Nuclide	Reaction	Threshold (Mev)
Th^{232}	(γ, f)	5.8
Pa^{232}	(n, f)	6.2
Th^{233}	(n, f)	6.4
U^{233}	(γ, f)	5.4
U^{234}	(d, pf)	5.2
U^{235}	(n, f)	5.7
U^{236}	(d, pf)	5.8
U^{237}	(n, f)	6.3
Np^{237}	(γ, f)	5.6
U^{238}	(γ, f)	5.8
Np^{238}	(n, f)	6.0
U^{239}	(n, f)	6.2
Pu^{239}	(γ, f)	5.4
Pu^{240}	(d, pf)	4.7
Pu^{241}	(n, f)	6.3
Am^{241}	(γ, f)	6.0
Am^{242}	(n, f)	6.4

nuclei.[15] The minimum at about 6 Mev occurs since the excitation energy is high enough to permit evaporation of a neutron which then reduces the excitation energy of the nucleus below the fission threshold.

The threshold energy is associated with the fission barrier and will be discussed in connection with the liquid-drop model of fission processes. Some representative values of threshold energy are given[16] in Table 5-1.

5.9   Spontaneous Fission

Most heavy nuclides undergo spontaneous fission in competition with the emission of an α-particle. A nucleus having $Z^2/A > 18$ undergoes spontaneous fission.[17] This is observable, although with a very small probability, in nuclides beyond Th^{232}. The phenomenon of spontaneous fission is dependent upon the mass number A. As the mass number increases, the fission rate increases. Figure 5-11 is a plot of half-lives for spontaneous fission by a particular mode for several nuclides[18] as a function of mass number. The figure indicates that even-even nuclides

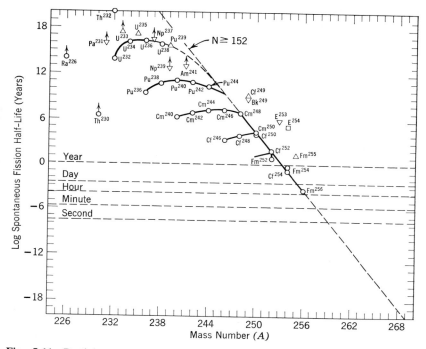

Fig. 5-11 Partial spontaneous-fission half-lives as a function of mass number: $\bigcirc$, even-even nuclide; $\triangle$, even-odd nuclide; $\triangledown$, odd-even nuclide; $\square$, odd-odd nuclide (Foreman and Seaborg[18]).

have a half-life that is shorter than that of even-odd species with the same mass number. For example, U^{235} which fissions with slow neutrons has a half-life of 1.8×10^{17} years and U^{238} which fissions with fast neutrons has a half-life of 8.0×10^{15} years. The same situation exists for Pu^{239} and Pu^{240}. For nuclides with a very high mass number like Cf^{254} and Fm^{256}, the principal decay mode is fission with a half-life of a few hours. The process of spontaneous fission which can be considered as a barrier-penetration phenomenon is discussed in the theoretical section.

The energetics of the fission process can be discussed using the semi-empirical mass formula Eq. (20). We assume for simplicity that a heavy nucleus of mass $M\,(A, Z)$ undergoes fission giving two lighter fragments of equal mass $M(A/2, Z/2)$ (symmetric fission). Then from Eq. (20), we can easily find that the energy of reaction Q is approximately given by

$$Q = a_s A^{2/3}(1 - 2^{1/3}) + a_c \frac{Z^2}{A^{1/3}}\left(1 - \frac{1}{2^{2/3}}\right)$$

The value of Q is positive for a heavy nucleus and contains terms involving surface tension and Coulomb energy. The importance of these two terms in the fission process will be evident in Section 5-11.

5.10   Mass and Energy Distribution of Fragments

The distribution of the masses of the fragments that result from fission shows that there are two predominant groups, light and heavy. This is

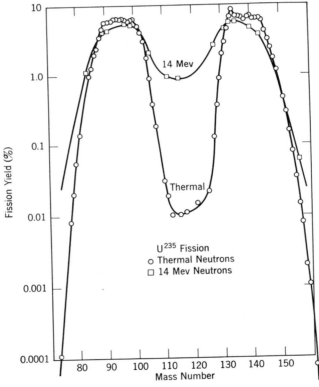

Fig. 5-12   Yield-mass curve for fission of U^{235} induced by neutrons. Curves plotted from "best" values taken from literature by S. Katcoff (quoted by Hyde[15]).

best illustrated if the percentage yield of the different elements is plotted against the mass number A. Figure 5-12 shows fission yield curves[15] for bombardment by thermal and high-energy neutrons. The peaks correspond to the light and heavy groups of fission fragments. The maxima for U^{235} are at $A = 95$ and $A = 139$. For Pu^{239} (not shown in the figure), the peaks occur at mass numbers 99 and 138. We note that the mass distribution of the fission process is highly asymmetric for thermal neutron bombardment; symmetric mass distribution occurs in only 0.01 % of the cases. There are also small, fine-structure peaks which probably result from the shell effect that favors the formation of certain mass pairs as compared to other neighboring mass pairs. As the incident neutron energy increases, the probability of the symmetric fission increases until finally an energy is reached where symmetric fission is the most favorable mode. The reason for the asymmetric nature of mass distribution is not yet properly understood.

Various suggestions have been made from time to time. For example, according to Bohr[19] the asymmetric nature of mass distribution for

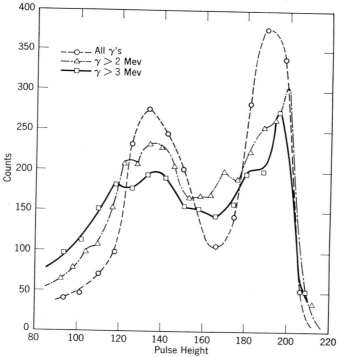

Fig. 5-13 Energy distribution of fission fragments (Cooperman and Roy[20]).

low-energy fission can be understood in terms of the splitting of the compound nucleus being dependent upon its spin and parity.

The kinetic-energy distribution of the fission fragments is similar to the mass distribution curve. There are two peaks; from the conservation of momentum, it is easy to see that the high-energy peak corresponds to the light fragment, whereas the low-energy one corresponds to the heavy fragment. Figure 5-13 presents the kinetic-energy distribution of fission fragments of U^{235} bombarded by thermal neutrons.[20] When the two fragments of fission are formed, they are in highly excited states which de-excite by the emission of neutrons, γ-rays, or conversion electrons. The curve corresponding to all γ-rays represents the normal distribution of kinetic energies of the fragments. However, if the kinetic-energy distribution is studied as a function of the energy of γ-rays by a coincidence technique, a fine structure in the distribution is observed. Figure 5-13 shows two distributions with energies greater than 2 and 3 Mev respectively. They exhibit the general features of the standard double-hump curve with a fine structure superimposed. It was concluded from this experiment that the higher-energy γ-rays are preferentially emitted for symmetric fission and by doubly magic number nuclei such as $N = 82$ and $Z = 50$.

We have briefly discussed some of the properties of fission. In the next section we examine various theories and see to what extent they have succeeded in explaining the properties of fission such as the fissionability of the elements and the double-hump mass-distribution curve.

5.11   Liquid-Drop Model

The first thorough theoretical treatment of the fission process based on the liquid-drop model was carried out by Bohr and Wheeler[21] in 1939. They considered a nucleus to be analogous to a charged liquid drop. The forces in the nucleus are the short-range, charge-independent nucleon-nucleon forces between neutrons and protons, and the Coulomb repulsive forces of the protons. The nuclear forces are compared with the surface tension force of a liquid. The nuclear shape represents a balance between the short-range attractive forces and the Coulomb repulsive forces. The surface tension effect and the Coulomb effect have been calculated in the expression for the empirical mass formula. When a heavy nucleus like U^{235} is excited through the capture of a thermal neutron, surface oscillations are set up in the liquid drop which distort it from its original shape. The Coulomb energy attempts to deform the drop even more. If the excitation energy is high enough, the Coulomb energy can overcome the surface energy and the nucleus separates into two or more intermediate masses. If fission does not occur, the excited compound nucleus emits either a γ-ray or a neutron and returns to a stable shape.

To treat the problem theoretically, the nucleus is considered as a uniformly charged drop of constant density and having a well-defined surface. The requirement of constant density of nuclear matter, that is, incompressibility, imposes the condition that the total volume of a drop remain constant. Hence the oscillations of the excited nucleus will deform the surface only. The drop is considered to deform from a spherical shape in such a way that it retains an axis of symmetry. In that case, the symmetry axis is chosen as the polar axis of the spherical coordinates. The distorted radial coordinate of a point on the surface can be expressed in terms of Legendre polynomials:

$$R(\theta) = R_0\left(1 + \sum_{l=0}^{\infty} \alpha_l P_l(\cos\theta)\right) \tag{26a}$$

where R_0 is the radius of the undeformed spherical drop, α_l are deformation parameters, and $P_l(\cos\theta)$ are the Legendre polynomials. The requirement of constant volume specifies that $\alpha_0 = 0$, and $\alpha_1 = 0$ because the center of mass of the drop is assumed to remain unchanged. Hence the expression becomes

$$R(\theta) = R_0(1 + \alpha_2 P_2 + \alpha_3 P_3 + \cdots) \tag{26b}$$

The surface energy of a spherical drop is defined as

$$E_{S_0} = \tau S = 4\pi R_0^2 \tau \tag{27a}$$

where τ and S are respectively the surface tension and the surface area. The surface energy E_S of the deformed drop is given by

$$E_S = \tau \int dS \tag{27b}$$

The surface area in Eq. (27b) is

$$S = \int_0^{2\pi} d\phi \int_0^{\pi} d\theta \sqrt{1 + \left(\frac{1}{R}\frac{\partial R}{\partial\theta}\right)^2}\, R^2 \sin\theta \tag{28a}$$

Using Eqs. (26a) and (28a) we obtain the form

$$S = 2\pi R_0^2 \int_{-1}^{1} \left\{\left[1 + \sum_{l=2}^{\infty} \alpha_l P_l\right]^2 + \left[\sum_{l=2}^{\infty} \alpha_l P_l'\right]^2\right\}^{1/2} \left[1 + \sum_{l=2}^{\infty} \alpha_l P_l\right] d(\cos\theta) \tag{28b}$$

According to Bohr and Wheeler, the surface energy of the deformed nucleus in terms of the deformation parameters α_l is

$$E_S = 4\pi R_0^2 \tau (1 + \tfrac{2}{5}\alpha_2^2 + \tfrac{5}{7}\alpha_3^2 + \cdots) \tag{28c}$$

The first term $4\pi R_0^2 \tau$ in the expansion is the surface energy of an undistorted drop as in Eq. (27a).

The Coulomb energy for the deformed drop is determined from the expression[17]

$$E_C = \tfrac{1}{2}\int V\rho\, d^3r = \tfrac{1}{2}\int V_0\rho_0\, d^3r + \int V_0\delta\rho\, d^3r + \tfrac{1}{2}\int \delta V\delta\rho\, d^3r \quad (29a)$$

where δV and $\delta\rho$ are changes in the electric potential and charge distribution due to the deformation.

$$V = V_0 + \delta V \qquad \text{and} \qquad \rho = \rho_0 + \delta\rho$$

It is also assumed that

$$\int V_0\delta\rho\, d^3r = \int \rho_0\delta V\, d^3r$$

The deformation is such that the deformation energy $V_0\,\delta\rho$ in changing the charge density by $\delta\rho$ at a constant potential V_0 is equal to the deformation energy $\rho_0\,\delta V$ in changing the potential by δV at constant charge density ρ_0. The first term is the electrostatic energy of an undistorted uniformly charged sphere.

$$E_{C_0} = \tfrac{1}{2}\int V_0\rho_0\, d^3r = \frac{3}{5}\frac{(Ze)^2}{R_0} \quad (29b)$$

The second term is the energy of a monopole redistribution of charge and is given by

$$E_{C_m} = \int V_0\,\delta\rho\, d^3r = \frac{3}{4\pi}\frac{(Ze)^2}{R_0^3}\int d\Omega\int_{R_0}^{R} R\, dR$$

$$= -\frac{3}{8\pi}\frac{(Ze)^2}{R_0}[\alpha_2^2 + \alpha_3^2 + \cdots] \quad (29c)$$

The last term of Eq. (29a) is due to the interaction between the multipole part of the potential field and the multipole charge distribution. This is obtained from

$$E_{CI} = \tfrac{1}{2}\int \delta V\,\delta\rho\, d^3r = \frac{3}{8\pi}\frac{Ze}{R_0^3}\sum_{l=2}^{\infty}\int d\Omega V(R_0,\theta)\int_{R_0}^{R} R^2\, dR$$

$$= \frac{9}{8\pi}\frac{(Ze)^2}{R_0}\sum_{l=2}^{\infty}\frac{1}{2l+1}|\alpha_l|^2 \quad (29d)$$

Adding Eqs. (29b), (29c), and (29d) we obtain for the Coulomb energy

$$E_C = \frac{3}{5}\frac{(Ze)^2}{R_0}[1 - \tfrac{1}{5}\alpha_2^2 - \tfrac{10}{49}\alpha_3^2 - \cdots] \quad (29e)$$

The total deformation energy E_T can be found by adding Eqs. (28c) and (29e). Using $R_0 = r_0 A^{1/3}$, we find

$$E_T = 4\pi r_0^2 A^{2/3} \tau [1 + \tfrac{2}{5}\alpha_2^2 + \tfrac{5}{7}\alpha_3^2 + \cdots]$$
$$+ \frac{3}{5}\frac{(Ze)^2}{r_0 A^{1/3}}[1 - \tfrac{1}{5}\alpha_2^2 - \tfrac{10}{49}\alpha_3^2 - \cdots] \tag{30a}$$

Equation (30a) can also be expressed as

$$E_T = E_{S_0}(1 + \tfrac{2}{5}\alpha_2^2 + \tfrac{5}{7}\alpha_3^2 + \cdots)$$
$$+ E_{C_0}(1 - \tfrac{1}{5}\alpha_2^2 - \tfrac{10}{49}\alpha_3^2 - \cdots) \tag{30b}$$

The change in energy due to the deformation of the drop, keeping only the α_2^2 term, is

$$\Delta E = (E_S + E_C) - E_{S_0} - E_{C_0} \simeq \tfrac{1}{5}\alpha_2^2[2E_{S_0} - E_{C_0}] \tag{30c}$$

Since the surface energy appears with a positive sign and the Coulomb energy with a negative one, the stability of a nucleus against spontaneous fission is defined in terms of ΔE being positive or negative.

If $\qquad$ ΔE is positive: $\qquad E_{C_0} < 2E_{S_0}$ $\quad$ the nucleus is stable

$\qquad\qquad$ ΔE is negative: $\qquad E_{C_0} > 2E_{S_0}$ $\quad$ the nucleus is unstable

A convenient quantity for discussing fission is the fissionability parameter χ defined as follows. When $\Delta E = 0$, then from Eq. (30c)

$$2E_{S_0} = E_{C_0}$$

which defines the following critical value for Z^2/A:

$$\left(\frac{Z^2}{A}\right)_c = \frac{40\pi r_0^3 \tau}{3e^2} \simeq 50 \tag{31a}$$

χ in terms of the critical value $(Z^2/A)_c$ is

$$\chi = \frac{Z^2/A}{(Z^2/A)_c} \tag{31b}$$

When $\chi < 1$, the nucleus is stable against spontaneous fission, and when $\chi > 1$, the nucleus is unstable against spontaneous fission.

The critical energy E_f for fission is defined as the energy necessary to deform a drop when it is about to split into two equal drops:

$$E_f = 4\pi r_0^2 \tau A^{2/3} f(\chi) = E_{S_0} A^{2/3} f(\chi) \tag{32a}$$

where χ is given by Eq. (31b). The critical energy to the first order in Z^2/A can be calculated by neglecting the second-order change in energy due to the neck joining the two fragments, and comparing only the sum of the surface energy and electrostatic energy for the original nucleus with the corresponding energy of two spherical nuclei of half the size which are in contact with each other. We find

$$E_f = 2(4\pi r_0^2)\tau\left(\frac{A}{2}\right)^{2/3} - 4\pi r_0^2\tau A^{2/3}$$
$$+ 2\left(\frac{3}{5}\right)\frac{(Ze/2)^2}{r_0(A/2)^{1/3}} + \frac{(Ze/2)^2}{2r_0(A/2)^{1/3}} - \frac{3}{5}\frac{(Ze)^2}{r_0 A^{1/3}} \quad (32b)$$

Dividing E_f by $4\pi r_0^2\tau A^{2/3}$ and rearranging, Eq. (32b) becomes

$$\frac{E_f}{4\pi r_0^2\tau A^{2/3}} = f(\chi) = 0.260 - 0.215\chi \quad (33)$$

For an uncharged droplet, $\chi = 0$ and therefore $f(0) = 0.260$. This condition implies that there are no electrostatic forces to aid the fission. The critical energy is just the work done against the surface tension in separating into two drops.

Let us consider now the case where $\chi \approx 1$. For this a small deformation from the spherical shape causes the drop to reach the critical shape and separate. The distortion energy according to Bohr and Wheeler, taking into consideration the α_4 term, is

$$E_T = 4\pi r_0^2\tau A^{2/3}\left[\frac{2}{5}\alpha_2^2 + \frac{116}{105}\alpha_2^3 + \frac{101}{35}\alpha_2^4 + \frac{2}{35}\alpha_2^2\alpha_4 + \alpha_4^2\right]$$
$$- \frac{3}{5}\frac{(Ze)^2}{r_0 A^{1/3}}\left[\frac{1}{5}\alpha_2^2 + \frac{64}{105}\alpha_2^3 + \frac{58}{35}\alpha_2^4 + \frac{8}{35}\alpha_2^2\alpha_4 + \frac{5}{27}\alpha_4^2\right] \quad (34a)$$

Minimizing E_T with respect to α_4 yields the critical value for α_4 in terms of α_2:

$$\alpha_4 = -\frac{243}{595}\alpha_2^2 \quad (34b)$$

Using this value, Eq. (33) may be expressed as

$$\frac{E_f}{4\pi r_0^2\tau A^{2/3}} = f(\chi) = \frac{98}{135}(1 - \chi)^3 - \frac{11368}{34425}(1 - \chi)^4 + \cdots \quad (34c)$$

By interpolating between the results obtained for $\chi \approx 0$ and $\chi \approx 1$ we can plot the fission threshold energy E_f as a function of χ. This plot is given in Fig. 5-14.[21] The region shown by dashed lines includes those heavy nuclei which undergo fission like U^{238}. The threshold energy for U^{235} from Table 5-1 is 5.7 Mev. This corresponds to a χ value of about 0.74 (from Fig. 5-14). From this we conclude that $(Z^2/A)_c \approx 48$ in agreement with experiment. A plot of some critical shapes is shown in Fig. 5-15.[22] One of the properties that has come from this analysis is the idea of a

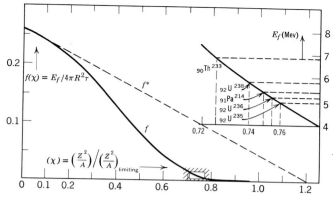

Fig. 5-14 The energy E_f required to produce a critical deformation leading to fission is divided by the surface energy $4\pi R^2\tau$ to obtain a dimensionless function of the quantity $\chi = $ (charge)^2/(10 × volume × surface tension). The behavior of the function $f(\chi)$ is calculated in the text for $\chi = 0$ and $\chi = 1$, and a smooth curve is drawn here to connect these values. The curve $f^*(\chi)$ determines for comparison the energy required to deform the nucleus into two spheres in contact with each other. Over the crosshatched region of the curve of interest for the heaviest nuclei, the surface energy changes but little. Taking for it a value of 530 Mev, we obtain the energy scale in the upper part of the figure. We estimate from the observations a value $E_f \sim 6$ Mev for U^{233}. Using the figure we thus find $(Z^2/A)_{\text{limiting}} = 47.8$ and can estimate the fission barriers for other nuclei, as shown (Bohr and Wheeler[21]).

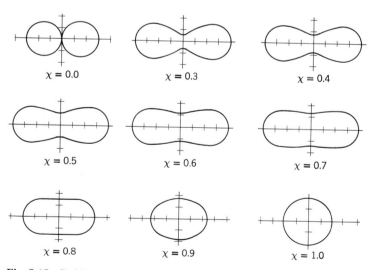

$\chi = 0.0$ $\chi = 0.3$ $\chi = 0.4$

$\chi = 0.5$ $\chi = 0.6$ $\chi = 0.7$

$\chi = 0.8$ $\chi = 0.9$ $\chi = 1.0$

Fig. 5-15 Saddle point shapes for various values of χ according to Cohen and Swiatecki.[22]

171

threshold energy or barrier potential. The potential energy associated with a deformation of the drop can be plotted as a function of some of the deformation parameters. The resulting plot which resembles a contour map is given in Fig. 5-16.[23] The coordinates α_2 and α_4 are only two of the many deformation parameters necessary to describe a general distortion

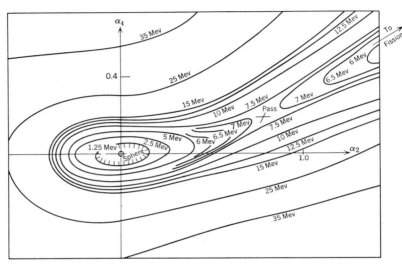

Fig. 5-16   Schematic contour map of the potential surface of the distorted drop. The two map coordinates are representative of the large set required to specify a general displacement of the drop. The contour lines are marked in Mev difference from the origin of the map coordinates, which is the undistorted spherical drop. Note the crater and the pass over the lip of the crater. The height of the pass is about right for a nucleus with $Z = 90$. The shape of the surface is adapted from an actual numerical calculation of the energy of distortion in an imaginary case where the distortion was restricted to a function of only the two parameters plotted for the map. The radius as a function of co-latitude angle, $R(\theta)$, was taken to be $R_0[1 + \alpha_2 P_2 + \alpha_4 P_4]$, and energy is plotted as a function of α_2 and α_4 as shown in the map (Segrè[23]).

of the liquid drop. Note the crater at the origin and the saddle point which is at about the threshold energy E_f. The saddle point corresponds to the critical distortion of the nucleus beyond which fission can take place. Bohr and Wheeler compare this saddle-point concept with a ball oscillating at the origin in the crater. If the ball receives some energy (neutron capture), it begins to oscillate in some complex manner about the origin. If the energy is sufficient, the ball will during some period move in a favorable direction to pass over the saddle point and escape, thus resulting in the fission of the nucleus.

5.12 Barrier Penetration

The preceding analysis was a classical one and describes gross features of fission. A more refined theory includes quantum effects and develops the idea of barrier penetration for fission. Actually spontaneous fission can be explained only in terms of leakage through the fission barrier. For the quantum mechanical treatment Hill and Wheeler[24] assume a one-dimensional inverted harmonic oscillator whose Hamiltonian is

$$H = -\frac{\hbar^2}{2B}\frac{\partial^2}{\partial\alpha_l^2} - \tfrac{1}{2}B\omega_l^2\alpha_l^2 + E_f \tag{35a}$$

where B is an inertia factor for the undistorted nucleus and α is the distortion parameter of Eq. (26a). ω_l is the frequency of distortion and E_f is a square-well barrier. The solution of the Schrödinger equation leads to the penetration factor P

$$P = \left\{1 + \exp\left[\frac{-2\pi(E - E_f)}{\hbar\omega_l}\right]\right\}^{-1} \tag{35b}$$

It is necessary to transform the kinetic energy and potential energy of the distorted drop into normal coordinates. For small values of α_l the kinetic energy is

$$T(\dot\alpha_l) = \tfrac{1}{2}\sum_{l=2}^{\infty} B_l(\dot\alpha_l)^2 \tag{35c}$$

B_l is the inertia term and is a function of the nuclear radius and mass; $\dot\alpha_l$ represents the instantaneous changes in α_l. The potential energy of the deformed nucleus is given by

$$V = \tfrac{1}{2}\sum_{l=2}^{\infty} C_l\alpha_l^2 \tag{35d}$$

where C_l is the stiffness constant of the surface and is a function of the nuclear radius, charge, and area. The total energy H is given by Eqs. (35c) and (35d) when undergoing oscillation

$$H = T + V = \tfrac{1}{2}\sum_{l=2}^{\infty} (C_l\alpha_l^2 + B_l\dot\alpha_l^2) \tag{36a}$$

The characteristic frequencies are obtained from

$$\omega_l = \left(\frac{C_l}{B_l}\right)^{1/2} \tag{36b}$$

Equation (36a) is a superposition (summed over all l's) of oscillations and is regarded as a harmonic oscillator whose displacement in terms of ω_l is given by

$$\alpha_l(t) = A_l \cos{(\omega_l + \delta_l)t} \tag{36c}$$

At some frequency ω_l the nucleus is in the saddle-point configuration resulting in $E \approx E_f$ in Eq. (35b), where the penetration factor $P = \frac{1}{2}$. The value of the $\hbar\omega_l$, when $E \approx E_f$, is given by

$$\hbar\omega_l \approx \hbar\left(-\frac{5}{4\pi}\frac{E_{S_0}}{B_2}\frac{\partial^2 E_f}{\partial \alpha_2^2}\right)^{\frac{1}{2}} \tag{36d}$$

$\hbar\omega_l$ is of the order of 1 Mev for nuclei with $A \approx 240$. An estimate of the lifetime t_0 for spontaneous fission from this calculation gives

$$t_0^{-1} \approx 2\pi\omega_2 \exp\left[\frac{-2\pi(E_f - E)}{\hbar\omega_l}\right] \tag{36e}$$

Seaborg[25] calculated E_f from a plot of spontaneous fission half-life versus Z^2/A for various heavy elements and found that the fission rate could be determined by the formula

$$t_0 = 10^{-21} \times 10^{178-3.75(Z^2/A)} \text{ sec} \tag{36f}$$

which is in contrast with the following expression calculated by Frankel and Metropolis[26] based upon barrier penetration.

$$t_0 = 10^{-21} \times 10^{7.85 E_f} \text{ sec} \tag{36g}$$

When Seaborg applied these results, he obtained the following equation for the barrier height

$$E_f = 19.0 - 0.36\frac{Z^2}{A} \tag{37}$$

Equation (37) is in good agreement with experiment but applies only over a small range of nuclei.

5.13   Comparison with Experiment

The potential energy of deformation of a drop or of a nucleus is characterized by the fissionability parameter defined in Eq. (31b). From this the threshold energy can be calculated using Eqs. (33) and (34c). Bohr and Wheeler in their paper indicated agreement of theory with experiment. The calculations from Eq. (34c) have been carried to the sixth power in χ. Table 5-2[17] shows that the agreement is poor. This discrepancy indicates that the threshold energy is not as sensitive to changes in χ

as one might expect. Also, even though values are derived from classical considerations, the quantum mechanical corrections are not likely to change the results appreciably. It seems clear from this large disagreement that the saddle-point energy represented by E_f for the liquid drop is not the threshold energy for fission.

The observed threshold energies are not a smooth varying function of χ as suggested by the theory. A major failing of the liquid-drop model is

Table 5-2 Comparison of Observed Thresholds with Liquid-Drop Model[a]

Nuclide	Z^2/A	χ	E_f (Liquid drop)	E_f (Exptl.)
Th^{233}	34.764	0.6939	15.58	6.44
Th^{232}	34.914	0.6969	15.08	5.95
U^{239}	35.414	0.7069	13.51	6.15
U^{238}	35.563	0.7099	13.06	5.80
Pa^{232}	35.696	0.7125	12.68	6.18
U^{237}	35.713	0.7129	12.63	6.40
U^{235}	36.017	0.7189	11.79	5.75
U^{233}	36.326	0.7251	10.96	5.49
Np^{238}	36.340	0.7254	10.92	6.04
Np^{237}	36.494	0.7285	10.53	5.49
Pu^{239}	36.971	0.7380	9.39	5.48

[a] The height of the saddle point E_f is computed through sixth order in $(1 - \chi)$. The observed thresholds, E_f (Exptl.), are deduced from photo- and neutron-induced fission (Wilets[17]).

that it does not predict asymmetric fission. This model will hold only when the energy of the bombarding neutrons is very high.

One result predicted by the liquid-drop model is that when $\chi \approx 1$ the nucleus is unstable against nuclear fission. There are no naturally occurring nuclides for which $\chi \approx 1$. In fact, U^{238} which is the heaviest nuclide in nature has $\chi \approx 0.72$. This suggests that the threshold barrier is very effective in preventing spontaneous fission.

5.14 Statistical Model of Fission

Fong[27] has proposed a theory for fission which predicts the asymmetric nature of the process. The theory is based upon the statistical model of the compound nucleus. We shall outline here a simplified version of the theory also due to Fong.[28] The probability of a fission mode is assumed to be proportional to the density of quantum states. To calculate the density of quantum states we approximate the nuclear configuration corresponding to a mode of fission specified by mass splitting, $A_1 : A_2$, by two spherical nuclei of mass numbers A_1 and A_2 in static contact, each excited by an energy E_1 and E_2, respectively. The density of quantum states of such a two-nucleus system is proportional to the level density of each component nucleus and thus proportional to their product. For the level density of a nucleus of mass number A excited by energy E, we use the following formula:

$$W_0(E) = C \exp\left(2\sqrt{aE}\right) \tag{38}$$

The parameters a and C are, of course, dependent on A. From analysis of nuclei in the region of fission fragments, Fong found that $a = 0.050\,A$ and $C = 0.38e^{-0.005A}$. Subscripts 1 and 2 will be used to indicate quantities relating to the light and the heavy fragments, respectively. Thus the density of quantum states of the two-nucleus sytem is given by

$$N \sim C_1 \exp\left(2\sqrt{a_1 E_1}\right) \cdot C_2 \exp\left(2\sqrt{a_2 E_2}\right) \tag{39}$$

Because the two fragments are formed in contact they must have equal nuclear temperature T. According to the statistical model of nuclei, we have

$$E_1 : E_2 = a_1 T^2 : a_2 T^2 = a_1 : a_2 \tag{40}$$

Denoting the total excitation energy (sum of E_1 and E_2) by E, we can write Eq. (38) by using Eq. (39) as follows

$$N \sim C_1 C_2 \exp\left[2\sqrt{(a_1 + a_2)E}\right] \tag{41a}$$

In particular, we have for symmetric fission, using subscript o to indicate quantities relating to symmetric fission,

$$N_o \sim C_o C_o \exp\left[2\sqrt{(a_o + a_o)E_o}\right] \tag{41b}$$

Since the parameter a is proportional to the mass number, we have

$$a_1 + a_2 = a_o + a_o \tag{42}$$

We assume that the ratio of probabilities of asymmetric to symmetric fission P/P_o is equal to N/N_o. Thus we have

$$\frac{P}{P_o} = \frac{C_1 C_2}{C_o C_o} \exp\left[2\sqrt{2a_o}\left(\sqrt{E} - \sqrt{E_o}\right)\right] \tag{43}$$

In general, the ratio of probabilities of any two modes A and B is

$$\frac{P_A}{P_B} = \frac{(C_1 C_2)_A}{(C_1 C_2)_B} \exp\left[2\sqrt{2a_o}\left(\sqrt{E_A} - \sqrt{E_B}\right)\right] \tag{44}$$

Since C_1 and C_2 are slowly varying parameters, they can be neglected compared to the rapidly varying exponential factor. Thus the probability of any fission mode is determined solely by the value of its total excitation energy E. Because of this exponential dependence, a small change in E can result in a large change in probability.

The value of E is determined by the following equation expressing energy conservation:

$$E = M^*(A, Z) - M(A_1, Z_1) - M(A_2, Z_2) - K - D \qquad (45)$$

where $M^*(A, Z)$ is the mass of the excited compound nucleus undergoing fission, $M(A_1, Z_1)$ and $M(A_2, Z_2)$ are masses of the primary fission fragments in their ground states, K is the total kinetic energy of the fragments, and D is the total deformation energy of the fragments. The deformation energy is introduced because the nascent fission fragments are deformed. The value of D depends on A_1, A_2, Z_1, Z_2, and K. Equation (45) shows that the excitation energy is different for different mass divisions, different charge divisions, and for different kinetic energy values. The corresponding density of quantum states (and the relative probability) is also different. Therefore, there will be a mass distribution, a charge distribution, and a kinetic energy distribution. This equation also shows that the excitation energy is different for different target nuclei, for different incident particles, and for different incident energies. Therefore, the relative fission probability varies with these fission conditions.

The accuracy of a quantitative theory along this line depends on: both the accuracy of the level density formula and the values of nuclear masses, fission kinetic energies, and deformation energies which determine the accuracy of the excitation energy E.

The experimental mass-distribution curve for thermal neutron incidence has two prominent peaks suggesting that asymmetric fission is preferable. Fong has derived the mass-distribution curve for $U^{235} + n^1$ fission and compared it with experimental results. The results of the comparison are presented in Fig. 5-17. The dots represent the experimentally determined fission products and the solid curve Fong's derivation. The agreement is most striking. Double peaks are illustrated in Fig. 5-17.

When fission is induced by high-energy neutrons, little of the energy goes into translational energy†; it consequently goes into excitation energy. Thus when the excitation energy is high, the small differences of the order

---

† A simple proof of the above can be given in the following way. Let m and v be the mass and velocity of the incident neutron and M and V those of the fissioning compound nucleus. From the conservation of the momentum, we find $V = (m/M)v$. Since M is very large compared with the mass of the neutron m, then V is small. Consequently, the kinetic energy of translation of the compound nucleus is small.

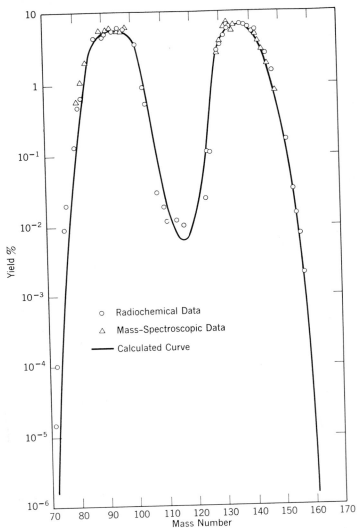

Fig. 5-17 Calculated mass-distribution curve of fission products of U^{235} induced by thermal neutrons, compared with experimental data (Fong[27]).

of a few Mev between the symmetric and asymmetric fission modes become less important. Symmetric and asymmetric fission will then have comparable probabilities.

Perring and Story[29] were not able to obtain a satisfactory fit to the fission data of Pu^{239} using Fong's theory. A four-humped curve was obtained from Fong's calculations instead of the observed two-peak curve. So Fong's theory has thus had only partial success. Furthermore, Fong's theory does not reproduce the fine structure that is observed in the mass-yield curve for fission of U^{235} with thermal neutrons.

5.15   Photofission

Bohr[19] proposed that the excitation energy of the compound nucleus appears mostly in the form of potential energy. At the saddle point (which corresponds to critical deformation of the unstable equilibrium beyond which fission can take place) the quantum states are widely separated and the nucleus is cold. The asymmetry in mass is determined when the nucleus passes the saddle point where one should expect rotational band levels 0^+, 1^-, 2^+, 3^-, . . . , which are characterized by antisymmetric wave functions. The compound nucleus will undergo asymmetric fission if it passes through any of the antisymmetric odd parity states. The photofission occurs through the 1^- channel by the absorption of an $E1$ photon. Sometimes fission may take place through the 2^+ channel by the absorption of an $E2$ photon.

Kivikas and Forkman[30] studied the symmetric to asymmetric photo-fission yield in U^{238} close to the saddle-point energy which is near the photofission threshold. The photofission in U^{238} was produced by photons of energies up to 6.56 Mev. The ratio of the symmetric fission yield to the asymmetric yield was ascertained by measuring the number of Cd^{117} and Ba^{139} nuclei formed in the fission process. Both of these are beta active and can be measured by the counter technique. The experimental results were then compared with the theoretical fission cross section near the threshold given by Halpern.[16] He deduced that the fission cross section σ_f was dependent upon a factor which measures the chance of concentrating an energy U_f on the fission oscillation. The cross section σ_f has been taken to be proportional to an integral over U_f up to the full nuclear excitation energy E_o. The expression used by Kivikas and Forkman[30] was obtained from the calculations of Halpern and is

$$\sigma_f(E) = \text{const} \int_0^{E_0} e^{-U_f/T} \frac{e^{(U_f - B_f)/E_P}}{1 + e^{(U_f - B_f)/E_P}} \, dU_f \qquad (46a)$$

where

B_f = fission barrier height

$$E_P = \frac{\hbar}{2\pi} \sqrt{\frac{K}{M}} \qquad (46b)$$

and where K defines the fission barrier form, M is the reduced mass of the

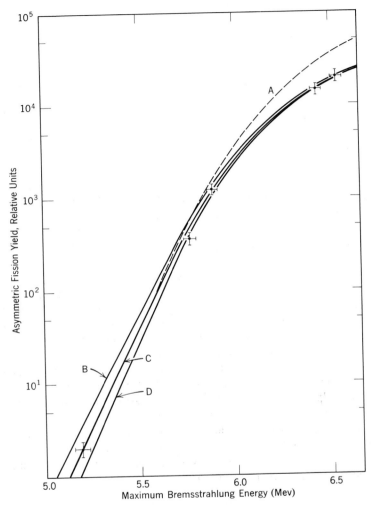

Fig. 5-18 Semilogarithmic plot of the asymmetric photofission yield as a function of maximum bremsstrahlung energy. Theoretical yields are given with the parameters (Kivikas and Forkman[30]). A: ($T = 0.6$ Mev; $B_f = 5.9$ Mev; $E_P = 85$ Kev), B: ($T = 0.6$ Mev; $B_f = 5.8$ Mev; $E_P = 90$ Kev), C: ($T = 0.6$ Mev; $B_f = 5.8$ Mev; $E_P = 85$ Kev), D: ($T = 0.6$ Mev; $B_f = 5.8$ Mev; $E_P = 80$ Kev).

two separating fragments, U_f is the fission oscillation energy, and T is the nuclear temperature. The first factor in the integral, $\exp\left(-U_f/T\right)$ in Eq. (46a), gives the probability that an amount of energy U_f will be concentrated in the fission oscillation. The second factor within the integral is the Hill and Wheeler[24] fission-barrier penetration factor. Below the barrier, $\sigma_f(E)$ varies steeply, and near the barrier $\sigma_f(E)$ is dominated by the term $\exp\left(-U_f/T\right)$ and is less energy-dependent.

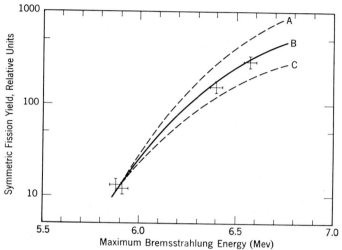

Fig. 5-19 Semilogarithmic plot of the symmetric photofission yield as a function of maximum bremsstrahlung energy. Theoretical yields are given with the parameters (Kivikas and Forkman[30]). A: ($T = 0.6$ Mev, $B_f = 6.0$ Mev, $E_P = 85$ Kev), B: ($T = 0.6$ Mev, $B_f = 5.9$ Mev, $E_P = 85$ Kev), C: ($T = 0.6$ Mev, $B_f = 5.8$ Mev, $E_P = 85$ Kev).

The asymmetric photofission yield as obtained by Kivikas and Forkman is given in Fig. 5-18, whereas the symmetric fission yield is shown in Fig. 5-19 with various sets of parameters. The formula given in Eq. (46a) describes both the symmetric and asymmetric fission yield rather well. For nuclear temperature $T = 0.6$ Mev, the best fit for asymmetric fission is obtained for $B_f = 5.80 \pm 0.05$ Mev which is roughly the same as $B_f = 5.90 \pm 0.05$ Mev for symmetric fission. The barrier form K is the same in both cases since E_P is about the same. It appears from the identical values of B_f and K in both cases that in symmetric fission the uranium nucleus passes over the fission barrier in the asymmetric valley as was previously noted by Johansson[31] and is different from the channel concept of Bohr.[19]

References

1. Evans, R. D., *The Atomic Nucleus*, McGraw-Hill Book Co., New York, 1955.
2. Blatt, John M., and V. F. Weisskopf, *Theoretical Nuclear Physics*, John Wiley and Sons, New York, 1952.
3. von Weizsäcker, C. F., *Z. Physik* **96**, 431, 1935.
4. Wigner, E. P., Quoted by E. Feenberg, *Rev. Mod. Phys.* **19**, 239, 1947.
5. Brandt, R., F. Werner, W. Wakano, R. Fuller, and J. Wheeler, *Proc. Intern. Conf. on Nucleidic Masses*, University of Toronto Press, 1960.
6. Mozer, F. S., *Phys. Rev.* **116**, 970, 1959.
7. Green, A. E. S., *Phys. Rev.* **95**, 1006, 1954; *Rev. Mod. Phys.* **30**, 569, 1958.
8. Hahn, B., D. G. Ravenhall, and R. Hofstadter, *Phys. Rev.* **101**, 1131, 1956.
9. Seeger, P. A., *Nucl. Phys.* **25**, 1, 1961.
10. Levy, H. B., *Phys. Rev.* **106**, 1265, 1957.
11. Zeldes, N., *Proc. Intern. Conf. on Nucleidic Masses*, University of Toronto Press, 1960.
12. Green, A. E. S., *Rev. Mod. Phys.* **30**, 569, 1958.
13. Hahn, O., and F. Strassman, *Naturwiss.* **27**, 11, 1939.
14. Smith, R. K., R. A. Nobles, and R. L. Henkel, *Bull. Am. Phys. Soc.* **II, 2**, 196, 1957.
15. Hyde, E. K., UCRL—9036, University of California, 1960.
16. Halpern, I., *Ann. Rev. Nucl. Sci.* **9**, 245, 1959.
17. Wilets, L., *Theories of Nuclear Fission*, Clarendon Press, Oxford, 1964.
18. Foreman, B., and G. T. Seaborg, *J. Inorg. Nucl. Chem.* **7**, 305, 1958.
19. Bohr, A., *Proc. Intern. Conf. Peaceful Uses Atomic Energy*, **2**, P/911, 151, 1955.
20. Cooperman, E. L., and R. R. Roy, *Phys. Rev.* **132**, 371, 1963.
21. Bohr, N., and J. Wheeler, *Phys. Rev.* **56**, 426, 1939.
22. Cohen, S., and W. J. Swiatecki, UCRL-10450, University of California, 1962.
23. Segrè, E., (Ed.), *Experimental Nuclear Physics*, Vol. II, John Wiley and Sons, New York, 1953.
24. Hill, D., and J. Wheeler, *Phys. Rev.* **89**, 1102, 1953.
25. Seaborg, G., *Phys. Rev.* **88**, 1429, 1952.
26. Frankel, S., and N. Metropolis, *Phys. Rev.* **72**, 914, 1947.
27. Fong, P., *Phys. Rev.* **89**, 332, 1953; *Phys. Rev.* **102**, 434, 1956.
28. The authors would like to express their thanks to Professor P. Fong for communicating to them the simplified presentation of his theory.
29. Perring, J. K., and J. S. Story, *Phys. Rev.* **98**, 1525, 1955.
30. Kivikas, T., and B. Forkman, *Nucl. Phys.* **64**, 420, 1965.
31. Johansson, S. A. E., *Nucl. Phys.* **22**, 529, 1961.

Problems

1. Find the Coulomb energy of the fragments Mo^{95} and La^{139} formed in the fission of $U^{235} + n$ (thermal).

2. Consider a nucleus undergoing fission into two fragments. Assuming the semi-empirical mass formula (neglecting pairing energy, shell effect, etc.), show that:

(a) the most probable division is into two symmetric fragments; and

(b) spontaneous fission is possible for values of $Z^2/A \geq 18$ (see Ref. 17).

3. Assuming symmetric fission, make a plot of potential energy (Mev) versus r, the distance of separation of the two fragments. For this purpose neglect the effect of prompt neutrons, γ-rays, etc.

4. Examine the change in the binding energy $B(A, Z)$ as a result of adding or removing a neutron or a proton.

5. Find an expression for the fission width Γ_f, and approximate this near the threshold (See Ref. 21).

6. Discuss some properties of nuclei as obtained from studies of masses (See Ref. 12).

6

NUCLEAR REACTIONS I: COMPOUND NUCLEUS AND STATISTICAL MODEL

Since Rutherford's discovery of the nuclear reaction process, a large amount of literature has been published. Formerly, the investigations were limited to establishing the process in various elements. The projectiles used were alpha particles from natural radioactive substances. However, with the advent of the high-energy accelerating machines, such as the Cockroft-Walton generator, Van de Graaff generator, and the cyclotron, the high-energy bombarding particles, protons, deuterons, alpha particles, and neutrons, are used to produce nuclear reactions in practically all elements of the periodic table. Studies on cross sections and angular distribution of the disintegration products, coupled with the various theoretical developments, have led to a better understanding of the nature of the nucleus and nuclear forces. In this chapter we shall discuss the theory of nuclear reactions to derive an expression for the cross section and then we shall examine the compound nuclear process. Examples of nuclear reactions will be cited to substantiate the various theoretical calculations.

6.1 Nuclear Reactions and Cross Sections

Consider a beam of neutrons incident on a Pb^{208} target. We may expect any one of the following processes to occur.

$$_{82}Pb^{208} + n \rightarrow {}_{82}Pb^{208} + n \quad \text{(elastic scattering)}$$

$$\rightarrow {}_{82}Pb^{208*} + n' \quad \text{(inelastic scattering, with subsequent emission of } \gamma\text{-rays from } {}_{82}Pb^{208*})$$

$$\rightarrow {}_{81}Tl^{208} + p \quad \text{(disintegration)}$$

$$\rightarrow {}_{81}Tl^{208*} + p' \quad \text{(disintegration, producing excitation in } Tl^{208} \text{ which then de-excites by } \gamma\text{-rays or conversion-electron emission)}$$

$$\rightarrow Pb^{209} + \gamma \quad \text{(capture process)}$$

$$\rightarrow {}_{80}Hg^{205} + \alpha$$

$$\rightarrow \text{etc.}$$

In the elastic scattering process, the initial and final states of the target nucleus are identical and the neutron emerges through the same channel that it entered. In all other processes, the channels are different and are characterized by their respective quantum states. The following expresses the total cross section of the process σ_T as composed of the scattering cross section σ_{sc} (including shape elastic and compound elastic) and reaction cross section σ_r:

$$\sigma_T = \sigma_{sc} + \sigma_r \tag{1a}$$

We next derive the expression for σ_{sc} and σ_r in the channel of the lth partial wave. To avoid including the Coulomb interaction, we confine our discussion to an incident neutron beam. The incident beam of unit density and of flux v described by a plane wave $\exp(ikz)$ along the z-axis can be written in the partial-wave expansion as follows (see Appendix):

$$e^{ikz} = \sum_{l=0}^{\infty} i^l (2l + 1) j_l(kr) P_l(\cos\theta)$$

$$\sim \sum_l \frac{i^{l+1}}{2kr} (2l + 1) \left\{ \exp\left[-i\left(kr - \frac{l\pi}{2} \right) \right] \right.$$

$$\left. - \exp\left[i\left(kr - \frac{l\pi}{2} \right) \right] \right\} P_l(\cos\theta) \qquad \text{for} \quad r \to \infty \tag{1b}$$

Equation (1b) contains both the incoming and the outgoing spherical wave. In nuclear reaction or scattering the amplitude of the outgoing spherical wave part of the plane wave is modified. The wave function $\psi(r)$ describing the outgoing wave after interaction is given by

$\psi(r) = e^{ikz} + \psi_{sc}$.

$\therefore \psi_{sc} = \psi(r) - e^{ikz}$

$$\psi(r) \sim \sum_l \frac{i^{l+1}}{2kr} (2l + 1) \left\{ \exp\left[-i\left(kr - \frac{l\pi}{2} \right) \right] \right.$$

$$\left. - \eta_l \exp\left[i\left(kr - \frac{l\pi}{2} \right) \right] \right\} P_l(\cos\theta) \qquad \text{for} \quad r \to \infty \tag{1c}$$

where η_l is a complex amplitude for the lth partial wave and is related to the phase shift by $\eta_l = |\eta_l| \exp(2i\delta_l)$. If $|\eta_l| = 1$, there is no change in the number of particles in the channel l and only elastic scattering will take place. If, however, $|\eta_l| < 1$, then both elastic scattering and nuclear reaction will take place. This condition holds for all values of l. If the incident particle is a charged particle instead of a neutron, the exponential terms in Eq. (1c) must be replaced by the appropriate Coulomb wave function. On the other hand, when polarization of the target nucleus and the existence of noncentral forces are taken into account, the factor $2l + 1$ must be replaced by a weighted sum over the magnetic quantum number m.

The elastically scattered wave function ψ_{sc}, which is the difference of Eqs. (1a) and (1b), is given by

$$\psi_{sc} = \sum_l \frac{i^{l+1}}{2kr} (2l + 1)(1 - \eta_l) \exp\left[i\left(kr - \frac{l\pi}{2}\right)\right] P_l(\cos\theta) \qquad (2a)$$

Consider a sphere of radius r_0 enclosing the scatterer; if r_0 is very much larger than the range of the nuclear forces, then the number scattered per second into the solid angle $d\Omega$ is equal to the number scattered through $r_0^2 \, d\Omega$, which is

$$N_s(\theta) \, d\Omega = \frac{\hbar}{2mi}\left(\frac{\partial\psi_{sc}}{\partial r} \psi_{sc}^* - \frac{\partial\psi_{sc}^*}{\partial r} \psi_{sc}\right)\bigg|_{r=r_0} r_0^2 \, d\Omega$$

$$= \frac{\hbar k}{m} |\psi_{sc}(r_0, \theta)|^2 \, r_0^2 \, d\Omega \qquad (2b)$$

where m is the mass of the incident particle. Hence the scattering cross section is

$$\sigma_{sc}(\theta) = \frac{N_s(\theta) \, d\Omega}{v \, d\Omega} = |\psi_{sc}(r_0, \theta)|^2 \, r_0^2$$

Using Eq. (2a) for ψ_{sc}, we obtain

$$\sigma_{sc}(\theta) = \frac{\pi}{k^2}\left|\sum_{l=0}^{\infty} \sqrt{2l+1}\,(1 - \eta_l) Y_l^0(\theta)\right|^2$$

Because of the orthonormality of Y_l^0, the total scattering cross section is given by

$$\sigma_{sc} = \sum_{l=0}^{\infty} \sigma_{sc,l}$$

where

$$\sigma_{sc,l} = \frac{\pi}{k^2} (2l + 1) |1 - \eta_l|^2 \qquad (2c)$$

We now derive an expression for the reaction cross section σ_r. It is determined by the number of particles, N_r, removed from the beam per second. N_r is the number of particles, in a sphere of radius r_0, which go into channels other than the entrance channel. It is calculated from the total wave function $\psi = e^{ikz} + \psi_{sc}$. The number N_r is the total net flux into this sphere and is thus

$$N_r = -\iint r_0^2 \, d\Omega j_r(r_0, \theta) = -\iint r_0^2 \, d\Omega \frac{\hbar}{2mi}\left(\frac{\partial\psi}{\partial r} \psi^* - \frac{\partial\psi^*}{\partial r} \psi\right) \qquad (2d)$$

Using the orthonormality of Y_l^0, we may write

$$N_r = -\frac{\hbar\pi}{2mik^2} \sum_l (2l+1) \left\{ \left[-ik \exp -i\left(kr - \frac{l\pi}{2}\right) - ik\eta_l \exp i\left(kr - \frac{l\pi}{2}\right) \right] \right.$$

$$\times \left[\exp i\left(kr - \frac{l\pi}{2}\right) - \eta_l^* \exp -i\left(kr - \frac{l\pi}{2}\right) \right] - \text{complex conjugate} \right\}$$

$$= \frac{\hbar\pi}{mk} \sum_l (2l+1)(1 - |\eta_l|^2) \tag{2e}$$

Therefore the total reaction cross section is

$$\sigma_r = \frac{N_r}{v} = \sum_{l=0}^{\infty} \sigma_{r,l} \tag{2f}$$

where

$$\sigma_{r,l} = \frac{\pi}{k^2}(2l+1)(1 - |\eta_l|^2) \tag{2g}$$

The total cross section is the sum of the scattering and reaction cross sections:

$$\sigma_{T,l} = \sigma_{\text{sc},l} + \sigma_{r,l} = \pi\lambda^2(2l+1)\{|1 - \eta_l|^2 + 1 - |\eta_l|^2\}$$

$$= \pi\lambda^2(2l+1)\{2 - \eta_l - \eta_l^*\} \tag{3}$$

When there is only scattering and no reaction, $|\eta_l|^2 = 1$. In terms of phase shifts, since $\eta_l = |\eta_l| \exp(2i\delta_l)$, this means purely real δ_l. In the case of any reaction, at least one of the δ_l is complex, so η_l has a magnitude of less than 1.

Since the number of outgoing particles cannot exceed the number of incident particles, it follows from Eqs. (1b) and (1c) that $|\eta_l| \leq 1$ for each l. Therefore the maximum value of $\sigma_{\text{sc},l}$ is obtained for

$$\eta_l = -1: \qquad \sigma_{\text{sc},l,\text{max}} = 4\pi\lambda^2(2l+1)$$

whence $\sigma_{r,l} = 0$; and maximum value of $\sigma_{r,l}$ is for $\eta_l = 0$, in which case $\sigma_{\text{sc},l} \neq 0$. There cannot be reaction without scattering. If particles are removed from the beam, it is as if there were added to the beam a scattered wave out of phase with the incident wave. The scattering and reaction cross sections can be represented diagrammatically as shown in Fig. 6-1, which indicates that although there cannot be any reaction without some scattering, there can be scattering without any reaction.

Consider a limiting case of a nucleus with a sharp edge of radius $R \gg \lambda$ so that a semiclassical discussion of trajectories is valid. We assume that

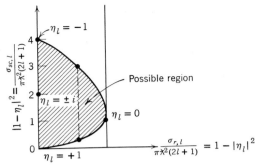

Fig. 6-1   Limits of scattering cross sections for a given reaction cross section.

If $\quad 1 - |\eta_l|^2 = \frac{1}{2}, \quad$ then $\eta_l = \dfrac{e^{i\alpha}}{\sqrt{2}},$

and α is real

For $\quad \alpha = 0, \quad |1 - \eta_l|^2 = \left| 1 - \dfrac{1}{\sqrt{2}} \right|^2 \simeq 0.09$

For $\quad \alpha = \pi, \quad |1 - \eta_l|^2 = \left| 1 + \dfrac{1}{\sqrt{2}} \right|^2 \simeq 2.9$

For $0 \leq \alpha \leq \pi$, cover dotted line in the figure.

all particles that strike the nucleus react. If the impact parameter is R_I, then

$$L = \hbar l = pR_I = \frac{\hbar R_I}{\lambda} \qquad \therefore l = \frac{R_I}{\lambda}$$

$$(l = 0, \lambda \gg , v \ll \cdots \substack{\text{LOW}\\\text{ENG}})$$

Therefore, all incident particles with $R_I \leq R$, or $l \leq R/\lambda$, react and all those with $l > R/\lambda$ pass by. The last condition gives $|\eta_l|^2 = 1$ for $l > R/\lambda$. For $l \leq R/\lambda$, the reaction is maximum, which corresponds to the condition $\eta_l = 0$. Then, since $R/\lambda \gg 1$, we find, from Eqs. (2f) and (2g),

$$\sigma_r = \pi\lambda^2 \sum_{l=0}^{R/\lambda} (2l + 1) = \pi\lambda^2 \left[2\,\frac{R/\lambda(R/\lambda + 1)}{2} + \frac{R}{\lambda} + 1 \right]$$

$$= \pi(R + \lambda)^2 \simeq \pi R^2 \tag{4}$$

Similarly, the scattering cross section is given by

$$\sigma_{sc} \simeq \pi R^2 \tag{5}$$

if the assumption is made that $\eta_l = 1$ for $l > R/\lambda$.

Adding Eqs. (4) and (5), the total cross section is

$$\sigma_T \simeq 2\pi R^2 \tag{6}$$

Equation (6) implies that σ_T is approximately twice the geometrical cross section of the nucleus for <u>fast</u> neutrons reacting with a large, totally absorbing nucleus. $\frac{R}{\lambda} \gg 1 \quad \therefore \; \lambda \ll , \; \lambda \gg \; \therefore \; HIGHENERGY \; NEUTRONS$

Equation (4) states that the reaction cross section σ_r is simply given by the geometrical cross section πR^2. This may be interpreted as due to the absence of any Coulomb interaction for a close collision of a fast neutron with a nucleus. Since any neutron striking the nucleus reacts, therefore the nucleus will appear opaque to a fast neutron. If the incident neutron beam is represented by a plane wave, then each nucleus should cast a shadow in the same way as an opaque disc in the path of a beam of light. Equation (5), known as the shadow-scattering (equation), corresponds to small-angle elastic scattering. <u>The equality of the reaction cross section</u> σ_r [Eq. (4)] and the scattering cross section σ_{sc} [Eq. (5)] implies that the <u>amount of energy absorbed by the opaque sphere is the same as the amount of energy diffracted by it.</u>

6.2   Resonance: Breit-Wigner Dispersion Formula for $l = 0$

The phenomenon of <u>resonance is observed</u> in nuclear reactions caused by the bombardment of nuclei <u>by</u> both <u>charged and uncharged particles.</u> <u>The resonance reaction is characterized by a sharp increase in the cross section.</u> The width at half maximum in the resonance cross-section curve <u>is correlated with the resonance width of the level from which the reaction products emerge.</u> A typical example[1] of resonance reaction for neutron-capture γ-ray is given in Fig. 6-2.

In our discussion, in this section, we consider only s-wave ($l = 0$) neutrons of low energy. We shall derive the Breit-Wigner formula in the neighborhood of a single isolated resonance level, ignoring the intrinsic spins of interacting particles.

In Chapter 3, we observed in (n-p) scattering for zero-energy neutrons that the phase shift δ is connected with the scattering length a_k and effective range r_0, the appropriate equations being given by

$$\lim_{k \to 0} \frac{\delta}{k} = -a_k \tag{7a}$$

$$k \cot \delta = -\frac{1}{a_k} + \frac{r_0 k^2}{2} \tag{7b}$$

We introduce $a(k)$ by defining

$$k \cot \delta = -\frac{1}{a(k)} \tag{7c}$$

for all values of k. <u>If there is no reaction, $a(k)$ is real.</u> For $\sigma_r \neq 0$, $a(k)$ is

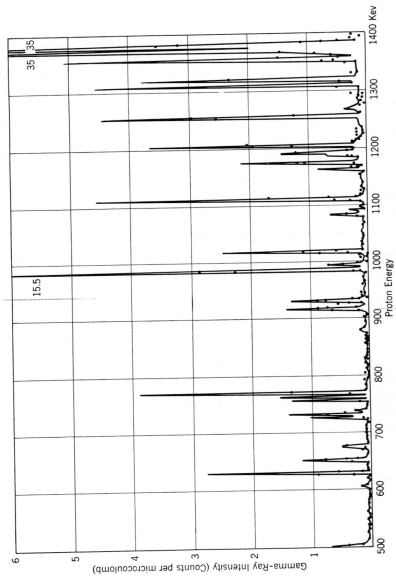

Fig. 6-2 Yield of the (p, γ) reaction in aluminum, as a function of the proton energy (Brostrom et al.[1]).

190

in general complex. By putting $a(k) = a$,

$$\eta = e^{2i\delta} = (\cos\delta + i\sin\delta)^2$$

$$= \left(\frac{1 - ika}{\sqrt{1 + k^2a^2}}\right)^2$$

$$= \frac{1 - ika}{1 + ika} \tag{8}$$

The scattering cross section σ_{sc} in Eq. (2c) and reaction cross section σ_r in Eq. (2f) are expressed in terms of the scattering length a by simply substituting the value of η from Eq. (8). Keeping in mind that $l = 0$,

$$\sigma_{sc} = \frac{\pi}{k^2}|1 - \eta|^2 = \frac{4\pi}{\left|\dfrac{1}{a} + ik\right|^2} \tag{9a}$$

$$\sigma_r = \frac{\pi}{k^2}(1 - |\eta|^2) = \frac{4\pi}{k}\frac{\mathrm{Im}\left(\dfrac{1}{a}\right)}{\left|\dfrac{1}{a} + ik\right|^2} \tag{9b}$$

For real a, σ_r in Eq. (9b) is zero.

We consider first the real a, in which case $\sigma_r = 0$. At resonance, the phase shift $\sim\pi/2$, so that we have

$$\frac{1}{a(E_0)} = 0 \tag{9c}$$

where E_0 is the energy at which the resonance occurs. Expanding $1/a(E)$ about E_0, we may write

$$\frac{1}{a(E)} = 0 + (E - E_0)\left[\frac{d}{dE}\left(\frac{1}{a}\right)\right]_{E_0} + \cdots \tag{9d}$$

We define

$$\left[\frac{d}{dE}\left(\frac{1}{a}\right)\right]_{E_0} = \frac{2k}{\Gamma_S} \tag{9e}$$

Limiting the expansion to the linear term and substituting in Eq. (9a) for σ_{sc}, we obtain

$$\sigma_{sc} = \frac{4\pi}{\left|(E - E_0)\dfrac{2k}{\Gamma_S} + ik\right|^2} = \frac{\pi\lambda^2\Gamma_S^2}{\left|(E - E_0) + i\dfrac{\Gamma_S}{2}\right|^2}$$

$$= \frac{\pi\lambda^2\Gamma_S^2}{(E - E_0)^2 + \left(\dfrac{\Gamma_S}{2}\right)^2} \tag{10}$$

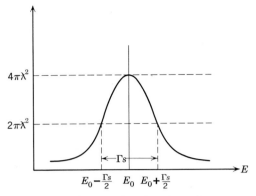

Fig. 6-3   This curve gives the schematic representation of the width Γ_s of a level of energy E_0 with a spread in energy of $\pm \Gamma_s/2$.

where Γ_S is defined as the width of the level from which the scattering takes place. It is the width at half maximum, as shown in Fig. 6-3. Equation (10) is the scattering cross-section formula known as the Breit-Wigner single-level formula. To derive an expression for the reaction cross section, we proceed as follows, keeping in mind that $a(E)$ is a complex function of the variable E.

Suppose $[1/a(E_0)] = 0$ for $E_0 = \epsilon_0 - [(i\Gamma_R)/2]$, where ϵ_0 and Γ_R are real. Expanding near E_0 we obtain

$$\frac{1}{a(E)} = 0 + (E - E_0)\left[\frac{d}{dE}\left(\frac{1}{a}\right)\right]_{E_0} + \cdots \tag{11a}$$

Let

$$\text{Re}\left[\frac{d}{dE}\left(\frac{1}{a}\right)\right]_{E_0} = \frac{2k}{\Gamma_S} \tag{11b}$$

$$\text{Im}\left[\frac{d}{dE}\left(\frac{1}{a}\right)\right]_{E_0} = k\alpha \tag{11c}$$

Then from Eqs. (11a), (11b), and (11c) and substituting for E_0, we obtain

$$\frac{1}{a(E)} = \left(E - \epsilon_0 + \frac{i\Gamma_R}{2}\right)\left(\frac{2k}{\Gamma_S} + ik\alpha\right)$$

$$= \frac{2k}{\Gamma_S}[E - E_R] + ik\left[\frac{\Gamma_R}{\Gamma_S} + \alpha(E - \epsilon_0)\right] \tag{11d}$$

where

$$E_R = \epsilon_0 + \frac{\alpha\Gamma_R\Gamma_S}{4} \tag{11e}$$

The cross section for scattering is given by

$$\sigma_{sc} = \frac{4\pi}{\left|\dfrac{1}{a} + ik\right|^2} = \frac{\pi\lambda^2\Gamma_S^2}{(E - E_R)^2 + \left(\dfrac{\Gamma_S + \Gamma_R + \alpha\Gamma_S(E - \epsilon_0)}{2}\right)^2} \quad (12)$$

For sharp resonance, α is small, so that near resonance, $\alpha(E - \epsilon_0)$ is very small. Therefore Eq. (12) is often written as

$$\sigma_{sc} = \frac{\pi\lambda^2\Gamma_S^2}{(E - E_R)^2 + \left(\dfrac{\Gamma_S + \Gamma_R}{2}\right)^2} \qquad \checkmark \quad l \qquad (13)$$

By substituting Eq. (11d) in Eq. (9b), we have

$$\sigma_r = \frac{\pi\lambda^2[\Gamma_R\Gamma_S + \Gamma_S^2\alpha(E - \epsilon_0)]}{(E - E_R)^2 + \left(\dfrac{\Gamma_S + \Gamma_R + \alpha\Gamma_S(E - \epsilon_0)}{2}\right)^2} \qquad (14a)$$

Again neglecting $\alpha(E - \epsilon_0)$, Eq. (14a) becomes

$$\sigma_r = \frac{\pi\lambda^2\Gamma_R\Gamma_S}{(E - E_R)^2 + \left(\dfrac{\Gamma_S + \Gamma_R}{2}\right)^2} \qquad \checkmark^2 \quad (14b)$$

✳ Equations (13) and (14b) are the Breit-Wigner formula for a single isolated level for neutrons and for $l = 0$.

The cross sections σ_{sc} and σ_r are determined by $a(k)$ whose physical description is not too clear. We shall therefore express the cross sections in terms of the nuclear radius R, and we assume that the nuclear forces are zero outside R. We can think of R as equivalent to the channel radius and composed of the radii of the target nucleus and the projectile. We still consider neutrons as projectiles with angular momentum $l = 0$. The radial wave function in terms of outgoing and incoming waves is given by

$$r\psi(r) = u(r) = u_{out}(r) + u_{in}(r) \qquad (15a)$$

where

$$u_{out}(r) = u^{(+)} \exp{(ikr)} \qquad (15b)$$
$$u_{in}(r) = u^{(-)} \exp{(-ikr)} \qquad (15c)$$

Since, outside the range of nuclear forces, the wave function is

$$\psi(r \geq R) = \frac{\sqrt{\pi}}{kr} \sum_l i^{l+1}\sqrt{2l + 1}\left\{\exp\left[-i\left(kr - \frac{l\pi}{2}\right)\right]\right.$$
$$\left. - \eta_l \exp\left[i\left(kr - \frac{l\pi}{2}\right)\right]\right\}Y_l^0(\theta) \quad (15d)$$

the radial wave function for $l = 0$ is

$$(r\psi)_{l=0} = u(r) = \frac{\sqrt{\pi}\, i}{k} \left[\exp\left(-ikr\right) - \eta \exp\left(ikr\right) \right] \tag{15e}$$

Comparing Eqs. (15b) and (15c) with (15e), we have

$$u^{(+)} = -\frac{\sqrt{\pi}}{k} i\eta$$
$$u^{(-)} = \frac{\sqrt{\pi}}{k} i \tag{16}$$

Now

$$\eta = \frac{-u^{(+)}(\infty)}{u^{(-)}(\infty)} = \frac{-u_{\text{out}}(R)\exp\left(-ikR\right)}{u_{\text{in}}(R)\exp\left(ikR\right)} \equiv \eta(R)\exp\left(-2ikR\right) \tag{17a}$$

where

$$\eta(R) = -\frac{u_{\text{out}}(R)}{u_{\text{in}}(R)} \tag{17b}$$

From Eq. (8),

$$\eta = \frac{1 - ika}{1 + ika}$$

We now define $a(R)$ as

$$\eta(R) = \frac{1 - ika(R)}{1 + ika(R)} \tag{17c}$$

so that

$$\checkmark \quad a(R) = \frac{1}{ik}\frac{1 - \eta(R)}{1 + \eta(R)} \tag{17d}$$

We note that

$$\left(\frac{ru'(r)}{u(r)}\right)_R = R\,\frac{-ik\exp\left(-ikR\right) - ik\eta\exp\left(ikR\right)}{\exp\left(-ikR\right) - \eta\exp\left(ikR\right)}$$
$$= -\frac{R}{a(R)} \tag{17e}$$

In expressing the reaction cross section σ_r in terms of $a(R)$ rather than a, using the relationship given by Eqs. (17c) and (17d), we obtain

$$\sigma_r = \pi\lambda^2(1 - |\eta|^2) = \pi\lambda^2[1 - |\eta(R)\exp\left(-2ikR\right)|^2]$$
$$= \pi\lambda^2(1 - |\eta(R)|^2) = 4\pi\lambda\,\frac{\text{Im}\left(\dfrac{1}{a(R)}\right)}{\left|\dfrac{1}{a(R)} + ik\right|^2} \tag{18}$$

The reaction cross section σ_r is a function of $a(R)$. Well below the resonance and far from the zeros of $1/[a(R)]$, we find that the reaction cross section $\sigma_r \sim \lambda \sim 1/v$. This is the well-known $1/v$ law.

The scattering cross section $\sigma_{\rm sc}$ in terms of $a(R)$, by using Eqs. (17c) and (17d), is

$$\sigma_{\rm sc} = \pi\lambda^2 |1 - \eta|^2 = 4\pi \left| \frac{1 - \eta}{2ik} \right|^2$$

$$= 4\pi \left| \frac{\exp(2ikR) - 1}{2ik} + \frac{1}{\dfrac{1}{a(R)} + ik} \right|^2$$

$$= 4\pi \left| \frac{\exp(ikR)\sin kR}{k} + \frac{1}{\dfrac{1}{a(R)} + ik} \right|^2 \tag{19}$$

The first term is the potential scattering amplitude whereas the second term is the resonance scattering amplitude. We recall from Eq. (9a) that $\sigma_{\rm sc}$ in terms of a, rather than $a(R)$, is

$$\sigma_{\rm sc} = 4\pi \left| \frac{1}{\dfrac{1}{a} + \dfrac{1}{ik}} \right|^2$$

(NO REACTION)

✱The potential scattering depends only on the nuclear size but the resonance *(REACTION)* scattering in addition depends on the internal details of the nucleus through $a(R)$. We have $a(R)$ given in terms of a logarithmic derivative, which should be continuous across R, and should therefore depend on the internal wave function.

For scattering resonances,

$$\left[\frac{d}{dE}\left(\frac{1}{a}\right) \right]_{E_0} = \frac{2k}{\Gamma_S} > 0$$

since $\Gamma_S > 0$. Hence, it follows from Eq. (11a) that below resonance, $1/a < 0$. For low energies,

$$\frac{\exp(ikR)\sin kR}{k} \simeq R > 0.$$

Therefore, from Eq. (19) we find that for low-energy scattering resonances, we have destructive interference with potential amplitude below resonance and constructive interference above resonance.

Away from resonance—near the zeros of $a(R)$—the denominator of the second term in Eq. (19) $\simeq \infty$, leaving only the first term to contribute to the scattering cross section. Under these conditions $[a(R) \simeq 0]$, Eq. (17e) gives $u(r = R) \simeq 0$, the boundary condition for an (almost) impenetrable sphere. Furthermore, at low energies ($kR \ll 1$) Eq. (19) gives

$\sigma_{\rm sc} \simeq (4\pi/k^2) \sin^2 kR \simeq 4\pi R^2$, the potential scattering for a rigid sphere. Phenomenologically, then, potential or "hard sphere" scattering represents the external portion of the total scattering as given by Eq. (19). The facts that $u(R) \simeq 0$ and that $u(r)$ and $u'(r)$ are continuous across the nuclear surface $r = R$ mean that the amplitude of $u(r)$ inside the nuclear surface is much reduced from that of the incident neutron. Thus the behavior of the total scattering cross section between resonance is very similar to that of a hard sphere.

From the first term of Eq. (19), we see that potential scattering, being a function of R, can give information regarding the size of the nucleus.

Near resonance $a(R)$ is very large, and the second term of Eq. (19) predominates. In this case Eq. (17e) dictates that the wave function of the incident neutron must match up with the internal wave function in such a way that $u'(R) = 0$. This in turn indicates that the amplitude of the incident neutron wave is a maximum at the surface, and the continuity conditions require the same of the internal wave function; that is, at some exceptional wave number corresponding to the resonance energy E_0, there is suddenly a large probability of the neutron beam penetrating the nucleus and interacting with the many nucleons inside the nucleus—hence the labeling of resonance scattering as an internal effect. Evidently resonance scattering can be considered a tunnel effect or a resonant penetration of the nuclear barrier resulting in the interaction of the target with a single isolated level.

The exact relationship of resonance scattering to the internal details of the nucleus is implicit in $a(R)$. In Eq. (17e), large $a(R)$ implies large $u(r)$—at least near the nuclear surface. At the relatively low energies where resonances occur, the nuclear energy levels are distinctly separated and a large wave function means a high probability of finding a particle at the energy E_0 associated with that wave function. Thus when an incident neutron at energy E_0 enters the nucleus, it finds itself at one of the nuclear energy levels and is strongly absorbed.

6.3 Breit-Wigner Dispersion Formula for all Values of l

The Breit-Wigner theory is worked out in terms of the logarithmic derivative f_l of the wave function evaluated at $r = R$ where R may be associated with the radius of the nuclear surface, which for this purpose may be assumed to be sharp. We define the complex logarithmic derivative f_l by

$$f_l = R\left(\frac{1}{u_l}\frac{du_l}{dr}\right)_{r=R} \tag{20a}$$

where u_l satisfies the potential-free Schrödinger equation

$$\frac{d^2 u_l}{dr^2} + \left(k^2 - \frac{l(l+1)}{r^2}\right) u_l(r) = 0 \tag{20b}$$

and is a superposition of the outgoing and incoming radial functions $u_l^{(+)}$ and $u_l^{(-)}$.

$$u_l(r) = a_+ u_l^{(+)}(r) + a_- u_l^{(-)}(r) \tag{20c}$$

$u_l^{(\pm)}$ are given by

$$
\begin{aligned}
u_l^{(\pm)}(r) &= \pm ikr[j_l(kr) \pm in_l(kr)] \\
&= ikr \begin{cases} h_l^{(1)}(kr) \\ -h_l^{(2)}(kr) \end{cases} \\
&\sim \exp\left[\pm i\left(kr - \frac{l\pi}{2}\right)\right] \qquad \text{for} \quad r \to \infty
\end{aligned} \tag{20d}
$$

$$[\text{For } l = 0 \qquad u_0(r) = a_+ e^{ikr} + a_- e^{-ikr}]$$

Comparing Eqs. (1c) and (20c), and using Eq. (20d), we find

$$\eta_l = -\frac{a_+}{a_-} \tag{20e}$$

From Eqs. (20a), (20c), and (20e), we can establish the relationship between η_l and f_l:

$$f_l = R \frac{a_+ u_l^{(+)\prime}(R) + a_- u_l^{(-)\prime}(R)}{a_+ u_l^{(+)}(R) + a_- u_l^{(-)}(R)} \tag{21a}$$

where primes indicate differentiation with respect to r. The logarithmic derivatives,

$$\left(R \frac{1}{u_l^{(\pm)}} \frac{du_l^{(\pm)}}{dr}\right)_{r=R} = S_l \pm iK_l$$

$$[S_0 = 0,\ K_0 = kR]\,, \tag{21b}$$

are complex, as is evident from Eq. (20c). From Eqs. (21a), (21b), (20c), (20d), and (20e), we obtain

$$
\begin{aligned}
\eta_l &= \frac{f_l - S_l + iK_l}{f_l - S_l - iK_l} e^{2i\xi_l} \\
&= \left(1 + \frac{2iK_l}{f_l - S_l - iK_l}\right) e^{2i\xi_l}
\end{aligned} \tag{21c}
$$

where

$$\frac{u_l^{(-)}(R)}{u_l^{(+)}(R)} = \exp(2i\xi_l) \qquad [\xi_0 = -kR] \tag{21d}$$

When we substitute Eq. (21c) in Eqs. (2c) and (2g) for the elastic scattering cross section and the reaction cross section, we obtain

$$\sigma_{sc} = \sum_l (2l + 1) \frac{\pi}{k^2} |A_l(\text{pot}) + A_l(\text{res})|^2 \tag{22a}$$

$$\sigma_r = \sum_l (2l + 1) \frac{\pi}{k^2} \frac{2K_l(f_l - f_l^*)}{[\frac{1}{2}(f_l + f_l^*) - S_l]^2 + [\frac{1}{2}(f_l - f_l^*) - K_l]^2} \tag{22b}$$

where

$$A_l(\text{pot}) = \exp(-2i\xi_l) - 1 \tag{22c}$$

$$A_l(\text{res}) = \frac{-2iK_l}{f_l - S_l - iK_l} \tag{22d}$$

$\bigstar$ $A_l(\text{pot})$ is called the "potential scattering" and corresponds to scattering by an impenetrable sphere of radius R. This follows because, for an infinitely hard core of radius R, we have $u(R) = 0$. Thus from Eq. (20a), $f_l \to \infty$, and therefore $A_l(\text{res}) \to 0$, leaving only the contribution $A_l(\text{pot})$ in the elastic scattering cross section; and also the reaction cross section $\sigma_r \to 0$ in this case. Generally, at low energies, $A_l(\text{pot})$ is expected to be small for $l \geq 1$ because of the centrifugal barrier. $A_l(\text{res})$ is identified with resonance scattering.

Resonance Condition

We next discuss the logarithmic derivative f_l, and hence the cross sections, as a function of energy. The f_l is a complex function of the energy E of the incident neutron. To obtain the condition for resonance, we consider the solutions inside and outside the potential region. Using the form of Eq. (20d), we can write these solutions as follows:

$$u_{in}(r) = A_{in} \sin\left[Kr - \frac{l\pi}{2} + \alpha(E)\right] \qquad \text{for} \quad r < R \tag{23a}$$

$$u_{out}(r) = A_{out} \sin\left[kr - \frac{l\pi}{2} + \beta(E)\right] \qquad \text{for} \quad r > R \tag{23b}$$

where α and β are complex functions of the energy. We assume that the potential $V_0 \approx 30$ to 40 Mev is a constant in the inside region $r < R$, and zero for $r > R$, so that

$$K = \frac{\sqrt{2m(E + V_0)}}{\hbar}, \qquad k = \frac{\sqrt{2mE}}{\hbar} \tag{23c}$$

From Eqs. (23a) and (23b), the logarithmic derivative is given by

$$f_l = KR \cot\left[KR - \frac{l\pi}{2} + \alpha(E)\right]$$

$$= kR \cot\left[kR - \frac{l\pi}{2} + \beta(E)\right] \tag{23d}$$

By equating the inside and outside wave functions at $r = R$,

$$\frac{A_{\text{in}}}{A_{\text{out}}} = \frac{\sin\left[kR - \frac{l\pi}{2} + \beta(E)\right]}{\sin\left[KR - \frac{l\pi}{2} + \alpha(E)\right]}$$

$$= \frac{kR}{\sqrt{f_l^2 + k^2R^2}} \frac{\sqrt{f_l^2 + K^2R^2}}{KR} \tag{23e}$$

Treating f_l as real, we find from Eq. (23e) that for $f_l \gg KR$, $A_{\text{in}}/A_{\text{out}} \sim k/K \ll 1$. But for $f_l = 0$, $A_{\text{in}}/A_{\text{out}} = 1$, and the neutron wave has penetrated inside the nucleus by the maximum amount. Thus the energy at which f_l vanishes corresponds to "resonance." Formally, the resonance energy E_r is defined by the equation

$$\text{Re}\,[f_l(E_r^l)] = 0 \tag{24a}$$

Expanding $f_l(E)$ about $E = E_r^l$, we have

$$f_l(E) = i\,\text{Im}\,f_l(E_r^l) + (E - E_r^l)\left(\frac{\partial f_l}{\partial E}\right)_{E=E_r^l} + \cdots \tag{24b}$$

Substituting Eq. (24b) into Eq. (22d), we obtain

$$A_l(\text{res}) = \frac{i\Gamma_\alpha}{E - E_{\text{res}}^l + \dfrac{i}{2}\Gamma} \tag{25a}$$

where

$$\Gamma_\alpha = \frac{-2K_l}{(\partial f_l/\partial E)_{E=E_r^l}}, \qquad \Gamma_r = \frac{2\,\text{Im}\,f_l(E_r^l)}{(\partial f_l/\partial E)_{E=E_r^l}} \tag{25b}$$

$$\Gamma = \Gamma_\alpha + \Gamma_r \tag{25c}$$

$$E_{\text{res}}^l = E_r^l + \frac{S_l}{(\partial f_l/\partial E)_{E=E_r^l}} \tag{25d}$$

Γ is the total width and Γ_r is the reaction width. E_{res}^l is the actual resonance energy which differs from the formal resonance energy by a small amount

$$\frac{S_l}{\left(\dfrac{\partial f_l}{\partial E}\right)_{E=E}}$$

(equal to zero for $l = 0$).

From Eqs. (25a), (22a), and (22b), the expressions for the elastic and reaction cross sections are given by

$$\sigma_{sc}^{(0)} = \frac{\pi}{k^2} \left| [\exp(-2ikR) - 1] + \frac{i\Gamma_\alpha}{E - E_{res}^0 + \frac{i\Gamma}{2}} \right|^2 \qquad \text{for } l = 0 \quad (26a)$$

$$\sigma_{sc}^{(l)} = (2l + 1) \frac{\pi}{k^2} \frac{\Gamma_\alpha^2}{(E - E_{res}^l)^2 + \left(\frac{\Gamma}{2}\right)^2} \qquad \text{for } l \geq 1 \quad (26b)$$

$$\sigma_r^{(l)} = (2l + 1) \frac{\pi}{k^2} \frac{\Gamma_\alpha \Gamma_r}{(E - E_{res}^l)^2 + \left(\frac{\Gamma}{2}\right)^2} \qquad (26c)$$

where, in $\sigma_{sc}^{(l)}$, the potential scattering term is dropped and, in $\sigma_{sc}^{(0)}$, use has been made of $\xi_0 = -kR$. Equations (26) are the Breit-Wigner one-level formulas. The reaction width Γ_r can be interpreted as the sum of all the partial widths except the incident channel width Γ_α.

$$\Gamma_r = \sum_{\beta \neq \alpha} \Gamma_\beta \qquad \Gamma = \sum \Gamma_\beta = \Gamma_\alpha + \Gamma_r$$

The scattering cross section $\sigma_{\beta \leftarrow \alpha}^{(l)}$ for scattering from the incident channel α into channel β is given by Eq. (26c).

$$\sigma_{\beta \leftarrow \alpha}^{(l)} = (2l + 1) \frac{\pi}{k^2} \frac{\Gamma_\alpha \Gamma_\beta}{(E - E_{res}^l)^2 + \left(\frac{\Gamma}{2}\right)^2} \qquad (27)$$

6.4 The Compound Nucleus

In 1936, Bohr proposed the compound-nucleus theory of nuclear reactions. According to this concept, the nuclear reaction takes place in two steps: (1) the incident particle together with the target nucleus forms the compound nucleus in which energy is shared among all the nucleons; (2) the compound nucleus then decays to the final products. Since the lifetime of the compound nucleus is much greater than the time taken by the incident particle to traverse the nucleus ($\sim 10^{-22}$ sec), it is assumed that the mode of decay of the compound nucleus is independent of the mode of its formation, except for the requirements of the various conservation laws. Therefore, to calculate the cross section of a nuclear reaction, it is necessary to determine the cross sections of the two processes, that is, the formation of the compound nucleus and its decay. The decay process can be treated statistically on the assumption that the probability of decay by the emission of different kinds of particles such as alpha, proton, neutron, etc, is the same. At low incident energy, the spacings of the levels are greater than the widths of the levels excited; consequently, the decay of the level will occur from the well-defined states of the compound nucleus. At low energies, the reaction is essentially an isolated resonance process. ✳ At high energies, however, the situation changes. Here the excited levels may overlap and the lifetime of the compound nucleus may be comparable with the transit time of a neutron through the nucleus; hence a departure from the compound nucleus concept may be expected.

In this section we shall limit ourselves to the low-energy region where the compound-nucleus hypothesis may be valid. Consider the reaction

$$x + X \rightarrow C \rightarrow y + Y \tag{28a}$$

According to the compound-nucleus hypothesis, the target nucleus X absorbs the incident particle x to form the compound nucleus C in which all the nucleons share the energy; then by the process of chance sufficient energy may be imparted to the particle y, which is then emitted leaving the final nucleus Y.

Since we are discussing low-energy processes, the intermediate state is well defined so that

$$\sigma(x, y) = \sigma_C(x) G_C(y) \tag{28b}$$

where $\sigma_C(x)$ is the cross section for the formation of the compound nucleus C by x and $G_C(y)$ is the probability that C decays with the emission of y, leaving a final nucleus Y.

Consider the case that the compound nucleus C decays with the emission of a different particle z giving the final nucleus Z, so that

$$x + X \rightarrow C \rightarrow z + Z \tag{28c}$$

and

$$\sigma(x, z) = \sigma_C(x) G_C(z)$$

For the same energy, angular momentum, and parity we assume the same $\sigma_C(x)$. Again, for the reaction

$$y + Y \rightarrow C \rightarrow z + Z \tag{28d}$$

we have

$$\sigma(y, z) = \sigma_C(y) G_C(z)$$

For the same compound nucleus, we assume the same $G_C(z)$.

Let the mean life of C be τ. The full width at half maximum satisfies the relation $\Gamma\tau = \hbar$. If $\Gamma_x, \Gamma_y, \Gamma_z, \ldots$ are the partial widths of the modes of decay $x, y, z, \ldots$, we can express the decay rate through the channel x by the relationship

$$G_C(x) = \frac{\Gamma_x}{\Gamma} \tag{29a}$$

where

$$\sum_x G_C(x) = 1 \quad \text{and} \quad \sum_x \Gamma_x = \Gamma \qquad (29b)$$

The mean lifetime of the decay modes $x, y, \ldots$ are

$$\tau_x = \frac{\hbar}{\Gamma_x}, \tau_y = \frac{\hbar}{\Gamma_y}, \cdots \qquad (29c)$$

Hence, we may write

$$\frac{1}{\tau} = \frac{\Gamma}{\hbar} = \frac{\Gamma_x + \Gamma_y + \cdots}{\hbar} = \frac{1}{\tau_x} + \frac{1}{\tau_y} + \cdots \qquad (29d)$$

Since the formation and decay of the compound nucleus are two independent processes according to Bohr's assumption, it is possible to find a relationship between Γ_x and $\sigma_C(x)$. From the theorem of reciprocity, we know

$$k_x^2 \sigma(x, y) = k_y^2 \sigma(y, x) \qquad (30a)$$

If there are intrinsic angular momenta for x, X, y, Y, we may write

$$(2I_x + 1)(2I_X + 1)k_x^2 \sigma(x, y) = (2I_y + 1)(2I_Y + 1)k_y^2 \sigma(y, x) \quad (30b)$$

Therefore, it follows that

$$k_x^2 \sigma_C(x) \frac{\Gamma_y}{\Gamma} = k_y^2 \sigma_C(y) \frac{\Gamma_x}{\Gamma} \qquad (30c)$$

or

$$k_x^2 \frac{\sigma_C(x)}{\Gamma_x} = k_y^2 \frac{\sigma_C(y)}{\Gamma_y} = k_z^2 \frac{\sigma_C(z)}{\Gamma_z} = \cdots = F \qquad (30d)$$

F is a function only of the state, that is, the angular momentum, energy, and parity of the compound nucleus, but independent of the channel. Therefore, from Eqs. (29a) and (30d) we may write

$$G_C(x) = \frac{\Gamma_x}{\Gamma} = \frac{k_x^2 \sigma_C(x)}{\Gamma F} = \frac{k_x^2 \sigma_C(x)}{\Gamma_x F + \Gamma_y F + \Gamma_z F + \cdots}$$

$$= \frac{k_x^2 \sigma_C(x)}{k_x^2 \sigma_C(x) + k_y^2 \sigma_C(y) + k_z^2 \sigma_C(z) + \cdots} \qquad (30e)$$

The validity of Bohr's hypothesis of the compound nucleus has been elegantly demonstrated by several experiments. In the following we discuss the experiment of Ghoshal[2] in which he produced the same compound nucleus Zn^{64*} with the bombardment of $_{28}Ni^{60}$ by alpha particles and

$_{29}Cu^{63}$ by protons. To produce the same excitation in Zn^{64*}, an additional 7 Mev was added to the kinetic energy of protons, that is,

$$E_\alpha = E_p + 7 \text{ Mev}$$

Thus,

$$c^2[M_\alpha + M_{Ni}] + 7 \text{ Mev} = c^2[M_p + M_{Cu^{63}}]$$

The reactions observed were

1. $_{28}Ni^{60}(\alpha, n)_{30}Zn^{63}$ 4. $_{29}Cu^{63}(p, n)_{30}Zn^{63}$

2. $_{28}Ni^{60}(\alpha, 2n)_{30}Zn^{62}$ 5. $_{29}Cu^{63}(p, 2n)_{30}Z^{62}$

3. $_{28}Ni^{60}(\alpha, pn)_{29}Cu^{62}$ 6. $_{29}Cu^{63}(p, pn)_{29}Cu^{62}$

Since the excitations produced through the two processes are the same, $G_C(x)$ is the same, for it depends only upon the excitation produced in the compound nucleus and not upon the mode of formation. Consequently, according to Bohr's hypothesis one should expect

$$\sigma(p, n):\sigma(p, 2n):\sigma(p, pn) = \sigma(\alpha, n):\sigma(\alpha, 2n):\sigma(\alpha, pn)$$

as was observed by Ghoshal. The results are accurate within 10%. It should be pointed out that Ghoshal's experiment was performed at high bombarding energies. The levels excited in the compound nucleus are more closely spaced and broader, and may partially overlap. In this energy range, since many resonance levels are involved, the variation of the cross section as a function of bombarding energy must involve many resonances. This is described by the continuum theory (Section 6.5). The theoretical treatment given here is applicable to low bombarding energy where the excited levels in the compound nucleus are discrete and widely spaced.

Consider the reactions $O^{16}(d, p)O^{17}$ and $N^{14}(\alpha, p)O^{17}$. These two reactions have the same compound nucleus F^{18} and the same final nucleus O^{17}. The former reaction was known[3] to decay by two groups of protons for a given excitation. In conformity with the compound-nucleus hypothesis, at the same excitation Roy[4] was able to observe two groups of protons through the (α, p)-reaction thus verifying that the mode of decay of the compound nucleus was independent of its mode of formation.

Similar confirmation was also made by John[5] in the heavy elements. He compared the excitation functions of (α, xn) reaction in Pb^{206} with those of (p, xn) in Bi^{209}. For the same excitation in the compound nucleus Po^{210}, according to Bohr, we should obtain

$$\sigma(p, 2n):\sigma(p, 3n):\sigma(p, 4n) = \sigma(\alpha, 2n):\sigma(\alpha, 3n):\sigma(\alpha, 4n)$$

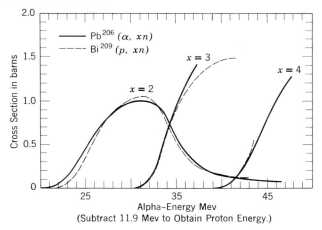

Fig. 6-4 Comparison of the excitation functions of $Pb^{206}(\alpha, xn)$ and $Bi^{209}(p, xn)$ (John[5]).

The experimental results which confirm this relationship are presented in Fig. 6-4.

6.5 Continuum Theory of Cross Section σ_C

The cross section σ_C for the formation of a compound nucleus is larger for neutrons than for charged particles. In the latter the Coulomb repulsion between the incident charged particle and the target nucleus is important.

In the medium and heavy elements, if the energy of the incident particle is large, then the individual level becomes broader and the levels are also more closely spaced.

The continuum theory of nuclear cross sections treats the individual level not separately but as an average over many resonances.

We shall consider neutrons with $l = 0$ as bombarding particles. Treated classically, the cross section σ_C for neutrons is merely given by the target area

$$\sigma_C = \pi R^2 \tag{31a}$$

where R is the radius of the nucleus.

Since the position of the particle is uncertain (quantum mechanically) by the amount of its wavelength $\lambdabar$, Eq. (31a) becomes

$$\sigma_C = \pi(R + \lambdabar)^2 \tag{31b}$$

Equation (31b) has to be modified by including the transparency T of the potential barrier. It is approximately given by

$$T = \frac{4kK}{(k + K)^2} \tag{31c}$$

where k = the wave number of the incident neutron

K = the internal wave number

Combining Eqs. (31b) and (31c), we obtain the cross section for the formation of the compound nucleus by s-wave neutrons,

$$\sigma_C \simeq \pi(R + \lambda)^2 \frac{4kK}{(k + K)^2} \qquad (32a)$$

For very small neutron energies, $k \ll K$ and $\lambda \gg R$, and thus Eq. (32a) becomes

$$\sigma_C \simeq \frac{4\pi}{kK} \qquad (32b)$$

The cross section for the formation of the compound nucleus for incident neutrons with angular momentum l can be obtained from Eq. (26c) and is

$$\sigma_{C \leftarrow \alpha}^{(l)} = \sum_\beta \sigma_{\beta \leftarrow \alpha}^{(l)}$$

$$= (2l + 1) \frac{\pi}{k^2} \frac{\Gamma_\alpha \Gamma}{(E - E_{\text{res}}^l)^2 + \left(\frac{\Gamma}{2}\right)^2} \qquad (33)$$

where α = incident channel

β = reaction channel

6.6 Statistical Theory of Nuclear Reactions

Nuclear reactions via the formation of the compound nucleus proceed as follows

$$A + a \rightarrow C \rightarrow B + b$$

where the incident particle a collides with the target nucleus A, forming the compound nucleus C which, after times much larger than the nuclear time (time of transit of a nucleon across the nucleus $\sim 10^{-22}$ sec), decays into B and b. According to Bohr, the incident and the target nuclei form a compound nucleus and the available excitation energy is distributed among the several particles of the compound nucleus in a completely random manner. After time $\sim 10^{-15}$ sec has elapsed, the excitation energy may possibly concentrate on any one particle which can then escape from the nucleus.

In light nuclei, the energy levels of the compound nucleus are generally well separated, that is, the spacing between the levels is much greater than the width of the levels (or the resolution of the measuring apparatus), and the theory of the compound nucleus can be described in terms of the resonance reaction. In the case of heavy nuclei, there are many degrees of freedom so the levels are relatively more closely spaced, and if the energy of excitation is sufficiently high, overlapping levels will be excited and the number of levels excited is too great for them to be treated individually. In such cases, using the other extreme method, that is, a statistical approach, may provide a good description. However, since the number of particles in the nucleus is finite and much smaller than the numbers required for the application of the laws of statistics, accurate agreement between theory and experiments is hardly to be expected.

In statistical thermodynamics the procedure is to employ the number of states per unit energy interval corresponding to the given energy E and to relate it to the entropy $S(E)$ of the system. We denote by $\rho(E)$ the density of states so that $\rho(E)\,dE$ is the total number of states of the nucleus within the excitation energy range dE. Then, according to the Boltzmann formula

$$S(E) = \ln \rho(E) \tag{34}$$

A more formal derivation of Eq. (34) is as follows.[6] We can define the thermodynamic free energy $F(\beta)$ of the nucleus at temperature $T = 1/\beta$ by

$$e^{-\beta F} = \int dE' \rho(E') e^{-\beta E'} \tag{35a}$$

We can invert the Laplace transform to obtain

$$\rho(E') = \frac{1}{2\pi i} \int_{\gamma-i\infty}^{\gamma+i\infty} d\beta e^{\beta(E'-F)} \tag{35b}$$

The above integral can be calculated by using the method of steepest descent (saddle-point method). The integrand has a saddle point at $\beta = \beta(E)$ given by

$$\frac{d}{d\beta}(\beta F) = E \tag{36a}$$

where E has been treated as an independent variable. We note from Eq. (36a) that

$$\frac{d}{dE}[\beta(E - F)] = \frac{d}{dE} S(E) = \beta = \frac{1}{T} \tag{36b}$$

where

$$S(E) = \beta(E - F) = \int_0^E dE' \beta(E') \tag{36c}$$

Equation (36b) corresponds to the usual definition of temperature in thermodynamics. After integrating, Eq. (35b) gives

$$\rho(E) = \frac{1}{\sqrt{-2\pi\, dE/d\beta}}\, e^S$$

so that

$$\frac{d}{dE} \ln \rho(E) = \frac{dS}{dE} - \frac{1}{2}\frac{d}{dE} \ln\left(-\frac{dE}{d\beta}\right)$$

$$= \frac{1}{T} - \frac{1}{2}\frac{d}{dE} \ln\left(T^2 \frac{dE}{dT}\right) \tag{37a}$$

which defines the statistical nuclear temperature. The last term in Eq. (37a) is negligible so that we obtain

$$\frac{d}{dE} \ln \rho(E) \simeq \frac{dS(E)}{dE} = \frac{1}{T} \tag{37b}$$

which is the same as Eq. (34)

It is now necessary to determine how the nuclear entropy S and the energy E of the nucleus depend on the nuclear temperature T. If we treat the nucleons in the nucleus as an ideal Fermi gas, similar to electrons in metal, we know that the thermal heat capacity $c = dE/dT$ is proportional to the temperature and therefore the energy E is proportional to T^2. Alternatively, if we consider the expansion of $E(T)$ at $T = 0$, then since

$$\left(\frac{dE}{dT}\right)_{T=0} = 0$$

(because of the Nernst heat theorem that the specific heat vanishes at $T = 0$), the first term in the expansion of E will be proportional to T^2. We may therefore write

$$E = aT^2 \tag{38a}$$

where a is a constant. The following expression for E which is a good fit of the experimental data is due to Lang and LeCouteur.[6]

$$E = \tfrac{1}{11}AT^2 - T + \tfrac{1}{8}A^{2/3}T^{7/3} \text{ Mev} \tag{38b}$$

where A is the mass number of the nucleus.

From Eqs. (38a) and (37b) we have

$$\frac{d}{dE} \ln \rho(E) = \sqrt{\frac{a}{E}}$$

or

$$\rho(E) \sim \exp\left(2\sqrt{aE}\right) \tag{39a}$$

which gives the general behavior of the density of states per unit energy interval $\rho(E)$ as a function of energy. An approximate result obtained by Ericson[8] is the following:

$$\rho(E) = \frac{1}{16}\left(\frac{\pi^2}{a}\right)^{1/4} E^{-5/4} \exp\left(2\sqrt{aE}\right) \tag{39b}$$

6.7 Evaporation Probability and Cross Sections for Specific Reactions

In statistical theory we assume that several states of the compound nucleus C are excited, that the mode of decay is independent of the mode of formation of the compound nucleus, and that there are several states of the residual nucleus B into which C can decay. Weisskopf[9] and Weisskopf and Ewing[10] have carried out the first calculations on the basis of the statistical model.

Let the energy of excitation of the compound nucleus C^* (where the asterisk signifies that the compound nucleus is formed in an highly excited state) be E_0. Then in the decay $C^* \rightarrow B + b$, we denote by E the energy of excitation of B, by ϵ the kinetic energy with which b is emitted, and by ϵ_{Cb} the binding energy of b with the compound nucleus C. Then

$$E_0 - \epsilon_{Cb} = E + \epsilon \tag{40}$$

The transition probability $w_{Bb \leftarrow C}$ per unit time for compound nucleus C^* to decay into B and b can be expressed in terms of the cross section $\sigma_{C \leftarrow Bb}$ for the formation of the compound nucleus C^* from B and b (reaction $B + b \rightarrow C^*$) by making use of the principle of detailed balancing. According to this principle, we have

$$|H'_{fi}|^2 = |H'_{if}|^2 \tag{41}$$

where H'_{fi} is the matrix element for the transition from the state i to the state f and H'_{if} is that for the reverse process. We note that according to the perturbation theory the transition probability w_{fi} per unit time is given by

$$w_{fi} = \frac{2\pi}{\hbar} \rho_f |H'_{fi}|^2$$

$$= \sigma_{fi} v_i \tag{42a}$$

where ρ_f is the density of final states per unit energy interval, σ_{fi} is the cross section for the process, and v_i is the incident flux. Combining Eqs. (41) and (42a) we obtain

$$\frac{w_{fi}}{\rho_f} = \frac{w_{if}}{\rho_i} = \frac{\sigma_{if} v_f}{\rho_i} \tag{42b}$$

With reference to the reaction $C \rightarrow B + b$, we use $i = C$ and $f = B + b$ so that $\rho_i = \rho_C$ and $\rho_f = \rho_{Bb}$. The density of states ρ_{Bb} is the product of the density of states ρ_B of B per unit energy range and the number of states in the momentum range dp into which the particle b can go. Particle b is taken to be free so that the latter number is

$$(2s + 1) \frac{4\pi p^2 \, dp}{(2\pi\hbar)^3}$$

where s is the spin of particle b. We therefore have from Eq. (42b) the result that the transition probability per unit time for the emission of b in the energy range $d\epsilon$ is given by

$$w_{Bb \leftarrow C}(\epsilon) \, d\epsilon = \frac{(2s + 1)m_b}{\pi^2\hbar^3} \frac{\rho_B(E)}{\rho_C(E_0)} \epsilon \sigma_{C \leftarrow Bb} \, d\epsilon \qquad (43)$$

where m_b is the mass of particle b and $\epsilon = p^2/2m_b$.

We define $\sigma_C(a)$ as the cross section for formation of the compound nucleus C through the incident channel a, and if w_0 denotes the sum of the probabilities of all possible modes of decay of the compound nucleus, then the cross section $\sigma_{Bb \leftarrow Aa}$ for the reaction $A + a \rightarrow C \rightarrow B + b$ is given by

$$\sigma_{Bb \leftarrow Aa} = \sigma_C(a) \frac{w_{Bb \leftarrow C}}{w_0} \qquad (44a)$$

where

$$w_0 = \sum_{B'b'} w_{B'b' \leftarrow C} \qquad (44b)$$

Combining Eqs. (43), (44a) and (44b) we obtain

$$\sigma_{Bb \leftarrow Aa} = \sigma_C(a) \frac{\displaystyle\int_0^{\epsilon_m} d\epsilon (2s_b + 1)m_b \epsilon \sigma_{C \leftarrow Bb} \rho_B(E)}{\displaystyle\sum \int_0^{\epsilon'_m} d\epsilon (2s_{b'} + 1)m_{b'} \epsilon \sigma_{C \leftarrow B'b'} \rho_{B'}(E)} \qquad (45)$$

where ϵ_m and ϵ'_m are the maximum energies available to particles b and b', respectively.

We may make Eq. (43) more explicit by introducing the statistical nuclear entropy and temperature. By using Eqs. (34), (37b), and (40),

$$w_{Bb \leftarrow C}(\epsilon) \, d\epsilon = \frac{(2s + 1)m_b}{\pi^2\hbar^3} \epsilon \sigma_{C \leftarrow Bb} \exp\left[S_B(E_0 - \epsilon_{bC} - \epsilon) - S_C(E_0)\right] d\epsilon.$$
$$(46)$$

We may assume $E_0 - \epsilon_{bC} \gg \epsilon$ since the compound nucleus excitation energy is usually higher than the kinetic energy of the particle emitted.

Also, if we assume that the density of levels in the compound nucleus and that in the residual nucleus are the same at the given energy of excitation, that is, $S_C(E) \simeq S_B(E)$, we have

$$S_B(E_0 - \epsilon_{bC} - \epsilon) \simeq S_C(E_0 - \epsilon_{bC}) - \epsilon \left(\frac{dS}{dE}\right)_{\epsilon=\epsilon_m=E_0-\epsilon_{bC}} \tag{47}$$

By substituting Eq. (47) in Eq. (46) and using Eq. (37b), we have

$$\begin{aligned} w_{Bb \leftarrow C}(\epsilon)\, d\epsilon &= \frac{(2s + 1)m_b}{\pi^2 \hbar^3} \epsilon \sigma_{C \rightarrow Bb} \\ &\quad \times \exp\left[S_C(E_0 - \epsilon_{bC}) - S_C(E_0)\right] \exp\left(-\frac{\epsilon}{T}\right) d\epsilon \\ &\simeq \frac{(2s + 1)m_b}{\pi^2 \hbar^3} \epsilon \sigma_{C \leftarrow Bb} \exp\left(-\frac{\epsilon_{bC}}{T_0} - \frac{\epsilon}{T}\right) d\epsilon \end{aligned} \tag{48}$$

where T is the nuclear temperature of the residual nucleus at its maximum excitation and T_0 is the temperature of the compound nucleus at excitation energy E_0. In the above approximations, the cross section for the emission of particles b of energy ϵ is independent of the energy of the incident particles a.

Equation (48) can be utilized to determine the ratio of the cross sections for reactions (a, n) and $(a, 2n)$ if the kinetic energy of the incident particle is below the threshold of the reaction $(a, 3n)$. We find that

$$\frac{\sigma(a, 2n)}{\sigma(a, n)} = \frac{\int_0^{\epsilon_m - \epsilon_{nB}} d\epsilon\, \epsilon\, e^{-\epsilon/T} G_B(n)}{\int_0^{\epsilon_m} d\epsilon\, \epsilon\, e^{-\epsilon/T}} \tag{49}$$

The upper limit for the kinetic energy in the reaction $(a, 2n)$ is less by an amount corresponding to the binding energy of the second neutron to the residual nucleus. Generally it is possible to take $G_B(n) \simeq 1$, assuming that neutron emission is predominant as soon as it becomes energetically possible, that is, if B is left in a highly excited state so that it can emit neutrons.

6.8 Experimental Results

In analyzing the results of compound nuclear statistical reactions, it should be carefully noted that the statistical model analysis of the experimental results is valid. Both direct and statistical processes may be present in the same reaction. The compound-nuclear reaction can be separated from the direct reaction on the basis of lifetime. The lifetime τ can be estimated from the measurements of the level width Γ since $\Gamma\tau = \hbar$. However, one practical way of separating the two processes is based upon the study of the angular distribution of disintegration products. The angular distribution of the emitted particle is symmetric* about 90° for the compound-nuclear reactions whereas in the direct reaction process (see Chapter 11) the symmetry is lacking. In addition, consideration must also be given to the level density.

For the reaction to be statistical, the compound system must involve many states and also the average level width must be larger than the average level spacing. The number of states involved should be large not only in the compound nucleus, but also in the final nucleus. There are many ways in which the experimental results can be compared with the predictions of the statistical theory of the compound nucleus—for example, angular distributions of disintegration products, energy distributions of the emitted particles, and excitation functions. The theories discussed in earlier sections have been refined by various workers, taking into account many detailed properties of nuclei. Hansen and Albert[11] compared their experimental results with theory, using modified forms[6,12] of level density expressions which took into account even-odd effects, pairing energies, and the angular momentum of the disintegration products. These modified forms are

$$\rho_{II} = \exp\{2[a(E + P_B(Z, N))]^{\frac{1}{2}}\} \tag{50a}$$

$$\rho_{IV} = [E + P_B(Z, N)]^{-2} \exp\{2[a(E + P_B(Z, N))]^{\frac{1}{2}}\} \tag{50b}$$

where $P_B(Z, N)$ are the pairing-energy parameters. The equations for the level densities are expressed in terms of parameters whose values have to be determined before any comparison with the experimental results can be made.

Hansen and Albert bombarded targets of V^{51}, Co^{59}, Cu^{63}, Cu^{66}, and Rh^{103} by protons of energies between 5 and 11 Mev. From studies of (p, n) and (p, p) cross sections in the above elements, they were able to compare their results with the predictions of the statistical model, as given in Figs. 6-5 and 6-6. The agreement between experimental results and prediction of theory is excellent. There does not appear to be any significant difference between the two theoretical values of the cross sections, calculated by using the level-density expressions given in Eqs. (50a) and (50b).

Blann and Merkel[13] studied the excitation function for the reactions $Ni^{58}(d, \alpha)$, $(d, \alpha p)$, $(d, \alpha n)$, $(d, 2pn)$, and $(d, 2np)$ and $Ni^{60}(d, 2\alpha)$ with deuteron energies in the range 0 to 24 Mev. They compared their results

---

* Assuming that the parity is conserved between the initial and final states, it can be shown (H. Feshbach, *Nuclear Spectroscopy*, Part B, edited by Ajzenberg and Selove) that the angular distribution involves Legendre polynomials of even l only.

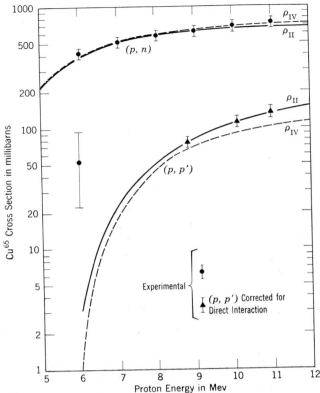

Fig. 6-5 Cross sections of $Cu^{65}(p, n)Zn^{65}$ and Cu^{65}-$(p, p')Cu^{65}$. The theoretical curves are calculated using $r_0 = 1.6F$ for the proton-reaction cross section and for the level densities

$$\rho_{II} = \exp \{2[a(E + P_B(Z, N))]^{1/2}\}$$

and

$$\rho_{IV} = [E + P_B(Z, N)]^{-2} \exp \{2[a(E + P_B(Z, N))]^{1/2}\}$$

(Hansen and Albert[11]).

with the statistical-model prediction with the assumptions that the nuclear-level density is

$$\rho(E) \propto (2J + 1)E^{-2} \exp [2(aE)^{1/2}]$$

The excitation energy E was corrected for pairing energy, and the parameter a was taken from an independent experiment. The analysis of the results indicated fair agreement with the statistical model of the compound nucleus.

Holbrow and Barschall[14] have studied the neutron spectra emitted from

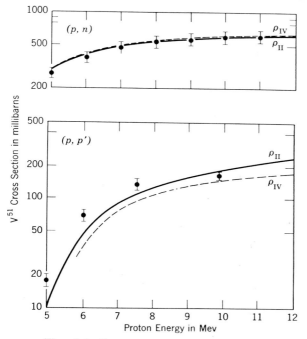

Fig. 6-6 Cross sections of $V^{51}(p, n)Cr^{51}$ and $V^{51}(p, p')V^{51}$. The theoretical curves are calculated using $r_0 = 1.5F$ for the reaction cross section of protons incident on V^{51} and $r_0 = 1.65F$ for the Coulomb barrier of the final nucleus. The level densities used are

$$\rho_{II} = \exp \{2[a(E + P_B(Z, N))]^{\frac{1}{2}}\}$$

and

$$\rho_{IV} = [E + P_B(Z, N)]^{-2} \exp \{2[a(E + P_B(Z, N))]^{\frac{1}{2}}\}$$

(Hansen and Albert[11]).

rhodium under bombardment by protons of energies between 5 and 12 Mev. The neutron energy E_n was measured by time-of-flight spectrometry. They compared their results with Weisskopf's evaporation theory,[9] from which the neutron spectrum $N(E_n)$ is given by

$$N(E_n) \propto E_n \exp \left(-\frac{E_n}{T}\right) \tag{51}$$

where E_n is the neutron energy and T is the nuclear temperature. Figure 6-7 gives the results of the comparison, showing $\log [N(E_n)/E_n]$ plotted against E_n. Excellent agreement has been obtained between the energies 7 and 10 Mev. The discrepancy observed at 11 and 12 Mev might have

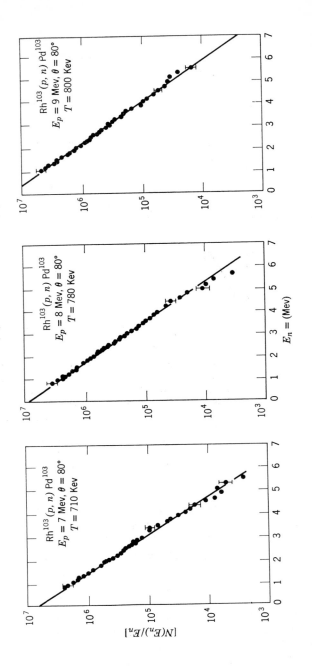

214

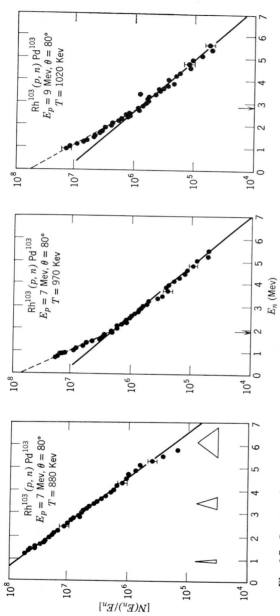

Fig. 6-7 Spectra of neutrons from the Rh(p, n) reaction at a neutron emission angle θ of 80° and at the bombarding energies E_p. Nuclear temperature T of Pd^{103} are given for each plot. The three triangles in the lower left-hand plot indicate the energy resolution of the spectrometer. The arrows indicate the maximum energy of neutrons from the $(p, 2n)$ reaction (Holbrow and Barschall[14]).

215

been due to the competing reaction $Rh^{103}(p, 2n)Pd^{102}$. This was thought possible because at the points where experimental and theoretical curves intersect, the energy of the neutrons corresponds closely to the neutron energy from the reaction $Rh^{103}(p, 2n)Pd^{102}$ which starts above 9 Mev. Another comparison with the statistical model can be made by studying the relative yield of the competing emitted particles, on which extensive data are available in the intermediate mass region. The relative widths can be expressed from the statistical formula for neutron and proton emission in terms of the residual proton density $\rho(E_p)$, neutron density $\rho(E_n)$, and inverse reaction cross sections for the two competing processes $\sigma(\epsilon_p)$ and $\sigma(\epsilon_n)$ as

$$\frac{\Gamma_p}{\Gamma_n} = \frac{\int \epsilon_p \sigma(\epsilon_p)\rho(E_p)\,d\epsilon_p}{\int \epsilon_n \sigma(\epsilon_n)\rho(E_n)\,d\epsilon_n} \tag{52a}$$

Equation (52a) can be simplified[15] by making an approximation. Expressing Eq. (52a) in terms of n-p separation energies S_n and S_p and effective height V' of the Coulomb barrier,

$$\frac{\Gamma_p}{\Gamma_n} = \exp\left[\frac{S_n - S_b - V'}{T}\right] \quad \text{and} \quad \sigma_p = \sigma_n\left(1 - \frac{V'}{\epsilon}\right) \tag{52b}$$

The separation energy can be calculated in terms of the difference between actual charge Z of the emitted particle and the charge Z_0 at the center of the stable valley for nuclei of that mass and by using the smooth properties of the nuclear-mass surface. Thus

$$\left.\begin{array}{l} M(Z, A) = M(Z_0, A) + \tfrac{1}{2}B(Z - Z_0)^2 \\ S_n - S_p = m_n - m_H + B(Z - Z_0) \end{array}\right\} \tag{52c}$$

B is a measure of the stable valley width. It is independent of Z, but in general varies with A. Substituting for $S_n - S_p$ from Eq. (52c) in the expression Eq. (52b) for Γ_p/Γ_n, we obtain

$$\frac{\Gamma_p}{\Gamma_n} = \exp\left[\frac{m_n - m_H + B(Z - Z_0) - V'}{T}\right] \tag{53}$$

where T is the nuclear temperature. In this expression no consideration has been given to the pairing correlations, which arise when distinction is made between odd or even nuclei, or shell effects. Bodansky et al.[15] have plotted the above expression of Γ_p/Γ_n as a function of proton richness $Z - 0.45A$. The data on proton yields are due to Allan[16] for neutron incident energy of 14 Mev and from Lassen and Sidorov[17] for alpha incident energy of 19 Mev. The results of the comparison are given in Fig. 6-8, where the neutron yields have been calculated from the total

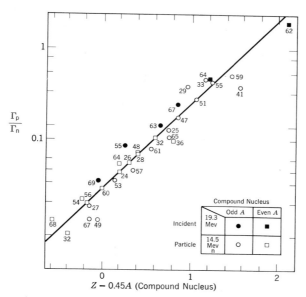

Fig. 6-8 Dependence of the ratio of proton to neutron evaporation probabilities upon the distance of the emitting nucleus from the center of the stable valley. The abscissa, $Z - 0.45A$, is a measure of this distance for intermediate-mass nuclei. The solid line represents an approximate empirical fit to points obtained mostly from data for incident neutrons and in part from data for incident alpha particles. (The mass number of the compound nucleus is given adjacent to each point) (Bodansky et al.[15]).

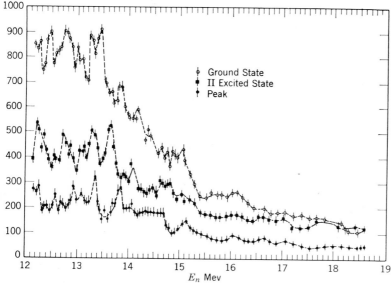

Fig. 6-9 Cross section in arbitrary units versus neutron energy from 12.15 to 18.4 Mev for $Si^{28}(n, \alpha)Mg^{25}$ (Colli et al.[18]).

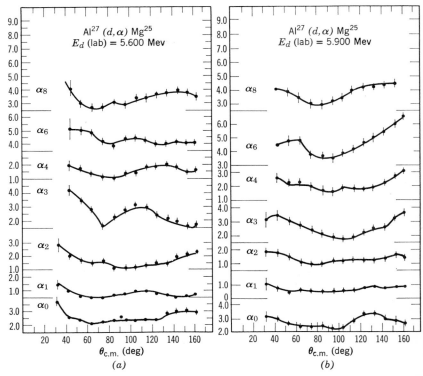

Fig. 6-10 Angular distributions taken at the following laboratory energies: 5.6 MeV(*a*), 5.9 MeV(*b*), 6.2 MeV(*c*), 6.5 MeV(*d*), 6.8 MeV(*e*), 7.4 MeV(*f*), 8.0 MeV(*g*). The beam energy spread was always less than 10 KeV. The α_0 to α_8 refer to the various groups of α-particles in the reaction and correspond to the excitations in which the final nucleus Mg^{25} is left. Summations of angular distributions over the different alpha groups and energies are given in (*h*) (Naqib et al.[19]).

cross sections. The ratio Γ_p/Γ_n from the preceding expression should vary exponentially with the proton richness as is also observed from the figure, thereby confirming the validity of the statistical model calculations.

We have stressed the importance of proper criteria to be used to analyze the experimental results. One of them is pertinent to the energy of the incident particle. If the energy resolution of the incident beam is of the same order of magnitude as the total width Γ of the compound nucleus, we observe the fluctuations, known as Ericson[8] fluctuations, in the cross sections of various transitions. One clear example[18] is shown in Fig. 6-9. The reaction studied was $Si^{28}(n, \alpha)Mg^{25}$ using neutrons of energy 12.15 to 18.4 Mev. The neutrons were produced by bombarding a thin target

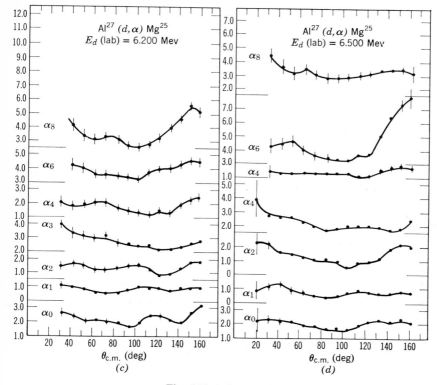

Fig. 6-10 *Continued*

of tritium with deuterons of energy 2.2 Mev obtained from the Van de Graaff generator. The energy fluctuation of the beam was 50 Kev between 12.15 and 15 Mev, and above 15 Mev it was of the order of 100 Kev. The three graphs of Fig. 6-9 starting from the top represent the state in which Mg^{25} was left in the ground state, 0.98 Mev state, and the unresolved states of 2.56 and 2.76 Mev. The energy spacing of the neutron group was in the region of 150 to 250 Kev. According to Ericson,[8] for large intervals of incident energy the fluctuation in the cross section is roughly given by

$$\overline{(\sigma - \bar{\sigma})^2} = \frac{\overline{2\sigma^2}}{n} \tag{54}$$

where $\bar{\sigma}$ is the mean value of the cross section and n is the number of final states. The experimental results confirm this relationship.

One of the criteria used to identify the statistical reaction process is the

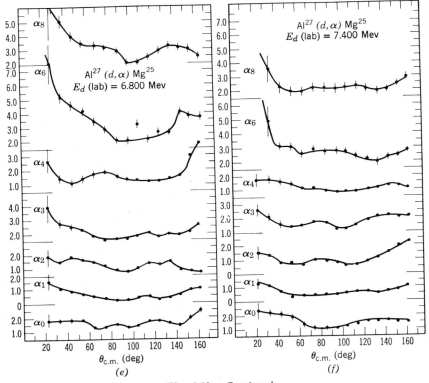

Fig. 6-10 *Continued*

symmetric angular distribution of disintegration products about 90°. However, this symmetry is destroyed if the energy spread δE of the incident beam is very much less than the width Γ of the level of the compound nucleus as is seen[19] in Fig. 6-10a to g. In this experiment, emission of various alpha groups was studied from the reaction $Al^{27}(d, \alpha)Mg^{25}$ with incident energy of the deuterons varying from 5.50 to 8.00 Mev. The energy spread of the incident beam δE was less than 10 Kev and the value of Γ was estimated to be 58 ± 8 Kev. On the other hand, if the cross section is averaged over a wide range of excitation energy of the compound nucleus or over many outgoing channels, the characteristic of the compound-nuclear statistical model—symmetry about 90°—can be obtained, as is seen in Fig. 6-10h. To obtain Fig. 6-10h, the cross sections for different alpha groups have been added for incident deuteron energy varying between 5.60 Mev and 6.80 Mev.

The cross sections of the nuclear reactions for the statistical process

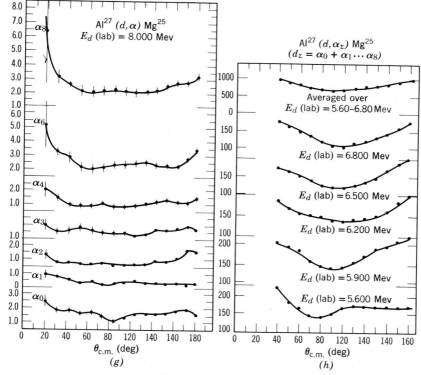

Fig. 6-10 *Continued*

diminish as a function of the bombarding energy since at higher energy many outgoing channels are available and the probability of decay through any particular channel diminishes. Thus the diminishing of nuclear cross section as a function of bombarding energy is also a characteristic by which one can separate compound-nuclear statistical reactions from other processes such as direct reactions.[20]

Another characteristic of the statistical reaction which has been observed is the so-called $(2I + 1)$ rule[21] which states that the cross sections in a specific nuclear reaction for the excitation of final states of spin I are proportional to $(2I + 1)$. It has been argued[22] that in order to observe the above proportionality the energy of the incident particles should be above the Coulomb barrier and that a large number of values of the angular momentum be involved. The above rule has been verified in many reactions. Naqib, Gleyvod, and Heydenberg[19] verified it in the reaction $Al^{27}(d, \alpha)Mg^{25}$ by studying the relative intensities of the different emitted alpha groups, which should be proportional to the statistical weights

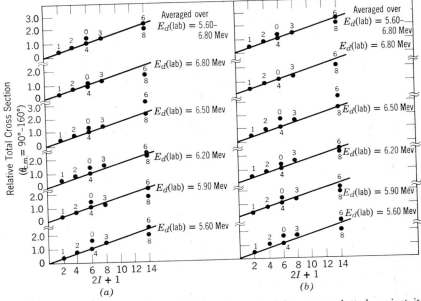

Fig. 6-11 The relative total cross section for each alpha group plotted against its statistical weight. Total cross sections were estimated by integration over $\theta_{c.m.} = 90°-160°(a)$ and $\theta_{c.m.} = 40°-160°(b)$. For the α_6 (triplet) and α_5 (doublet) groups the statistical weight was obtained by summing over the statistical weights of the members. A spin assignment $I = \frac{7}{2}$ was used for the third member of the α_6 triplet (Naqib et al.[19]).

$(2I + 1)$ of the corresponding residual states. Figure 6-11 gives the integrated cross section plotted against the total statistical weight for each group. The results indicate excellent agreement with the rule.

It was mentioned that the compound-nuclear statistical model requires symmetric angular distribution about 90°, but it does not necessarily follow that the angular distribution should be isotropic. In fact, if higher angular momenta are involved in the compound system, the angular distribution of the disintegration product may be anisotropic. This is evident from Fig. 6-12 (Bodansky[23]) plotted from the data of various experiments.[24] The illustration shows that the higher the angular momentum carried by the incident and outgoing particles, the greater the anisotropy, although the angular distribution is symmetric. The anisotropy depends on the angular velocity of the compound nucleus and may provide information on the nuclear moment of inertia which would be equal to the rigid body value according to the Fermi gas model.

Finally, we discuss the statistical parameter a. The value of a depends upon the mass number A. To calculate the level density in which the

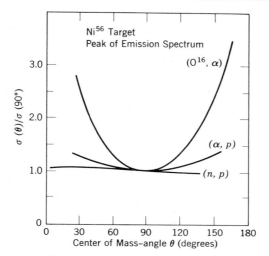

Fig. 6-12 Examples of anisotropies in the angular distributions of emitted particles. The reactions studied and the emission energies examined have been chosen to emphasize the compound-nuclear contribution (Bodansky[23]).

parameter a is involved, we must know the variation of a as a function of mass number. In the region of doubly magic number nuclei the value of a shows a dip.[25] Various level density formulas can be used to estimate a. Such calculations have been performed[26] using the expression of level density $\rho(E, j)$ due to Lang and Le Couteur,[6]

$$\rho(E, j) = \frac{6^{-\frac{1}{2}}}{2^{\frac{3}{2}} \times 12} \pi \hbar^3 y^{-\frac{3}{2}} g_0^{\frac{1}{2}} (2j + 1)$$

$$\times \exp \left(-\frac{(j + \frac{1}{2})^2 \hbar^2}{2yt} \right) \frac{\exp (2\sqrt{aU})}{(U + t)^2} \quad (55)$$

This formula represents the density of levels with spin for a given excitation energy E; U is the effective excitation energy and is given by $E + P$, where P is the pairing energy; y is the moment of inertia of the nucleus, and g_0 the average energy density of the less bound nucleons in the nucleus. The value of $a = (\pi^2 g_0)/6$. The parameter t is related to U and a by the expression $U = at^2 - t$. Experiments with neutrons indicate that $\rho(E)$ increases rapidly with increasing value of the mass number A.

Figure 6-13 gives the value of a collected from various experiments.[27] The experimental values of a are in agreement with the values calculated[26] from Eq. (55) for slow neutron resonances. The dip predicted from the shell model[25] can be seen for doubly magic nucleus $_{82}Pb^{208}$ from Fig. 6-13.

In conclusion, we may say that the statistical model gives a reasonably good description of nuclear reaction. However, valid comparison of experimental results with theoretical results can only be made when the final states involved are many, when $\Gamma \gg D$, and when the average value of the cross section over a large range of incident energies is considered. It is also necessary to make a judicious choice of incident energy so that

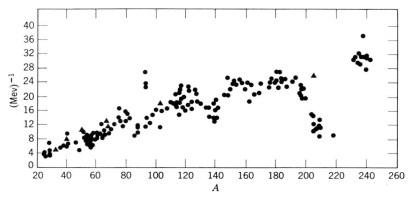

Fig. 6-13 Values of the parameter a obtained from resonances of slow neutrons and from neutron and proton spectra (Facchini[27]).

the statistical model is applicable. Before appropriate analysis can be made, other competing processes such as direct reaction must be separated from the data of the statistical process. The usefulness of the statistical model in the analysis of nuclear reaction data has been well established.

References

1. Brostrom, K. J., T. Huus and R. Tangen, *Phys. Rev.* **71**, 661, 1947.
2. Ghoshal, S. N., *Phys. Rev.* **80**, 939, 1950.
3. Pollard, E., and P. W. Davison, *Phys. Rev.* **72**, 736, 1947.
4. Roy, R. R., *Phys. Rev.* **82**, 227, 1951.
5. John, W., *Phys. Rev.* **103**, 704, 1956.
6. Lang, J. M. B., and K. J. Le Couteur, *Proc. Phys. Soc.* **67A**, 586, 1954.
7. Bethe, H. A., *Rev. Mod. Phys.* **9**, 69, 1937.
8. Ericson, T., *Adv. Phys.* **9**, 425, 1960.
9. Weisskopf, V. F., *Phys. Rev.* **52**, 295, 1937.
10. Weisskopf, V. F., and D. H. Ewing, *Phys. Rev.* **57**, 472, 1940.
11. Hansen, L. F., and R. D. Albert, *Phys. Rev.* **128**, 291, 1962.
12. Hurwitz, H., and H. A. Bethe, *Phys. Rev.* **81**, 898, 1951; Weinberg, I. G., and J. M. Blatt, *Am. J. Phys.* **21**, 124, 1953; Newton, T. D., *Can. J. Phys.* **34**, 804, 1956.
13. Blann, M., and G. Merkel, *Phys. Rev.* **131**, 764, 1963.
14. Holbrow, C. H., and H. H. Barschall, *Nucl. Phys.* **42**, 269, 1963.

15. Bodansky, D., R. K. Cole, W. G. Cross, C. R. Gruhn, and I. Halpern, *Phys. Rev.* **126**, 1082, 1962.
16. Allan, D. L., *Nucl. Phys.* **24**, 274, 1961.
17. Lassen, N. O., and V. A. Sidorov, *Nucl. Phys.* **19**, 579, 1960.
18. Colli, L., I. Lori, M. G. Marcazzan, and M. Milazzo, *Proc. Conf. Direct Interactions Nucl. Reaction Mech.*, 1962, p. 387, Gordon and Breach Science Publishers Inc., New York, 1963.
19. Naqib, I. M., R. Gleyvod, and N. P. Heydenberg, *Nucl. Phys.* **66**, 129, 1965.
20. Wolfenstein, L., *Phys. Rev.* **82**, 690, 1951; Hauser, W., and H. Feshbach, *Phys. Rev.* **87**, 366, 1952.
21. Enge, H. A., *Phys. Rev.* **94**, 730, 1954.
22. MacDonald, N., *Nucl. Phys.* **33**, 110, 1962.
23. Bodansky, D., *Proc. Conf. Direct Interactions Nucl. Reaction Mech.*, 1962, p. 230. Gordon and Breach Science Publishers, Inc., New York, 1963.
24. Knox, W. J., A. R. Quinton, and C. E. Anderson, *Phys. Rev.* **120**, 2120, 1960; Glover, R. N., and K. H. Purser, *Nucl. Phys.* **24**, 431, 1961.
25. Newton, T. D., *Can. J. Phys.* **34**, 804, 1956.
26. Erba, E., U. Facchini, and E. Saetta Menichella, *Nuovo Cimento* **22**, 1237, 1961.
27. Facchini, U., *Proc. Conf. Direct Interactions Nucl. Reaction Mech.*, 1962, p. 245. Gordon and Breach Science Publishers, Inc., New York, 1963.

Problems

1. Consider the nuclear reaction

$$A + a = B + b$$

where A, B are heavy particles, a and b light particles. Using principle of detailed balance, derive an expression for the ratio of the cross sections $\sigma(A \to B)$ and $\sigma(B \to A)$, in terms of the spins of A, B; a and b. (See R. Durbin, H. Loar, and J. Steinberg, *Phys. Rev.* **83**, 646, 1951.)

2. Show how to derive

$$T = \frac{4kK}{(K + k)^2}$$

3. From the relations

$$\frac{1}{T} = \frac{dS}{dU} \quad \text{and} \quad \rho(U) = \frac{\exp S(U)}{\left(2\pi T^2 \dfrac{dU}{dt}\right)^{1/2}}$$

and assuming that $U = aT^n$, show that

$$\rho(U) \propto \frac{U^{-1}}{\left(1 + \dfrac{1}{n}\right)} \exp\left[\frac{n}{n-1} a^{1/n} U^{1-1/n}\right]$$

(Hint: Assume that U can be represented as a power series in T and $dU/dT \to 0$ as $T \to 0$, then it follows that the expansion must start with a term at best quadratic in T.)

4. From the statistical model show that

$$\frac{\Gamma_p}{\Gamma_n} = \frac{\int \epsilon_p \sigma(\epsilon_p) w(U_p) \, d\epsilon_p}{\int \epsilon_n \sigma(\epsilon_n) w(U_n) \, d\epsilon_n}$$

5. Show that in a compound nuclear reaction, the angular distribution of emitted particles with respect to the direction of incidence is symmetric about 90°

6. Show that the average spacing between energy levels according to the statistical model of the nucleus is given by

$$D(U) = \frac{1}{\rho(U)} = T\left(2\pi \frac{dU}{dT}\right)^{\frac{1}{2}} e^{-S}$$

where $\rho(U)$ is the number of energy levels in range dU, U is the average energy of excitation of the nucleus, T is "nuclear temperature" in units of energy, and S is "nuclear entropy." (See Ref. 7.)

7. There are several methods to associate a temperature with a nucleus in an ideal gas law statistically, such as

$$E = aT^2; \quad E = \tfrac{1}{11} AT^2 - T + \tfrac{1}{8}A^{\frac{2}{3}}T^{\frac{7}{3}}.$$

Compare these using $A = 25$.

7

NUCLEAR MODEL I: NUCLEAR-SHELL MODEL

7.1   Introduction

In the early stage of its development, one of the main objectives of the shell model was to reproduce the so-called magic numbers. As more refinements were introduced, it was found that this model was capable of explaining not only the magic numbers but also many other nuclear properties such as spin, magnetic moment, and energy levels. The success of the model is astonishing and more so when one considers that basically the model is simple.

The first part of this chapter deals with the extreme single-particle model. In this model it is assumed that the nucleons in the nucleus move independently in a mean potential. Two cases, infinite square-well and harmonic-oscillator potentials, are considered in order to understand some of the properties of nuclei including the magic numbers. The addition of the spin-orbit potential eliminates some of the difficulties experienced with the above two potentials. Various experimental results have been successfully analyzed in terms of the extreme single-particle model.

In this model the properties of the nucleus are attributed to the single unpaired nucleon. A simple model such as this which describes the properties of many nuclei fairly well has also some exceptions in that the model does not explain some observed properties. Hence some refinements have been introduced in this model, and the single-particle model has evolved. Here the nucleus is visualized as consisting of filled shells that contain the maximum number of neutrons and protons permitted by the Pauli exclusion principle and unfilled shells containing the remaining number of neutrons and protons to form the particular nucleus. States of several particles are involved, and with this modification it is found that the nuclear shell model can explain many nuclear properties such as spin, magnetic moment, nuclear isomerism, and stripping reaction.

In contrast to these two models, in the individual-particle model (also known as the independent-particle model) all the particles in the nucleus are taken into account. In the treatment of this model, L-S and j-j coupling schemes have been introduced which provide a complete set of wave functions. The relation between L-S and j-j coupling schemes has been developed. The predictions of the model have been analyzed and compared with the experimental results of energy levels and binding energies of nuclei.

7.2   Single-Particle Potentials

In the single-particle shell model, the nucleons in the nucleus are assumed to move in a common (mean) potential. Most of the nucleons are paired so that a pair of nucleons contribute zero spin and zero magnetic moment. The paired nucleons thus form an inert core, and therefore the predicted spin and magnetic moment of even-even nuclei is zero. In the case of odd-A nuclei the properties of the nucleus are characterized by the unpaired nucleon, and for odd-odd nuclei by the unpaired proton and neutron.

To determine how the nucleons fill the various quantum states of the nucleus, that is, the spectrum of quantum states into which any one of the nucleons can enter, it is necessary to specify the mean potential to which each nucleon is subjected. Very strong experimental evidence exists which supports the point of view that when a nucleus contains 2, 8, 20, 50, 82, or 126 protons or neutrons—the so-called "magic numbers"—a shell closure occurs, that is, the energy level just above the shell-closure level is separated by a larger energy spacing than those within the shell (See Fig. 7-1). In a nuclear shell model attempts are made to understand this shell-closure property and predict electromagnetic and nuclear ground-state properties of the nucleus in terms of the uncorrelated motion of single particles in the specified mean potential. In the following we consider the level scheme predicted by (1) the infinite "square" potential well and (2) the infinite harmonic-oscillator potential well. In these two cases we can obtain an exact solution and they provide two contrasting viewpoints. The square well has an infinitely sharp edge whereas the harmonic-oscillator potential diminishes steadily at the edge. The nuclear potential is expected to be in between these two extremes and we desire to arrive at the correct single-particle quantum states by interpolating between these two. Actually, a potential which is intermediate between the square well and the harmonic-oscillator well and which also has an experimental basis, is the Woods-Saxon[1] potential obtained by fitting the data on nucleon-nucleus scattering. This potential, which is flat at the center and falls off smoothly to zero at the edge of the nucleus, is given by

$$V(r) = -V_0/[1 + \exp \mu(r - R)] \tag{1}$$

where $\mu^{-1} \simeq 0.5 \times 10^{-13}$ cm and $R \simeq 1.33A^{\frac{1}{3}} \times 10^{-13}$ cm, A being the mass number of the nucleus, and $V_0 \simeq 50$–60 Mev. For $\mu \to \infty$, $V(r) = -V_0$ for $r < R$, $V(r) = 0$ for $r > R$, and the potential corresponds to the square well.

For the Woods-Saxon potential, an exact solution cannot be obtained, and numerical methods are employed. In fact, even in the square well and the harmonic-oscillator well, solutions in terms of known mathematical functions are only possible provided the former falls off infinitely sharply and the latter extends to infinity. However, for the consideration of low-lying bound states it is not of great importance whether the wells are cutoff or not.

General Considerations for Motion in a Mean Potential

The eigenstates available to a nucleon of mass M moving in a (mean) spherically symmetric potential $V(r)$ are determined by the solutions of the Schrödinger equation

$$\left[\nabla^2 + \frac{2M}{\hbar^2}(E - V(r))\right]\psi(\mathbf{r}) = 0 \tag{2}$$

where E is the energy eigenvalue. The solutions can be given in the form:

$$\psi_{nlm}(\mathbf{r}) = u_{nl}(r) Y_{lm}(\theta, \phi) \tag{3}$$

where $Y_{lm}(\theta, \phi)$ are the spherical harmonics and u_{nl} is the radial function. The set of quantum numbers $n\ l\ m$ determines an eigenstate corresponding to an eigenvalue E_{nl} (which is independent of m and hence $(2l + 1)$-fold degenerate). The quantum number $n*$ is associated with the number of nodes in the radial function including a possible node at the origin, and l determines the parity which is odd (or even) for odd (or even) l.

Square-Well of Infinite Depth

In the infinite square well, the radial solutions $u_{nl}(r)$ which are regular at the origin are the spherical Bessel functions (of half-integral-order)

$$u_{nl}(r) = j_l(kr) = r^{-\frac{1}{2}} J_{l+\frac{1}{2}}(kr) \tag{4}$$

* Note that the n here has a slightly different meaning from the "n", or "principal quantum number" used in atomic physics. There, the number of nodes in the radial function is given by $n - l$.

$$k = \sqrt{\frac{2ME}{\hbar^2}} \qquad (5)$$

The energy eigenvalues are determined by the boundary condition at $r = R$:

$$j_l(k_{nl}R) = 0 \qquad (6)$$

that is, the eigenvalue $k_{nl}R$ is thus the nth zero of the lth spherical Bessel function j_l. The level l is $2(2l + 1)$ fold degenerate (the factor 2 being due to two spin states). The closed shells occur for neutron or proton numbers $\sum_l 2(2l + 1)$, with $l = 0, 1, 2, \ldots$, namely, at numbers 2, 8, 20, ... The spectroscopic symbols $s, p, d, \ldots$, represent the states $l = 0, 1, 2, \ldots$. In practice the lowest $l = 0$ state is written as $1s$. The $1s$ state can accept two particles, one with spin up and the other with spin down. The next state to be filled is $1p$ which has a capacity of six particles, giving altogether a total of eight particles in the well. After an energy gap, the $1d$ level is filled with 10 particles, making a total of 18 particles in the well. The magic number 20 is reached by filling the $2s$ state with an additional two particles. In this way, we find that the following sequence of levels[2] is predicted by the square-well potential of infinite depth.

$$nl(2(2l + 1), \sum_l 2(2l + 1); k_{nl}R) = 1s(2, 2; 3 \cdot 14),$$

$$1p(6, 8; 4 \cdot 49), 1d(10, 18; 5 \cdot 76), 2s(2, 20; 6 \cdot 28),$$

$$1f(14, 34; 6 \cdot 99), 2p(6, 40; 7 \cdot 73), 1g(18, 58; 8 \cdot 18),$$

$$2d(10, 68; 9 \cdot 10), 3s(2, 70; 9 \cdot 43), 1h(22, 92; 9 \cdot 36),$$

$$2f(14, 106; 10 \cdot 42), 3p(6, 112; 10 \cdot 90),$$

$$1i(26, 138; 10 \cdot 51), 2g(18, 156; 11 \cdot 71)$$

where inside the parentheses, the first argument gives the number of particles in the state nl, the second argument refers to the number of particles accumulating up to level nl, and the third number is the eigenvalues $k_{nl}R$ which are the zeros[2] of the spherical Bessel functions (Eq. 6). The magic numbers 50, 82, and 126 are not reproduced by the square-well model.

Harmonic-Oscillator Potential Well

The harmonic-oscillator potential is given by

$$V(r) = \tfrac{1}{2}M\omega^2 r^2 \qquad (7)$$

where ω is the classical angular frequency of the oscillator. By substituting Eqs. (7) and (3) in Eq. (2), the radial function satisfies the following differential equation:

where

$$\left[\frac{d^2}{dr^2} - \frac{l(l+1)}{r^2} + \frac{2M}{\hbar^2}(E_{nl} - V(r))\right]R_{nl}(r) = 0 \qquad (8)$$

$$R_{nl}(r) = ru_{nl}(r) \qquad (9)$$

Here, n signifies the number of nodes in $R_{nl}(r)$, including the one at the origin. The solutions of Eq. (8) are given by

$$R_{nl}(r) = N_{nl}\exp\left(-\tfrac{1}{2}\nu r^2\right)r^{l+1}v_{nl}(r) \qquad (10)$$

where $\nu = (M\omega)/\hbar$ and $v_{nl}(r)$ is the associated Laguerre polynomial

$$v_{nl}(r) = L_{n+l-\frac{1}{2}}^{l+\frac{1}{2}}(\nu r^2)$$

$$= \sum_{k=0}^{n-1}(-1)^k 2^k \binom{n-1}{k}\frac{(2l+1)!!}{(2l+2k+1)!!}(\nu r^2)^k \qquad (11)$$

and the N_{nl} are determined by the normalization condition

$$\int_0^\infty R_{nl}^2(r)\,dr = 1 \qquad (12)$$

Explicitly,

$$N_{nl}^2 = \frac{2^{l-n+3}(2l+2n-1)!!}{\sqrt{\pi}\,(n-1)!\,[(2l+1)!!]^2}\,\nu^{l+\frac{3}{4}} \qquad (13)$$

The energy eigenvalue corresponding to the eigenfunction

$$\psi_{nlm}(\mathbf{r}) = \frac{R_{nl}(r)}{r}Y_{lm}(\theta,\phi) \qquad (14)$$

is

$$E_{nl} = \hbar\omega(2n+l-\tfrac{1}{2}) \qquad (15)$$

$$= \hbar\omega(\Lambda + \tfrac{3}{2}) = E_\Lambda \qquad (16)$$

with

$$n = 1, 2, 3, \ldots, \qquad l = 0, 1, 2, \ldots,$$

$$\Lambda = 2n + l - 2 \qquad (17)$$

The degeneracy corresponding to each l value is $2(2l+1)$ as before. However, the eigenstates corresponding to the same value of $2n+l$ (same value of Λ) are also degenerate. Since $2n = \Lambda - l + 2 = $ even, for a given value of Λ, the degenerate eigenstates are

$$(n, l) = \left(\frac{\Lambda + 2}{2}, 0\right), \left(\frac{\Lambda}{2}, 2\right), \ldots, (2, \Lambda - 2), (1, \Lambda) \qquad \text{for} \quad \Lambda = \text{even}$$

$$(n, l) = \left(\frac{\Lambda + 1}{2}, 1\right), \left(\frac{\Lambda - 1}{2}, 3\right), \ldots, (2, \Lambda - 2), (1, \Lambda)$$

$$\text{for} \quad \Lambda = \text{odd} \quad (18)$$

so that the number of neutrons or protons with the eigenvalue E_Λ for $\Lambda =$ even (or odd) is (setting $l = 2k$ or $2k + 1$ according to whether Λ is even or odd)

$$N_\Lambda = \sum_{k=0}^{\Lambda/2} 2[2(2k) + 1] \qquad \text{for even } \Lambda$$

$$N_\Lambda = \sum_{k=0}^{(\Lambda-1)/2} 2[2(2k + 1) + 1] \qquad \text{for odd } \Lambda$$

$$N_\Lambda = (\Lambda + 1)(\Lambda + 2) \qquad \text{in either case} \qquad (19)$$

and the accumulating total number of particles for all levels up to Λ is

$$\sum_\Lambda N_\Lambda = \tfrac{1}{3}(\Lambda + 1)(\Lambda + 2)(\Lambda + 3) \qquad (20)$$

The single-particle level scheme predicted by the infinite harmonic-oscillator well is given in Table 7-1.

In the harmonic-oscillator potential, the levels appear in groups such as $1s$; $1p$; $1d$, $2s$; $1f$, $2p$; $1g$, $2d$, $3s$; etc. These grouped levels are degenerate, occupying the same energy state, whereas in the infinite square-well potential, the degeneracy is split. Closed shells occur at 2, 8, and 20, which are in agreement with experimental evidence, but predicted shell closures at higher nucleon numbers are in disagreement.

Table 7-1   Infinite Harmonic-Oscillator Well: Single-Particle States

$\Lambda = 2n + l - 2$	$E/\hbar\omega$	Degenerate States nl for Each Λ	N_Λ = Number of Particles in Λ	$\sum_\Lambda N_\Lambda$ = Accumulating Number
0	3/2	$1s$	2	2
1	5/2	$1p$	6	8
2	7/2	$2s, 1d$	12	20
3	9/2	$2p, 1f$	20	40
4	11/2	$3s, 2d, 1g$	30	70
5	13/2	$3p, 2f, 1h$	42	112
6	15/2	$4s, 3d, 2g, 1i$	56	168

Radial Density Distribution

The radial density distribution is given by

$$\rho(r) = \sum_{nl} u^2_{nl}(r)$$

Malenka,[3] and Levinger and Kent[4] have carried out calculations of $\rho(r)$ for square wells of infinite and finite depth. The density falls off to zero smoothly at the edge for infinite wells, but faster than experimental results indicate. In the harmonic-oscillator well, the density is peaked at the center and decreases approximately linearly to zero with the distance from the center.

It is easy to estimate[5] the harmonic-oscillator frequency and hence the spacing of the oscillator levels. Since, for the harmonic-oscillator potential, the expectation value of the kinetic energy in any state is equal to the expectation value of the potential energy, the total single-particle energies in a nucleus of mass number A are

$$E = M\omega^2 A \langle r^2 \rangle \tag{21}$$

where the mean square radius $\langle r^2 \rangle$ can be estimated from the relation[6]

$$\langle r^2 \rangle \simeq \tfrac{3}{5} R_C^2 \tag{22}$$

with the Coulomb radius $R_C \simeq 1.2 A^{\frac{1}{3}} \times 10^{-13}$ cm. Assuming an equal number of neutrons and protons and that all energy states up to E_{Λ_0} are occupied, we have

$$A = \sum_{\Lambda=0}^{\Lambda_0} 2N_\Lambda = \tfrac{2}{3}(\Lambda_0 + 1)(\Lambda_0 + 2)(\Lambda_0 + 3)$$

$$\simeq \tfrac{2}{3}(\Lambda_0 + 2)^3 + \text{terms of order } (\Lambda_0) \tag{23}$$

and

$$\frac{E}{\hbar\omega} = \sum_{\Lambda=0}^{\Lambda_0} 2N_\Lambda(\Lambda + \tfrac{3}{2})$$

$$\simeq \tfrac{1}{2}(\Lambda_0 + 2)^4 - \tfrac{1}{3}(\Lambda_0 + 2)^3 + \cdots \tag{24}$$

Eliminating $(\Lambda_0 + 2)$ from Eqs. (23) and (24) and retaining terms of the highest powers of $(\Lambda_0 + 2)$, we obtain

$$\frac{E}{\hbar\omega} \simeq \tfrac{1}{2}(\tfrac{3}{2}A)^{\frac{4}{3}} \tag{25}$$

From Eqs. (21), (22), and (25) we obtain

$$\hbar\omega \simeq 41 \, A^{-\frac{1}{3}} \text{ Mev} \tag{26}$$

The giant dipole resonances which are observed in photonuclear reactions can be discussed in terms of the simple relationship given in Eq. (26). The cross section of photonuclear reactions shows broad resonance peaks in different elements at an incident photoenergy of 20 Mev, with a width at half-maximum varying from 3 to 10 Mev. This phenomenon can be interpreted according to the shell model as resulting from the absorption of the electric dipole gamma rays, and the resonance peaks are due to the transitions between the states whose $\Delta l = \pm 1$. In addition, the resonance energies at which peaks are observed for different A vary somewhat, but not too greatly, from the predicted values of Eq. (26), thus confirming approximately the above relationship.

From Table (7-1) we see that the closure of a shell for the harmonic oscillator potential occurs corresponding to neutron or proton numbers 2, 8, 20, 40, 70, 112, and 168, whereas the square-well potential suggests magic numbers at 2, 8, 18, 20, 34, 40, 58, 68, 70, 92, 106, 112, 138, and 156. Experimentally observed values are 2, 8, 20, 50, 82, and 126. The truth may lie in between the two extremes: the harmonic-oscillator and square-well potentials. Tentative interpolation between these does not change the sequence of the levels except for the $1h$, $3s$ states and the $1i$, $3f$ states, but the spacings of the levels are somewhat different. In 1949 an approach was proposed which is intermediate between the harmonic oscillator and the square well, as discussed in the next section.

7.3   Spin-Orbit Potential

To obtain the magic numbers 28, 50, 82, and 126, Mayer,[7] and Haxel, Jensen, and Suess[8] suggested that a spin-orbit potential should be added to the centrally symmetric potential. This results in the splitting of the $j = l \pm \frac{1}{2}$ levels. The choice of the sign of the radial part $f(r)$ of the spin-orbit potential

$$-f(r)(\mathbf{l} \cdot \mathbf{s}) \tag{27}$$

where $\mathbf{s}$ is the intrinsic spin, is such that the $j = l + \frac{1}{2}$ level is depressed relative to the $j = l - \frac{1}{2}$ level. Since $\mathbf{j} = \mathbf{l} + \mathbf{s}$ we have for the expectation value of the operator $\mathbf{l} \cdot \mathbf{s}$ for states with definite l, s, j:

$$
\begin{aligned}
\langle \mathbf{l} \cdot \mathbf{s} \rangle &= \tfrac{1}{2}\{\langle j^2 \rangle - \langle l^2 \rangle - \langle s^2 \rangle\} \\
&= \frac{j(j+1) - l(l+1) - s(s+1)}{2} \\
&= \begin{cases} \tfrac{1}{2}l & \text{for } j = l + \tfrac{1}{2} \\ -\tfrac{1}{2}(l+1) & \text{for } i = l - \tfrac{1}{2} \end{cases}
\end{aligned}
\tag{28}
$$

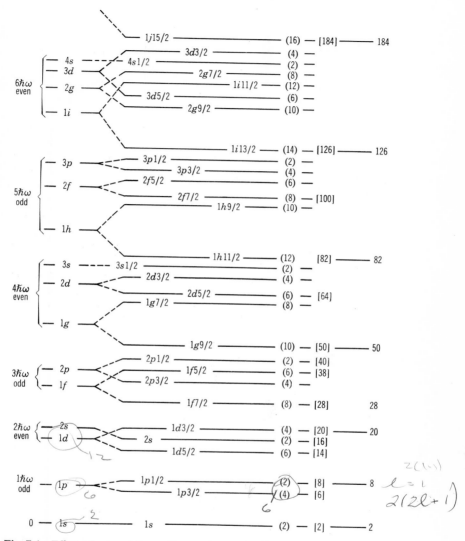

Fig. 7-1 Effect of spin-orbit coupling on the level system of a well of a shape intermediate between the square and oscillator wells. The number of particles of one kind (neutrons or protons) in the various shells are indicated in parentheses. The accumulating numbers are given in square brackets (Mayer and Jensen[9]).

The energy shifts from the central value are

$$\Delta E_{nl}(j = l + \tfrac{1}{2}) = -\tfrac{1}{2} l \int d\mathbf{r} \, |\psi_{nl}(\mathbf{r})|^2 f(r)$$

$$\Delta E_{nl}(j = l - \tfrac{1}{2}) = \tfrac{1}{2}(l + 1) \int d\mathbf{r} \, |\psi_{nl}(\mathbf{r})|^2 f(r) \tag{29}$$

and the total spin-orbit energy splitting is

$$\Delta(\Delta E_{nl}) = \Delta E_{nl}(j = l - \tfrac{1}{2}) - \Delta E_{nl}(j = l + \tfrac{1}{2})$$

$$= (l + \tfrac{1}{2}) \int d\mathbf{r} \, |\psi_{nl}(\mathbf{r})|^2 f(r) \tag{30}$$

The spin-orbit interaction splits each of the higher ($1f$, $1g$, $1h$, and $1i$) single-particle levels so that the $j = l + \tfrac{1}{2}$ level ($2j$ in number) is lowered into the band corresponding to the oscillator-level band below. Fig. 7-1 illustrates[9] the effect of spin-orbit coupling on the level scheme of a well intermediate between the square and the oscillator well and the resulting shell closures at the magic numbers.

The spin-orbit level scheme presents some interesting features. We note, for example, the odd-parity $1h_{11/2}$-level is grouped with the even-parity $3s_{1/2}$ level. Although the energy difference between these levels is small, they are markedly different in their spins. Similarly, other levels such as even-parity $1g_{9/2}$ and odd-parity $2p_{1/2}$, or even-parity $1i_{13/2}$ and odd-parity $3p_{1/2}$, are banded together.

7.4 Analysis of Shell Model Predictions

With the introduction of the spin-orbit force to the central potential, the shell model not only reproduces the magic numbers but also explains and predicts a large number of observed phenomena in odd-mass nuclei. In the following we describe briefly the success and failure of the extreme single-particle model with reference to some aspects of the experimental results.

Spin

The shell model has been very successful in predicting the ground-state spin of a large number of odd-A nuclei. According to this model, the neutron and proton levels fill independently. Because of the Pauli exclusion principle, each level can be filled with a maximum of two protons whose spins are antiparallel and two neutrons of opposite spins. Each pair of nucleons couple their j values to give a total of zero, so that the angular momentum is determined by the last unpaired nucleon. A consequence of this statement is that all even-even nuclei should have $J = 0$

in their ground state, which, in fact, is observed experimentally. The shell model is unable to make predictions concerning the odd-odd nuclei since from the model it is not known how the last neutron and the last proton couple their j's. For odd-even nuclei, the angular momentum is determined by the level occupied by the last nucleon.

Some actual examples are now presented. Consider the nuclei $_6C^{13}$ and $_7N^{13}$: the shells are filled according to $(1s_{1/2})^2|(1p_{3/2})^4(1p_{1/2})^1$. If it is C^{13}, the last unpaired nucleon is a neutron and has a spin $\frac{1}{2}$; if it is N^{13}, the last particle is a proton with spin $\frac{1}{2}$. The ground-state spin, according to the single-particle model for each of these nuclei, is $\frac{1}{2}$, a value which is observed experimentally.

As another example, consider $_8O_9^{17}$ and $_9F_8^{17}$:

$$(1s_{1/2})^2 \,\big|\, (1p_{3/2})^4(1p_{1/2})^2 \,\big|\, (1d_{5/2})^1,$$

the model predicts $\frac{5}{2}$ which is also the observed value for the ground-state spin for each of these nuclei. Finally, for $_{16}S_{17}^{33}$, experimentally the spin has been observed to be $\frac{3}{2}$. The single-particle model gives the same value

$$_{16}S_{17}^{33}: (1s_{1/2})^2 \,\big|\, (1p_{3/2})^4(1p_{1/2})^2 \,\big|\, (1d_{5/2})^6(2s_{1/2})^2(1d_{3/2})^1$$

In this way, numerous examples can be cited where the shell model has been successful in predicting the spins. However, a simple model such as this must have some exceptions, which we now discuss.

The nuclei $_{22}Ti_{25}^{47}$ and $_{25}Mn_{30}^{55}$:

$$(1s_{1/2})^2 \,\big|\, (1p_{3/2})^4(1p_{1/2})^2 \,\big|\, (1d_{5/2})^6(2s_{1/2})^2(1d_{3/2})^4 \,\big|\, (1f_{7/2})^5;$$

hence the model indicates the ground-state spins of these nuclei should be $\frac{7}{2}$ instead of the observed $\frac{5}{2}$.

Consider the nuclei $_{33}As_{42}^{75}$ and $_{28}Ni_{33}^{61}$:

$$(1s_{1/2})^2 \,\big|\, (1p_{3/2})^4(1p_{1/2})^2 \,\big|\, (1d_{5/2})^6(2s_{1/2})^2(1d_{3/2})^4 \,\big|\, (1f_{7/2})^8 \,\big|\, (2p_{3/2})^4(1f_{5/2})^1$$

Experimentally, both nuclei have spin $\frac{3}{2}$ rather than $\frac{5}{2}$ as is indicated by the model. Similar kinds of exceptions have been observed for neutron numbers 57, 59, and 61.

Many such exceptions have been eliminated by modifying the rules and stating that if the high-spin shell, say, $(1f_{5/2})$ comes after low-spin shell $(2p_{3/2})$, the high-spin shell fills faster, pairing its particles before the low-spin shell can be filled completely. Following this rule, we may write for As^{75} and Ni^{61}:

$$(1s_{1/2})^2 \,\big|\, (1p_{3/2})^4(1p_{1/2})^2 \,\big|\, (1d_{5/2})^6(2s_{1/2})^2(1d_{3/2})^4 \,\big|\, (1f_{7/2})^8 \,\big|\, (2p_{3/2})^3(1f_{5/2})^2$$

that is, there is a strong tendency for particles to form pairs in higher l states, even at some expense in energy. This can be put into the model in the form of a pairing potential, which gives paired nucleons a lower energy than unpaired ones, and which increases with increasing l.

7.5 Single-Particle Model

In the extreme single-particle model which we have discussed up to now, the properties of the nucleus are ascribed to the single unpaired nucleon moving in a potential due to the remaining nucleons. The angular momenta of the nucleons of an even-even nucleus couple to total angular momentum J equal to zero. A nucleus with odd mass-number A is considered to consist of an even-even core with total core angular momentum $J_c = 0$, and the angular momentum state of the outer nucleon is governed by the level scheme of the common potential modified by a strong spin-orbit potential.

A refinement of the extreme single-particle model is the single-particle model in which states of several particles are involved. The nucleus consists of filled shells which contain the maximum number of neutrons and protons allowed by the Pauli principle and unfilled shells containing, say, k "loose" particles. The nuclear configuration is

$$(n_1 l_1 j_1)^{2(2j_1+1)}(n_2 l_2 j_2)^{2(2j_2+1)} \dots (n_i l_i j_i)^{2(2j_i+1)}(nlj)^k \tag{31}$$

where $(nlj)^k$ may involve several states (configuration mixing).

In this model all the loose particles are considered in describing the properties of the nucleus. The nuclear wave function is represented by the configuration of its loose particles and given by the following Slater determinant

$$\Psi^\nu = \begin{vmatrix} \psi^{\nu_1}(\mathbf{r}_1) & \cdots & \psi^{\nu_1}(\mathbf{r}_k) \\ \cdot & & \cdot \\ \cdot & & \cdot \\ \cdot & & \cdot \\ \psi^{\nu_k}(\mathbf{r}_1) & \cdots & \psi^{\nu_k}(\mathbf{r}_k) \end{vmatrix} \equiv (nlj)^k \tag{32}$$

where $\psi^{\nu_i}(\mathbf{r}_i)$ are a set of complete orthonormal single-particle wave functions, $\mathbf{r}_i$ is the position vector, and ν_i denotes all the relevant quantum numbers. Equation (32) assumes that the nucleons move independently and the only correlations between nucleons are due to the Pauli principle, that is, the wave function is totally antisymmetric. All the different states of the k particles, each with the same (nlj), are degenerate in energy; the degeneracy is removed by considering the two-particle interaction $V_x(r)$, which is usually taken to be of one of the following forms

$$V_x(r) = \begin{cases} V_0 e^{-br^2} P_x & \text{(Gaussian)} \\[2mm] V_0 \dfrac{e^{-br}}{r} P_x & \text{(Yukawa)} \end{cases} \tag{33}$$

where P_x stands for the Wigner, Majorana, Bartlett, or Heisenberg exchange operators P_W, P_M, P_B, or P_H, and the parameters V_0 and b are taken to be the ones obtained by fitting the two-nucleon experimental data. The matrix element of $V_x(r)$ between two-nucleon states $|\nu_1\nu_2\nu\rangle$ and $|\nu_3\nu_4\nu\rangle$, where ν specifies the composite state of the two-nucleon system, is given by

$$\langle\nu_1\nu_2\nu|\,V_x(r)\,|\nu_3\nu_4\nu\rangle \tag{34}$$

7.6   Total Spin J for Various Configurations $(j)^k$

The total spin J of the nucleus is determined by assuming that j of the individual nucleon is a good quantum number. The **j**'s of the k_p loose protons couple to give a total spin $\mathbf{J}_p$, and those of $k_n = k - k_p$ loose neutrons couple to yield $\mathbf{J}_n$. The total spin of the nucleus is $\mathbf{J} = \mathbf{J}_p + \mathbf{J}_n$. In order to obtain the state of k_p (or k_n) protons (or neutrons) of spin $\mathbf{J}_p$ (or $\mathbf{J}_n$), it is necessary to form linearly independent combinations of single-particle states, with the corresponding total spin, which are anti-symmetric in all particles (Pauli principle). In Table 7-2 are listed[9] the number of states of each total spin J of k protons (or neutrons) satisfying the requirement of antisymmetry. The table is obtained by a tedious chain calculation, arriving at the result for the $(j)^k$ configuration from the $(j)^{k-1}$ configuration, etc. For the case of two like particles, it is easy to see that the odd J states are absent because of the requirement of antisymmetry with respect to exchange. The two-particle state of angular momentum $(J, J_z = M)$ of two particles in the state of configuration (n, l, j) is

$$\psi_J^M(\mathbf{r}_1, \mathbf{r}_2) = u_n(r_1)u_n(r_2) \sum_{m=-j}^{j} \langle jjm\,M-m\mid JM\rangle\chi_j^m(1)\chi_j^{M-m}(2)$$
$$= -u_n(r_2)u_n(r_1) \sum_m \langle jjm\,M-m\mid JM\rangle\chi_j^m(2)\chi_j^{M-m}(1) \tag{34a}$$

where in the last expression the antisymmetry of the total wave function has been used. Substituting $m' = M - m$, replacing the summation over m by m' (which also takes the same set of values as m), and dropping the prime, we obtain

$$\psi_J^M(\mathbf{r}_1, \mathbf{r}_2) = -u_n(r_2)u_n(r_1) \sum_m \langle jj\,M-m\,m\mid JM\rangle\chi_j^{M-m}(2)\chi_j^m(1)$$
$$= -(-1)^{2j-J}u_n(r_2)u_n(r_1) \sum_m \langle jjm\,M-m\mid JM\rangle\chi_j^{M-m}(2)\chi_j^m(1)$$
$$= -(-1)^{2j-J}\psi_J^M(\mathbf{r}_1, \mathbf{r}_2) \tag{34b}$$

where we have used the following property of the Clebsch-Gordan coefficients

$$\langle j_1 j_2 m_1 m_2\mid JM\rangle = (-1)^{j_1+j_2-J}\langle j_1 j_2 m_2 m_1\mid JM\rangle \tag{34c}$$

Table 7-2 Possible Total Spin J for Various Configurations $(j)^k$ (Mayer and Jensen[9])

$j = \frac{3}{2}$
$k = 1 \quad \frac{3}{2}.$
$ = 2 \quad 0, 2.$

$j = \frac{5}{2}$
$k = 1 \quad \frac{5}{2}.$
$ = 2 \quad 0, 2, 4.$
$ = 3 \quad \frac{3}{2}, \frac{5}{2}, \frac{9}{2}.$

$j = \frac{7}{2}$
$k = 1 \quad \frac{7}{2}.$
$ = 2 \quad 0, 2, 4, 6.$
$ = 3 \quad \frac{3}{2}, \frac{5}{2}, \frac{7}{2}, \frac{9}{2}, \frac{11}{2}, \frac{15}{2}.$
$ = 4 \quad 0, 2 \text{ (twice)}, 4 \text{ (twice)}, 5, 6, 8.$

$j = \frac{9}{2}$
$k = 1 \quad \frac{9}{2}.$
$ = 2 \quad 0, 2, 4, 6, 8.$
$ = 3 \quad \frac{3}{2}, \frac{5}{2}, \frac{7}{2}, \frac{9}{2} \text{ (twice)}, \frac{11}{2}, \frac{15}{2}, \frac{17}{2}, \frac{21}{2}.$
$ = 4 \quad 0 \text{ (twice)}, 2 \text{ (twice)}, 3, 4 \text{ (3 times)}, 5, 6 \text{ (3 times)}, 7, 8, 9, 10, 12.$
$ = 5 \quad \frac{1}{2}, \frac{3}{2}, \frac{5}{2} \text{ (twice)}, \frac{7}{2} \text{ (twice)}, \frac{9}{2} \text{ (3 times)}, \frac{11}{2} \text{ (twice)}, \frac{13}{2} \text{ (twice)}, \frac{15}{2} \text{ (twice)}, \frac{17}{2} \text{ (twice)}, \frac{19}{2}, \frac{21}{2}, \frac{25}{2}.$

$j = \frac{11}{2}$
$k = 1 \quad \frac{11}{2}.$
$ = 2 \quad 0, 2, 4, 6, 8, 10.$
$ = 3 \quad \frac{3}{2}, \frac{5}{2}, \frac{7}{2}, \frac{9}{2} \text{ (twice)}, \frac{11}{2} \text{ (twice)}, \frac{13}{2}, \frac{15}{2} \text{ (twice)}, \frac{17}{2}, \frac{19}{2}, \frac{21}{2}, \frac{23}{2}, \frac{27}{2}.$
$ = 4 \quad 0 \text{ (twice)}, 2 \text{ (3 times)}, 3, 4 \text{ (4 times)}, 5 \text{ (twice)}, 6 \text{ (4 times)}, 8 \text{ (4 times)}, 9 \text{ (twice)}, 10 \text{ (3 times)}, 11, 12 \text{ (twice)}, 13, 14, 16.$
$ = 5 \quad \frac{1}{2}, \frac{3}{2} \text{ (twice)}, \frac{5}{2} \text{ (3 times)}, \frac{7}{2} \text{ (4 times)}, \frac{9}{2} \text{ (4 times)}, \frac{11}{2} \text{ (5 times)}, \frac{13}{2} \text{ (4 times)}, \frac{15}{2} \text{ (5 times)}, \frac{17}{2} \text{ (4 times)}, \frac{19}{2} \text{ (4 times)}, \frac{21}{2} \text{ (3 times)}, \frac{23}{2} \text{ (3 times)}, \frac{25}{2} \text{ (twice)}, \frac{27}{2} \text{ (twice)}, \frac{29}{2}, \frac{31}{2}, \frac{35}{2}.$
$ = 6 \quad 0 \text{ (3 times)}, 2 \text{ (4 times)}, 3 \text{ (3 times)}, 4 \text{ (6 times)}, 5 \text{ (3 times)}, 6 \text{ (7 times)}, 7 \text{ (4 times)}, 8 \text{ (6 times)}, 9 \text{ (4 times)}, 10 \text{ (5 times)}, 11 \text{ (twice)}, 12 \text{ (4 times)}, 13 \text{ (twice)}, 14 \text{ (twice)}, 15, 16, 18.$

Since $2j = $ odd, it is evident from Eq. (34b) that for $J = $ odd,

$$\psi_J^M(\mathbf{r}_1, \mathbf{r}_2) = 0.$$

The states of the nucleus can be specified by $(nlj)^k$, where k is the number of nucleons in the unfilled state nlj. In light nuclei $(A < 50)$, because the Coulomb field is negligible, the shells begin to fill with neutrons and protons together. A light nucleus can be considered as consisting of a few closed shells together with k nucleons consisting of neutrons and protons in the unfilled nlj shell. The situation changes for heavier nuclei where the Coulomb field plays an important part. Because of Coulomb repulsion, protons and neutrons may not fill the same orbit together. Instead protons may fill a state with one configuration whereas neutrons may fill another state with a different configuration.

In light nuclei, when a shell is filled by both neutrons and protons together, the concept of isotopic spin plays an important role. According to this formalism, each nucleon possesses an isotopic spin $\mathbf{t}_i$ and the total isotopic spin of the nucleus is $\mathbf{T} = \sum_{i=1}^{A} \mathbf{t}_i$. The third component t_{i3} of the isotopic spin vector t_i of the ith nucleon describes the state of a nucleon. The third component t_3 for a proton is $+\frac{1}{2}$, and for neutron it is $-\frac{1}{2}$. The total isotopic spin T is a good quantum number which together with the total angular momentum J can be used to classify the states of the configuration $(nlj)^k$. However, as Z increases, because of increased Coulomb repulsion, the neutrons and protons may not fill the orbits simultaneously. In this case T may not be a good quantum number for the nucleus.

The quantum numbers J and T cannot describe a state without ambiguity because there is frequently more than one way to obtain a given J and T. Consider the following example. Suppose there are two neutrons and one proton in the $j = \frac{5}{2}$ level. The two neutrons together can have an antisymmetric state with $J_n = 0$, 2, or 4. To each of these J_n values the $j = \frac{5}{2}$ of the proton can be added vectorially to obtain the resultant $J = \frac{5}{2}$. Thus for $J = \frac{5}{2}$ there are three different eigenstates which give the same value of J. For three identical $j = \frac{5}{2}$ particles, say neutrons, there is only one totally antisymmetric state with $J = \frac{5}{2}$ with total isotopic spin $T = \frac{3}{2}$. For the two neutrons and one proton there are two states with $J = \frac{5}{2}$ and $T = \frac{1}{2}$. In the limit of very short-range forces, it is possible to have one eigenstate corresponding to the lowest energy.[9]

In addition to J and T, two additional quantum numbers are needed to define a state, the seniority number S and the reduced isotopic spin t. They can be explained by assuming that the lowest-energy wave functions can be constructed with a maximum number of $+m_j$, $-m_j$ pairs of nucleons in one level.

Let us now consider the preceding case of three nucleons in the $j = \frac{5}{2}$ level. The possible values for the $3m_j$ to give the total $M = \sum m_j = \frac{5}{2}$, not all three m_j being the same, are: $(\frac{5}{2}, \frac{5}{2}, -\frac{5}{2})$, $(\frac{5}{2}, \frac{3}{2}, -\frac{3}{2})$, $(\frac{5}{2}, \frac{1}{2}, -\frac{1}{2})$, and $(\frac{3}{2}, \frac{3}{2}, -\frac{1}{2})$, $(\frac{3}{2}, \frac{1}{2}, \frac{1}{2})$. The first three contain $+m_j$, $-m_j$ pairs, but the last two do not. A rule can be formulated by saying that the first three sets occur, but the last two do not. We generalize this statement by introducing the concept of seniority number S. Imagine removing from a given level all nucleon pairs that have $J = 0$ and $T = 1$ (like above $+m_j$, $-m_j$ pairs). The seniority number S is the number of particles left after removal of these pairs. The reduced isotopic spin t is the isotopic spin state of S particles that are left after removal of $J = 0$, $T = 1$ pairs. With the addition of the two quantum numbers, S and t, it is possible to specify the states of a general configuration $(nlj)^k$.

We shall now discuss the value of the total angular momentum J which is obtained for odd-odd nuclei.

Nordheim's Rules

Suppose we have a given number of neutrons of the configuration $(n_n, l_n, j_1)^{k_n}$ coupled to j_1 and similarly protons $(n_p, l_p, j_2)^{k_p}$ coupled to j_2. The possible value of the total angular momentum J is given by

$$|j_1 - j_2| \leq J \leq j_1 + j_2.$$

The problem is to find the value of J for the ground state of odd-odd nuclei. By studying the spin and parity in β-decay, Nordheim[10] proposed two empirical coupling rules which predict the ground-state spin J of odd-odd nuclei. The Nordheim coupling rules governing the coupling of the angular momenta of the proton and neutron indicate the tendency for the spins of the proton and neutron to line up parallel. The two rules for the ground state are:

(1) strong rule,

$$J = |J_1 - J_2| \quad \text{for} \quad j_1 = l_1 \pm \tfrac{1}{2} \quad \text{and} \quad j_2 = l_2 \mp \tfrac{1}{2}$$

(2) weak rule,

$$|J_1 - J_2| \leq J \leq J_1 + J_2 \quad \text{for} \quad j_1 = l_1 \pm \tfrac{1}{2} \quad \text{and} \quad j_2 = l_2 \pm \tfrac{1}{2}$$

For the weak rule the value of J tends toward the maximum value. The symbols j and l with the subscript 1 and 2 represent the total and orbital angular momenta of the single particle obtained using the shell model from the adjacent odd-A nuclei. The total angular momentum of the odd-A nucleus is denoted by J_1 or J_2.

Brennan and Bernstein[11] have modified Nordheim's rules by analyzing experimental results. For configurations in which both the odd protons and odd neutrons are particles (or holes) in their respective unfilled subshells, the coupling rules for such levels are given by

$$(1) \quad J = |J_1 - J_2| \quad \text{for} \quad j_1 = l_1 \pm \tfrac{1}{2} \quad \text{and} \quad j_2 = l_2 \mp \tfrac{1}{2}$$

$$(2) \quad J = |J_1 \pm J_2| \quad \text{for} \quad j_1 = l_1 \pm \tfrac{1}{2} \quad \text{and} \quad j_2 = l_2 \pm \tfrac{1}{2}$$

$$(3) \quad J = J_1 + J_2 - 1$$

Distinction has been made[11] between J_1 (or J_2) and the single-particle momentum j_1 (or j_2) to include cases of high seniority in which $j_1 \neq J_1$ (or $j_2 \neq J_2$).

Rule (3) applies to a configuration in which there is a combination of particles and holes but it is not rigorous.

Stripping Reactions

The spin and parity of a nuclear level can also be obtained from the single-particle model analysis of the (d, p) type of nuclear reactions. The parity of a state is given by $(-1)^l$. Experimentally we obtain the l-value from the measurement of cross sections and from the angular distribution of the outgoing proton in the (d, p) process. The value of l and hence the parity can then be compared with the predictions of the single-particle model.

The stripping (d, p) and pickup (d, t) types of reaction provide valuable information about the shell structure of nuclei in the region of the 82-neutron closed shell. The shell-model predictions for the neutron states in the $N = 82$ to 126 shell are $2f_{7/2}$, $1h_{9/2}$, $3p_{3/2}$, $1i_{13/2}$, $2f_{5/2}$, and $3p_{1/2}$. In the reaction $Ce^{140}(d, p)Ce^{141}$, it is predicted that the neutron states to be expected in Ce^{141} are those given above. In fact, the ground-state spin has been measured[12] to be $\frac{7}{2}$ and is consistent with the shell-model assignment of $2f_{7/2}$ for the eighty-third neutron. Holm and Martin[13] studied the reaction $Ce^{140}(d, p)Ce^{141}$ and observed eight groups of protons, leading to levels in Ce^{141} at excitation energies of 0, 0.65, 1.12, 1.35, 1.47, 1.77, 2.15, and 2.41 Mev. From a study of the angular distribution and relative cross sections, spins and parities were assigned for some of these states. The values obtained from the shell-model analysis of their results are: $\frac{7}{2}^-$ for the ground state; $\frac{3}{2}^-$ for the 0.65 and the 1.12-Mev states; $\frac{5}{2}^-$ for the 1.77 Mev state; and $\frac{1}{2}^-$ for the 2.41-Mev state.

The reactions $Ce^{140}(d, p)Ce^{141}$ and $Ce^{142}(d, t)Ce^{141}$ have been similarly analyzed by Fulmer, McCarthy, and Cohen.[14] The shell-model analysis of this experiment confirms some of the results of Duffield and Langer.[12] Additional levels have also been identified whose spin assignments have been given.

7.7 Nuclear Isomerism

There is a large number of nuclei that are found in excited states with a half-life ranging from about a microsecond to many years, which are of extremely long duration on the nuclear time scale ($\sim 10^{-22}$ sec). These nuclei are known as isomers. The nuclei de-excite by the emission of γ-rays, internal-pair or conversion electrons. We shall confine our discussion to those nuclei which decay by γ-rays with a measurable half-life. The emitted γ-rays are classified as electric (E) or magnetic (M) multipoles depending upon the change of spin and parity in the transition. The problem is to understand how γ-rays for which there is no Coulomb barrier can remain confined for such a long time within the nucleus. The single-particle model has succeeded in explaining the phenomenon of nuclear isomerism.

It was mentioned previously, in the spin-orbit level scheme, that sometimes a high-spin state is depressed and is grouped with the low-spin states, opposite in parity but differing in energy by only a small amount. Some examples are: $2p_{1/2}$ and $1g_{9/2}$; $3s_{1/2}$, $2d_{3/2}$, $2d_{5/2}$, and $1h_{11/2}$; $1h_{9/2}$, $2f_{7/2}$, $2f_{5/2}$, $3p_{3/2}$, $3p_{1/2}$, and $1i_{13/2}$. If a γ-ray is now emitted from an excited state that has a high-spin value to a lower state, usually the ground state, with low-spin value, then there is a large spin change involved in this low-energy transition, which leads to a low probability and thus long life.

Consider $_{19}K^{41}_{22}$ which is known to decay by γ-rays of 1.3 Mev with a half-life of 6.6×10^{-9} sec. The spin-orbit level scheme is

$$(1s_{1/2})^2 \mid (1p_{3/2})^4(1p_{1/2})^2 \mid (1d_{5/2})^6(2s_{1/2})^2(1d_{3/2})^3$$

The extreme single-particle model interprets this γ-ray to be M2 arising in transition from the $f_{7/2}$ excited state to the ground state $d_{3/2}$ with a change of parity. Many of these transitions can be understood with the help of the single-particle model.

7.8   Magnetic Moment

The shell model is able to make good predictions for the magnetic moment of nuclei. The magnetic moments of the proton and neutron are respectively 2.79 and -1.91 nuclear magnetons. Assuming the angular momentum of the deuteron is zero, the configuration of the deuteron is $1s^2$ so that its magnetic moment is equal to the sum of the magnetic moments of the proton and neutron in the $1s^2$ configuration. The magnetic moment of the deuteron should be $2.79 - 1.91 = 0.88$ nm, which compares favorably with the measured magnetic moment, 0.86 nm, of the deuteron. For H^3, the configuration is $1s^3$. From the Pauli principle the capacity of the $1s$ level is 4 and the filled $1s$ level will have a vanishing magnetic moment. For H^3 in the $1s^3$ configuration, the place of the proton remains vacant, and the configuration can be represented by a hole $1s^{-1}$. The magnetic moment of H^3 should be that of a proton, 2.79 nm, which is in close agreement with the measured value 2.98 nm. Similarly for He^3 in which one neutron is unfilled, the magnetic moment of He^3 is that of the last neutron, -1.91 nm, which within limits of accuracy compares favorably with the experimental value of -2.13 nm. The spin of H^3 and He^3 should be given by the unpaired nucleon in each case and should be $\frac{1}{2}$. In B^{10}, the configuration is that of the closed shell of C^{12} less two nucleons, one neutron and one proton each in the $1p_{3/2}$ state, that is, it is $C^{12}(1p_{3/2})^{-2}$, giving a spin value of 3. The magnetic moment of B^{10} arises from (1) the orbital motion of the proton in the $l = 1$ state and (2) the spin magnetic moments of the neutron and proton, thus giving a value of 1.88 nm, which is in good agreement with the experimental value 1.80 nm. In Ne^{20} the

Table 7-3 Comparison of Observed and Predicted Values of the Spin and Magnetic Moment of Light Nuclei (Landau and Smorodinsky[15])

Nucleus	Spin	Magnetic Moment	Configuration	Magnetic Moment (Theoretical)
	Measured Values			
n	$\frac{1}{2}$	-1.91	$1s_{1/2}$	
H^1	$\frac{1}{2}$	2.79	$1s_{1/2}$	
H^2	1	0.86	$1s^2_{1/2}$	0.88
H^3	$\frac{1}{2}$	2.98	$1s^3_{1/2}$	2.79
He^3	$\frac{1}{2}$	-2.13	$1s^3_{1/2}$	-1.91
He^4	Closed shell		$1s^4_{1/2}$	
Li^6	1	0.82	$He^4\ 2s^2_{1/2}$	0.88
Li^7	$\frac{3}{2}$	3.26	$He^4\ 1p^3_{1/2}$	3.07
Be^9	$\frac{3}{2}$	-1.17	$He^4\ 1p^5_{3/2}$	-1.14
B^{10}	3	1.80	$He^4\ 1p^6_{3/2}$	1.88
B^{11}	$\frac{3}{2}$	2.69	$He^4\ 1p^5_{3/2}\ 2s^2_{1/2}$	Not unique
C^{12}	Closed shell		$1s^4_{1/2}\ 1p^8_{3/2}$	
C^{13}	$\frac{1}{2}$	0.70	$C^{12}\ 1p_{1/2}$	0.64
N^{14}	1	0.40	$C^{12}p^2_{1/2}$	0.40
N^{15}	$\frac{1}{2}$	-0.28	$C^{12}p^3_{1/2}$	-0.24
O^{16}	Closed shell		$1s^4_{1/2}\ 1p^8_{3/2}\ 1p^4_{1/2}$	
O^{17}	$\frac{5}{2}$	-1.89	$O^{16}d_{5/2}$	-1.91
F^{19}	$\frac{1}{2}$	2.63	$O^{16}2s^3_{1/2}$	2.79
Ne^{20}	Closed shell		$1s^4_{1/2}\ 1p^8_{3/2}\ 1p^4_{1/2}\ 2s^4_{1/2}$	
Na^{21}	$\frac{3}{2}$	<0	$Ne^{20}\ 2p_{3/2}$	-1.91
Na^{22}	3	1.75	$Ne^{20}\ 2p^2_{3/2}$	1.88
Mg^{25}	$\frac{5}{2}$	-0.85	$O^{16}\ 1d^9_{5/2}$	-1.06
Si^{23}	Closed shell		$1s^4_{1/2}\ 1p^8_{3/2}\ 1p^4_{1/2}\ 1d^{12}_{5/2}$	

configuration is that of a closed shell, $1s^4_{1/2}\ 1p^8_{3/2}\ 1p^4_{1/2}\ 2s^4_{1/2}$, with zero spin and magnetic moment.

The magnetic moments of light nuclei can be predicted according to the shell model by the above procedure. Table 7-3 gives a comparison[15] of observed and predicted values of the spin and magnetic moment of light nuclei.

7.9 Configuration Mixing

The shell-model wave functions may often be mixtures of several configurations. As long as the interaction between nucleons can be considered as not disturbing the states predicted by the effective single-particle potential, configuration mixing can be ignored and the shell-model wave function will be a pure (nlj) configuration. However, as a result of strong, interparticle interactions the shell-model wave function Ψ may consist of superpositions of two or more configurations Ψ^ν:

$$\Psi = \sum_\nu a_\nu \Psi^\nu \tag{35}$$

where the nuclear configurations may be of the following form

$$(n_1 l_1 j_1)^{k_1}(n_2 l_2 j_2)^{k_2} \cdots (n_i l_i j_i)^{k_i}$$

The majority of k's will correspond to filled states, that is, $k_m = 2j_m + 1$, with only one or two unfilled shells.

The shell-model wave function Ψ is determined by diagonalizing the interaction $V_x(r)$. As an illustration of a calculation that takes into account a configuration mixing from immediately higher configurations, we briefly describe a calculation due to Redlich[16] for F^{18} and O^{18}. The calculations were performed for two-particle configurations of the $1d_{5/2}$, $2s_{1/2}$, and $1d_{3/2}$ shell. The potential energy of one particle was taken as

$$V(r_1) = \frac{1}{2m}(\hbar \nu r_1)^2 \tag{36}$$

where m is the mass of the nucleon, $\mathbf{r}_1$ is the position vector, and ν is determined from

$$\langle r_1 \rangle^2 = \int_0^\infty r_1^2 R_{1d}^2(r_1)\,dr_1 = \frac{7}{2\nu} = (1.43 A^{1/3} \times 10^{-13})^2 \tag{37}$$

that is, the $1d_{5/2}$ particle is assumed to be just at the outer edge of the nucleus and R_{1d} is the radial part of the harmonic-oscillator wave function. For $A = 18$, $\hbar\omega = \hbar^2\nu/m = 10.3$ Mev. The parameters for the Gaussian potential in Eq. (33)[17] are $V_0 = -70.8$ Mev and $b^{-1} = 2.245 \times 10^{-26}$ cm². The interaction used is $\frac{1}{2}(V_W + V_M)$, and diagonalization of $\frac{1}{2}(V_W + V_M) + \Delta(j_1) + \Delta(j_2)$ is carried out (W and M respectively refer to ordinary and exchange forces), where

$$\langle j_1 j_2 JT | \Delta(j_1) | j_1' j_2' JT \rangle = a(j_1)\,\delta(j_1, j_1')\,\delta(j_2, j_2')$$

$$a(j_1) = \begin{cases} 0 & \text{if } j_1 = \frac{5}{2} \\ 0.875 \text{ Mev} & \text{if } j_1 = \frac{1}{2} \\ 5.08 \text{ Mev} & \text{if } j_1 = \frac{3}{2} \end{cases}$$

takes into account the energy differences between single-particle levels due to spin-orbit splitting in O^{17}. For O^{17}, the observed energy difference

Table 7-4 Matrices of $-\frac{1}{2}(V_W + V_M) - \Delta(j_1) - \Delta(j_2)$ in Mev (Redlich[16])

| | $T = 0, J = 1$ | | | | | | $T = 1, J = 0$ | | |
	$d_{5/2}^2$	$d_{5/2}d_{3/2}$	$s_{1/2}^2$	$d_{3/2}^2$	$d_{3/2}s_{1/2}$		$d_{5/2}^2$	$d_{3/2}^2$	$s_{1/2}^2$
$d_{5/2}^2$	2.10	2.15	0.82	−1.61	−0.60	$d_{5/2}^2$	3.72	3.04	1.21
$d_{5/2}d_{3/2}$	2.15	−0.47	1.24	−0.51	0.79	$d_{3/2}^2$	3.04	−7.68	0.98
$s_{1/2}^2$	0.82	1.24	1.46	−0.44	0	$s_{1/2}^2$	1.21	0.98	1.46
$d_{3/2}^2$	−1.61	−0.51	−0.44	−8.39	1.12				
$d_{3/2}s_{1/2}$	−0.60	0.79	0	1.12	−3.35				

between the $\frac{3}{2}+$ and $\frac{5}{2}+$ states is 5.08 Mev and between the $\frac{1}{2}+$ and $\frac{5}{2}+$ states is 0.875 Mev. T is the isotopic spin. The ground states of F^{18} and O^{18} are expected to be $(T, J) = (1, 0)$ and $(0, 1)$ respectively. The matrix elements of $\frac{1}{2}(V_W + V_M) + \Delta(j_1) + \Delta(j_2)$ between the various configurations are given in Table 7-4. Diagonalization of this matrix determines the shell-model wave function $\Psi(T, J)$ and the maximum eigenvalue λ_{TJ}.

$$\Psi(0, 1) = 0.732\psi(d_{5/2}^2) + 0.477\psi(d_{5/2}\,d_{3/2}) + 0.464\psi(s_{1/2}^2)$$
$$- 0.131\psi(d_{3/2}^2) - 0.009\psi(d_{3/2}s_{1/2}) \tag{38}$$
$$\lambda_{01} = 4.03 \text{ Mev}$$

$$\Psi(1, 0) = 0.895\phi(d_{5/2}^2) + 0.370\phi(s_{1/2}^2) + 0.243\phi(d_{3/2}^2) \tag{39}$$
$$\lambda_{10} = 5.05 \text{ Mev}$$

The calculations of Redlich show that the ground state of F^{18} is an admixture of $1d_{5/2}$, $2s_{1/2}$, and $1d_{3/2}$ states. The evaluation of the matrices indicate that the ground state of F^{18} is a $(0, 1)$ state as observed.

In recent years a large number of shell-model calculations have been done assuming diverse potentials. These calculations predict spins of both the ground and the excited states, the energy levels of nuclei, and the magnetic moment. The shell-model calculations have been less successful with the quadrupole moment. An extensive calculation has been done by Glaudemans, Wiechers, and Brussaard[18] for nuclei ranging from Si^{29} to Ca^{40}. In these calculations, it was assumed that the two outer shells, $2s_{1/2}$ and $1d_{3/2}$, are in the central field provided by the inert central core of Si^{28}. The interaction matrix elements were expressed in terms of 17 parameters, 2 for the binding energies of the $2s_{1/2}$ and $1d_{3/2}$ shells to the Si^{28} core and 15 for the interactions of the various nucleons in different configurations of the $2s_{1/2}$ and $1d_{3/2}$ shells. The 17 parameters were evaluated by the method of least-square fit, and the energies and wave functions of 377 states in the $2s_{1/2}$, $1d_{3/2}$ shell were calculated. Some of their results are given in Figs 7-2 and 7-3.

The energy-level configurations of some isotopes of Si, P, S, and Cl are given together with the calculated values. We note excellent agreements for spins, parity, and energy-level assignment between the computed values and the experimental results for many nuclei. On the other hand,

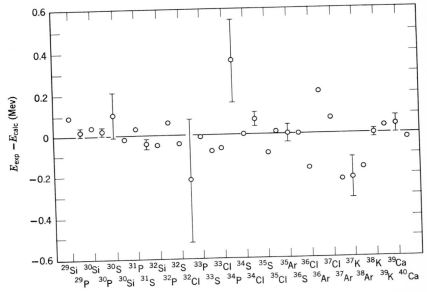

Fig. 7-2   Difference between experimental and calculated ground-state binding energies. The bars represent the experimental errors larger than 0.01 Mev (Glaudemans et al.[18]).

there are quite a few levels which are not reproduced. For example, the experimentally observed $\frac{5}{2}+$ level at 2.23 Mev in S^{31} and P^{31} is not predicted by the theory.

Figure 7-2 gives the differences between the calculated and theoretical values of the ground-state binding energies for nuclei between Si^{29} and Ca^{40}. With the exceptions of Cl^{36}, Ar^{36}, Ar^{37}, and Ar^{38}, deviations greater than 0.15 Mev have been attributed to inaccuracies in the experiments.

7.10   Individual (Independent)-Particle Model

In the individual-particle model, all the A particles in the nucleus are taken into account. This model is also referred to as the many-particle shell model. The wave function $\Psi^{\nu}(r)$ for one configuration of the nucleus

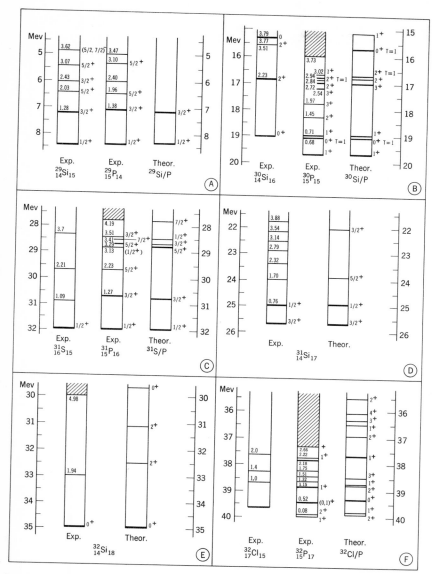

Fig. 7-3 Comparison of the theoretical level energies and spins with the experimental data. The levels indicated by bold lines were used in the fitting process. The vertical axis represents the excitation energy relative to the binding energy of the ^{28}Si core, with the Coulomb energy of the outer particles subtracted. Hatching indicates areas of high level density (Glaudemans et al.[18]).

is the properly antisymmetrized Slater determinant of the single-particle wave functions ψ^{ν_i} for all the A particles, where ν_i specifies the quantum state. Thus

$$
\Psi^\nu(r) = \begin{vmatrix} \psi^{\nu_1}(\mathbf{r}_1) & \cdots & \psi^{\nu_1}(\mathbf{r}_A) \\ \cdot & & \cdot \\ \cdot & & \cdot \\ \cdot & & \cdot \\ \psi^{\nu_A}(\mathbf{r}_1) & \cdots & \psi^{\nu_A}(\mathbf{r}_A) \end{vmatrix} \tag{40}
$$

The Ψ^ν are solutions of the Schrödinger equation

$$
H_1 \Psi^\nu = E_1 \Psi^\nu \tag{41a}
$$

where

$$
H_1 = \sum_{i=1}^{A} \left[-\frac{\hbar^2}{2m} \nabla_i^2 + V_1(\mathbf{r}_i) \right] \tag{41b}
$$

and $V_1(\mathbf{r}_i)$ is a suitably chosen common single-particle potential in which each nucleon moves. This potential is frequently taken to be the harmonic oscillator potential. The Hamiltonian of the A-nucleon system is given by

$$
H = -\frac{\hbar^2}{2m} \sum_{i=1}^{A} \nabla_i^2 + \sum_{i<j=2}^{A} V_{ij}(\mathbf{r}_{ij}) \tag{41c}
$$

where $V_{ij}(\mathbf{r}_{ij})$ is the two-nucleon interaction between nucleons i and j. The actual wave function Ψ of the nucleus is obtained by solving the Schrödinger equation

$$
H\Psi = E\Psi \tag{41d}
$$

In practice, Ψ is taken to be a linear superposition of Ψ^ν, that is,

$$
\Psi = \sum_\nu a_\nu \Psi^\nu \tag{42}
$$

The nuclear wave function Ψ and the energy eigenvalue E are determined by diagonalizing the matrix $(\Psi^\mu| H |\Psi^\nu)$. For a complete set of anti-symmetric Ψ^ν (with $\nu \to \infty$), the diagonalization of the matrix $(\Psi^\mu| H |\Psi^\nu)$ would yield an exact expansion of Ψ. But taking a large set of Ψ^ν would involve a prohibitive amount of work, and generally only a few terms in the summation on the right-hand side of Eq. (42) are retained. Actually, a few values of ν are sufficient to determine a Ψ which is a good approximation of the nuclear wave function, provided the set of Ψ^ν's chosen is such that some of them are fairly close to the actual wave function. The above procedure[19] of diagonalization is equivalent to a variational procedure of minimizing the total energy E with respect to the coefficients of the linear combination, Eq. (42), where

$$E = \int \Psi^*(T + V)\Psi \tag{43}$$

and $T = -\hbar^2/(2m) \sum_i \nabla_i^2$ is the total kinetic energy; V, the total potential energy, is given by

$$V = \sum_{i<j=2}^{A} v_{ij} \tag{44a}$$

$$= \sum_{i=1}^{A} V_1(\mathbf{r}_i) + \left(\sum_{i<j=2}^{A} v_{ij} - \sum_{i=1}^{A} V_1(\mathbf{r}_i) \right) \tag{44b}$$

In Eq. (44b), the potential energy is separated into two parts; the choice of the single-particle potential $V_1(\mathbf{r}_j)$ is arbitrary, and its main purpose is to provide a first set of wave functions Ψ^ν (Eqs. (41a) and (41b)). The calculations for the nucleus are carried out with the interparticle potential V.

The L-S and j-j coupling schemes which describe the wave functions of the independent-particle model are discussed below.

7.11   Russell-Saunders Coupling (L-S Coupling)

It is necessary to form wave functions which are totally antisymmetric with respect to permutation of all coordinates of the A nucleons. The lowest nuclear state consists of several closed shells $n_i l_i$ containing $\sum_i 4(2l_i + 1)$ nucleons and one unfilled shell nl. The relative positions of levels of this configuration can be considered by ignoring the closed shell. But if we are interested in the interaction between different configurations, we have to form a wave function antisymmetric in all the nucleons. If the interaction is central, then for the k particles under consideration, the total orbital angular momentum $\mathbf{L} = \mathbf{l}_1 + \mathbf{l}_2 + \cdots + \mathbf{l}_k$ and the total intrinsic spin $\mathbf{S} = \mathbf{s}_1 + \mathbf{s}_2 + \cdots + \mathbf{s}_k$ are both constants of motion, and the nuclear wave function should be formed according to this mode of coupling provided the nuclear spin-orbit interactions can be considered weak compared to the central force experienced by each nucleon. This scheme of coupling is referred to as the Russell-Saunders (or L-S) coupling. The single-particle wave function is of the form

$$\phi(nlstm_lm_sm_t) = u_{nl}(r)Y_l^{m_l}(\theta, \phi)\chi_s^{m_s}\chi_t^{m_t} \tag{45}$$

where n is the total quantum number, l, s, t are the orbital angular momentum, spin, and isospin and m_l, m_s, m_t their z-components with $\mathbf{s} = \mathbf{t} = \frac{1}{2}$.

The two-particle states $\phi(l^2LM)$ are formed as in Eq. (34a). The multiplicities of the state are $2T + 1$ and $2S + 1$ where

$$\mathbf{T} = \mathbf{t}_1 + \mathbf{t}_2, \qquad \mathbf{S} = \mathbf{s}_1 + \mathbf{s}_2$$

T and S are the total isospin and spin. The totally antisymmetric states of two particles are

$$^{3\,1}L, {}^{1\,3}L \qquad \text{with} \quad L = 0, 2, \ldots, 2l(\text{even})$$
$$^{1\,1}L, {}^{3\,3}L \qquad \text{with} \quad L = 1, 3, \ldots, 2l - 1 \ (\text{odd}) \qquad (46)$$

where the superscripts are the values $2T + 1$ and $2S + 1$.

In the case of two particles, it is a straightforward procedure to construct antisymmetric wave functions. For two particles, any wave function can be expressed in terms of a symmetric and an antisymmetric wave function which form a basis. When the number of particles $k > 2$, the basis functions consist of not only functions which are antisymmetric and symmetric with respect to all the particles but also those which have intermediate symmetry. These are classified into sets which are labeled

Table 7-5 *L-S* Coupled Wave Functions for the *p*-Shell (Elliot and Lane[22])

n	$[\lambda]$	L	$(2T + 1, 2S + 1)$
0	[0]	s	(1 1)
1	[1]	p	(2 2)
2	[2]	s, d	(1 3) (3 1)
	[1 1]	p	(1 1) (3 3)
3	[3]	p, f	(2 2)
	[2 1]	p, d	(2 2) (2 4) (4 2)
	[1 1 1]	s	(2 2) (4 4)
4	[4]	sdg	(1 1)
	[3 1]	pdf	(1 3) (3 1) (3 3)
	[2 2]	sd	(1 1) (1 5) (5 1)·(3 3)
	[2 1 1]	p	(1 3) (3 1) (3 3) (3 5) (5 3)
5	[4 1]	$pdfg$	(2 2)
	[3 2]	pdf	(2 2) (2 4) (4 2)
	[3 1 1]	sd	(2 2) (2 4) (4 2) (4 4)
	[2 2 1]	p	(2 2) (2 4) (4 2) (2 6) (6 2) (4 4)
6	[4 2]	sd^2fg	(1 3) (3 1)
	[4 1 1]	pf	(1 1) (3 3)
	[3 3]	pf	(1 1) (3 3)
	[3 2 1]	pd	(1 3) (3 1) (3 3)^2 (1 5) (5 1) (3 5) (5 3)
	[2 2 2]	s	(1 3) (3 1) (3 5) (5 3) (1 7) (7 1)

by the partitions $[\lambda] \equiv [\lambda_1, \lambda_2 \cdots \lambda_p]$ of k such that

$$\lambda_1 \geq \lambda_2 \cdots \geq \lambda_p \quad \text{and} \quad \sum_i \lambda_i = k \qquad (47)$$

The set $[\lambda]$ are the basis functions which spread out the irreducible representation $[\lambda]$ of the symmetric group S_k and are invariant under any permutation of the particles.[20] The partitions $[\lambda]$ are representable by a Young tableau, with λ_i blocks in the ith row. For example,

$$[\lambda] \equiv [3\ 2\ 1] = \text{Young tableau}$$

We will not go into the details of construction of the coupled wave functions. An account of the group theoretical discussion involved is given by Elliot.[21] In Table 7-5,[22] the complete list of states in the p-shell is given. This was first derived by Hund[23] and later by John[24] using group theory.

7.12   *j-j* Coupling Scheme

The L-S coupling is satisfactory for purely central forces in which the total orbital angular momentum $\mathbf{L} = \sum\limits_{i=1}^{k} \mathbf{l}_i$ and the total intrinsic spin $\mathbf{S} = \sum\limits_{i=1}^{k} \mathbf{s}_i$ are good quantum numbers, and therefore we couple $\mathbf{L}$ and $\mathbf{S}$ to form the total angular momentum $\mathbf{J} = \mathbf{L} + \mathbf{S}$. However, the shell-model interpretation is based on the introduction of a strong spin-orbit potential

$$V_{LS} = \xi \sum_i (\mathbf{l}_i \cdot \mathbf{s}_i) \qquad (48)$$

which couples the spin and orbital momenta of each particle into a total angular momenta $\mathbf{j} = \mathbf{l} + \mathbf{s}$, leading to an energy level of a single particle corresponding to each value of $j = l \pm \frac{1}{2}$. In a purely spin-orbit potential, since j is a good quantum number, a satisfactory description of the nuclear state would be obtained by coupling the individual j's of the nucleons into a total angular momentum

$$J = \mathbf{j}_1 + \mathbf{j}_2 + \cdots + \mathbf{j}_k = \sum \mathbf{j}_i$$

This is called the *j-j* coupling scheme.

Now the intrinsic spin and the orbital angular momenta of each particle are coupled to form a total particle angular momentum j and in this

Table 7-6 j-j-Coupled Wave Functions for the $p_{3/2}$ Shell (Elliot[21])

k	$[f]$	T	$(\rho_1\,\rho_2\,\rho_3)$	J
1	[1]	$\frac{1}{2}$	(1 0 0)	$\frac{5}{2}$
2	[2]	0	(2 0 0)	1, 3, 5
	[1 1]	1	(0 0 0)	0
			(1 1 0)	2, 4
3	[2 1]	$\frac{1}{2}$	(1 0 0)	$\frac{5}{2}$
			(2 1 0)	$\frac{1}{2}, \frac{3}{2}, \frac{5}{2}, (\frac{7}{2})^2$ $\frac{9}{2}, \frac{11}{2}, \frac{13}{2}$
	[1 1 1]	$\frac{3}{2}$	(1 0 0)	$\frac{5}{2}$
			(1 1 1)	$\frac{3}{2}, \frac{9}{2}$

pure coupling scheme the shells are labeled by nlj. The wave functions of k particles are classified by their symmetry $[\lambda]$ with respect to permutations of the coordinates in j-space. This is done by the group theoretical methods of Racah and has been carried out by Flowers.[25] The group of transformations which is used in the j-j coupling scheme is called the Symplectic group. The transformation properties of the states which appear in this group are denoted by two labels (S, t), the seniority S and the reduced isotopic spin t defined earlier. The complete set of j-j-coupled states for the $p_{3/2}$ shell are given[21,22] in Tables 7-6 and 7-7.

Table 7-7 j-j-Coupled Wave Functions for the $p_{3/2}$ Shell (Elliot and Lane[22])

n	$[\lambda]$	T	(σ)	(s, t)	J
0	[0]	0	(0 0)	(0, 0)	0
1	[1]	$\frac{1}{2}$	(1 0)	$(1, \frac{1}{2})$	$\frac{3}{2}$
2	[2]	0	(2 0)	(2, 0)	1, 3
	[1 1]	1	(0 0)	(0, 0)	0
			(1 1)	(2, 1)	2
3	[2 1]	$\frac{1}{2}$	(1 0)	$(1, \frac{1}{2})$	$\frac{3}{2}$
			(2 1)	$(3, \frac{1}{2})$	$\frac{1}{2}, \frac{5}{2}, \frac{7}{2}$
	[1 1 1]	$\frac{3}{2}$	(1 0)	$(1, \frac{1}{2})$	$\frac{3}{2}$
4	[2 2]	0	(0 0)	(0, 0)	0
			(1 1)	(2, 1)	2
			(2 2)	(4, 0)	2, 4
	[2 1 1]	1	(2 0)	(2, 0)	1, 3
			(1 1)	(2, 1)	2
	[1 1 1 1]	2	(0 0)	(0, 0)	0

7.13 Transformation between the *L-S* and the *j-j* Coupling Schemes

Since both the *L-S* and the *j-j* coupling schemes provide a complete set of wave functions, it should be possible to relate them. We consider the case of two particles with spin and orbital angular momenta s_1, s_2, l_1, l_2 and total angular momenta j_1 and j_2. In the *L-S* coupling we have

$$\mathbf{S} = \mathbf{s}_1 + \mathbf{s}_2 \qquad \mathbf{L} = \mathbf{l}_1 + \mathbf{l}_2 \tag{49}$$

forming a resultant

$$\mathbf{J} = \mathbf{L} + \mathbf{S} \tag{50}$$

In the *j-j* coupling we have

$$\mathbf{j}_1 = \mathbf{l}_1 + \mathbf{s}_1 \qquad \mathbf{j}_2 = \mathbf{l}_2 + \mathbf{s}_2 \tag{51}$$

forming

$$\mathbf{J} = \mathbf{j}_1 + \mathbf{j}_2 \tag{52}$$

Denoting the *L-S* coupled wave function by $|(l_1 l_2)L(s_1 s_2)S, JM\rangle$ and the *j-j* coupled wave function by $|(l_1 s_1)j_1(l_2 s_2)j_2, JM\rangle$, we have

$$|(l_1 l_2)L(s_1 s_2)S, JM\rangle = \sum \langle (l_1 s_1)j_1(l_2 s_2)j_2, JM \mid (l_1 l_2)L(s_1 s_2)S, JM\rangle$$
$$\cdot |(l_1 s_1)j_1(l_2 s_2)j_2, JM\rangle \tag{53}$$

where the transformation coefficient

$$\langle (l_1 s_1)j_1(l_2 s_2)j_2, JM \mid (l_1 l_2)L(s_1 s_2)S, JM\rangle$$

is to be obtained by the rearrangement of the order of vector coupling. It can be shown that

$$\langle (l_1 l_2)L(s_1 s_2)S, JM \mid (l_1 s_1)j_1(l_2 s_2)j_2, JM\rangle$$
$$= [(2L + 1)(2S + 1)(2j_1 + 1)(2j_2 + 1)]^{1/2} \sum_x (2x + 1)W(Ls_1 Js_2, xS)$$
$$\times W(Ls_1 \tfrac{1}{2}j_1, x\tfrac{1}{2})W(j_1 \tfrac{1}{2}Js_2, xj_2)$$
$$= [(2L + 1)(2S + 1)(2j_1 + 1)(2j_2 + 1)]^{1/2} \begin{Bmatrix} L\, l_1\, l_2 \\ S\, \tfrac{1}{2}\, \tfrac{1}{2} \\ J\, j_1\, j_2 \end{Bmatrix} \tag{54}$$

where the *W*'s are the Racah functions and { } are the Wigner 9-*j* symbols. These coefficients have been tabulated by Kennedy and Cliff.[26]

7.14 Coefficient of Fractional Parentage (cfp)

To calculate the matrix elements of the interaction, Bacher and Goudsmit[27] introduced the method of fractional parentage. The method was further developed by Racah.[28] This method enables us to express a state of k particles in terms of states of $(k - 1)$ particles, or $(k - 2)$ particles, and so on.

We denote by $\Psi'^{(k)}$ the antisymmetric wave function of the k particles 1, 2, ..., k in the configuration l^k, by $\Psi'^{(k-1)}$ the wave function for particles 1, 2, ..., $k-1$ in the configuration l^{k-1}, and by ϕ_k the single-particle wave function of the kth particle. Then the k-particle wave function $\Psi'^{(k)}$ can be written in terms of the $(k-1)$-particle wave function $\Psi'^{(k-1)}$ and the single-particle wave function $\phi_k(l_k m_k)$ in the following manner

$$\Psi'^{(k)}(l^k \alpha LM) = \sum_{\alpha' L', \phi_k} \langle \Psi'^{(k)}(l^k \alpha L)\{|\Psi'^{(k-1)}(l^{k-1} \alpha' L'), \phi_k\rangle$$
$$\times \{\Psi'^{(k-1)}(l^{k-1} \alpha' L'), \phi_k LM\} \qquad (55)$$

where α and α' represent any additional quantum numbers which may be required to specify the wave functions completely.

$$\langle \Psi'^{(k)}(l^k \alpha L)\{|\Psi'^{(k-1)}(l^{k-1} \alpha' L'), \phi_k\rangle$$

are the coefficients of fractional parentage and $\{\Psi'^{(k-1)}(l^{k-1} \alpha' L'), \phi_k LM\}$ imply vector coupling of the kth particle in the state l_k to the allowed $(k-1)$ particles in the state $l^{k-1} \alpha' L'$; that is,

$$\{\Psi'^{(k-1)}(l^{k-1} \alpha' L'), \phi_k LM\}$$
$$= \sum_{m_k M'} \langle L' l_k M' m_k \mid LM \rangle \Psi'^{(k-1)}(l^{k-1} \alpha' L'M') \phi_k(l_k m_k) \qquad (56)$$

Similar expressions can be written in the j^k configuration representation. Tables of *cfp* have been prepared.[29] For the sake of brevity, we shall write Eq. (55) in the following form

$$\Psi'^{(k)} = \sum_{\Psi'^{(k-1)}, \phi_k} \langle \Psi'^{(k)}\{|\Psi'^{(k-1)}, \phi_k\rangle\{\Psi'^{(k-1)}, \phi_k\} \qquad (57)$$

Equation (57) can be employed to express the matrix elements of the interaction $V = \sum_{i<j} v_{ij}$ between two k-particle states in terms of two $(k-1)$-particle states. Because of the antisymmetry $\langle \Psi'^{(k)} | v_{ij} | \Psi'^{(k)'} \rangle$ has the same value for any pairs i and j, and using Eq. (57) we have

$$\langle \Psi'^{(k)} | V | \Psi'^{(k)'} \rangle = \frac{k(k-1)}{2} \langle \Psi'^{(k)} | v_{12} | \Psi'^{(k)'} \rangle$$

$$= \frac{k(k-1)}{2} \sum_{\Psi'^{(k-1)}, \phi_k} \sum_{\Psi'^{(k-1)'}, \phi_{k'}} \langle \Psi'^{(k)}\{|\Psi'^{(k-1)}, \phi_k\rangle$$
$$\times \langle \Psi'^{(k)'}\{|\Psi'^{(k-1)'} \phi_{k'}\rangle \langle \Psi'^{(k-1)} | v_{12} | \Psi'^{(k-1)'} \rangle \qquad (58)$$

which may be rewritten in the form

$$\langle \Psi'^{(k)} | V | \Psi'^{(k)'} \rangle = \frac{k}{k-2} \sum_{\substack{\Psi'^{(k-1)}, \Psi'^{(k-1)'} \\ \phi_k, \phi_{k'}}} \langle \Psi'^{(k)}\{|\Psi'^{(k-1)}, \phi_k\rangle$$
$$\times \langle \Psi'^{(k)'}\{|\Psi'^{(k-1)'} \phi_{k'}\rangle \langle \Psi'^{(k-1)} | V | \Psi'^{(k-1)'} \rangle \qquad (59)$$

The wave function $\Psi'^{(k)}$ of k particles can be expressed in terms of the wave function $\Psi'^{(k-2)}$ of $k - 2$ particles and $\phi^{(2)}_{k-1,k}$ of the last two $(k - 1)$th and kth particles in a manner similar to Eqs. (56) and (57). We have

$$\Psi'^{(k)} = \sum_{\Psi^{(k-2)}, \phi^{(2)}} \langle \Psi'^{(k)}\{|\Psi'^{(k-2)}\phi^{(2)}\rangle\{\Psi'^{(k-2)}, \phi^{(2)}_{k-1,k}\} \tag{60}$$

The *cfp* are now $\langle \Psi'^{(k)}\{|\Psi'^{(k-2)}\phi^{(2)}\rangle$, which are related to the *cfp* of Eq. (57) as follows

$$\langle \Psi'^{(k)}\{|\Psi'^{(k-2)}\phi^{(2)}\rangle = \sum_{\Psi^{(k-1)}} \{(2\Psi'^{(k-1)} + 1)(2\phi^{(2)} + 1)\}^{1/2}$$
$$\times W(\Psi'^{(k-2)}l\Psi'^{k}l, \Psi'^{(k-1)}\phi^{(2)})$$
$$\times \langle \Psi'^{(k)}\{|\Psi'^{(k-1)}\rangle\langle\Psi'^{(k-1)}\{|\Psi'^{(k-2)}\rangle \tag{61}$$

where[22] the (Racah) function W is actually a product of three Racah functions.

The matrix elements of the interactions V are now given by

$$\langle \Psi'^{(k)}| V |\Psi'^{(k)'}\rangle = \frac{k(k - 1)}{2} \langle \Psi'^{(k)}| v_{k-1\,k} |\Psi'^{(k')}\rangle$$
$$= \frac{k(k - 1)}{2} \sum_{\substack{\Psi^{(k-2)}, \phi^{(2)} \\ \phi^{(2)'}}} \langle \Psi'^{k}\{|\Psi'^{(k-2)}\phi^{(2)}\rangle$$
$$\times \langle \Psi'^{(k)'}\{|\Psi'^{(k-2)}\phi^{(2)'}\rangle\langle\phi^{(2)}| v_{k-1,k} |\phi^{(2)'}\rangle \tag{62}$$

which expresses the matrix elements in terms of the two-body matrix elements. The $(k - 2)$-particle states contributing nonzero matrix elements have to be the same in $\Psi'^{(k)}$ and $\Psi'^{(k)'}$.

The individual-particle model has been successfully applied for predicting the energy-level configuration and also the binding energies of light nuclei. We shall present some results obtained by Amit and Katz.[30] They have applied the effective-interaction method (in which nucleons moving in a central field interact with each other through a residual interaction) to the $1p$ shell using intermediate coupling to calculate the binding energies and levels of nuclei ranging from Be[8] to O[15]. Similar calculations were also performed earlier by Kurath.[31] In the calculations of Amit and Katz, no specific interaction potential was assumed other than that it is charge-independent and that the two-particle interaction is central. In addition, it was also assumed that only $1p$ nucleons were responsible for the low-lying energy levels. Figure 7-4 gives the spin, parity, and position of the energy levels of O[15] and N[14]. For O[15] we note that the $\frac{1}{2}^-$ and $\frac{3}{2}^-$, which are the only $1p$ levels, are reproduced accurately. Similar agreement is also found for N[14].

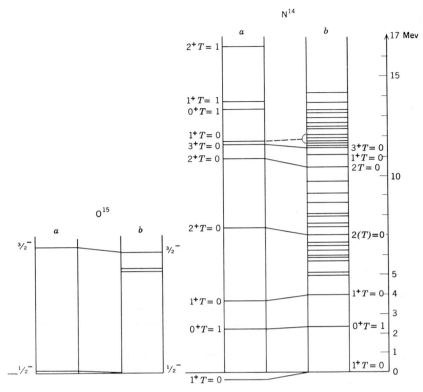

Fig. 7-4   Energy-level schemes (a) calculated, (b) experimental (Amit and Katz[30]).

The intermediate coupling-scheme calculations for the absolute values of the binding energies for nuclei $8 \leq A \leq 16$ are shown in Table 7-8. The close agreement between the theoretical values and the experimental results seem to indicate the validity of the above scheme for the $1p$ shell nuclei. There are two possible ways we can interpret this agreement: either the ground state of these nuclei consists mostly of the lowest jj configurations or, as is observed by Amit and Katz, the interaction between the configurations is contained for ground states in the parameters of the effective interaction used.

7.15   Beta Decay

The nuclear-shell model gives a good account of the various properties of nuclei. The nuclear-shell structure is quite well understood with the aid of this model. One other application of the shell model which we shall

Table 7-8 Energy Levels Involved in the Final Procedure (Amit and Katz[30])

Nucleus	E_x	$T; J^\pi$	Nuclear Binding Energy Experimental	Calculated	Exptl. − Calc.
Be^8	0	0; 0$^+$	−82.22	−81.48	−0.74
Be^8	2.90	0; 0$^+$	−85.12	−85.94	+0.82
Be^8	11.7	0; 4$^+$	−93.92	−93.91	−0.01
Be^9	0	$\frac{1}{2}; \frac{3}{2}-$	−80.55	−80.43	−0.12
Be^9	2.43	$\frac{1}{2}; \frac{5}{2}-$	−82.98	−83.58	+0.60
B^{10}	1.74	1; 0$^+$	−73.85	−74.12	+0.27
B^{10}	7.56	1; 0$^+$	−79.67	−79.38	−0.29
B^{10}	0.72	0; 1$^+$	−72.83	−72.66	−0.17
B^{10}	2.15	0; 1$^+$	−74.26	−74.37	+0.11
B^{10}	3.58	0; 2$^+$	−75.69	−74.94	−0.75
B^{10}	4.77	0; 2$^+$	−76.88	−76.78	−0.10
B^{10}	5.16	1; 2$^+$	−77.27	−77.55	+0.28
B^{10}	8.89	1; 2$^+$	−81.00	−80.10	−0.90
B^{10}	0	0; 3$^+$	−72.11	−71.82	−0.29
B^{11}	0	$\frac{1}{2}; \frac{3}{2}-$	−60.64	−60.62	−0.02
B^{11}	5.03	$\frac{1}{2}; \frac{3}{2}-$	−65.67	−65.62	−0.05
B^{11}	6.81	$\frac{1}{2}; \frac{3}{2}-$	−67.45	−67.40	−0.05
B^{11}	4.46	$\frac{1}{2}; \frac{5}{2}-$	−65.10	−64.68	−0.42
B^{11}	6.76	$\frac{1}{2}; \frac{7}{2}-$	−67.40	−67.40	−0.00
C^{12}	0	0; 0$^+$	−41.94	−42.25	+0.31
C^{12}	7.66	0; 0$^+$	−49.60	−50.16	+0.56
C^{12}	12.73	0; 1$^+$	−54.67	−54.90	+0.23
C^{12}	15.11	1; 1$^+$	−57.05	−57.79	+0.74
C^{12}	16.11	1; 2$^+$	−58.05	−58.01	−0.04
C^{12}	18.37	1; 2$^+$	−60.31	−59.65	−0.66
N^{13}	0	$\frac{1}{2}; \frac{1}{2}-$	−36.99	−36.64	−0.35
N^{13}	3.68	$\frac{1}{2}; \frac{3}{2}-$	−40.50	−40.98	+0.48
B^{13}	0	$\frac{3}{2}; \frac{3}{2}-$	−52.39	−52.29	−0.10
N^{14}	2.31	1; 0$^+$	−28.75	−28.63	−0.12
N^{14}	0	0; 1$^+$	−26.44	−26.08	−0.36
N^{14}	3.95	0; 1$^+$	−30.39	−30.03	−0.36
N^{14}	7.03	0; 2$^+$	−33.47	−33.78	+0.31
N^{14}	10.43	1; 2$^+$	−36.87	−37.25	+0.38
N^{14}	11.38	0; 3$^+$	−37.82	−37.99	+0.17
O^{15}	0	$\frac{1}{2}; \frac{1}{2}-$	−15.60	−15.70	+0.10
O^{15}	6.15	$\frac{1}{2}; \frac{3}{2}-$	−21.75	−21.88	+0.13

mention is that of beta decay. The theory of beta decay discussed in Chapter 13 shows that the beta-decay lifetime can be understood in terms of certain selection rules. The lifetime, on the other hand, depends upon the relative parity and angular momenta of the states involved. The nuclear-shell model is able to predict spins and parities of many unstable nuclei which decay by beta emission. The success has been remarkable, particularly in odd-A nuclei. We shall give only a few examples.

The lightest nucleus known which decays by β-emission is the neutron. The neutron decays to a proton with a half-life of 12.8 min. The measured spin of the proton is $\frac{1}{2}$, which is consistent with the shell-model assignment of $s_{1/2}$. Consider $_{10}Ne^{19}$ which decays to F^{19} by β^+-emission with a half-life of 18.2 sec. The shell-model configuration gives a spin $s_{1/2}$ for F^{19}, which is in accord with the measured value. $_{20}Ca^{45}$ decays to $_{21}Sc^{45}$ by β^--emission; the measured and predicted value of the spin of Sc^{45} is $f_{7/2}$.

We have given only some limited examples of beta decay to indicate the extent of agreement with the predictions of the shell model. In conclusion, we should remark that the model has been invaluable in our understanding of nuclear properties and shell structure.

References

1. Woods, R. D., and D. S. Saxon, *Phys. Rev.* **95**, 577, 1954.
2. Feenberg, E., *Shell Theory of the Nucleus*, Princeton University Press, 1955; *Handbook of Mathematical Functions with Formulas, Graphs, and Mathematical Tables*, M. Abramowitz and I. A. Stegun, eds., U.S. Department of Commerce, National Bureau of Standards, Applied Mathematics Series **55**, p. 467, 1964.
3. Malenka, B. J., *Phys. Rev.* **86**, 68, 1952.
4. Levinger, J. S., and D. C. Kent, *Phys. Rev.* **95**, 418, 1954.
5. Moszkowski, S. A., "Models of Nuclear Structure," in *Handbuch Der Physik*, vol. 39, p. 411, S. Flügge, ed., Springer Verlag, Berlin, 1957.
6. Hahn, B., D. G. Ravenhall, and R. Hofstadter, *Phys. Rev.* **101**, 1131, 1956.
7. Mayer, M. G., *Phys. Rev.* **75**, 1969, 1949.
8. Haxel, O., J. H. D. Jensen, and H. E. Suess, *Phys. Rev.* **75**, 1766, 1949.
9. Mayer, M. G., and J. H. D. Jensen, *Elementary Theory of Nuclear Shell Structure*, John Wiley and Sons, New York, 1955.
10. Nordheim, L. W., *Phys. Rev.* **78**, 294, 1950; *Rev. Mod. Phys.* **23**, 322, 1951.
11. Brennan, M. H., and A. M. Bernstein, *Phys. Rev.* **120**, 927, 1960.
12. Duffield, R. B., and L. M. Langer, *Phys. Rev.* **84**, 1065, 1951.
13. Holm, G. B., and H. J. Martin, Jr., *Phys. Rev.* **122**, 1537, 1961.
14. Fulmer, R. H., A. L. McCarthy, and B. L. Cohen, *Phys. Rev.* **128**, 1302, 1962.
15. Landau, L., and Ya. Smorodinsky, *Lectures on Nuclear Theory*, Plenum Press, Inc., New York, 1959.
16. Redlich, M. G., *Phys. Rev.* **95**, 448, 1954.
17. Blatt, J. M., and J. D. Jackson, *Phys. Rev.* **76**, 18, 1949.
18. Glaudemans, P. W. M., G. Wiechers, and P. J. Brussaard, *Nucl. Phys.* **56**, 529, and 548, 1964.

19. Redlich, M. G., *Phys. Rev.* **99**, 1421, 1955.
20. Rutherford, D. E., *Substitutional Analysis*, Edinburgh University Press, Edinburgh, 1948; Yamanouchi, T., *Proc. Physic. math. Soc.* Japan, **19**, 436, 1937.
21. Elliot, J. P., *Selected Topics in Nuclear Theory*, p. 157, International Atomic Energy Agency, Vienna, 1963.
22. Elliot, J. P., and A. M. Lane, "The Nuclear Shell Model," in *Handbuch Der Physik*, vol. 39, p. 241. S. Flügge, ed., Springer Verlag, Berlin, 1957.
23. Hund, F., *Z. Physik* **105**, 202, 1937.
24. Jahn, H. A., *Proc. Roy. Soc. (London)* **A201**, 516, 1950.
25. Flowers, B. H., *Proc. Roy. Soc. (London)* **A212**, 248, 1952.
26. Kennedy, J. M., and M. J. Cliff, Chalk River Report CRT, p. 609, 1955.
27. Bacher, R. F., and S. Goudsmit, *Phys. Rev.* **46**, 948, 1934.
28. Racah, G., *Phys. Rev.* **63**, 367, 1943.
29. Jahn, H. A., and H. Van Wieringen, *Proc. Roy. Soc. (London)* **A209**, 509, 1951; Jahn, H. A., *Proc. Roy. Soc. (London)* **A205**, 192, 1951; Racah, G., *Phys. Rev.* **76**, 1352, 1949; Edmonds, A. R., and B. H. Flowers, *Proc. Roy. Soc. (London)* **A214**, 515, 1952.
30. Amit, D., and A. Katz, *Nucl. Phys.* **58**, 388, 1964.
31. Kurath, D., *Phys. Rev.* **101**, 216, 1956.

Problems

1. Write out the shell configuration for $_{30}Zn^{67}$, $_{43}Tc^{99}$, $_{12}Mg^{25}$, and $_{57}La^{139}$; and compare the spin obtained from the shell model with the experimental values.

2. (a) Find an expression for the interaction of the particles in the j-shell, assuming a closed j-j coupling shell of identical particles.

(b) Derive the corresponding expression when one more particle is added to the closed shell.

3. For two particles and for J odd show that $\Psi_J^M(\mathbf{r}_1, \mathbf{r}_2) = 0$.

4. Derive an expression for the magnetic moment μ of a nucleus using the independent-particle model. Using the level scheme given in the text, find theoretical values of the magnetic moment for the following nuclei: $_1H^2$, $_2He^3$, $_5B^{10}$, $_7N^{14}$, and $_8O^{17}$. Compare these values with experimental ones.

5. Discuss the merits and demerits of the extreme single-particle model, single-particle model, and independent-particle model.

6. Show that the spin-orbit doublet separation

$$(\Delta E)_{ls} = E_{J=l-\frac{1}{2}} - E_{J=l+\frac{1}{2}}$$

is proportional to $(2l + 1)$.

7. Determine the harmonic oscillator frequencies ω appropriate to the nuclei O^{17}, Ca^{41}, and Ni^{60}.

8. Express the wave function $|(d_{5/2})^1(p_{3/2})^1\rangle$ with $M = 3$ in terms of the singlet and triplet state form.

9. What do you infer from Nordheim's rules about the existence of odd-odd nuclei with ground states 0^+ or 1^-?

8

NUCLEAR MODEL II: UNIFIED (COLLECTIVE) MODEL

8.1 Introduction

The unified model* was developed by Bohr[1] and by Bohr and Mottelson.[2] The collective model is useful in explaining the large values of the electric quadrupole moments found for a number of nuclides of odd-A far removed from the closed-shell nuclei. Large values of quadrupole moment cannot be obtained by the j-j coupling scheme. Rainwater[3] noted that if the nuclei are assumed to be deformed so that they have permanent nonspherical shapes (spheroidal shapes), the many protons in the nucleus can give large values of the electric quadrupole moments. The deformation of the nucleus can occur as a result of the polarizing action of one or more loosely bound nucleons on the remaining nucleus, which is the basis of the collective behavior.

The collective mode is more evident when one considers the excitations of the even-even nuclei. Over the last several years a large amount of data has been accumulated on the excitation of even-even nuclei that indicates that they all have ground-state spin and parity 0^+ and the first excited state 2^+. The γ-rays emitted from the first excited state to the ground state in even-even nuclei show that the transitions are of the electric quadrupole type ($E2$). Such transitions are identified with various vibrational and rotational bands. The unified model encompasses some

---

* The names unified and collective model are used here interchangeably. Both represent collective effects with certain differences. The unified model is a hybrid of the liquid-drop model and distorted-shell model, that is, the shell-model potential is assumed nonspherical and the nucleons move approximately independently rather than being strongly coupled as in the case of the liquid-drop model. The collective model refers to a simpler model in which the nucleus is considered to consist of a core and extra core particles with the core being treated as a liquid drop.

262

properties of both the shell model and the liquid-drop model. The principal assumption, that differs from that of the independent-particle model, states that, in the unified model, a number of nearly loose particles move in a slowly varying potential that arises from nuclear deformation. This deformation in the shape of the nucleus leads to modes of excitation which are classified as vibrational and rotational. The observed excitations of even-even and odd-A nuclei far removed from the closed shells indicate energy level-spacings characteristic of the vibrational and rotational spectra. De-Shalit[4] has described some excited states of odd-A nuclei in terms of excitation of the even-even core.

The collective properties are evident if the lowest single-particle state is coupled to the core excitation. Detailed calculations have been made by Kisslinger and Sorensen[5] for investigating the low-energy states of spherical nuclei considering first the pairing correlation[6] between the neutrons and protons individually, and then the quadrupole force among all the pairs of particles.

The concept of pairing energy (δ-term) has already appeared in Chapter 5 in the discussion of binding energy. We have seen that even-even nuclei (containing protons as well as neutrons in pairs) are energetically favored as compared with odd-even, even-odd, and odd-odd nuclei. The pairing energy can be defined by considering a nucleus with both Z and N even. If we successively add two protons to the nucleus, then the pairing energy of the proton pair can be thought of as binding energy of these two protons minus twice the binding energy of the $(Z + 1)$th proton. The pairing energy of a neutron pair can be similarly defined. The magnitude of the pairing energy determines the successive filling of closely adjacent levels.

For closed-shell nuclei, the pairing forces are dominant and the nucleus retains its spherical shape. However, deformation occurs when additional nucleons start to fill the unfilled shell outside the closed shell. The nucleus gradually reaches ellipsoidal shape, and the collective motion appears in the form of vibrational and rotational modes of excitation.

The calculations based on the unified model are extensive, and it is sometimes difficult to differentiate precisely among the various approaches made. However, a large number of these calculations have succeeded, at least in a semiquantitative way, in explaining various nuclear properties such as level energies, transition probabilities, reaction rates, and moments.

8.2 Nuclear Rotational Motion: Rotational Energy Spectra and the Nuclear Wave Functions for Even-Even Nuclei

Let us consider the collective rotational motion of nuclei which have axial symmetry. This is similar to the rotation of a symmetric top. The following are two sets of orthogonal systems of axes: (1) body-fixed reference frame: 1, 2, 3 axes; and (2) laboratory-fixed reference frame: x-, y-, z-axes. In system 1 the body-fixed reference frame is attached to the rotating body. The 3-axis is used as the axis of symmetry. If $\mathscr{I}_3$ and $\mathscr{I}$ are the moments of inertia for rotations[3] about symmetry-axis 3 and about an axis perpendicular to it, and $\mathbf{I}$ is the total angular momentum operator with components I_1, I_2, and I_3 along the body-fixed axes, the Hamiltonian is given by

$$H = \sum_{i=1}^{3} \frac{\hbar^2}{2\mathscr{I}_i} I_i^2 = \frac{\hbar^2}{2\mathscr{I}} (\mathbf{I}^2 - I_3^2) + \frac{\hbar^2}{2\mathscr{I}_3} I_3^2 \tag{1}$$

where (for the symmetric top) $\mathscr{I}_1 = \mathscr{I}_2 = \mathscr{I}$.

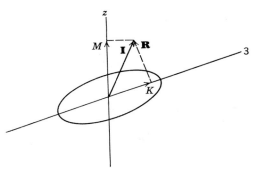

Fig. 8-1 Schematic diagram for angular momenta in deformed nuclei.

The nuclear wave functions are the D-functions which are the transformation functions for the spherical harmonics under finite rotations. Thus the spherical harmonic $Y_{lm}(\Omega)$ transforms as in Eq. (2a) under a rotation through Euler angles θ, ϕ, and ψ [counterclockwise rotation θ ($0 \leq \theta \leq 2\pi$) about the z-axis, followed by a rotation ϕ ($0 \leq \phi \leq \pi$) about the new y-axis, and a rotation ψ ($0 \leq \psi \leq 2\pi$) about the new z-axis]

$$Y_{lm}(\Omega) = \sum_{m'=-l}^{l} Y_{lm'}(\Omega') D_{mm'}^{l}(\theta, \phi, \psi) \tag{2a}$$

where Ω and Ω' are the initial and final polar angles (θ, ϕ) and (θ', ϕ'), and m and m' can independently take any of the values $-l, -l+1, \ldots, l-1, l$.

Let us denote by M the component of the angular momentum $\mathbf{I}$ along the z-axis (laboratory frame) and by K the component of $\mathbf{I}$ along symmetry-axis 3 (body frame), as shown in Fig. 8-1. We then obtain the following relations satisfied by the angular momentum operator:

$$\mathbf{I}^2 D^I_{MK} = I(I + 1)D^I_{MK} \tag{2b}$$

$$I_z D^I_{MK} = M D^I_{MK} \tag{2c}$$

$$I_3 D^I_{MK} = K D^I_{MK} \tag{2d}$$

A normalized wave function corresponding to the Hamiltonian in Eq. (1) is

$$\Psi^I_{MK} \equiv |IMK\rangle = \left[\frac{2I + 1}{8\pi^2}\right]^{1/2} D^I_{MK}(\theta, \phi, \psi) \tag{3a}$$

and the energy eigenvalues are

$$E_{IK} = \frac{\hbar^2}{2\mathscr{I}}[I(I + 1) - K^2] + \frac{\hbar^2}{2\mathscr{I}_3}K^2 \tag{3b}$$

For even-even axially symmetric nuclei $K = 0$. This follows because even-even spherical nuclei do not show rotational spectra and therefore do not rotate about the axis of symmetry; thus the angular momentum about a symmetry axis vanishes. The wave function and energy spectrum for even-even nuclei are given by

$$\Psi^I_{M0} \equiv |IM0\rangle = i^{-M}\left[\frac{2I + 1}{8\pi^2}\right]^{1/2} D^I_{M0}(\theta, \phi)$$

$$= Y_{IM}(\theta, \phi) \tag{3c}$$

$$E_I = \frac{\hbar^2}{2\mathscr{I}} I(I + 1) \tag{3d}$$

where, in Eq. (3c), the factor i^{-M} has been inserted so that Ψ^I_{M0} corresponds to Y_{IM}.

Because a spheroid is invariant with respect to rotation by π about any axis passing through the center, the wave function (3a) should be invariant with respect to rotation by π about, say, the 1-axis, that is, under a transformation of the Euler angles

$$\theta \to \pi + \theta \qquad \phi \to \pi - \phi \qquad \psi \to \psi$$

We designate this rotation by an operator

$$R_1 (\theta \to \pi + \theta, \phi \to \pi - \phi, \psi \to \psi).$$

Invariance under R_1 requires that the normalized wave function be

$$\Psi^I_{MK} \equiv |IMK\rangle = \left[\frac{2I + 1}{8\pi^2}\right]^{1/2} \frac{1}{\sqrt{2}}(1 + R_1)D^I_{MK}(\theta, \phi, \psi)$$

$$= \left[\frac{2I + 1}{16\pi^2}\right]^{1/2}[D^I_{MK} + (-1)^{I+K}D^I_{M,-K}] \tag{4a}$$

since

$$R_1 D^I_{MK}(\theta,\phi,\psi) = e^{i\pi(I+K)} D^I_{M,-K}(\theta,\phi,\psi)$$

$$R_1^2 = 1 \qquad R_1 \Psi^I_{MK} = \Psi^I_{MK} \tag{4b}$$

From Eq. (4a), it follows that

$$\text{if} \quad K = 0, \quad \text{for} \quad \Psi^I_{MK} \neq 0, \quad \text{we require} \quad I = 0, 2, 4, \ldots \tag{4c}$$

In other words, for $K = 0$, only even angular-momentum I states are allowed.

If the nucleus has additional (internal) degrees of freedom associated with the rotational motion, denoted by χ_i, then the correct wave function replacing Eq. (4a) is the product wave function

$$\Psi^I_{MK} \equiv |IMK\rangle = \left[\frac{2I+1}{16\pi^2}\right]^{\frac{1}{2}} [D^I_{MK}\chi_i + (-1)^{I+K} D^I_{M,-K} R_1\chi_i] \tag{4d}$$

where we have assumed that the total wave function is the product of the two wave functions.

8.3   Odd-A Nuclei: Energy Spectrum and Wave Function

In this section we discuss odd-A nuclei which consist of an even-even core and a loosely bound (unpaired) nucleon. Let $\mathbf{j}$ denote the intrinsic angular momentum of the nucleon. Because of axial symmetry about the body-fixed 3-axis, the component j_3 of $\mathbf{j}$ along the symmetry axis is a constant of motion. The total angular momentum $\mathbf{I} = \mathbf{R} + \mathbf{j}$, where $\mathbf{R}$ is the angular momentum associated with the rotation (of the even-even core). The total Hamiltonian for the system is

$$H = H_{\text{rot}} + H_{\text{p}} + V(\mathbf{r}) \tag{5a}$$

where H_{rot} is the Hamiltonian for the rotator, H_{p} is the Hamiltonian for the odd-particle (nucleon), and $V(\mathbf{r})$ is the interaction potential between the particle and the rotator, $\mathbf{r}$ being the radius vector in the body-fixed reference frame. Writing H_{rot} in full, we have

$$H_{\text{rot}} = \sum_{i=1}^{3} \frac{\hbar^2}{2\mathscr{I}_i} R_i^2 = \frac{\hbar^2}{2\mathscr{I}} (\mathbf{R}^2 - R_3^2) + \frac{\hbar^2}{2\mathscr{I}_3} R_3^2$$

$$= \frac{\hbar^2}{2\mathscr{I}} (\mathbf{I} - \mathbf{j})^2 \tag{5b}$$

where in the last term we have made use of the fact that the component of the angular momentum R_3 of the rotator about its symmetry axis is zero, so that $I_3 = R_3 + j_3 = j_3$. The total Hamiltonian can be rewritten as

$$H = H_0 + H_{\text{ro}}^0 + H_{\text{coupl}} \tag{5c}$$

where

$$H_0 = H_p + V(\mathbf{r}) + \frac{\hbar^2}{2\mathscr{I}} j^2 \tag{5d}$$

$$H_{\text{rot}}^0 = \frac{\hbar^2}{2\mathscr{I}} (\mathbf{I}^2 - 2I_3 j_3) = \frac{\hbar^2}{2\mathscr{I}} (\mathbf{I}^2 - 2j_3^2) \tag{5e}$$

$$H_{\text{coupl}} = -\frac{\hbar^2}{2\mathscr{I}} (2I_1 j_1 + 2I_2 j_2)$$

$$= -\frac{\hbar^2}{2\mathscr{I}} [I_+ j_- + I_- j_+] \tag{5f}$$

with

$$I_\pm = I_1 \pm iI_2 \qquad j_\pm = j_1 \pm ij_2 \tag{5g}$$

We denote the solutions of H_0 by $\chi_\Omega(\mathbf{r})$ where Ω is the eigenvalue of the operator j_3. Ω is a constant of motion since the potential $V(\mathbf{r})$ is axially symmetric. (If the potential $V(\mathbf{r})$ is spherically symmetric, then j would be a constant of motion.) A normalized eigenfunction of the Hamiltonian in Eq. (5c) is

$$\Psi_{\Omega MK}^I \equiv |I\Omega MK\rangle = \sqrt{\frac{2I+1}{8\pi^2}} \, \chi_\Omega(r) D_{MK}^I(\theta, \phi, \psi) \tag{6a}$$

Because of axial symmetry, the nuclear wave function, Eq. (6a), should be invariant with respect to the rotation of the body fixed frame about the symmetry axis by an arbitrary amount α. The operator for this rotation is $R_3 \, (\theta \to \theta, \phi \to \phi, \psi \to \psi + \alpha)$. Under* R_3,

$$R_3 D_{MK}^I = e^{iK\alpha} D_{MK}^I \tag{6b}$$

$$R_3 \chi_\Omega = e^{-i\Omega\alpha} \chi_\Omega \tag{6c}$$

Therefore, from Eqs. (6a) to (6c), it is clear that the requirement

$$R_3 \Psi_{\Omega MK}^I = \Psi_{\Omega MK}^I \tag{6d}$$

is satisfied, provided

$$\Omega = K \tag{6e}$$

The additional invariance which must be considered is R_1—rotation by π about the 1-axis. The effect of R_1 on D has already been considered in Eq. (4b). To investigate the transformation of χ_Ω under R_1, we expand χ_Ω in terms of wave functions $\chi_{j\Omega}$ which are eigenstates of the angular momentum j,

$$\chi_\Omega = \sum_j a_{j\Omega} \chi_{j\Omega} \tag{7a}$$

* The exponents in Eqs. (6b) and (6c) have opposite signs, because D is the wave function (of the body system) with respect to the laboratory system, whereas χ is the wave function with respect to the body system.

Furthermore, $\chi_{j\Omega}$ (in body system) is related to the wave function $\chi'_{j\Omega}$ (in laboratory system) by the relation

$$\chi_{j\Omega} = \sum_{\Omega'} \chi'_{j\Omega'} D_{\Omega'\Omega}^{j*} \tag{7b}$$

Under R_1,

$$R_1\chi_{j\Omega} = \sum_{\Omega'} \chi'_{j\Omega'} R_1 D_{\Omega'\Omega}^{j*}$$

$$= e^{-i\pi(j+\Omega)} \sum_{\Omega'} \chi'_{j\Omega'} D_{\Omega',-\Omega}^{j*}$$

$$= e^{-i\pi(j+\Omega)}\chi_{j,-\Omega} \tag{7c}$$

Thus, from Eqs. (4a), (4b), (6b) to (6e), and (7c), we find that the normalized nuclear wave function which is invariant under the operations R_1 and R_3 is given by the following expressions in the two cases (1) $K = \Omega \neq 0$ and (2) $K = \Omega = 0$.

Case 1. $K = \Omega \neq 0$

$$\Psi_{MK}^I \equiv |IMK\rangle = \left[\frac{2I+1}{16\pi^2}\right]^{1/2}[\chi_K(\mathbf{r})D_{MK}^I + (-1)^{I-j}\chi_{-K}(\mathbf{r})D_{M,-K}^I] \tag{7d}$$

where the term $(-1)^{-j}$ acts separately on each j-component of χ_Ω.

Case 2. $K = \Omega = 0$

For this case, only certain values of the total angular momentum I of the nucleus are allowed. If the wave function of the odd particle contains even (odd) values of j, then I of the nucleus must be even (odd). This is found to be the case in the low-lying states of even-even nuclei. The normalized wave function is given by

$$\Psi_{M0}^I \equiv |IM\rangle = \frac{1}{\sqrt{2\pi}}\chi_0(\mathbf{r})Y_{IM}(\theta, \phi) \tag{7e}$$

The symmetrization in Eq. (7d) is such that the parity of the nuclear wave function Ψ_{MK}^I is the same as that of χ_K. The parity operator P involves inversion of the coordinates of all particles. P operating on χ_K inverts the coordinates of χ_K, and its operation on D_{MK}^I is equivalent to an inversion of the nuclear surface through the origin. Using Eqs. (7a), (7b), and (7d) we can rewrite Ψ_{MK}^I

$$\Psi_{MK}^I = \left[\frac{2I+1}{16\pi^2}\right]^{1/2} \sum_{j,K'} a_{jK}\chi'_{jK'}(1 + R_1)\{D_{MK}^I(\theta, \phi, \psi)D_{K'K}^{j*}(\theta, \phi, \psi)\}$$

$$= \text{independent of the angle } \psi \tag{7f}$$

Therefore, the parity operator P is equivalent to the rotation R_1 (rotation by π about the 1-axis), so that

$$P(1 + R_1) = R_1(1 + R_1) = R_1 + 1$$

Hence, $P\Psi^I_{MK} = P\chi'_{jK'}$; that is, the parity of the nuclear wave function is the same as the parity of the particle wave function in the laboratory coordinates.

Energy Eigenvalues

The eigenvalues of the Hamiltonian H, Eq. (5e), can be determined using the wave function Ψ^I_{MK} in Eqs. (7d) and (7e). We consider the following two cases.

1. *The particle-rotation Hamiltonian* (*Coriolis term*). $H_{\text{coupl}} \sim 0$ if the particle is tightly bound to the rotator so that the energy-level separations of H_0 are large compared to the rotational energies. The eigenvalues E_I of $H_0 + H^0_{\text{rot}}$ are given by (the rotational spectrum)

$$E_I = E_0 + \frac{\hbar^2}{2\mathscr{I}} [I(I+1) - 2K^2] \tag{8a}$$

with

$$I = K, K+1, \ldots \tag{8b}$$

2. *Special case of* $K = \frac{1}{2}$. Since the nuclear wave function contains both $\pm K$ values there is considerable modification of the energy spectrum, because H_{coupl} has diagonal matrix elements. Using the wave function Ψ^I_{MK} of Eq. (7d), we find that

$$E_I = E_0 + \frac{\hbar^2}{2\mathscr{I}} [I(I+1) - 2K^2 + \delta_{K,\frac{1}{2}} a(-1)^{I+\frac{1}{2}} (I + \frac{1}{2})] \tag{8c}$$

where

$$a = (-1)^l \langle -\tfrac{1}{2} | j_- | +\tfrac{1}{2} \rangle = - \sum_j |a_{j\frac{1}{2}}|^2 (-1)^{j+\frac{1}{2}} (j + \tfrac{1}{2}) \tag{8d}$$

Here $(-1)^l$ is the parity of χ and a is called the decoupling parameter since it corresponds to a partial decoupling of the particle motion from the rotator. For all known rotational spectra in heavy elements with $K = \frac{1}{2}$, a lies between -1 and $+1$. On the other hand, for light nuclei, a has been found to have large values, resulting in a partial inversion of the level ordering. In Eq. (8c) we have made use of the following matrix relations:

$$\langle IMK | I_\pm | IMK \pm 1 \rangle = [(I \mp K)(I \pm K + 1)]^{\frac{1}{2}} \tag{8e}$$

$$\langle j\Omega | j_\mp | j\Omega \pm 1 \rangle = [(j \mp \Omega)(j \pm \Omega + 1)]^{\frac{1}{2}} \tag{8f}$$

A large amount of data is available for even-even nuclei with spin sequence 0^+ for the ground state, 2^+ for the first excited state, and $2'^+$ or 4^+ for the second excited state (the spin of second excited state is often denoted by $2'$ instead of 2) for axially symmetric nuclei. The rotational

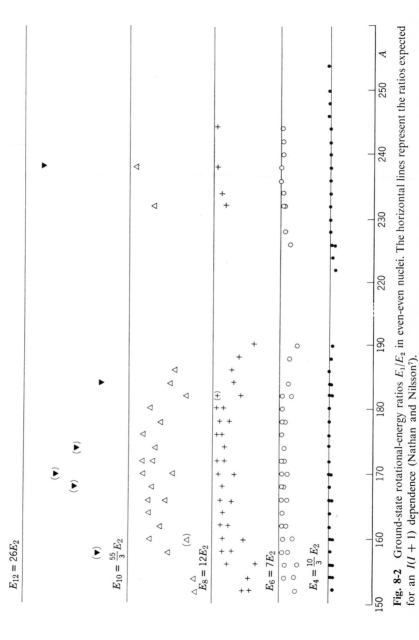

Fig. 8-2 Ground-state rotational-energy ratios E_I/E_2 in even-even nuclei. The horizontal lines represent the ratios expected for an $I(I + 1)$ dependence (Nathan and Nilsson[7]).

energy spectrum, Eq. (3b) with $K = 0$ for even-even nuclei, is explained well by the energy formula

$$E_I = \frac{\hbar^2}{2\mathscr{I}} I(I + 1) \tag{8g}$$

as can be seen from Fig. 8-2.[7] However, we note systematic deviation from the rotational spectrum. This deviation can be explained by adding a correction term of the form $I^2(I + 1)^2$ to the energy. Thus in the next approximation the energy is given by

$$E_I = \frac{\hbar^2}{2\mathscr{I}} I(I + 1) - BI^2(I + 1)^2. \tag{8h}$$

The value of B can be calculated from the energy of the 4^+ state, which is approximately given by $\hbar^2/2\mathscr{I} \times 10^{-3}$ for even-even nuclei with $154 \leq A \leq 180$. The deviation from the rotational spectrum may be thought of as due to a weak coupling between the rotational mode of motion, and either vibrational or particle mode. This coupling depending on $\mathbf{I}^2$ contributes to a small change in energy given by the second term of Eq. (8h).

8.4 Nuclear Moments

We have seen that for several nuclei the nuclear moments can be understood in terms of the shell-model schemes. However, there are some exceptions that can be interpreted satisfactorily only within the framework of collective motion. In fact, the nuclear deformation of odd-A nuclei is attributed to the presence of an electric quadrupole moment, and the rotational spectrum observed is due to electric quadrupole transitions.

We denote

$M'_{lm} = $ multipole operator of order (l, m) in the laboratory system

$M_{lm} = $ multipole operator of order (l, m) in the body-fixed system

Then

$$M'_{lm} = \sum_{m'} D^l_{mm'} M_{lm'} \tag{9a}$$

The transition probability for a gamma-ray emission of a multipole of order l is given by

$$T(l) = \frac{8\pi(l + 1)}{l[(2l + 1)!!]^2} \frac{1}{\hbar} \left(\frac{\Delta E}{\hbar c}\right)^{2l+1} B(l) \tag{9b}$$

where the "reduced transition probability" $B(l)$ is

$$B(l; I_i \to I_f) = \sum_{m M M'} |\langle I_f M'| M'_{lm} |I_i M \rangle|^2 \tag{9c}$$

Conservation of angular momentum and parity π in a nuclear transition leads to the following selection rules

$$|I_i - I_f| \leq l \leq I_i + I_f$$

$$\pi_i \pi_f = (-1)^l \qquad \text{for electric transitions}$$

$$\pi_i \pi_f = (-1)^{l+1} \qquad \text{for magnetic transitions}$$

(9d)

Electric Quadrupole Moment $(l = 2)$

In the calculation of the electric quadrupole operator $M'_{2m}(E)$, it is necessary to take the form of the wave function Ψ^I_{MK} given by Eq. (7d). However, the crossterms which couple the two components of the wave function contribute to the matrix element only for $2K \leq l$. If this case is not considered, it is sufficient to use Eq. (6a) (with $\Omega = K$) as the wave function. The matrix element of M'_{l0} is given by

$$\langle I'M'K| M'_{l0} |IMK\rangle = \frac{[(2I + 1)(2I' + 1)]^{1/2}}{8\pi^2} \sum_{m'} \langle \chi_K(\mathbf{r}')| M_{lm'} |\chi_K(\mathbf{r}')\rangle$$

$$\times \int (D^{I'}_{M'K})^* D^l_{0m'} D^I_{MK} \, d\Omega$$

(10a)

where

$$d\Omega = \sin \phi \, d\phi \, d\theta \, d\psi$$

Using the following relations

$$\frac{1}{8\pi^2} \int (D^{I'}_{M'K'})^* D^l_{mm'} D^I_{MK} \, d\Omega = \frac{1}{(2I' + 1)} \langle lImM \mid I'M'\rangle \langle lIm'K \mid I'K'\rangle$$

(10b)

$$\langle I1M0 |IM\rangle = \frac{M}{\sqrt{I(I + 1)}}$$

(10c)

$$\langle I2M0 \mid IM\rangle = \frac{3M^2 - I(I + 1)}{\sqrt{I(I + 1)(2I - 1)(2I + 3)}}$$

(10d)

we obtain

$$\langle I'M'K| M'_{l0} |IMK\rangle = \sqrt{\frac{(2I + 1)}{(2I' + 1)}} \sum_{m'} \langle \chi_K(\mathbf{r}')| M_{lm'} |\chi_K(\mathbf{r}')\rangle$$

$$\times \langle lI0M \mid I'M'\rangle \langle lIm'K \mid I'K\rangle$$

$$= \sum_{m'} \sqrt{\frac{2I + 1}{2I' + 1}} \, \delta_{MM'} \delta_{m'0} \langle \chi_K(\mathbf{r}')| M_{l0} |\chi_K(\mathbf{r}')\rangle$$

$$\times \langle lI0M \mid I'M\rangle \langle lI0K \mid I'K\rangle$$

(10e)

More explicitly, for $l = 1$ and $l = 2$, we have

for $l = 1$:

$$\langle I'M'K | M'_{10} | IMK \rangle = \sqrt{\frac{2I + 1}{2I' + 1}} \, \delta_{MM'} \langle \chi_K | M_{10} | \chi_K \rangle$$
$$\times \langle 1I0M | I'M \rangle \langle 1I0K | I'K \rangle \tag{11a}$$

for $l = 2$:

$$\langle I'M'K | M'_{20} | IMK \rangle = \sqrt{\frac{2I + 1}{2I' + 1}} \, \delta_{MM'} \langle \chi_K | M_{20} | \chi_K \rangle$$
$$\times \langle 2I0M | I'M \rangle \langle 2I0K | I'K \rangle \tag{11b}$$

For $I' = I$, the matrix elements of the angular momentum and quadrupole moment operators are given by

$$\langle j_z \rangle_{IMK} = \langle j_3 \rangle_{IMK} \frac{MK}{I(I + 1)} \tag{11c}$$

$$\langle Q \rangle_{IMK} = Q_0 \frac{[3M^2 - I(I + 1)][3K^2 - I(I + 1)]}{I(I + 1)(2I - 1)(2I + 3)} \tag{11d}$$

where the angular momentum operator j_z and the quadrupole moment operator Q are in the laboratory system, and j_3 and Q_0 are their values in the body-fixed system. The Q operator is related to M_{20} as follows:

$$\langle \chi_0 | M_{20} | \chi_0 \rangle = \sqrt{\frac{5}{16\pi}} \, eQ_0 \tag{11e}$$

$$Q_0 = \langle \chi_0 | (3z^2 - r^2) | \chi_0 \rangle \tag{11f}$$

The "reduced transition probability" $B(E2; I \to I')$ for an electric quadrupole transition between two members of the same rotational band with quantum number K is obtained from Eqs. (9c), (10c), and (11e)

$$B(E2; IK \to I'K) = \frac{5}{16\pi} e^2 Q_0^2 |\langle I2K0 | I'K \rangle|^2 \tag{12a}$$

where we have used

$$\sum_{M_1, M_2, M} |\langle I_1 I_2 M_1 M_2 | IM \rangle|^2 = (2I + 1) \tag{12b}$$

For Coulomb excitation, the $B(E2)$ reduced transition probability in the case of a symmetric rotator (even-even nuclei) is given by

$$B(E2; I \to I + 2) = \frac{5}{16\pi} e^2 Q_0^2 |\langle I2\,0\,0 | I + 2, 0 \rangle|^2$$

$$= \frac{15}{32\pi} e^2 Q_0^2 \frac{(I + 1)(I + 2)}{(2I + 1)(2I + 3)} \tag{12c}$$

For odd nuclei, the $B(E2)$ value is obtained from Eq. (12a).

The nonspherical nuclei have rotational levels that are due to the very fast electric quadrupole transition probability $B(E2; I \rightarrow I')$, which, according to Eq. (12a), increases as the value of the electric quadrupole moment Q_0 increases as is evident[8] from Table 8-1.

Experimentally, Q_0 is usually determined from the Coulomb excitation. The target nucleus is bombarded by protons, deuterons, alpha particles, or even heavier ions, raising the nucleus to an excited state which then de-excites by the emission of γ-rays. The higher excited states sometimes

Table 8-1 The Reduced Transition Probability (Perlman[8])

Nucleus	E_γ (Kev)	$B(E2)\ 0 \rightarrow 2$ ($e^2 \times 10^{-48}\,\mathrm{cm}^4$)	Q_0 ($10^{-24}\,\mathrm{cm}^2$)
Em^{218}	325	0.88	3.0
Ra^{222}	111	4.4	6.6
Th^{226}	72	6.8	8.3
U^{230}	52	8.9	9.5
U^{238}	45	11.1	10.5
Pu^{238}	44	11.9	11.0
Gd^{152}	344	0.8	—

may not be reached through Coulomb excitation; if so, the possibility of radioactive nuclei which decay by the emission of high-energy γ-rays is considered. If the transition takes place between the ground state for which $I = 0$ and the first excited state $I = 2$ of even-even nuclei, then $B(E2) = (5/16\pi)\, e^2 Q_0^2$. Under certain assumptions, the experimental values of the intrinsic quadrupole moment Q_0 may provide information concerning the shape of nuclei. These assumptions are related to the nature of nuclear deformation.

Nuclear Deformation

If the nucleus is considered as a uniformly charged spheroid, then by taking the radial coordinate of the surface of the nucleus as

$$R \simeq R_0[1 + \beta\, Y_{2\,0}(\theta, \phi)] \tag{13a}$$

the intrinsic quadrupole moment Q_0 is

$$Q_0 = e \int d^3r \rho(r) \langle IM| (3z^2 - r^2) |IM\rangle_{M=I} \tag{13b}$$

$$= \frac{3}{\sqrt{5\pi}} Z e R_0^2 \beta[1 + 0.36\beta + \cdots] \tag{13c}$$

From the observed values of Q_0, we can determine β. The deformation parameter β can also be related to the difference ΔR between the major and minor semi-axes.

$$\beta = \frac{4}{3}\sqrt{\frac{\pi}{5}}\frac{\Delta R}{R_0} = 1.06\frac{\Delta R}{R_0} \tag{13d}$$

Magnetic Dipole Moment

The magnetic dipole moment $\boldsymbol{\mu}$ for an odd-A nucleus arises from the angular momentum $\mathbf{R}$ of the rotator and the total spin $\mathbf{j}$ of the last (odd) nucleon. Thus

$$\boldsymbol{\mu} = (g_R\mathbf{R} + g_l\mathbf{l} + g_s\mathbf{s}) \tag{14a}$$

where

$$\mathbf{j} = \mathbf{l} + \mathbf{s} \tag{14b}$$

$$\mu = g_j j = \langle g_R R_z + g_l l_z + g_s s_z\rangle_{M=I} \tag{14c}$$

and g_l, g_s are the g-factors for the last particle (in units of one nuclear magneton, $g_{sn} = -3.826$, $g_{sp} = 5.585$, $g_{ln} = 0$, $g_{lp} = 1$; n and p stand for neutron and proton, respectively). g_R is the g-factor for rotational (collective) motion. It may be reasonable to estimate $g_R \approx Z/A$. The total angular momentum $\mathbf{I}$ of the nucleus is defined as

$$\mathbf{I} = \mathbf{R} + \mathbf{j} \tag{14d}$$

so that

$$\boldsymbol{\mu} = g_R\mathbf{I} + \boldsymbol{\mu}' \tag{14e}$$

where

$$\boldsymbol{\mu}' = (g_l\mathbf{l} + g_s\mathbf{s} - g_R\mathbf{j})$$
$$= (\mu'_{-1}, \mu'_0, \mu'_{+1}) \tag{14f}$$

with

$$\mu'_0 = \mu'_z \qquad \mu'_{\pm 1} = \mp\frac{1}{\sqrt{2}}(\mu'_x \pm i\mu'_y). \tag{14g}$$

μ'_m ($m = 0, \pm 1$) can be transformed to the internal coordinate system by the relation

$$\mu'_m = \sum_{m'} D'_{mm'}\mu_{m'} \tag{15a}$$

The evaluation of the matrix elements of μ'_m follows a pattern similar to the calculations of the quadrupole operator.

By defining the magnetic dipole operator as

$$M_{lm} = \frac{e\hbar}{2Mc}\sqrt{\frac{3}{4\pi}}\mu_m \tag{15b}$$

the "reduced magnetic dipole transition probability" for an $M1$ transition between two members of the same rotational band for axially symmetric deformed nuclei is (except for $K = \frac{1}{2}$)

$$B(M1; I_i \rightarrow I_f) = \frac{3}{4\pi}\left(\frac{e\hbar}{2Mc}\right)^2 \sum |\langle I_f, M_f = I_f, K| \mu_m |I_i, M_i = I_i, K\rangle|^2$$

$$= \left(\frac{3}{4\pi}\right)\left(\frac{e\hbar}{2Mc}\right)^2 (g_K - g_R)^2 K^2 |\langle I_i 1 K 0 | I_f K\rangle|^2 \quad (15c)$$

where

$$\mathbf{I} = K\hat{e}_3 + \mathbf{R}, \qquad \boldsymbol{\mu} = g_K K\hat{e}_3 + g_R \mathbf{R} \quad (15d)$$

The emission of electric quadrupole or magnetic dipole radiation is dependent on the parameter K which is a constant of motion since K is the value of the projection of the angular momentum $\mathbf{I}$ parallel to the nuclear symmetry axis. Consequently, the transition is governed by what is known as the K-selection rule.[9] For transitions from band K_i to band K_f the rule states $\lambda \geq |K_i - K_f| \equiv \Delta K$. The importance of this rule has been noted in quite a few transitions. In addition to the K-selection rule there is another one, known as the intensity rule, also due to Alaga et al.[9] This determines the alternate modes of decay or branching ratios. For transitions $\lambda \leq K_f + K_i$, or if K_f or K_i is zero, the intensity rule states that

$$\frac{B(\lambda; I_i \rightarrow I_f')}{B(\lambda; I_i \rightarrow I_f)} = \frac{|\langle I_i \lambda K_i K_f - K_i | I_f' K_f\rangle|^2}{|\langle I_i \lambda K_i K_f - K_i | I_f K_f\rangle|^2} \quad (16)$$

This intensity rule is valid for E2 as well as higher multipole transitions.

We have already seen that the deformed even-even nuclei give rise to a rotational spectrum due to electric quadrupole transitions of low-lying states. In most cases the transition between second $(2'+)$ and first excited states $2'+ \rightarrow 2^+$, is of the E2 type. However, the selection rule does not prohibit the magnetic dipole (M1) transition of a cascade $2'+ \rightarrow 2^+ \rightarrow 0^+$. Davydov and Filippov[10] give definite expressions for such transitions. Because of the smallness of the effect it is hard to detect M1 transitions. These mixed transitions are of considerable interest. The mixing ratio δ is defined by

$$\delta = \pm\sqrt{\frac{\text{intensity of } E2}{\text{intensity of } M1}} \quad (17)$$

The sign of δ depends upon the relative phase of the reduced matrix element. The value of δ can be ascertained from γ–γ angular correlation measurements of the transition $2'+ \rightarrow 2^+ \rightarrow 0^+$. The $2^+ \rightarrow 0^+$ transition is pure E2. Figure 8-3[11] gives the variation of $\log (\delta/E_\gamma)^2$ as a function of the neutron number N where E_γ is the energy of transition. The dotted lines are due to single-particle estimates[12] and the Davydov-Filippov model. The figure indicates that δ increases as a function of the neutron number with exceptions at magic numbers 28, 50, 82, and 126. At these neutron numbers the mixing ratios diminish by a factor of two or three from the values predicted by the Davydov-Filippov model. This is of course not unexpected, since rotational-level calculations are effective at a region far removed from the closed shells. Grechukhin[13] has calculated in great detail the magnetic transitions of even nuclei which show collective quadrupole-type excitations. He has shown that $\delta^2(E2/M1)$ is sensitive to the admixture of single-particle excitations in the collective states of the nucleus. The mixing ratio δ in the mixed transitions $I_i(M1 + E2)I_f$ for different transitions such as $I_1 \to I_2$ and $I_3 \to I_4$ is, according to the collective model,

$$\frac{\delta^2\left(\dfrac{E2}{M1}, I_1 \to I_2\right)}{\delta^2\left(\dfrac{E2}{M1}, I_3 \to I_4\right)} = \frac{\omega_{12}^2 f(I_3, I_4)}{\omega_{34}^2 f(I_1, I_2)} \qquad (18)$$

where ω is the frequency of the γ-ray emitted in the transitions between the two states. Calculations show that

$$\left[\frac{B(M1)}{B(E2)}\right] = 0.286 \times 10^5 A^{-4/3}$$

for the single-particle excitation and

$$\left[\frac{B(M1)}{B(E2)}\right] = f(I_1, I_2) \times 10^4 A^{-10/3}$$

for collective-model excitations. The function $f(I_1, I_2)$ for different transitions has the values: $f(2 \to 2) = 84$; $f(3 \to 2) = 96$; $f(3 \to 3) = 180$; $f(3 \to 4) = 180$; $f(4 \to 4) = 308$; $f(5 \to 4) = 288$; $f(5 \to 5) = 468$; and $f(6 \to 5) = 420$. Numerous experimental data have been compared for different transitions. The results are given in Fig. 8-4[13] which shows the dependence of $[B(M1)/B(E2)]$ on A. The analysis of the data indicates that $\delta_{exp}^2 \le \delta_{coll}^2$. This deviation of the experimental values from the (theoretical) collective-model values of the mixing ratio may be due to the admixture of single-particle excitations with the collective states. Taking into consideration the single-particle contributions to only M1

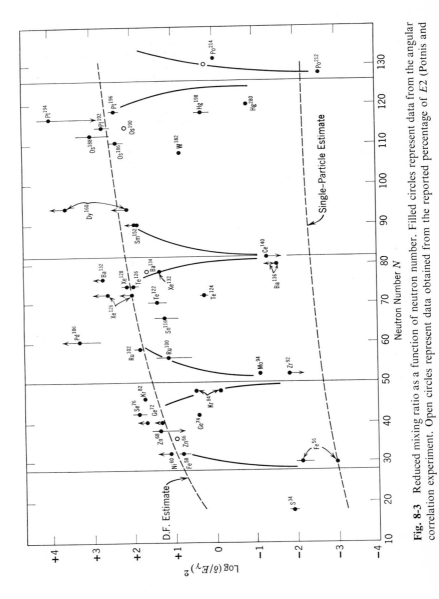

Fig. 8-3 Reduced mixing ratio as a function of neutron number. Filled circles represent data from the angular correlation experiment. Open circles represent data obtained from the reported percentage of $E2$ (Potnis and Rao[11]).

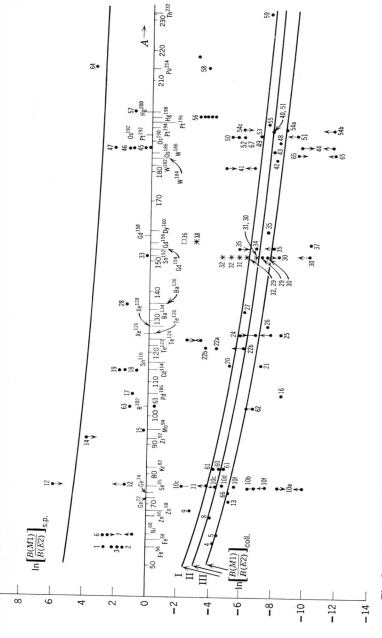

Fig. 8-4 Experimental and theoretical values for $Z/g_R = A$ of the quantities $[B(M1)/B(E2)]$ are compared. Curves I, II, and III correspond to the following transitions: $I_1 \rightarrow I_2$: I to $(4 \rightarrow 4)$, $(4 \rightarrow 5)$; II to $(3 \rightarrow 4)$, $(3 \rightarrow 3)$; and III to $(2 \rightarrow 2)$, $(3 \rightarrow 2)$ (Grechukhin[13]).

transitions (neglecting the contributions to E2), Grechukhin[13] obtains approximately

$$\delta^2\left(\frac{E2}{M1}, I_1 \to I_2\right) \approx \frac{1}{\left[1 + a^2\left(\frac{\mu_n}{\beta g_R}\right)^2\right]} \delta^2\left(\frac{E2}{M1}, I_1 \to I_2\right)_{\text{coll}} \qquad (19a)$$

where

$$\delta^2\left(\frac{E2}{M1}, I_1 \to I_2\right)_{\text{coll}} = \frac{441}{500} \frac{1}{f(I_1, I_2)} \left(\frac{Z\omega M R_0^2}{g_R}\right)^2 \qquad (19b)$$

and

$$f(I_1, I_2) = (I_1 + I_2 + 3)(I_2 - I_1 + 2)(I_1 - I_2 + 2)(I_1 + I_2 - 1). \qquad (19c)$$

g_R is the gyromagnetic ratio for nuclear collective excitations, R_0 is the nuclear radius, Z is the effective charge, M is the nucleon mass, and ω is the frequency of the emitted radiation. The parameter a^2 determines the admixture of single-particle to nuclear collective excitations and depends upon the specific model used for collective excitation calculations. In Fig. 8-4 are also given the theoretical estimates from the single-particle model. In a majority of the transitions, $\delta^2_{\text{exp}} < \delta^2_{\text{th}}$ for collective transitions. It seems then that one should first separate the true collective quadrupole transitions for comparison, or take into account the contribution of single-particle excitation to the M1 transition, since the quantity δ^2 changes substantially when single-particle excitation is added to the collective mode.

8.5   Collective Vibrational Excitations

We consider the nucleus to be a dynamic system which can perform small oscillations about the equilibrium shape. The oscillations can be analyzed in terms of normal modes; for small oscillation amplitudes, they can be treated as independent. Since the energies involved in vibrational excitations are of the order of several hundred Kev to Mev, the coupling between the vibrational and intrinsic motions need no longer be weak as was the case with rotational motion. It is therefore to be expected that the agreement of the experimental data with the theoretical predictions in vibrational spectra would not be as good as that in the rotational spectra.

The vibrational states are known to occur not only among spherical even-even nuclei but also among deformed nuclei. The spin sequence for the ground, first, and second excited states is 0^+, 2^+, $2'^+$ or 4^+, although infrequent 0^+, 1^- or 3^- states have also been reported for the second excited state. The ratio of the energy of the second and the first excited state when plotted as a function of neutron number is about 2.2 when $N \leq 88$. This is evident from Fig. 8-5a.[14] It can also be seen that there is a sudden change in E_2/E_1 between $N = 88$ and $N = 90$. The electric quadrupole E2 transitions are much more frequent than E1 transitions. The other known properties are that the $2^+ \to 0^+$ transition is pure E2 and that the $2'^+ \to 2^+$ transitions can be a mixture of (E2 and M1) with a preponderance of E2.

8.6 Collective Oscillations: Liquid-Drop Model

The nucleus is considered as an incompressible liquid drop with a sharp surface, and the nuclear wave function is described in terms of the radius vector specifying the nuclear surface. If R_0 is the radius of the nucleus if it were spherical, the equation for the surface can be written[15]

$$R(\theta, \phi) = R_0 \left[1 + \sum_{\lambda, \mu} \alpha_{\lambda\mu} Y^*_{\lambda\mu}(\theta, \phi) \right] \tag{20a}$$

where $Y_{\lambda\mu}$ are the spherical harmonics and $\alpha_{\lambda\mu}$ are deformation parameters which determine the nuclear shape. The subscript μ takes the values $-\lambda$ to $+\lambda$, so that there are $2\lambda + 1$ modes of deformation of order λ. The lowest mode of surface deformation corresponds to quadrupole mode ($\lambda = 2$), since a deformation of order $\lambda = 1$ is equivalent to a translation of the whole system. For $\lambda = 2$, the five values of $\mu = -2$ to $+2$ correspond to five independent modes which represent ellipsoidal shapes. The mode with $\mu = 0$ (for all λ values) has symmetry with respect to arbitrary rotation about the z-axis and therefore represents an axially symmetric nuclear shape.

The surface oscillations come about as a result of the variation of the deformation parameters $\alpha_{\lambda\mu}$ which, although quantum-mechanical variables, may be treated here as being classical and time dependent. Because of surface oscillation, there is collective transport of nuclear matter within the nucleus. Assuming irrotational flow (vortex-free flow), the velocity field at points inside the surface is given by

$$\mathbf{v} \simeq R_0^2 \sum_{\lambda, \mu} \frac{1}{\lambda} \dot{\alpha}_{\lambda\mu} \, \text{grad} \left\{ \left(\frac{r}{R} \right)^\lambda Y_{\lambda\mu} \right\} \tag{20b}$$

where higher orders in $\dot{\alpha}_{\lambda\mu}$ have been neglected, that is, $\dot{\alpha}_{\lambda\mu}$ is assumed to be small. The kinetic energy T of nuclear mass transport in the nucleus is

$$T = \tfrac{1}{2} \sum_{\lambda, \mu} B_\lambda |\dot{\alpha}_{\lambda\mu}|^2 \tag{20c}$$

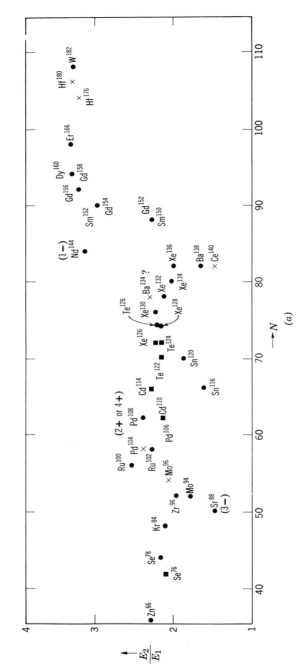

Fig. 8-5(a) Ratio of energies E_2/E_1 as function of neutron number N ($36 \leq N \leq 108$). The character of the second excited state of the nucleus is denoted by ▲ (0+), ■ (2+), × (4+), and ● (not known, unless given in parentheses) (Scharf-Goldhaber and Weneser[14]).

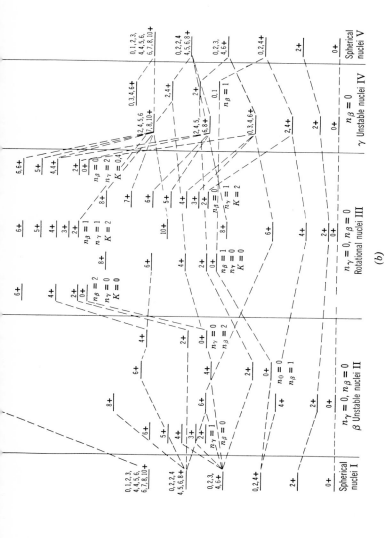

Fig. 8-5(b) Relationships between the levels in spherical, deformed, β-unstable, and γ-unstable nuclei. Vertical solid lines separate the various nuclear species. Spins are given on top of the levels. Related states are connected by dashed lines (Sheline[20]).

283

where B_λ corresponds to the moment of inertia of the nucleus with respect to changes in deformation and can be calculated from Eq. (20b) under the assumption of irrotational flow by using Rayleigh's[16] method

$$B_\lambda = \frac{3}{4\pi} \frac{MAR_0^2}{\lambda} = \frac{\rho R_0^5}{\lambda} \tag{20d}$$

ρ being the density of nuclear matter. The potential energy for collective motion is

$$V = \tfrac{1}{2} \sum_{\lambda,\mu} C_\lambda |\alpha_{\lambda\mu}|^2 \tag{20e}$$

where C_λ are the deformability coefficients which measure the resistance of the nucleus against deformation. The total Hamiltonian H is given by

$$H = E_0 + \sum_{\lambda,\mu} H_{\lambda\mu} \tag{20f}$$

where

$$H_{\lambda\mu} = \tfrac{1}{2} B_\lambda |\dot{\alpha}_{\lambda\mu}|^2 + \tfrac{1}{2} C_\lambda |\alpha_{\lambda\mu}|^2 \tag{20g}$$

and E_0 is the energy of the nucleus for a spherically symmetric shape. The C_λ, which has been evaluated by Bohr and Wheeler,[17] is given by

$$C_\lambda = \frac{\lambda - 1}{4\pi} \left[(\lambda + 2)E_S - \frac{10}{2\lambda + 1} E_c \right] \tag{20h}$$

where E_S and E_c are the surface and Coulomb energies respectively for a spherical shape. The classical frequency of oscillation ω_λ from Eq. (20g) is

$$\omega_\lambda = \sqrt{\frac{C_\lambda}{B_\lambda}} \tag{20i}$$

The Hamiltonian in Eq. (20g) can be quantized by introducing $\pi_{\lambda\mu}$, the variable canonically conjugate to $\alpha_{\lambda\mu}$,

$$\pi_{\lambda\mu} = B_\lambda \dot{\alpha}_{\lambda\mu}^* \tag{21a}$$

The quantized Hamiltonian is

$$H_{\lambda\mu} = \frac{1}{2B_\lambda} |\pi_{\lambda\mu}|^2 + \tfrac{1}{2} C_\lambda |\alpha_{\lambda\mu}|^2 \tag{21b}$$

whose energy eigenvalues (levels) are the harmonic-oscillator energies:

$$E = E_0 + \sum_{\lambda,\mu} (n_{\lambda\mu} + \tfrac{1}{2})\hbar\omega_\lambda \tag{21c}$$

where $n_{\lambda\mu}$ is the number of oscillators or phonons in the $\lambda\mu$-mode of oscillation.

The wave function for the lowest (ground) state corresponding to all $n_{\lambda\mu} = 0$ is

$$\Psi_0 = N \exp\left[-\sum_{\lambda,\mu} \frac{B_\lambda \omega_\lambda}{2\hbar}(\alpha_{\lambda\mu})^2\right] \tag{21d}$$

where N is the normalization constant. The wave function of the one-phonon state of mode $\lambda\mu$ of energy $\hbar\omega_\lambda$ relative to the ground state is

$$\Psi_1 = N_1 \alpha_{\lambda\mu}^* \Psi_0 \tag{21e}$$

The state Ψ_0 [Eq. (21d)] is nondegenerate and corresponds to angular momentum zero, whereas the state Ψ_1 is $(2\lambda + 1)$-fold degenerate and therefore corresponds to an angular momentum λ. From Eqs. (20h), (20i), and (20d) we obtain the excitation energy for the $\lambda\mu$-mode (neglecting Coulomb energy)

$$\hbar\omega_\lambda \simeq 13\lambda^{3/2} A^{-1/2} \text{ Mev} \tag{21f}$$

From Eqs. (20d) and (20h), for low-lying states it is sufficient to consider only small values of λ as the frequency of emitted radiation ω_3 (for $\lambda = 3$) is about twice the value of ω_2 and $\omega_4 = 3\omega_2$. The excitation energy of the collective mode from Eq. (21c) is

$$\sum_{\lambda,\mu} (n_{\lambda\mu} + \tfrac{1}{2})\hbar\omega_\lambda$$

The angular momentum of a phonon in the state $\lambda\mu$ is λ, its z-component is μ, and the parity is $(-1)^\lambda$, the value of λ being ≥ 2 for surface oscillations. As a result, the spin and parity of the ground state and first excited state should be respectively 0^+ and 2^+, which have been confirmed experimentally for even-even nuclei. The first excited state is one $\lambda = 2$ phonon state. The spin and parity of the second excited state can be obtained from considering that the energy of one $\lambda = 3$ phonon is roughly equal to the energy of two $\lambda = 2$ phonons. Therefore the spin and parity of the second excited state are 3^- or any one of the values 0^+, 2^+, and 4^+ obtained from the combination of two angular momenta of two units. Experimentally, 2^+, sometimes 4^+, and occasionally 3^- are observed.

Equation (21f) suggests that the energy of the emitted γ-rays should decrease as a function of mass number, which is in agreement with experimental observations. In collective oscillations, since all the nucleons are involved, the electric quadrupole transition E2 between the first excited state and the ground state should be stronger than one would expect from a single-particle model. Experimentally, the E2 transition is more often at least one order of magnitude larger than the prediction of a single-particle model. The analogy between the liquid-drop model and the collective mode of vibration has some limitations. These arise from the fact that the energy of the first excited state for the collective type of nuclei is of the order of a few hundred Kev, whereas the energy of the same state from the liquid-drop model is of the order of a few Mev.

8.7 Quadrupole Deformation

We next consider ellipsoidal shapes, restricting the discussion to the quadrupole deformation $\lambda = 2$ in Eq. (20a). The surface of the ellipsoid is described by $R(\theta', \phi')$, and the deformation $\delta R(\theta', \phi')$ from the radius R_0 of the sphere (of the same volume) is

$$\delta R(\theta', \phi') = R(\theta', \phi') - R_0$$

$$= R_0 \sum_{\mu=-2}^{2} \alpha_{2\mu}^* Y_{2\mu} \tag{22a}$$

where the deformation parameter $\alpha_{2\mu}$ and the polar angles θ', ϕ' are with respect to the laboratory system. Since δR is real, we obtain

$$\alpha_{2,-\mu} = (-1)^\mu (\alpha_{2\mu})^* \tag{22b}$$

Equation (22b) implies that there are only five independent deformation constants $\alpha_{2\mu}$ ($\mu = -2$ to $+2$)—two specifying the shape and three describing the orientation.

In the body-fixed reference frame in which the coordinate axes coincide with the principal axes, we denote the deformation parameters $\alpha_{2\mu}$ by $a_{2\mu}$. The relationship between deformation in the two coordinate systems is

$$\sum_{\mu} a_{2\mu}^* Y_{2\mu}(\theta, \phi) = \sum_{\nu} a_{2\nu}^* Y_{2\nu}(\theta, \phi)$$

$$= \sum_{\nu} a_{2\nu}^* \sum_{\mu} D_{\mu\nu}^2(\theta, \phi, \psi) Y_{2\mu}(\theta', \phi') \tag{22c}$$

so that

$$\alpha_{2\mu} = \sum_{\nu} a_{2\nu} D_{\mu\nu}^{2*}(\theta, \phi, \psi) \tag{22d}$$

Since, in terms of the principal axes, the product of inertia is zero, we define the following

$$a_{20} = \beta \cos \gamma \tag{23a}$$

$$a_{21} = a_{2\,-1} = 0 \tag{23b}$$

$$a_{22} = a_{2,-2} = \frac{1}{\sqrt{2}} \beta \sin \gamma \tag{23c}$$

where β and γ are new parameters whereby the a's are defined. The deformations δR_j along the principal axes $j = 1, 2, 3$ (nuclear body-fixed axes) are obtained from

$$\delta R(\theta, \phi) = R_0 \sum_{\mu=-2}^{2} a_{2\mu}^* Y_{2\mu}(\theta, \phi)$$

and are given by

$$\delta R_1\left(\frac{\pi}{2}, 0\right) = \sqrt{\frac{5}{4\pi}} \beta R_0 \cos\left(\gamma - \frac{2\pi}{3}\right)$$

$$\delta R_2\left(\frac{\pi}{2}, \frac{\pi}{2}\right) = \sqrt{\frac{5}{4\pi}} \beta R_0 \cos\left(\gamma - \frac{4\pi}{3}\right)$$

$$\delta R_3(0, \phi) = \sqrt{\frac{5}{4\pi}} \beta R_0 \cos \gamma$$

that is, by

$$\delta R_j = \sqrt{\frac{5}{4\pi}} \beta R_0 \cos\left(\gamma - \frac{2\pi j}{3}\right) \tag{23d}$$

The parameter β is a measure of the deviation from sphericity and γ determines the shape of the nucleus as indicated in Table 8-2.

Table 8-2 Nuclear Shapes for Different Values of γ

γ	Shape	Symmetry Axis
0	Spheroid-prolate (football-shaped)	3-Axis
π	Spheroid-oblate (dish-shaped)	3-Axis
$2n\pi/3$	Spheroid-prolate }	
$(2n + 1)\pi/3$	Spheroid-oblate }	1- or 2-Axis
$\neq n\pi/3$	Ellipsoid (3 unequal axes along principal axes)	
$n = $ integer		

The kinetic energy for collective oscillations is given by Eq. (20c). In terms of the parameters β and γ, using Eqs. (23a) to (23c), and Eq. (22d), we obtain

$$T_{\lambda=2} = \tfrac{1}{2} B_2(\dot{\beta}^2 + \beta^2\dot{\gamma}^2) + \tfrac{1}{2}\sum_{j=1}^{3} I_j\omega_j^2 \tag{24a}$$

where B_2 is the mass parameter for collective quadrupole oscillations, ω is the angular velocity of the principal axes with respect to the laboratory (space)-fixed axes, and I_j are effective moments of inertia

$$I_j = 4B_2\beta^2 \sin^2\left(\gamma - \frac{2\pi}{3}j\right)$$

$$= \frac{15}{4\pi} I_{\text{rig}}\beta^2 \sin^2\left(\gamma - \frac{2\pi}{3}j\right) \tag{24b}$$

where I_{rig} is the moment of inertia of a rigid sphere of radius R_0, given by

$$I_{\text{rig}} = \frac{16\pi}{15} B_2 \tag{24c}$$

B_2 is given by Eq. (20d). The second term in Eq. (24a) corresponds to rotational kinetic energy. But since β^2 is small, very little of the kinetic energy of the nucleus takes part in the rotation. Furthermore, from Eq. (24b), for $\gamma = 0$ or π and $j = 3$, we have $I_3 = 0$, which implies that the 3-axis is an axis of symmetry. There is good experimental evidence of this result. In the spherical nuclei, low-lying rotational states have not been observed. The particles may show collective vibrations instead of a rotation about the axis.

8.8   Nuclear Moments

For even-even nuclei, since the intrinsic spin of the nucleus is zero ($I_0 = 0$), any angular momentum $\mathbf{I}$ and the magnetic moment $\boldsymbol{\mu}$ of the nucleus would arise from collective motion.

$$\boldsymbol{\mu} = g_c \mathbf{I} \tag{25a}$$

where g_c is the gyromagnetic ratio for collective motion. The matrix elements of $\boldsymbol{\mu}$ for M1 transitions are zero, since the matrix elements of the angular momentum operator $\mathbf{I}$ between different (nondegenerate) states vanishes. For E2 transitions, the reduced transition matrix, summed over all possible final states, is

$$\sum_f B(E2; i \rightarrow f) = \sum_f \left(\frac{3}{4\pi} R_0^2 Ze\right)^2 \sum_{\mu=-2}^{2} |\langle f| \alpha_{2\mu} |i\rangle|^2 \tag{25b}$$

$$= \left(\frac{3}{4\pi} R_0^2 Ze\right)^2 \langle i| \beta^2 |i\rangle \tag{25c}$$

where we have used that for a uniformly charged drop the corresponding electric multipole is

$$\mu(E\lambda\mu) = \frac{3}{4\pi} R_0^2 Ze\alpha_{\lambda\mu} \tag{25d}$$

For even-even nuclei, the matrix element in Eq. (25b) contributes significantly for transitions only between the ground state and the first excited states; and other transitions are strongly inhibited.[18]

For even-even nuclei, not far from the magic numbers, the departures from spherical shape are small, so that their equilibrium shape may be assumed to be spherical and collective oscillations about the spherical shape may be well approximated by quadrupole deformations. The Hamiltonian describing the collective motion is

$$H_{coll} = \frac{1}{2B_2} \sum_{\mu=-2}^{2} |\pi_{2\mu}|^2 + \tfrac{1}{2}C_2 \sum_{\mu=-2}^{2} |\alpha_{2\mu}|^2 \tag{26a}$$

The energy eigenvalue for the state containing n phonons, each having an angular momentum 2 and even parity, is

$$E_n = (n + \tfrac{5}{2})\hbar\omega_2 \tag{26b}$$

where

$$\hbar\omega_2 = \hbar\sqrt{\frac{C_2}{B_2}} \tag{26c}$$

is the uniform spacing between non-degenerate levels. The values of the mass parameter B_2 and the effective surface tension C_2 can be calculated from the energy difference and from the electric quadrupole transition rate between the first excited state and the ground state. Temmer and Heydenberg[19] observed that for even-even nuclei with $22 \leq Z \leq 52$, C_2 increases near the closed-shell nuclei. The same effect has also been noted for the mass parameter term B_2.

According to Bohr, the spin sequence of spherical nuclei removed from a closed shell is 0^+ for the ground state, 2^+ for the first excited state, and 0^+, 2^+, 4^+ etc. for the second excited state. In a deformed nucleus, on the other hand, one expects 0^+, 2^+, 4^+, 6^+, etc., for the ground-state rotational band, and a γ-vibration with a mixture of a rotational band with spin sequence 2^+, 3^+, 4^+, 5^+ etc., and a β-vibration with a superimposed rotational band with spin 0^+, 2^+, 4^+, 6^+ etc. Sheline[20] has proposed a relationship between the states of deformed nuclei and spherical nuclei, although in the latter case, there is no rotational motion. According to him the 2^+ first vibrational states of spherical nuclei are related to the 2^+ state of the ground-state rotational band; the second 2^+ members of the vibrational states of spherical nuclei are related to the 2^+ γ-vibrational band heads; and the second 4^+ members of the vibrational states are related to the 4^+ members of the ground-state rotational bands. Figure 8-5b on p. 283 illustrates[20] a schematic relationship between spherical and deformed nuclei as proposed by Sheline from the consideration of spins and parities of the two types of nuclei discussed. The β-unstable-vibration involves an infinitely long nucleus and has no physical meaning (hence the use of quotation marks).

The energy of vibrational levels above the ground state is shown[20] as a function of the neutron number in Fig. 8-6 for positive parity levels of even-even nuclei in the rare earth and actinide region. The figure is divided into vertical sections showing the regions of spherical and non-spherical nuclei. The smooth trends of the vibrational levels are noticeable for the particular way in which the vibrations of the spherical nuclei join those of the deformed nuclei. Between the neutron numbers 110 and 120, the 4^+ state of the ground-state rotational band and the 2^+ γ-vibrational band head join smoothly with the second vibrational state of the spherical

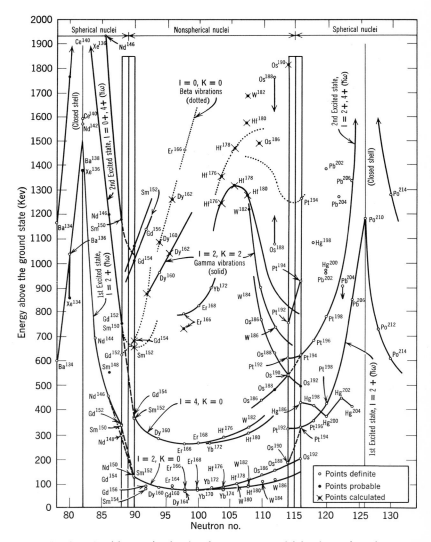

Fig. 8-6 Positive parity levels of even-even nuclei in the regions between closed neutron shells 82 and 126. Only 0+, 2+, and 4+ members of the ground-state bands are plotted; lines connecting the β vibrations are dotted and those connecting the γ vibrations are solid; higher members of the β- and γ-vibrational bands are not plotted (Sheline[20]).

region. The vibrations are relatively near the ground state at the beginning of the region of deformation. However, they seem to go monotonically upward through the region of deformation, and downward at its end. On the other hand, the γ-vibrations are complex and show rather wide fluctuations. To sum up, it appears that the vibrations of positive parity in the region of change from spherical to deformed or vice versa are very frequent in nuclei. The rotational levels due to E2 transitions are easy to reach through the Coulomb excitation process. However, the vibrational levels, because of their higher energy values, are difficult to excite.

The ratio of $B(E2)$ values for some electric quadrupole transitions for a few vibrational states in deformed even-even nuclei have been calculated by Davidson and Davidson.[21] The reduced transition probability $B(E2)$ from the state INn to the state $I'N'n'$ is given by the expression

$$B(E2; INn \rightarrow I'N'n') \equiv B_a(E2; IN \rightarrow I'N')S_{vv'} \qquad (26d)$$

where I is the spin of the state, N the ordinal of that spin, and n the ordinal of the β-vibrational band. The B_a term represents the pure rotational reduced transition probability and

$$S_{vv'} = (Z_1 Z_1'/ZZ' I_v I_{v'})(Z/Z_1)^{2M+2}(\mu\beta_0)^{2M} I_{vv'} \qquad (26e)$$

$$I_{vv'} = \int_0^\infty D_v(\sqrt{2}\,[y - Z_1])\, y^M D_{v'}(\sqrt{2}\,[R_z y - Z_1'])\, dy \qquad (26f)$$

D_v are the Weber functions, $R_z = (Z_1'Z/Z_1Z')$, Z_1 is a known function of v, I_v is a normalization integral, and μ is the stiffness parameter of the nucleus.

Figure 8-7 gives[21] the ratio of Coulomb excitation from the ground state to the first 2[+] state in the β-vibration band and ground-state band, that is,

$$B(E2; 011 \rightarrow 212)/B(E2; 011 \rightarrow 211)$$

The intraband transition is much more dependent upon the stiffness parameter μ of the nucleus than on γ. The experimentally determined Coulomb excitation ratios are also shown in Fig. 8-7. The value of μ has been determined for each case from the ratio of the energy of the beta band to the energy of the first excited state, that is, E(012)/E(211).

A comparison of the calculation of Davidson and Davidson with experimental results is given in Table 8-3. The asymmetry parameter η, the value of which is given in the table, refers to the negative parity state π^-, and the asymmetry parameter γ to the positive parity state. With some exceptions the experimental values are in reasonably good agreement with the predictions of the theory. Essentially, the calculations of Davidson and Davidson for the ratios of electric quadrupole reduced transition probabilities are based upon a collective model. However, distinction has been made between transitions between positive parity states and transitions between negative parity states. In the first, an asymmetric core model with β-vibrations has been used, and in the second, one with ξ-vibrations. The reduced transition probability has been divided into two factors, an adiabatic term $B_a(E2)$ and $B(E2)$ due to the vibration on the deformation parameter.

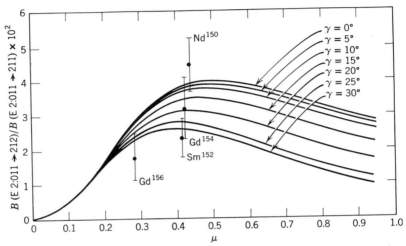

Fig. 8-7 Ratio of Coulomb-excitation transition probabilities for the excitation of the lowest 2+ states in the ground and beta-vibrational bands from the 0+ ground state plotted as a function of μ for different values of γ. The experimental values and errors for Nd^{150}, Sm^{152}, Gd^{154}, and Gd^{156} are from Ref. 22. The value of μ has been assigned from the energy ratio $E(012)/E(211)$ (Davidson and Davidson[21]).

Before concluding, we should point out that the situation is more complex in odd-A nuclei. The vibrational levels are difficult to detect experimentally. This is because the low-lying single-particle states are in competition with the vibrational states of odd-A nuclei. The unpaired odd nucleons are coupled to the collective oscillation. If this coupling can be neglected, the collective vibrational excitation spectrum can be observed.

8.9 Davydov and Filippov's Model

Davydov and Filippov[10] have calculated the energy states and the electric and magnetic transition probabilities for rotational levels of even

Table 8-3 Comparison Between Experiment and Theory for E2 Branching Ratios of Positive- and Negative-Parity Bands of W^{182} and Th^{228} and for Positive-Parity Bands of Sm^{152}. The First Column Gives the Initial and Final States for the Transitions Where $I_i N_i n_i - I_f N_f n_f$; I Is the Spin of a Level, N the Ordinal of the Level, and n the Ordinal of the Vibration Band. The Second and Third Columns Give Experimental Values and References for Sm^{152}, W^{182}, and Th^{228}; the Fourth Column, the Adiabatic Ratio, While the Fifth Column Gives the Ratio Including the Vibrational Contribution (Davidson and Davidson[21]).

Transitions	Experiment $B(E2)$	Ref.	Theory $B_a(E2)$	$B(E2)$
Sm^{152}, π^+, $\gamma = 11.3°$, $\mu = 0.396$				
$\dfrac{011 \rightarrow 212}{011 \rightarrow 211}$	0.023 ± 0.006	(a)	1.0	0.036
$\dfrac{212 \rightarrow 411}{212 \rightarrow 211}$	6.7 ± 1.8	(b)	1.81	4.22
$\dfrac{212 \rightarrow 011}{212 \rightarrow 411}$	0.048 ± 0.015	(b)	0.386	0.088
$\dfrac{221 \rightarrow 011}{221 \rightarrow 211}$	0.44 ± 0.02	(c)	0.502	0.453
W^{182}, π^+, $\gamma = 10.93°$, $\mu = 0.28‡$				
$\dfrac{221 \rightarrow 011}{221 \rightarrow 211}$	0.69 / 0.70	(d) / (e)	0.522	0.507
$\dfrac{221 \rightarrow 211}{221 \rightarrow 411}$	1†	(d)	11.52	10.96
$\dfrac{212 \rightarrow 011}{212 \rightarrow 211}$	0.57	(d)	0.708	0.600
$\dfrac{212 \rightarrow 211}{212 \rightarrow 411}$	0.833	(d)	0.547	0.405
$\dfrac{421 \rightarrow 211}{421 \rightarrow 411}$	0.2	(d)	0.158	0.150
$\dfrac{421 \rightarrow 411}{421 \rightarrow 611}$	1†	(d)	5.21	4.98
$\dfrac{621 \rightarrow 411}{621 \rightarrow 611}$	0.17	(d)	0.068	0.066

Table 8-3 (Contd.)

Transitions	Experiment $B(E2)$	Ref.	Theory $B_a(E2)$	$B(E2)$
W^{182}, π^-, $\eta = 83.5°$, $\mu = 1.0$				
$411 \to 211$	0.883	(d)		
$411 \to 311$	0.556	(e)	0.631	0.563
$421 \to 211$	1.	(d)		
$421 \to 311$	1.28	(e)	6.86	6.11
Th^{228}, π^+, $\gamma = 9.1°$, $\mu = 0.30$				
$221 \to 411$				
$221 \to 211$	0.09 ± 0.02	(f)	0.073	0.080
$221 \to 211$				
$221 \to 011$	2.32 ± 0.28	(f)	1.72	1.81
$421 \to 611$				
$421 \to 411$	≤ 0.25	(f)	0.151	0.165
$421 \to 411$				
$421 \to 211$	6.25 ± 0.8	(f)	4.66	5.12
$311 \to 411$				
$311 \to 211$	0.66 ± 0.08	(f)	0.600	0.658
Th^{228}, π^-, $\eta = 12.3°$, $\mu = 0.258$				
$211 \to 311$				
$211 \to 111$	<0.3	(f)	0.212	0.215
$321 \to 111$				
$321 \to 311$	0.36 ± 0.04	(f)	0.502	0.495
$411 \to 511$				
$411 \to 311$	0.75 ± 0.02	(f)	0.371	0.379

† Unobserved.

‡ Experimental errors are not given for the transition ratios of W^{182}.

References:

(a) Yoshizawa, Y., B. Elbek, B. Herskind, and M. C. Olesen, *Proc. Conf. Reactions Complex Nuclei*, 3rd, p. 289, University of California Press, Berkeley, 1963; Elbek, B., M. C. Olesen, and S. Skilbreid, *Nuclear Phys.* **19**, 523, 1960.

(b) Greenberg, J. S., G. C. Seaman, E. V. Bishop, and D. A. Bromley, *Phys. Rev. Letters* **11**, 211, 1963.

(c) Nathan, O., and S. Hultberg, *Nuclear Phys.* **10**, 118, 1959.

(d) Harmatz, B., T. H. Handley, and J. W. Mihelich, *Phys. Rev.* **123**, 1758, 1961.

(e) Gallagher, C. J., and J. O. Rasmussen, *Phys. Rev.* **112**, 1730, 1958.

(f) Arbman E. E., S. Bjørnholm, and O. B. Nielsen, *Nuclear Phys.* **21**, 406, 1960.

atomic nuclei which do not possess axial symmetry. We shall briefly
outline their theory and compare its predictions with some of the experimental results.

Davydov and Filippov consider the energy states of an even nucleus
corresponding to rotation of the nucleus as a whole with no change of its
internal state, and write the following operator for the rotational energy
of the nucleus:

$$H = \sum_{\lambda=1}^{3} \frac{\hbar^2 J_\lambda^2}{2I_\lambda} \tag{27a}$$

$$= \sum_{\lambda=1}^{3} \frac{A J_\lambda^2}{2 \sin^2\left(\gamma - \frac{2\pi}{3}\lambda\right)} \tag{27b}$$

where the expression for I_λ is substituted from Eqs. (24b) and (24c). The
parameter A has the dimension of energy and is $\hbar^2/4B_2\beta^2$; γ gives the
deviation of the shape of the nucleus from axial symmetry and has values
between 0 and $\pi/3$. The nucleus is considered symmetric between these
two limits exclusive of these two extreme values. Because of the symmetry
conditions imposed on the wave function, the only allowed values of J
for even nuclei are those which correspond to a completely symmetric
representation of the group D_2. There are no rotational states of the
required symmetry for $J = 1$. There are two states for $J = 2$, one for
$J = 3$, three for $J = 4$, two for $J = 5$, etc. The energies in units of $A =
\hbar^2/4B_2\beta^2$ of the two levels of required symmetry for $J = 2$ are

$$\mathscr{E}_1(2) = \frac{9(1 - \sqrt{1 - \frac{8}{9}\sin^2(3\gamma)})}{\sin^2(3\gamma)} \tag{27c}$$

$$\mathscr{E}_2(2) = \frac{9(1 + \sqrt{1 - \frac{8}{9}\sin^2(3\gamma)})}{\sin^2(3\gamma)} \tag{27d}$$

For $J = 3$, the energy of the level is

$$\mathscr{E}(3) = \frac{18}{\sin^2(3\gamma)} \tag{27e}$$

$\mathscr{E}_1(2) + \mathscr{E}_2(2) = \mathscr{E}(3)$ gives the relationship for levels of $J = 2$ and
$J = 3$. For spin 5, the energy levels are given by

$$\mathscr{E}_\tau(5) = \frac{45 \pm 9\sqrt{9 - 8\sin^2(3\gamma)}}{\sin^2(3\gamma)} \qquad \tau = 1, 2 \tag{27f}$$

where $\tau = 1$ with the minus sign and $\tau = 2$ with the plus sign. The
computed energy levels for various values of γ are given in Fig. 8-8.
For $\gamma = 0$, we obtain the energy levels corresponding to axially symmetric
nuclei as treated, for example, by Bohr and Mottelson.[2]

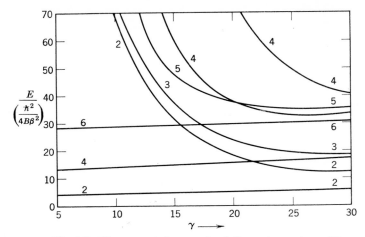

Fig. 8-8 The computed energy levels for various values of the deformation parameter γ (Davydov and Filippov[10]).

The Davydov and Filippov model also predicts the transition probabilities between the rotational states of the second excited state of spin 2 and the first excited state of spin 2 or to the ground state of spin 0 of an even nucleus. The first and second levels of spin 2 are known as the one- and two-phonon vibrations of the nuclear surface. The reduced transition probability $B(E2)$ for three transitions in terms of γ are:

$$B(E2; J = 2, \tau = 1 \rightarrow J = 0) = \frac{1}{2}\left(\frac{e^2 Q_0^2}{16\pi}\right)\left[1 + \frac{3 - 2\sin^2(3\gamma)}{\sqrt{9 - 8\sin^2(3\gamma)}}\right] \quad (28a)$$

for the first excited state to the ground state; for the second excited state to the ground state the reduced transition probability is

$$B(E2; J = 2, \tau = 2 \rightarrow J = 0) = \frac{1}{2}\left(\frac{e^2 Q_0^2}{16\pi}\right)\left[1 - \frac{3 - 2\sin^2(3\gamma)}{\sqrt{9 - 8\sin^2(3\gamma)}}\right] ; \quad (28b)$$

and for the second to the first excited state, the value is

$$B(E2; J = 2, \tau = 2 \rightarrow J = 2, \tau = 1) = \left(\frac{e^2 Q_0^2}{16\pi}\right)\left[\frac{10}{7}\frac{\sin^2(3\gamma)}{9 - 8\sin^2(3\gamma)}\right]$$

$$(28c)$$

The factor $(e^2 Q_0^2/16\pi)$ is the reduced electric quadrupole transition probability between rotational levels of spin 2 and 0 for axially symmetric nuclei. The ratios of various reduced transition probabilities can be calculated from these expressions.

The Davydov and Filippov theory has predicted successfully many rotational levels including those of higher excitation. From this theory

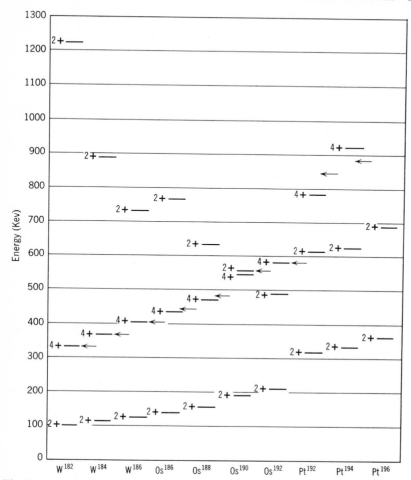

Fig. 8-9 Low-lying levels for even-even nuclei in the transition region from spheroidal to spherical shape (McGowan and Stelson[23]).

we can calculate the parameter γ, which determines the deviation from the axial symmetry known as γ-vibration, by taking the ratio of the energies of the first and second excited states of spin 2^+. By knowing the value of γ and the energy of the first excited state 2^+, we can obtain the theoretical value of the energy and hence the position of the first excited state of spin 4^+. McGowan and Stelson[23] (Fig. 8-9) studied the low-lying transitions by Coulomb excitation produced in even nuclei by bombardment with 4 to 5 Mev protons. Their results for the position of the first 4^+ state are in good agreement with the values predicted by Davydov and

Table 8-4 Comparison of $B(E2)$ Values with Those Predicted from the Davydov and Filippov Model. γ is Deduced from the Position of the First and Second 2^+ States (McGowan and Stelson[23])

Nucleus	γ in Degrees	$\dfrac{B(E2, 2' \to 2)}{B(E2, 2 \to 0)}$ Theory	Expt.	$\dfrac{B(E2, 2' \to 0)}{B(E2, 2 \to 0)}$ Theory	Expt.	$\dfrac{B(E2, 2' \to 2)}{B(E2, 2' \to 0)}$ Theory	Expt.
W^{184}	13.9	0.12	0.07 ± 0.02	0.051	0.038 ± 0.021	2.40	1.9 ± 0.4
W^{186}	16.0	0.18	0.12 ± 0.02	0.061	0.048 ± 0.010	3.05	2.5 ± 0.5
Os^{188}	19.1	0.32	0.19 ± 0.06	0.071	0.070 ± 0.022	4.60	2.8 ± 0.4
Os^{190}	22.3	0.58	0.41 ± 0.09	0.067	0.071 ± 0.017	8.7	5.8 ± 1.1
Os^{192}	25.3	0.94	0.98 ± 0.26	0.042	0.102 ± 0.023	23.5	9.5 ± 2.4
Pt^{194}	—	—	0.59 ± 0.14	—	0.004 ± 0.001	—	135 ± 20

Filippov. McGowan and Stelson also compared the ratios of $B(E2)$ values with those predicted by the Davydov and Filippov model. The results are given in Table 8-4 .The levels 2′, 2, and 0 correspond to the second excited state ($2'^+$), first excited state (2^+) and ground state (0^+). Good agreement is indicated between the theory and experiment. However, a recent experiment of DeBoer, Goldring, and Winkler[24] shows somewhat limited agreement with the $B(E2)$ values predicted by the asymmetric rotator model of Davydov and Filippov as can be observed from Table 8-5.

Another approach has been tried in the study of even-even nuclei. The electric quadrupole transition probabilities between the lowest excited states and ground state are frequently determined by the Coulomb excitation technique. If the bombarding particles are light, such as protons, deuterons, or alpha particles, then, the probability of excitation being small, the process is well described by the first-order perturbation theory.[25] But if the incident particles are heavy, like oxygen ions, the excitation probability may approach unity, in which case the perturbation treatment may not be applicable. The oxygen-ion bombardment of a target nucleus may produce multiple Coulomb excitations. The theory of this process has been developed by Alder and Winther.[26] Graetzer and Bernstein[27]

Table 8-5 Comparison of the $B(E2)$ ratios with the Predictions of the Davydov-Filippov Model (DeBoer et al.[24])

Isotope	$\dfrac{B(E2, 2' \to 2)}{B(E2, 2 \to 0)}$ Theory	Expt.	$\dfrac{B(E2, 2' \to 0)}{B(E2, 2 \to 0)}$ Theory	Expt.	$\dfrac{B(E2, 2' \to 2)}{B(E2, 2' \to 0)}$ Theory	Expt.
Gd^{160}	0.064	0.053 ± 0.016	0.031	0.023 ± 0.007	1.78	2.3 ± 0.5
W^{186}	0.18	0.051 ± 0.015	0.061	0.028 ± 0.009	3.05	1.9 ± 0.4
Os^{188}	0.32	0.13 ± 0.04	0.071	0.048 ± 0.014	4.60	2.2 ± 0.6
Os^{192}	0.94	0.22 ± 0.09	0.042	0.026 ± 0.008	23.5	8.6 ± 1.7

performed experiments to test their calculations regarding double E2 excitation of the spin 4, even-parity rotational levels in even-even non-spherical nuclei. In this experiment they used oxygen ions of energies 14 to 50 Mev to bombard targets of Sm^{152}, Sm^{154}, Gd^{160}, Dy^{162}, Er^{170}, Yb^{176}, $Hf,^{180}$, and W^{189}. The advantage of using heavy ions like oxygen

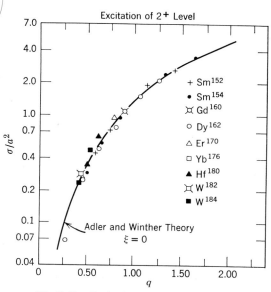

Fig. 8-10 Excitation of 2+ Level

+ Sm^{152}
• Sm^{154}
⊠ Gd^{160}
○ Dy^{162}
△ Er^{170}
□ Yb^{176}
▲ Hf^{180}
⊠ W^{182}
■ W^{184}

Adler and Winther Theory
$\xi = 0$

Fig. 8-10 Excitation of the 2+ rotational level of the ground-state band compared with the Alder-Winther theory. The estimated uncertainty is about 7% in values of σ/a^2 and about 3% in values of q. The Dy^{162} point plotted at $q = 0.276$ is based on a single measurement (Graetzer and Bernstein[27]).

as projectiles is that the Coulomb excitation probability in the target nucleus is high in comparison with the nuclear excitation.

The transition from the second excited state 4+ to first 2+ and from the first to ground state 0+ were observed. The B(E2) values obtained from the cross sections for excitation of the 2+ levels were found to be in satisfactory agreement with those obtained from lifetime measurements and from inelastic scattering of protons, deuterons, and alpha particles. The cross section for the double E2 excitation of the spin 4+ rotational levels is in qualitative agreement with the theory of Alder and Winther for even-even nonspherical nuclei. Figures 8-10 and 8-11 give the comparison of the experimental results with the theory. The ordinates σ/a^2

represent the cross section of double excitation divided by the square of one-half of the distance of the closest approach of the incident particles to the target nucleus. The parameter q depends upon the quadrupole moment Q_0 of the deformed nucleus.

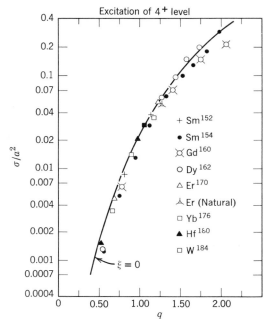

Fig. 8-11 Experimental results of double E2 Coulomb excitation compared with the Alder-Winther theory. The estimated uncertainty is about 13% in values of σ/a^2 and about 3% in q. The Sm[154] and Gd[160] points at $q = 1.95$ and $q = 2.03$, respectively, are each based on single determinations of the cross sections (Graetzer and Bernstein[27]).

Although this is not the appropriate place to discuss Alder and Winther's theory in detail, we shall indicate certain features of this calculation. When the bombardment of the target nucleus is by low Z-value projectiles, the excitation probability is small and, as mentioned earlier, the first-order perturbation theory is adequate for the process. However, as the probability of excitation increases as a result of the bombardment of target nucleus by heavy ions, the perturbation method breaks down. If one uses higher than a first-order perturbation expansion, a large number of parameters appear in the calculations. On the other hand, the theory of Alder and Winther uses the sudden approximation[28] which avoids a perturbation expansion. The method depends upon the assumption of a definite model of a nucleus in terms of a small number of parameters which are relatively easy to determine.

8.10 Nilsson Potential

In the shell theory the spherically symmetric self-consistent field is introduced by a phenomenological shell-model potential. The nuclear wave functions are then constructed by filling the lowest available states in the potential. Nilsson[29] has proposed an analogous procedure except that the self-consistent potential is deformed; the Nilsson model represents the self-consistent potential by an axially symmetric oscillator potential with spin-orbit coupling. The single particle wave functions (the Nilsson orbitals) are obtained by solving the Schrödinger equation with this potential.

Nilsson[29] introduced a term proportional to $\mathbf{l} \cdot \mathbf{l}$ and a spin-orbit term proportional to $\mathbf{l} \cdot \mathbf{s}$ in the Hamiltonian of an anisotropic oscillator in order to obtain the detailed characteristics of heavy, strongly deformed nuclei. The $\mathbf{l}^2$ term favors large l values and the $\mathbf{l} \cdot \mathbf{s}$ term takes into account the strong spin-orbit coupling of the nucleons. The interaction of one nucleon with the nuclear field is thus represented by a single-particle Hamiltonian of the following form

$$H = H_0 + C\mathbf{l} \cdot \mathbf{s} + D\mathbf{l}^2 \tag{29a}$$

where

$$H_0 = -\frac{\hbar^2}{2M} \nabla'^2 + \frac{M}{2}(\omega_x^2 x'^2 + \omega_y^2 y'^2 + \omega_z^2 z'^2) \tag{29b}$$

with x', y', z' being the coordinates of a particle in a coordinate system fixed in the nucleus. Considering the case of cylindrical symmetry, and introducing a single parameter of deformation, Nilsson writes

$$\omega_x^2 = \omega_0^2(1 + \tfrac{2}{3}\delta) = \omega_y^2 \qquad \omega_z^2 = \omega_0^2(1 - \tfrac{4}{3}\delta) \tag{30a}$$

with

$$\omega_x \omega_y \omega_z = \text{constant} \tag{30b}$$

which is the condition of the constant volume of the nucleus. From Eqs. (30a) and (30b), the dependence of ω_0 on δ is given by

$$\omega_0(\delta) = \omega_0^0(1 - \tfrac{4}{3}\delta^2 - \tfrac{16}{27}\delta^3)^{-\frac{1}{6}} \tag{31}$$

where $\omega_0^0 = \omega_0(\delta = 0)$. The parameter δ is related to the parameter β of Bohr and Mottelson by the relation

$$\delta \simeq \frac{3}{2}\sqrt{\frac{5}{4\pi}}\,\beta$$

The Hamiltonian H_0 can be rewritten in the form

$$H_0 = H_0^0 + H_\delta \tag{32a}$$

where

$$H_0^0 = \tfrac{1}{2}\hbar\omega_0[-\nabla^2 + r^2], \qquad \mathbf{r} = \sqrt{\frac{M\omega_0}{\hbar}}\,\mathbf{r}', \tag{32b}$$

is spherically symmetric, and

$$H_\delta = -\delta\hbar\omega_0\frac{4}{3}\sqrt{\frac{\pi}{5}}\,r^2 Y_{20} \tag{32c}$$

represents the coupling of the particle to the axis of the deformation.

The representation chosen by Nilsson is with the H_0^0 diagonal, together with l^2, l_z, and s_z. The base vectors used are $|N l \Lambda \Sigma\rangle$ where N represents the total number of oscillator quanta, and l, Λ, Σ are the quantum numbers corresponding to the operators l^2, l_z, s_z, respectively. The operator $j_z = l_z + s_z$ commutes with the total Hamiltonian H. The quantum number corresponding to j_z is denoted by $\Omega = \Lambda + \Sigma$, which represents the component of the nucleon total angular momentum along the nuclear axis.

Nilsson obtains the following form for the total Hamiltonian:

$$H = H_0^0 + H_\delta + C\mathbf{l}\cdot\mathbf{s} + D l^2 \tag{33a}$$

$$= H_0^0 + k\hbar\omega_0^0 R \tag{33b}$$

where

$$k = -\frac{1}{2}\frac{C}{\hbar\omega_0^0} \tag{34a}$$

$$R = \eta U - 2\mathbf{l}\cdot\mathbf{s} - \mu l^2 \tag{34b}$$

with

$$\mu = 2\frac{D}{C} \qquad \eta = \frac{\delta}{k}\frac{\omega_0(\delta)}{\omega_0^0} \tag{34c}$$

and U is obtained from

$$H_\delta = \delta\hbar\omega_0 U = k\hbar\omega_0^0\eta U \tag{35a}$$

giving

$$U = -\frac{4}{3}\sqrt{\frac{\pi}{5}}\,r^2 Y_{20} \tag{35b}$$

The diagonalization of the dimensionless matrix R is then carried out in the representation chosen. The operator R depends on the two parameters η and μ, with η a deformation parameter and μ independent of the deformation. R is treated as a function of η and is diagonalized for a sequence of η-values. The eigenvalues of R belonging to certain N and Ω are denoted by $r^{N\Omega}(\eta)$. The corresponding energy eigenvalues of the total Hamiltonian are thus

$$E^{N\Omega} = (N + \tfrac{3}{2})\hbar\omega_0(\delta) + k\hbar\omega_0^0 r^{N\Omega} \tag{36}$$

where $\omega_0(\delta)$ is defined in Eq. (31).

The properties of odd nuclei are understood in terms of the Nilsson model. This model describes the states of motion of the particles in the potential field of a core. It has been successful in describing the properties of the heavier deformed nuclei.

In recent years the rotational collective model has been successfully applied[30] to odd-A light nuclei in the $1d$-shell. The properties which have been calculated are magnetic and quadrupole moments, nuclear levels, reduced transition probability $B(E2)$, spins and parities of nuclei such as Al^{25}, F^{19}, $Ne^{21,23}$, Mg^{25}, Al^{27}, Si^{29}, P^{31}, and many others. The calculations of these nuclei lie within the framework of the Nilsson model with some modifications. The basic approach to the theoretical calculations is that the energy levels are grouped into rotational bands specified by an intrinsic single-particle state calculated for a deformed nuclear potential. The deformation of the nucleus is determined from various parameters such as the quadrupole moment, etc. Knowing the deformation, we can use the eigenvalues and eigenfunctions corresponding to the single-particle shell model, and a comparison between the theory and experimental quantities can be made.

The parameter μ in Eq. (34c) determines the depression of higher levels. The spacing of the oscillator level is $\hbar\omega_0$, and the parameter k in Eq. (34a) determines the spin-orbit splitting.

In the absence of any band mixing, the observed electric quadrupole moment Q_{obs} is related to the intrinsic quadrupole moment Q_0 by

$$Q_{\text{obs}} = \frac{3K^2 - I(I + 1)}{(I + 1)(2I + 3)} Q_0 \tag{37a}$$

where I is the total angular momentum of the nucleus and K is the component of I along the 3-axis in the body-fixed coordinate system. To calculate δ, the intrinsic quadrupole moment Q_0 is equated to the quadrupole moment of a uniformly charged spheroid with deformation δ. Thus

$$Q_0 = \tfrac{4}{5}ZeR_0^2 \, \delta(1 + 0.17\delta + \cdots) \tag{37b}$$

where $R_0 = r_0 A^{1/3}$. In the d-shell region the value of the spin-orbit parameter k as suggested by Nilsson[29] is 0.05. However, higher values, ranging from 0.07 to 0.1, have been used by Bhatt[30] to obtain better agreement with the experimental results. Nilsson performed the diagonalization of R with $\mu = 0$, for $N = 0, 1, 2$. Bishop[30] observed that, for

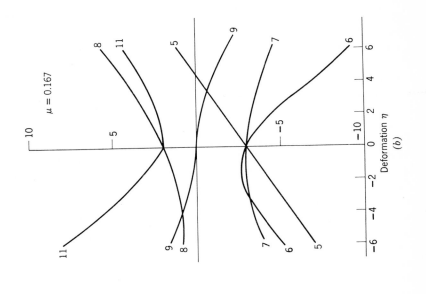

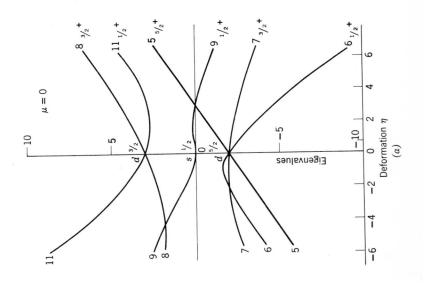

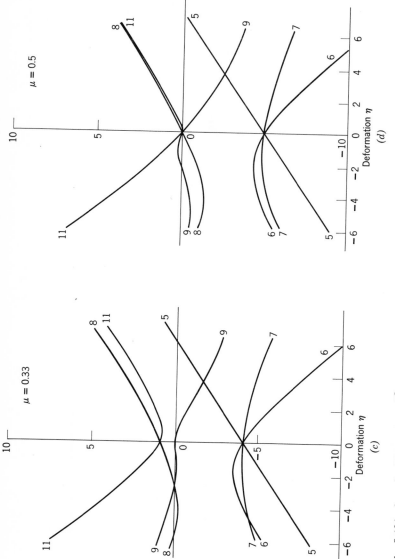

Fig. 8-12(*a, b, c, d*) Eigenvalues $r^{N}\Omega$ of the operator R as a function of the deformation η and for four different values of the parameter μ. The ordinate must be multiplied by $k\hbar\omega_0^0$ to give the energy of the individual orbits in excess of $3.5\hbar\omega_0(\delta)$ (Bishop[30]).

305

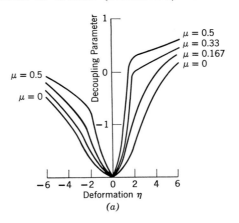

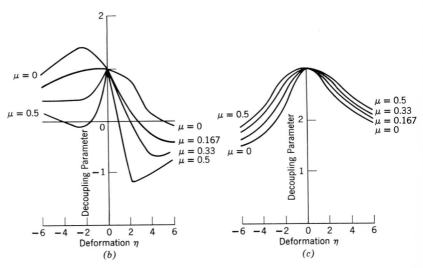

Fig. 8-13(a, b, c) Plot of the decoupling parameter against deformation for orbits 11, 9, and 6, which each have $N = 2$ and $\Omega = 1/2$ (Bishop[30]).

some nuclei, in order to obtain a good fit with the observed nuclear spectra, the value of μ has to be nonzero. He has recalculated the eigenvalues and eigenfunctions for the deformed Nilsson potential with the addition of the term μI^2 for $N = 2$ and for different values of Ω. Figure 8-12a, b, c, d gives a plot of the eigenvalues $r^{N\Omega}$ of the operator R as a function of the deformation η for four different values of the parameter μ, and Fig. 8-13a, b, c gives a plot of the decoupling parameter for the orbits $\Omega = \frac{1}{2}$. These calculations can be used successfully to interpret some of the nuclear properties which cannot be reproduced from Nilsson's model. This has been accomplished by introducing a correction term μl^2 to the oscillator potential.

We shall present some examples discussed by Bishop; first, that of Al^{27}. Its ground-state configuration is

$$\nu\{O^{16}; d_{5/2}(\tfrac{1}{2}^2, \tfrac{3}{2}^2, \tfrac{5}{2}^2)\}$$

$$\pi\{O^{16}; d_{5/2}(\tfrac{1}{2}^2, \tfrac{3}{2}^2, \tfrac{5}{2}^1)\}$$

The deformation parameter δ is found to be $+0.35$ from the measured value of the quadrupole moment $Q = +0.15 \times 10^{-24}\,\text{cm}^2$ and by using Eq. (37b). The excited-state sequence in Al^{27}, starting with the first, is $0.842\,\text{Mev}(\tfrac{1}{2}^+)$, $1.013\,\text{Mev}(\tfrac{3}{2}^+)$, and $2.729\,\text{Mev}(\tfrac{5}{2}^+)$, which suggests a rotational band on orbit 9. The value of $\hbar^2/2\mathscr{I}$ and a can be calculated from the formula

$$E_{\text{rot}} = \frac{\hbar^2}{2\mathscr{I}}\left[I(I+1) + a(-1)^{I+\frac{1}{2}}(I+\tfrac{1}{2})\right] \tag{38}$$

giving $\hbar^2/2\mathscr{I} = 218\,\text{Kev}$ and $a = -0.58$. The value $218\,\text{Kev}$ is consistent with values obtained for $\hbar^2/2\mathscr{I}$ in the neighboring nuclei. The value of the decoupling parameter $a = -0.58$ is obtained from Fig. 8-13b for $\mu = 0.33$, $\eta = +3.2$. If k is taken to be 0.125, from Fig. 8-12c we note that the first excited state is located above the ground state at 856 Kev, which is in excellent agreement with the measured value of 842 Kev. Since Nilsson suggests $\mu = 0$ for the d-shell region, we could not reach this excited state following Nilsson's calculations. As another example, we consider Mg^{25}. The ground-state configuration is

$$\pi\{O^{16}; d_{5/2}(\tfrac{1}{2}^2, \tfrac{3}{2}^2)\}$$

$$\nu\{O^{16}; d_{5/2}(\tfrac{1}{2}^2, \tfrac{3}{2}^2, \tfrac{5}{2}^1)\}$$

From the consideration of the first excited state the decoupling parameter $a = -0.2$. Assuming that it is on orbit 9, then from Fig. 8.13b we note $\eta > +6$. However, we note from Fig. 8-12a that for $\eta > +6$, orbit 9 is lower in energy than orbit 5. This discrepancy is removed if one considers curves for nonzero values of μ. The difference in eigenvalues for orbits 9 and 5 is given by*

$$\Delta r = \frac{0.58}{(0.125 \times 41 \times 25^{-\frac{1}{3}})} = \frac{\Delta E}{k\hbar\omega_0^0} = 0.331$$

* For the level spacing of the harmonic oscillator the usual estimate $\hbar\omega_0^0 \approx 41A^{-\frac{1}{3}}\,\text{Mev}$ is used.

For $\mu = 0.167$, from Fig. 8-12b, this difference of eigenvalues is obtained for $\eta = 3.2$ which corresponds to $a = -0.15$ from Fig. 8-13b. For $\mu = 0.33$, one obtains $\eta = +3.3$ and $a = -0.52$. Hence we should expect closer agreement with experiment for a value of μ slightly higher than 0.167. We see then that modified calculations of Bishop do indeed eliminate some of the discrepancies and give better agreement than those of Nilsson.

Another extensive calculation has been performed by Bhatt[30] within the framework of the extreme single-particle Nilsson model. Nuclei in the $1d$-$2s$ shell were grouped according to their last nucleon number. In these calculations the effect of band mixing was included. Bhatt consistently varied the parameters such as k, $\hbar\omega_0^0$, η, and μ. He found excellent agreement for energy spectrum, magnetic moments, and $B(E2)$ values for odd-mass nuclei with Z or $N = 9$, 11, and 13. Some of his results are shown in Tables 8-6 and 8-7. The ground-state magnetic

Table 8-6 Magnetic Moments of the Ground States of Odd-Mass Nuclei in the $1d$-$2s$ Shell (Bhatt[30])

Group	Nucleus	Deformation η	Level Spin	Calculated	Experimental[a]
I	$_9F^{19}$	4	$\frac{1}{2}$	2.54	2.63
		4	$\frac{5}{2}$	3.65	3.5
II	$_{10}Ne_{11}^{21}$	3	$\frac{3}{2}$	-0.60	-0.66
		4	$\frac{3}{2}$	-0.90	
	$_{11}Na^{23}$	3	$\frac{3}{2}$	2.27	2.22
		4	$\frac{3}{2}$	2.87	
III	$_{10}Ne_{13}^{23}$	-4	$\frac{5}{2}$	-1.081	
	$_{12}Mg_{13}^{25}$	-4	$\frac{5}{2}$	-1.037	-0.86
	$_{13}Al_{14}^{27}$	-4	$\frac{5}{2}$	3.77	3.64
IV	$_{14}Si_{15}^{29}$		$\frac{1}{2}$		-0.555
	$_{15}P_{16}^{31}$	-3	$\frac{1}{2}$	1.30	1.13
	$_{15}P_{16}^{31}$	-2	$\frac{1}{2}$	1.93	
V	$_{16}S_{17}^{33}$	-3	$\frac{3}{2}$	0.6	0.63
		-2	$\frac{3}{2}$	1.04	
	$_{17}Cl^{35}$	-2	$\frac{3}{2}$	0.86	0.821

[a] For $_9F^{19}$ the magnetic moment of the first excited state $\frac{5}{2}^+$ is also calculated. For the g-factor of the "core" $g_R = Z/A$ is used. All experimental values are taken from nuclear data sheets.

moments show very good agreement between the theoretical and experimental values. The same is true for the $B(E2)$ values for different nuclei with the exception of Ne^{21} and Mg^{25}. For the case of Mg^{25}, the calculated transition probabilities $B(E2; \frac{5}{2} \to \frac{3}{2})$ or $B(E2; \frac{5}{2} \to \frac{1}{2})$ have about the same values. These values are roughly five times smaller than the experimental values. This may suggest that the admixture of $(K = \frac{3}{2})$

Table 8-7 The Transition Probabilities† $B(E2, I_i \to I_f)$ (Bhatt[30])

Group	Nucleus	Deformation η	Initial State	Final State	$B(E2)$ ($e^2 \times 10^{-50}$ cm^4)	Experiment ($e^2 \times 10^{-50}$ cm^4)	Ref.
I	$_9F^{19}$	4	$\frac{1}{2}$	$\frac{5}{2}$	0.04	0.04	(d)
II	$_{11}Na^{23}$	4	$\frac{3}{2}$	$\frac{5}{2}$	0.84	1.00	(d)
	$_{10}Ne^{21}_{11}$	4	$\frac{3}{2}$	$\frac{5}{2}$	0.8	2.50	(d)
III	$_{12}Mg^{25}_{13}$	3	$\frac{5}{2}$	$\frac{1}{2}$	0.006	0.008, 0.005	(a, b)
	$_{12}Mg^{25}_{13}$	3	$\frac{5}{2}$	$\frac{3}{2}$	0.0054	0.028	(b)
	$_{12}Mg^{25}_{13}$	3	$\frac{5}{2}$	$\frac{7}{2}$	0.870	1.3, 1.095	(c, b)
	$_{13}Al^{25}_{13}$	3	$\frac{5}{2}$	$\frac{1}{2}$	0.051	0.057	(a)
	$_{12}Al^{27}_{14}$	3	$\frac{5}{2}$	$\frac{1}{2}$	0.060	0.170	(b)
	$_{13}Al^{27}_{14}$	3	$\frac{5}{2}$	$\frac{3}{2}$	0.053	0.300	(b)
	$_{13}Al^{27}_{14}$	3	$\frac{5}{2}$	$\frac{7}{2}$	1.38	1.00	(c)
IV	$_{15}P^{31}_{16}$	-2	$\frac{1}{2}$	$\frac{3}{2}$	0.07	1.00	(d)
		-4	$\frac{1}{2}$	$\frac{3}{2}$	0.17		

† In calculating the matrix elements, the effective charge is taken as $e_{eff} = e(1 + Z/A)$ for the odd proton and $e_{eff} = e(Z/A)$ for the odd neutron.
(a) Ferguson, A. T. C., M. A. Grace, and J. O. Newton, *Nuclear Phys.* **17**, 1, 1960.
(b) Lemberg, I. Kh., as quoted in Ref. (c).
(c) Rasmussen, V. K., F. R. Metzger, and C. P. Swann, *Phys. Rev.* **123**, 1386, 1961.
(d) Gove, H. E., *Proc. Intern. Conf. on Nuclear Structure*, p. 451, University of Toronto Press, 1960.

and $(K = \frac{1}{2})$-bands in the ground state $\frac{5}{2}^+$ and the excited state 3^+ should be much larger than Nilsson's model stipulated. The properties of nuclei with Z or $N = 15$ are not described by the calculation, which may be because the $d_{5/2}$-shell is just filled and the deformation is small. Consequently the single-particle Nilsson model may not be valid.

Bhatt's calculations on energy spectra for N or $Z = 11$ together with the experimental level scheme is represented in Fig. 8-14. For η somewhat greater than 2 and $\mu = 0$, the levels of O^{19} can be reproduced from theoretical calculations. There is a shift in the position of the $\frac{7}{2}^+$ level in the mirror pairs Ne^{21}–Na^{21} and Mg^{23}–Na^{23} without any significant change in the levels corresponding to $\frac{5}{2}^+$ or $\frac{1}{2}^+$. The position of the $\frac{1}{2}^+$ level in Na^{23} [$(K = \frac{1}{2})$-band] can be obtained with a μ-value other than zero. Perhaps $\mu \approx 0.1$ should fix the $(K = \frac{1}{2})$-band in relation to other levels.

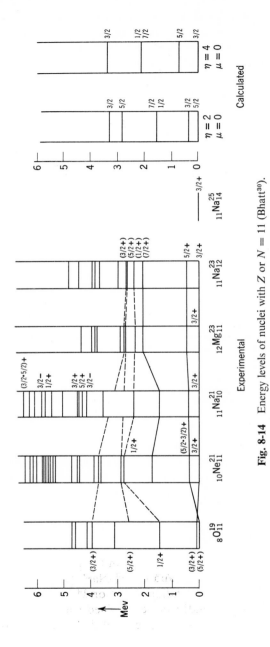

Fig. 8-14 Energy levels of nuclei with Z or $N = 11$ (Bhatt[30]).

A large band mixing for N or $Z = 11$ group with considerable deviation from the rotational level is noticeable. The fact that Nilsson's model is able to reproduce the energy levels, in particular, of O^{19} and Na^{23}, shows the validity of the model.

8.11   Coupling Between Modes of Collective Excitation

The collective motion can be treated as purely rotational provided that the rotational frequency is so slow that the intrinsic structure is not perturbed appreciably. There is ample experimental evidence for a purely rotational spectrum $I(I + 1)$, but as the frequency of rotation increases, the centrifugal force distorts the nuclear shape, thus causing rotation-vibration interactions. Also rotation-particle coupling contributes when the nonadiabatic perturbation of the particle structure becomes important due to Coriolis forces.

Rotation-Vibration Interaction

Spheroidal shapes.   The deformation potential for small deviations from equilibrium can be written as

$$V(\beta) = E_0 + \tfrac{1}{2}C_\beta(\beta - \beta_0)^2 \tag{39a}$$

with vibrational frequency ω_β given by

$$\omega_\beta = \sqrt{\frac{C_\beta}{B_2}} \tag{39b}$$

E_0 is the energy at equilibrium, C_β the restoring constant, and B_2 the mass parameter (see Eq. (24a)).

Adding the rotational energy to Eq. (39a), we obtain the total energy $E(\beta)$ as

$$E(\beta) = E_0 + \frac{B_2\omega_\beta^2}{2}(\beta - \beta_0)^2 + \frac{\hbar^2}{6B_2\beta^2}I(I + 1) \tag{39c}$$

The equilibrium shape of the rotating nucleus can be determined by minimizing the energy. The minimum occurs at

$$\beta = \beta_0\left[1 + 12\left(\frac{\hbar^2}{2\mathscr{I}_0}\right)^2\frac{I(I + 1)}{(\hbar\omega_\beta)^2}\right] \tag{40a}$$

where

$$\mathscr{I}_0 = 3B_2\beta_0^2 \quad \text{and} \quad \mathscr{I} = 3B_2\beta^2 \tag{40b}$$

are the moments of inertia for the unperturbed state and the perturbed system [as given by Eqs. (24b)]. The rotational energy is now given by

$$E_{\text{rot-vib}} = \frac{\hbar^2}{2\mathscr{I}_0}I(I + 1) + E_\beta'I^2(I + 1)^2 \tag{40c}$$

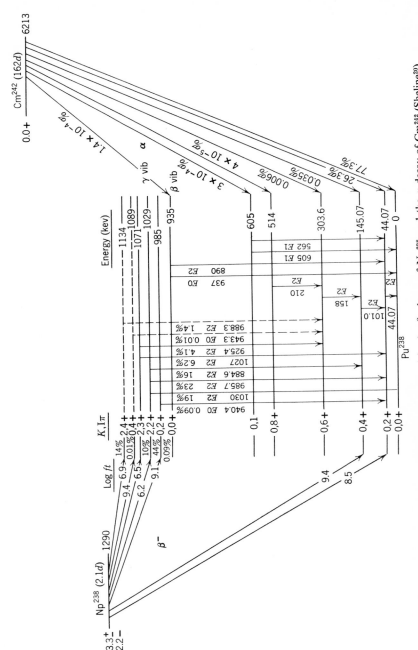

Fig. 8-15 Energy levels of Pu²³⁸ as determined in the β⁻-decay of Np²³⁸ and the α-decay of Cm²⁴² (Sheline[20]).

312

where

$$E'_\beta = -\frac{12}{(\hbar\omega_\beta)^2}\left(\frac{\hbar^2}{2\mathscr{I}_0}\right)^3 \tag{40d}$$

Ellipsoidal Shapes

The case of ellipsoidal vibrations about the equilibrium shape with fixed β corresponding to a perturbation by γ-vibrations has been discussed by Bohr.[15] The corrections are of smaller magnitude and are given by the replacement of E'_β in Eq. (40d) by

$$E'_\gamma = -\frac{4}{(\hbar\omega_\gamma)^2}\left(\frac{\hbar^2}{2\mathscr{I}_0}\right)^3 \tag{40e}$$

From Eqs. (40c) to (40e) we find that

$$\frac{\Delta E}{\left[\dfrac{\hbar^2}{2\mathscr{I}_0}I(I+1)\right]} = -\frac{1}{I(I+1)}\left[\frac{12}{(\hbar\omega_\beta)^2}+\frac{4}{(\hbar\omega_\gamma)^2}\right]\left(\frac{\hbar^2}{2\mathscr{I}_0}I(I+1)\right)^2 \tag{40f}$$

The β- and γ-vibrational corrections to the energy are negative. By using the 2^+ and 4^+ states of the ground-state rotational band of even-even nuclei, it is possible to calculate both $\hbar^2/2\mathscr{I}_0$ and B_2 by considering the decay scheme of a nucleus whose ground-state rotational band and β- and γ-vibrational bands are well known, such as Pu^{238}.[31] In Fig. 8-15 we have reproduced the decay scheme given by Sheline[20] who has recalculated some of the lines of the rotational ground-state band. Table 8-8 by Sheline gives the value of B_2 and $\hbar^2/\mathscr{I}_0$ for some nuclei.

8.12   Rotation-Particle Coupling

The quantum number K which is the projection of the total angular momentum $\mathbf{I}$ along the axis of symmetry of the nucleus is never an exact quantum number since it is coupled to the intrinsic structure of the rotating system. The rotation of the nuclear-symmetry axis causes a partial decoupling of the intrinsic motion from the instantaneous collective field, and the Hamiltonian is not separable precisely into intrinsic and rotational parts. The Coriolis force which couples the intrinsic particle motion with the collective rotation is given, by Eq. (5f), as

$$H_{\text{rot-par}} = -\frac{\hbar}{2\mathscr{I}}(I_+j_- + I_-j_+) \tag{41}$$

The term $H_{\text{rot-par}}$ can be treated as a perturbation for strongly deformed nuclei. The operators $I_\pm$ have matrix elements only for states which

Table 8-8 Rotational Constants for the Ground-State Bands of Nuclei and Calculation of Vibrational Levels. Only those Nuclei are Treated in which Either a β- or a γ-Vibration or both are Experimentally known (Sheline[20])

Nucleus	Ground-State Rotational Band 2 + (Kev)	4 + (Kev)	6 + (Kev)	Exptl. Obs γ-Vib 2 + (Kev)	Exptl. Obs β-Vib 0 + (Kev)	$\hbar^2/\mathscr{I}_0$ (Kev)	$B_2 \times 10^{-3}$	Calc. γ-Vib. (Kev)	Calc. β-Vib. (Kev)
Sm^{152}	121.79	366.39		1086		42.29	141.36	–	651
Gd^{154}	123.07	371.07		998		42.70	139.86	–	674
Gd^{156}	88.97	288.2	584.9	1152		30.02	29.89	–	874
Dy^{160}	87.0	284		964		29.26	21.43	–	1084
Er^{166}	80.85	265.1	554.1	1221.8	~1450	27.14	15.71	728	–
W^{182}	100.09	329.36	680.38	903.3		33.55	15.25	–	1695
W^{184}	111.20	364.04		768		37.35	23.68	–	2329
Os^{186}	137.2	437	868.9	633		46.62	72.60	–	1484
Os^{188}	154.9	478	1047	557	(1086)		276.18	–	1810
Os^{190}	188	547		966		65.65	21.64	–	517
Th^{228}	57.8	186.6	371.6		803	19.53	4.00	1029	–
U^{234}	43.25	143.05	296.15			14.47	3.32	(1029)	–
Pu^{238}	44.07	145.07	303.59	1029	935	14.73		–	(935)

differ by one unit in K, that is, $H_{rot\text{-}par}$ mixes up states of different K. The term in Eq. (41) can be treated by the second-order perturbation theory. The energy contribution arising from it is proportional to $I(I + 1)$ and is therefore interpretable as a "renormalization" of the moment of inertia of the ground-state band to a higher value. The moment of inertia of the excited state is decreased by an equal amount.

Besides renormalizing the moment of inertia, the rotational-particle coupling also causes a departure of the energy spectrum from the $I(I + 1)$ law.

The rotational mixing is small and may not cause any change in level structure. However, in odd nuclei the density of the excited states is much higher than in even nuclei; odd nuclei also have greater moments of inertia. This has been attributed to the fact that Coriolis mixing is more important in odd nuclei than in even.[32]

8.13   Core Excitation

The de-excitation of the various excited states of nuclei has been the subject of a most extensive study both experimentally and theoretically. We have already discussed these transitions in the single-particle model in which a nucleon moves from one state to another, and in the collective model in which the excitations, which include rotational and vibrational modes, are due to the collective motion of many nucleons.

There is still another model—the core-excitation model, suggested by Lawson and Uretsky.[33] In this model, which describes the energy spectrum of odd nuclei, it is thought that the energy spectrum is due to the excitation of the even-even core, and the odd nucleon moves in an orbit away from the core. The energy spacing of the odd nucleon orbit is large compared with the excitation energies of the core nucleons.

De-Shalit[4] has extended the core-excitation calculations by obtaining the transition rates and magnetic moments. We shall discuss both $_{79}Au^{197}$ and $_{81}Tl^{197}$ in the light of core excitation as developed by Braunstein and De-Shalit[34] (see Fig. 8-16). It should be remarked that a recent study by Griesacker and Roy[35] using β-γ and γ-γ coincidence techniques have established a new level, 155 Kev, lying between the 77-Kev and 268 Kev levels in $_{79}Au^{179}$ in addition to some new gamma lines arising in transitions between various states. However, since our primary interest is to point out the analysis made by Braunstein and De-Shalit according to the core-excitation model, we have retained their decay scheme. According to this model the 79th proton in Au^{197} moves in a $d_{3/2}$ orbit, whereas the 81st proton in Tl^{197} moves in an $s_{1/2}$ orbit. The positive parity excited states of Au^{179} are due to the coupling of the odd nucleon to the 2^+ state of the

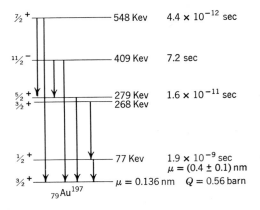

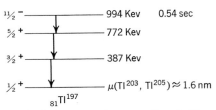

Fig. 8-16 Decay schemes of $_{79}Au^{197}$ and $_{81}Tl^{197}$ (Braunstein and De-Shalit[34]).

core which gives $\frac{1}{2}^+$, $\frac{3}{2}^+$, $\frac{5}{2}^+$, and $\frac{7}{2}^+$ states for 79 protons. Similarly, for the 81st proton in Tl^{197} the $\frac{3}{2}^+$ and $\frac{5}{2}^+$ states are obtained. The mathematical treatment of this scheme is as follows.

Consider the core in the angular momentum state J_c coupled to the odd proton in a state j, thus forming the state $|J_c j, J\rangle$ of total angular momentum J. Braunstein and De-Shalit allow slight admixtures whenever they can lead to large effects in the calculations of magnetic moments of these states, M1 and E2 transitions between them, and their quadrupole moments. The wave functions of the various states in Au^{197} taken are

$$|\tfrac{3}{2}\rangle_1 = a\,|0\,\tfrac{3}{2}, \tfrac{3}{2}\rangle + \sqrt{1 - a^2}\,|2\,\tfrac{3}{2}, \tfrac{3}{2}\rangle$$

$$|\tfrac{1}{2}\rangle\ \ = |2\,\tfrac{3}{2}, \tfrac{1}{2}\rangle$$

$$|\tfrac{3}{2}\rangle_2 = a\,|2\,\tfrac{3}{2}, \tfrac{3}{2}\rangle - \sqrt{1 - a^2}\,|0\,\tfrac{3}{2}, \tfrac{3}{2}\rangle$$

$$|\tfrac{5}{2}\rangle\ \ = b\,|2\,\tfrac{3}{2}, \tfrac{5}{2}\rangle + \sqrt{1 - b^2}\,|0\,\tfrac{5}{2}, \tfrac{5}{2}\rangle$$

$$|\tfrac{11}{2}\rangle = |0\,\tfrac{11}{2}, \tfrac{11}{2}\rangle$$

$$|\tfrac{7}{2}\rangle\ \ = |2\,\tfrac{3}{2}, \tfrac{7}{2}\rangle$$

where a mixture of the $\frac{3}{2}^+$ states is included since these states are observed close to each other. An admixture of a $d_{5/2}$ single particle state in $|\frac{5}{2}\rangle$ is also introduced since it affects strongly the M1 to ground-state transition. The values of the parameters a and b are chosen by fitting the observed magnetic moments, M1 transitions, and the two g-factors, g_p and g_c, of the $d_{3/2}$ proton and the core. The model then predicts the magnetic moment of the $|\frac{1}{2}\rangle$ state and the E2 transitions in good agreement with the experimental values. The model also predicts lifetimes and static moments of excited states.

References

1. Bohr, A., *Dan. Mat.-Fys. Medd.* **26**, No. 14, 1952.
2. Bohr, A., and B. R. Mottelson, *Dan. Mat-Fys. Medd.* **27**, No. 16, 1953.
3. Rainwater, J., *Phys. Rev.* **79**, 432, 1950.
4. De-Shalit, A., *Phys. Rev.* **122**, 1530, 1961.
5. Kisslinger, L. S., and R. A. Sorensen, *Rev. Mod. Phys.* **35**, 853, 1963.
6. Belyaev, S. T., *Dan. Mat.-Fys. Medd.* **31**, No. 11, 1959.
7. Nathan, O., and S. G. Nilsson, *Collective Nuclear Motion and The Unified Model, Alpha- Beta- and Gamma-Ray Spectroscopy*, Vol. I, p. 601, North-Holland Publishing Co. Amsterdam, 1965.
8. Perlman, I., *Proc. of the Intern. Cong. on Nucl. Structure*, p. 547, University of Toronto Press, 1960.
9. Alaga, G., K. Alder, A. Bohr, and B. R. Mottelson, *Dan. Mat.-Fys Medd.* **29**, No. 9, 1955.
10. Davydov, A. S., and G. F. Filippov, *Nucl. Phys.* **8**, 237, 1958.
11. Potnis, V. R., and G. N. Rao, *Nucl. Phys.* **42**, 620, 1963.
12. Moszkowski, S. A., *Theory of Multipole Radiation, Alpha- Beta- and Gamma-Ray Spectroscopy*, Vol. 2, 863, North-Holland Publishing Co., Amsterdam, 1965.
13. Grechukhin, D. P., *Nucl. Phys.* **40**, 422, 1963.
14. Scharff-Goldhaber, G., and J. Weneser, *Phys. Rev.* **98**, 212, 1955,
15. Bohr, A., *Dan. Mat.-Fys. Medd* **27**, No. 14, 1952.
16. Rayleigh, Lord, *The Theory of Sound* Vol. 2, Sec. 364, Macmillan and Co., London, 1877.
17. Bohr, N., and J. A. Wheeler, *Phys. Rev.* **56**, 426, 1939.
18. Wilets, L., and M. Jean, *Phys. Rev.* **102**, 788, 1956.
19. Temmer, G. M., and N. P. Heydenberg, *Phys. Rev.* **104**, 967, 1956.
20. Sheline, R. K., *Rev. Mod. Phys.* **32**, 1, 1960.
21. Davidson, J. P., and M. G. Davidson, *Phys. Rev.* **138B**, 316, 1965.
22. Yoshizawa, Y., B. Elbek, B. Herskind, and M. C. Olesen, *Proc. Conf. Reactions Complex Nuclei, 3rd, California*, p. 289, University of California Press, Berkeley, 1963; Elbek, B., M. C. Olesen, and O. Skilbreid, *Nuclear Phys.* **19**, 523, 1960.
23. McGowan, F. K., and P. H. Stelson, *Phys. Rev.* **122**, 1274, 1961.
24. de Boer, J., G. Goldring, and H. Winkler, *Phys. Rev.* **134B**, 1032, 1964.
25. Alder, K., A. Bohr, T. Huus, B. Mottelson, and A. Winther, *Rev. Mod. Phys.* **28**, 432, 1956; *ibid.* **30**, 353, 1958.
26. Alder, K., and A. Winther, *Phys. Rev.* **91**, 1578, 1953.
27. Graetzer, R., and E. M. Bernstein, *Phys. Rev.* **129**, 1772, 1963.

28. Alder, K., and A. Winther, *Dan. Mat.-Fys. Medd.* **32**, No. 8, 1960; Alder, K., *Proc. Conf. Reactions Complex Nuclei*, 3rd, California, p. 253, University of California Press, Berkeley, 1963.
29. Nilsson, S. G., *Dan. Mat.-Fys. Medd.* **29**, No. 16, 1955.
30. Litherland, A. E., H. McManus, E. B. Paul, D. A. Bromley, and H. E. Gove, *Can. J. Phys.* **36**, 378, 1958; Paul, E. B., *Phil. Mag.* [8] **2**, 311, 1957; Bishop, G. R., *Nucl. Phys.* **14**, 376, 1959/60. Bhatt, K. H., *Nucl. Phys.* **39**, 375, 1962.
31. Albridge, R. G., and J. M. Hollander, UCRL Report No. 8034, November, 1957; Perlman, I., and J. O. Rasmussen, *Handbuch der Physik*, vol. 42, 109, S. Flügge, ed., Springer Verlag, Berlin, 1957; Baranov, S. A., and K. N. Shlyagin, *Atomnya Energ.* **1**, 52, 1956. Smith, W. G., and J. M. Hollander, *Phys. Rev.* **101**, 746, 1956.
32. Kerman, A. K., *Dan. Mat.-Fys. Medd.* **30**, No. 15, 1956; Alaga, G., K. Alder, A. Bohr, and B. Mottelson, *Dan. Met.-Fys. Medd.* **29**, No. 9, 1956.
33. Lawson, R. D., and J. L. Uretsky, *Phys. Rev.* **108**, 1300, 1957.
34. Braunstein, A., and A. De-Shalit, *Phys. Letters* **1**, 264, 1962.
35. Griesacker, P. B., and R. R. Roy, *Nuclear Phys.* **50**, 41, 1964.

Problems

1. Carry out the transformation of the kinetic energy

$$T = \tfrac{1}{2}\sum_{\mu} B \, |\dot{\alpha}_{\mu}|^2$$

into the β, γ coordinates.

2. The magnetic moment for the case of a single particle coupled to the surface can be written as:

$$\mu = \langle g_S S_z + g_l l_z + g_R R_z \rangle_{M=J} = g_j j$$

where $\mathbf{R} = \mathbf{J} - \mathbf{j}$, $g_R = Z/A$, and g_S, g_l, S_z, l_z refer to the odd nucleon. Using the weak-coupling wave function Ψ of the ground state with $M = J$, (with coupling parameter f), that is,

$$\Psi(J = j) = |\, j; 00; jj \rangle + \sum_{j',\lambda} |\, j'; 1\lambda; jj \rangle a_{j'\lambda}$$

$$a_{j'\lambda} = f\sqrt{\frac{8\pi}{5}}\, \langle j \| Y_\lambda \| j' \rangle \hbar\omega_\lambda / (\hbar\omega_\lambda + E_{j'} - E_j),$$

show that

$$\langle j_z \rangle = [j + \sum_{j',\lambda} |a_{j'\lambda}|^2 \sum_m m \langle j'\, 2m\, j - m \,|\, jj \rangle^2][1 - \sum |a_{j'\lambda}|^2]$$

and

$$\mu = g_j j - j(g_j - g_R) f^2 \left[\frac{3(2j - 1)(2j + 3)}{8j^2(j + 1)^2} \right]$$

for $\lambda = 2$ (*Physics of the Nucleus*, M. A. Preston, Addison-Wesley Co., Inc., Massachusetts, p. 325, 1962).

3. Using the Appendix and the relations given in Section 8.4, derive Eq. (10e) in detail.

4(a) The relationship between the deformation parameter β of Bohr and Mottelson (Eq. 13a) and δ of Nilsson (Eq. 30a) may be found by comparing two equations in Chapter 8. Use these equations to verify the relationship

$$\delta \simeq \frac{3}{2}\sqrt{\frac{5}{4\pi}}\,\beta$$

4(b) Derive the relationship between the deformation parameter β and the difference between the major and minor semiaxes ΔR as found in Eq. (13d).

5. In deriving Eq. (21f) the numerical value, 13, of the constant depends upon the value one assumes for the surface tension in $E_S = 4\pi R^2 \tau$ in Eq. (20h). Without inserting a value for τ, rederive Eq. (21f), and thereby determine the value of τ one must assume in order to get the numerical constant in (21f). Compare this value with the one found (or derived) elsewhere in the text.

6. Derive Eq. (11d) (cf. Problem 8-3) and go on to verify equation (37a), making use of the definitions

$$\langle Q \rangle = \sqrt{\frac{5}{16\pi}}\,e\,Q_{\mathrm{obs}} \quad \text{and} \quad \langle \chi_K | \, M_{20} \, | \chi_K \rangle = \sqrt{\frac{5}{16\pi}}\,e\,Q_0$$

9

MANY-BODY TREATMENT
OF THE NUCLEUS

9.1 Introduction

The shell model (including the collective model) has been extremely successful in explaining nuclear properties. The basic assumption made is that each nucleon moves in a common potential (spherically symmetric plus a spin–orbit interaction for the shell model, and ellipsoidal in the collective model) so that the state of the nucleus is specified by a configuration, that is, by a set of quantum numbers for each nucleon. The theoretical basis and justification of the shell model have until now been lacking and, in fact, they seemingly involve a contradiction. The nuclear forces are believed to be strong at short internucleon distances, whereas the assumption of the shell model treats the motion of each nucleon, in a common potential, almost independently of the others, thus leading to well-defined states for the nucleon. However, there is sufficient experimental evidence[1,2] that the strong two-nucleon force exists inside the nucleus. The fact that, in processes like high-energy π-meson capture, photoelectric effects caused by high energy (>100 Mev) γ-ray, and pickup reactions, a large amount of energy can be transferred to the nucleus without appreciable change in its momentum indicates that the nucleons inside the nucleus must have large momenta,* and hence that the nuclear wave function contains components corresponding to large momenta of the individual nucleons. This implies[2] that the potential inside the nucleus fluctuates violently from point to point, a situation which would be compatible with the existence of strong two-body interactions inside the nucleus.

* From conservation of momentum it follows that in order for a nucleon to absorb large amounts of energy without appreciable change in its momentum, the nucleon must have had a large momentum before it absorbed the π-meson or the γ-ray.

The theory of the nuclear many-body problem, based on the two-body interaction, has been developed by Brueckner et al.[3-6] and Bethe.[2] Its mathematical formulation is based largely on Watson's theory[7] of multiple scattering. In a series of papers the properties of nuclear matter (infinite nucleus) were investigated, assuming that the nuclear wave functions could be taken as plane waves. Brueckner, Gammel, and Weitzner,[5] and others[6] have considered the case of finite nuclei. In all these calculations, the starting point is the two-nucleon interaction[8,9] which is in accord with the scattering experiments. Since this potential has an infinite repulsive core, the theory has been worked out in terms of the reaction matrix whose matrix elements in general are finite. The theory attempts in a self-consistent manner to derive from the two-body interaction the common potential in which each nucleon moves. However, because the solution of the exact self-consistent problem involves great computational difficulties, various approximations have been made at different stages of the calculation.

For the most part, only two-particle excitations have been taken into account. Corrections from three or more particle excitations are small and are usually neglected. Brueckner and Gammel[4] investigated the effect of the two-body potential on the wave function describing the two-particle interactions. Their finding was that for distances $\geqslant 10^{-13}$ cm, the wave function for the two-particle motion approaches its unperturbed values; this implies that for distances of the order of 10^{-13} cm the particles move as though they were free particles. This is referred to as the *healing*[10] distance. This result has a bearing on the role of the three—and more— nucleon interactions in the nucleus. Since the average distance of separation between two nucleons in nuclear matter is $\simeq 1.66 \times 10^{-13}$ cm, if two nucleons are within the healing distance ($\simeq 10^{-13}$ cm), the simultaneous probability of a third (or fourth) nucleon being within the healing distance of either of the first two is very small. Thus interactions among three and more particles, which can result in the formation of clusters of three or more particles, contribute little to nuclear properties.

An important aspect of the calculations for the nucleus which distinguishes it from the scattering problem is the inclusion of the Pauli exclusion principle. Because momentum states up to the Fermi momentum

$$p_{\rm F} = \hbar k_{\rm F} = \hbar(\tfrac{3}{2}\pi^2\rho)^{1/3}$$

(where ρ is the particle density in uniform matter) are filled, the nucleons can be excited only into momentum states greater than $p_{\rm F}$. The Pauli exclusion principle is largely responsible for the healing of the wave function in the nucleus. In free-particle scatterings, however, the scattered wave differs from the free-particle wave function by an amount governed by the phase shift.

9.2 Reaction Matrix

The principal feature of the Brueckner theory is the replacement of the two-body potential v by the reaction matrix K for the scattering of two nucleons while moving in nuclear matter. The reason for doing this is that the nucleon-nucleon potential contains a repulsive core at small distances so that the matrix elements of v will have large contributions from the core. The reaction matrix K for the scattering of two nucleons can be written symbolically as

$$K = v + v \frac{1}{E_0 - H_0} K \tag{1a}$$

Consider the scattering of two nucleons initially in the states i, j going to states i', j'. In a notation similar to that of Bethe,[2] the reaction matrix is given by

$$\langle i'j' | K | ij \rangle = \langle i'j' | v | ij \rangle_N$$
$$+ \sum_{i''j''} \langle i'j' | v | i''j'' \rangle_N \frac{Q}{e} \langle i''j'' | K | ij \rangle \tag{1b}$$

where the subscript N signifies that matrix elements are to be taken between the determinant wave functions which describe the initial and the final configurations of the nucleus. The matrix element

$$\langle i'j' | v | ij \rangle_N = 0 \quad \begin{cases} (1) \text{ if } i = j \text{ or } i' = j' \\ (2) \text{ or if any one of the states } i, j, i' \text{ or } j' \text{ is the} \\ \qquad \text{same as that already occupied by another} \\ \qquad \text{nucleon in the nucleus} \end{cases}$$

$$= \langle i'j' | v | ij \rangle_P - \langle j'i' | v | ij \rangle_P \tag{2a}$$

where the subscript P denotes the taking of matrix elements without regard to the presence of other nucleons in the nucleus. More explicitly the matrix elements are defined by

$$\langle i'j' | v | ij \rangle_P = \int \phi_{i'}^*(\mathbf{r}_i) \phi_{j'}^*(\mathbf{r}_j) v(\mathbf{r}_{ij}) \phi_i(\mathbf{r}_i) \phi_j(\mathbf{r}_j) \, d^3 r_i \, d^3 r_j \tag{2b}$$

where $\phi_i(\mathbf{r})$ are the single-particle wave functions that satisfy the Schrödinger equation corresponding to the common potential $\langle \mathbf{r}' | V | \mathbf{r} \rangle$ in which each individual nucleon moves, that is,

$$\frac{1}{2M} \nabla^2 \phi_i(\mathbf{r}) + E_i \phi_i(\mathbf{r}) = \int d^3 r' \langle \mathbf{r}' | V | \mathbf{r} \rangle \phi_i(\mathbf{r}') \tag{2c}$$

The single-particle potential $V(\mathbf{r}, \mathbf{r}')$ is determined by the diagonal elements of the K-matrix:

$$\langle \mathbf{r}'| V |\mathbf{r}\rangle = V(\mathbf{r}, \mathbf{r}') = \sum_i \phi_i^*(\mathbf{r}) \sum_j \{\langle ij| K |ij\rangle - \langle ij| K |ji\rangle\} \phi_i(\mathbf{r}') \quad (2d)$$

We define the operator Q in Eq. (1b) by

$$Q = 0 \quad \begin{cases} \text{if the energy denominator } e = 0 \\ \text{or if in the transition the Pauli} \\ \text{exclusion principle is violated} \end{cases}$$
$$= 1 \quad \text{otherwise} \quad (3a)$$

The energy denominator $-e$ is the excitation energy and is the difference in energies of the nucleus when the nucleons are in the states i', j' (states i, j unfilled), and when in the states i, j (states i', j' unfilled).

$$-e = E_N(i', j') - E_N(i, j) \quad (3b)$$

It has been shown by Bethe,[2] using the procedures of Brueckner and Levinson[3] and of Eden,[11] that the energy of the nuclear configuration with states i occupied is

$$E \simeq \sum_i \langle i| T |i\rangle + \sum_{ij} \langle ij| K |ij\rangle + w_c \quad (4a)$$

where T is the kinetic-energy operator of the nucleon, and w_c is an energy contribution which is nearly the same for all states of low excitation. From Eqs. (3b) and (4a), the excitation energy $-e_{i'j';ij}$ of nucleons in the states i and j in the presence of the remaining nucleons is

where

$$-e_{i'j';ij} = \mathscr{E}_{i'j';ij} + \delta K_{i'j';ij} \quad (4b)$$

$$\mathscr{E}_{i'j';ij} = \langle i'| T |i'\rangle + \sum_{k \neq i'} \langle i'k| K |i'k; ij \text{ unfilled}, j'\rangle$$
$$- \langle i| T |i\rangle - \sum_{k \neq i} \langle ik| K |ik\rangle$$
$$+ \text{terms } [(i' \leftrightarrow j') + (i \leftrightarrow j)] \quad (4c)$$

and

$$\delta K_{i'j';ij} = \langle i'j'| K |i'j'\rangle - \langle i'j| K |i'j\rangle - \langle ij'| K |ij'\rangle + \langle ij| K |ij\rangle \quad (4d)$$

In Eq. (4c), "unfilled" after ij refers to those states which are empty and j' is the extra occupied state. Also in Eq. (4b), terms corresponding to interaction between any two nucleons k, l which are different from i, j cancel out. The second and third terms on the right-hand side of Eq. (4d) involve excitation of only one nucleon. The contribution $\delta K_{i'j';ij}$ in Eq. (4b) can be neglected in comparison with $\mathscr{E}_{i'j';ij}$ since $\delta K_{i'j';ij}$ involves interaction between only one pair of nucleons, whereas Eq. (4c) involves interaction between one nucleon and A others. Therefore, $\delta K_{i'j';ij}$ is of relative order $1/A$ compared to $\mathscr{E}_{i'j';ij}$. We will take the following:

$$-e_{i'j';ij} \simeq \mathscr{E}_{i'j';ij} \tag{4e}$$

The reaction matrix $\langle i'k | K | i'k; \bar{i}\bar{j}, j' \rangle$ (where the bars denote the unfilled states) satisfies the following integral equation:

$$\langle i''k'' | K | i'k; \bar{i}\bar{j}, j' \rangle = \langle i''k'' | v | i'k \rangle_N - \sum \langle i''k'' | v | i'''k''' \rangle_N$$

$$\times \frac{Q_{ik}}{\mathscr{E}_{i'''j'k''';ijk}} \langle i'''k''' | K | i'k; \bar{i}\bar{j}, j' \rangle \tag{5a}$$

where $\mathscr{E}_{i'''j'k''';ijk}$ is defined similarly to Eq. (4c), but with additional contributions arising from the third pair of indices.

The energy E_i of the nucleon in the state i is

$$E_i = \langle i | T | i \rangle + \sum_{k \neq i} \langle ik | K | ik \rangle \tag{5b}$$

We note from Eq. (4c) that the excitation energy

$$\mathscr{E}_{i'j';ij} \neq E_{i'} + E_{j'} - E_i - E_j \tag{5c}$$

since the second term on the right-hand side of Eq. (4c) depends on states which are unoccupied and occupied. The equality sign in Eq. (5c) can be inserted if we can neglect the correction in the interaction energy of a pair arising because of the presence of the other nucleons. The third and the fourth terms in Eq. (4c) correspond to the energy of the nucleon in the state i in the initial (chosen) configuration. We can write Eq. (5c) with the equality sign after adding $\delta E_{i'j';ij}$ on the right-hand side, where $\delta E_{i'j';ij}$ takes into account the effect in energy differences arising from the change in the nuclear configuration; namely, in the nuclear state labeled by $i'j'$, certain states are empty and certain states are occupied relative to the initial (chosen) configuration. Rewriting Eq. (1b), we have

$$K_{i'j';ij} = \langle i'j' | K | ij \rangle$$

$$= \langle i'j' | v | ij \rangle_N - \sum_{i''j''} \langle i'j' | v | i''j'' \rangle_N \frac{Q}{\mathscr{E}_{i''j'';ij}} \langle i''j'' | K | ij \rangle \tag{6a}$$

where

$$\mathscr{E}_{i'j';ij} = E_{i'} + E_{j'} - E_i - E_j + \delta E_{i'j';ij} \tag{6b}$$

and

$$E_i = \langle i | T | i \rangle + \sum_{k \neq i} \langle ik | K | ik \rangle \tag{6c}$$

Equation (6a) is a form of the Brueckner-Bethe-Goldstone (BBG) equation. Written completely, the above equations are a complicated structure of an infinite ladder of equations (coupled integral equations), which have to be solved in a self-consistent manner. Brueckner and Gammel[4] have shown that the ladder can be reduced to a single equation without approximation by introducing a parameter with an infinite range in the denominator of the integral equations for the K-matrices. Bethe[2] has shown that it is often possible to approximate Eq. (6b) by neglecting the $\delta E_{i'j';ij}$ term.

For the Yukawa, square-well, etc., types of potentials without a repulsive core, the sum term on the right-hand side of Eq. (5a) or (6a) is small, so that $K \approx v$, and therefore the second term in Eq. (4c) does not depend on the states $\bar{ij}, j'$. In a repulsive core interaction, the difference between the matrix v and the reaction matrix K is large. But the main contribution to the sum in Eq. (6a) originates from intermediate states of high energies; thus the kinetic-energy contribution $\langle i| T |i \rangle$ in Eq. (4c) is much larger than the interaction energy K, and therefore the approximation of neglecting δE is justifiable.

9.3 Transformation to Coordinate Space: Nuclear Matter

We consider the nucleus to be infinite so that plane waves can be taken as basis states. In this approximation, the total momentum $\mathbf{P}$ of any two nucleons is conserved throughout their motion in the infinite nucleus (matrix elements of the potential v, and therefore of the reaction matrix K, are diagonal in total momentum). If $\mathbf{p}_1$ and $\mathbf{p}_2$ are the initial momenta of the two nucleons and $\mathbf{p}_1'$ and $\mathbf{p}_2'$ denote the momenta after scattering within nuclear matter, we have

$$\mathbf{P} = \mathbf{p}_1 + \mathbf{p}_2 = \mathbf{p}_1' + \mathbf{p}_2' \tag{7a}$$

The relative momenta are defined by

$$\mathbf{p} = \tfrac{1}{2}(\mathbf{p}_1 - \mathbf{p}_2) \qquad \mathbf{p}' = \tfrac{1}{2}(\mathbf{p}_1' - \mathbf{p}_2') \tag{7b}$$

From Eqs. (7a) and (7b), we obtain

$$\mathbf{p}_1 = \tfrac{1}{2}\mathbf{P} + \mathbf{p} \qquad \mathbf{p}_2 = \tfrac{1}{2}\mathbf{P} - \mathbf{p} \tag{7c}$$

$$\mathbf{p}_1' = \tfrac{1}{2}\mathbf{P} + \mathbf{p}' \qquad \mathbf{p}_2' = \tfrac{1}{2}\mathbf{P} - \mathbf{p}' \tag{7d}$$

In momentum representation Eq. (6) is (note abbrev. $p_1 p_2$ for p_1, p_2 etc.)

$$\langle \mathbf{p}_1' \mathbf{p}_2' | K | \mathbf{p}_1 \mathbf{p}_2 \rangle = \langle \mathbf{p}_1' \mathbf{p}_2' | v | \mathbf{p}_1 \mathbf{p}_2 \rangle - \sum_{\mathbf{p}_1'' \mathbf{p}_2''} \frac{\langle \mathbf{p}_1' \mathbf{p}_2' | v | \mathbf{p}_1'' \mathbf{p}_2'' \rangle \langle \mathbf{p}_1'' \mathbf{p}_2'' | K | \mathbf{p}_1 \mathbf{p}_2 \rangle}{\mathscr{E}(\mathbf{p}_1'' \mathbf{p}_2''; \mathbf{p}_1 \mathbf{p}_2)}$$

$$\cdot f(\mathbf{p}_1'', \mathbf{p}_2'') \tag{8a}$$

where the step function $f(\mathbf{p}_1'', \mathbf{p}_2'')$, which takes into account the Pauli principle, is defined by

$$f(\mathbf{p}_1'', \mathbf{p}_2'') = 1 \qquad \text{if both } p_1'' \text{ and } p_2'' > p_F \text{ (Fermi momentum)}$$
$$= 0 \qquad \text{otherwise} \tag{8b}$$

and

$$\mathscr{E}(\mathbf{p}_1''\mathbf{p}_2''; \mathbf{p}_1\mathbf{p}_2) = E(\mathbf{p}_1'') + E(\mathbf{p}_2'') - E(\mathbf{p}_1) - E(\mathbf{p}_2) + \delta E(\mathbf{p}_1''\mathbf{p}_2'', \mathbf{p}_1\mathbf{p}_2) \tag{8c}$$

$$E(\mathbf{p}_1) = \langle \mathbf{p}_1 | \, T \, | \mathbf{p}_1 \rangle + \sum_{\mathbf{p}_2 \neq \mathbf{p}_1} \langle \mathbf{p}_1\mathbf{p}_2 | \, K \, | \mathbf{p}_1\mathbf{p}_2 \rangle \tag{8d}$$

In the approximation that v and K are diagonal in the total momentum, Eq. (8a) becomes

$$\langle \mathbf{p}' | \, K(\mathbf{P}) \, | \mathbf{p} \rangle = \langle \mathbf{p}' | \, v \, | \mathbf{p} \rangle + \sum_{\mathbf{p}''} \frac{\langle \mathbf{p}' | \, v \, | \mathbf{p}'' \rangle \langle \mathbf{p}'' | \, K(\mathbf{P}) \, | \mathbf{p} \rangle}{\mathscr{E}(\mathbf{p}'', \mathbf{p}, \mathbf{P})} f(\mathbf{p}'', \mathbf{P}) \tag{9a}$$

where $\mathbf{p}''$ is defined similarly to $\mathbf{p}$ and $\mathbf{p}'$ in Eq. (7b), and

$$f(\mathbf{p}'', \mathbf{P}) = 1 \qquad \text{if both } |\tfrac{1}{2}\mathbf{P} \pm \mathbf{p}''| > p_F$$
$$= 0 \qquad \text{otherwise} \tag{9b}$$

To transform Eq. (9a) to coordinate space, we introduce the center-of-mass coordinate $\mathbf{R}$ and the relative coordinate $\mathbf{r}$ which are canonically conjugate to $\mathbf{P}$ and $\mathbf{p}$, respectively.

$$\mathbf{R} = \tfrac{1}{2}(\mathbf{r}_1 + \mathbf{r}_2) \qquad \mathbf{r} = \mathbf{r}_1 - \mathbf{r}_2 \tag{10a}$$

The plane wave function representing two nucleons with relative variables $\mathbf{p}$ and $\mathbf{r}$ is given by

$$\langle \mathbf{r} \, | \, \mathbf{p} \rangle = e^{i\mathbf{p} \cdot \mathbf{r}} \tag{10b}$$

Introducing a complete set of orthonormal states, we have

$$\langle \mathbf{p}' | \, v \, | \mathbf{p} \rangle = \int d\mathbf{r}' d\mathbf{r} \, \langle \mathbf{p}' \, | \, \mathbf{r}' \rangle \langle \mathbf{r}' | \, v \, | \mathbf{r} \rangle \langle \mathbf{r} \, | \, \mathbf{p} \rangle \tag{10c}$$

Using Eq. (10c) and similar relations, Eq. (9a) becomes

$$\int d\mathbf{r} \, d\mathbf{r}' \, \langle \mathbf{p}' \, | \, \mathbf{r}' \rangle \langle \mathbf{r}' | \, K \, | \mathbf{r} \rangle \langle \mathbf{r} \, | \, \mathbf{p} \rangle$$

$$= \int d\mathbf{r} \, d\mathbf{r}' \, \langle \mathbf{p}' \, | \, \mathbf{r}' \rangle \langle \mathbf{r}' | \, v \, | \mathbf{r} \rangle \langle \mathbf{r} \, | \, \mathbf{p} \rangle + \sum_{\mathbf{p}''} \int d\mathbf{r} \, d\mathbf{r}' \, d\mathbf{r}'' \, d\mathbf{r}'''$$

$$\times \frac{\langle \mathbf{p}' \, | \, \mathbf{r}' \rangle \langle \mathbf{r}' | \, v \, | \mathbf{r}'' \rangle \langle \mathbf{r}'' \, | \, \mathbf{p}'' \rangle \langle \mathbf{p}'' \, | \, \mathbf{r}''' \rangle \langle \mathbf{r}''' | \, K \, | \mathbf{r} \rangle \langle \mathbf{r} \, | \, \mathbf{p} \rangle}{\mathscr{E}(\mathbf{p}'', \mathbf{p}, \mathbf{P})} f(\mathbf{p}'', \mathbf{P}) \tag{10d}$$

Multiplying Eq. (10d) by $e^{i\mathbf{p}'\cdot\mathbf{r}_1}e^{-i\mathbf{p}\cdot\mathbf{r}_2}$, integrating over $d\mathbf{p}'\,d\mathbf{p}$, and relabeling the $\mathbf{r}$'s, we obtain

$$\langle\mathbf{r}'|\,K\,|\mathbf{r}\rangle = \langle\mathbf{r}'|\,v\,|\mathbf{r}\rangle + \int d\mathbf{r}''\,d\mathbf{r}'''\langle\mathbf{r}'|\,v\,|\mathbf{r}''\rangle\mathscr{G}(\mathbf{r}'',\mathbf{r}''',\mathbf{P})\langle\mathbf{r}'''|\,K\,|\mathbf{r}\rangle \quad (11a)$$

where the Green's function $\mathscr{G}(\mathbf{r}'',\mathbf{r}''',\mathbf{p}'',\mathbf{P})$ is given by

$$\mathscr{G}(\mathbf{r}'',\mathbf{r}''',\mathbf{P}) = \sum_{\mathbf{p}''}\frac{\langle\mathbf{r}''\,|\,\mathbf{p}''\rangle\langle\mathbf{p}''\,|\,\mathbf{r}'''\rangle}{\mathscr{E}(\mathbf{p}'',\mathbf{p},\mathbf{P})}f(\mathbf{p}'',\mathbf{P}) \quad (11b)$$

9.4 Two-Particle Wave Function

We denote by ϕ_{ij} the unperturbed wave function of two nucleons in the states i and j. The perturbed wave function ψ_{ij} when potential v is acting between the two nucleons is the solution of an integral equation which can be written symbolically as follows:

$$\psi = \phi + \mathscr{G}v\psi \quad (12a)$$

where $\mathscr{G}$ is the appropriate Green's function. In terms of ψ, the K-matrix can be written in the form

$$K_{i'j';ij} = \langle i'j'|\,K\,|ij\rangle = (\phi_{i'j'},K\phi_{ij})$$
$$= (\phi_{i'j'},v\psi_{ij}) \quad (12b)$$

The integral equation (12a), written in full, becomes

$$\psi_{ij}(\mathbf{r}_1,\mathbf{r}_2) = \phi_{ij}(\mathbf{r}_1,\mathbf{r}_2) + \int d\mathbf{r}'_1\,d\mathbf{r}'_2\,d\mathbf{r}''_1\,d\mathbf{r}''_2\mathscr{G}_{ij}(\mathbf{r}_1,\mathbf{r}_2;\mathbf{r}'_1,\mathbf{r}'_2)$$
$$\cdot\,\langle\mathbf{r}'_1,\mathbf{r}'_2|\,v\,|\mathbf{r}''_1,\mathbf{r}''_2\rangle\psi_{ij}(\mathbf{r}''_1,\mathbf{r}''_2) \quad (13a)$$

where

$$\mathscr{G}_{ij}(\mathbf{r}_1,\mathbf{r}_2;\mathbf{r}'_1,\mathbf{r}'_2) = \sum_{i'j'}\frac{\phi_{i'j'}(\mathbf{r}_1,\mathbf{r}_2)\phi^*_{i'j'}(\mathbf{r}'_1,\mathbf{r}'_2)}{\mathscr{E}_{i'j';ij}} \quad (13b)$$

In terms of the relative and center-of-mass coordinates, we have

$$\psi_{ij}(\mathbf{r},\mathbf{R}) = \phi_{ij}(\mathbf{r},\mathbf{R}) + \int d\mathbf{r}'\,d\mathbf{R}'\,d\mathbf{r}''\,d\mathbf{R}''\mathscr{G}_{ij}(\mathbf{r},\mathbf{R};\mathbf{r}',\mathbf{R}')$$
$$\cdot\,\langle\mathbf{r}',\mathbf{R}'|\,v\,|\mathbf{r}'',\mathbf{R}''\rangle\psi_{ij}(\mathbf{r}'',\mathbf{R}'') \quad (13c)$$

Assuming that the two-nucleon potential is diagonal in the center-of-mass coordinate,

$$\langle\mathbf{r}',\mathbf{R}'|\,v\,|\mathbf{r}'',\mathbf{R}''\rangle = \delta(\mathbf{R}'-\mathbf{R}'')\langle\mathbf{r}'|\,v\,|\mathbf{r}''\rangle, \quad (13d)$$

and that the center-of-mass dependence of the wave functions can be factored out, we obtain from Eq. (13c)

$$\psi_{ij}(\mathbf{r}) = \phi_{ij}(\mathbf{r}) + \int d\mathbf{r}'\,d\mathbf{r}''\mathscr{G}_{ij}(\mathbf{r},\mathbf{r}')\langle\mathbf{r}'|\,v\,|\mathbf{r}''\rangle\psi_{ij}(\mathbf{r}'') \quad (13e)$$

If we assume further that the two-nucleon potential is local, that is,

$$\langle \mathbf{r}' | \, v \, | \mathbf{r}'' \rangle = \delta(\mathbf{r}' - \mathbf{r}'')v(\mathbf{r}') \tag{14a}$$

the integral equation satisfied by $\psi_{ij}(\mathbf{r})$ is

$$\psi_{ij}(\mathbf{r}) = \phi_{ij}(\mathbf{r}) + \int d\mathbf{r}' \mathscr{G}_{ij}(\mathbf{r}, \mathbf{r}')v(\mathbf{r}')\psi_{ij}(\mathbf{r}') \tag{14b}$$

where

$$\mathscr{G}_{ij}(\mathbf{r}, \mathbf{r}') = \sum_{i'j' \neq ij} \frac{\phi_{i'j'}(\mathbf{r})\phi^*_{i'j'}(\mathbf{r}')}{\mathscr{E}_{i'j';ij}} \tag{14c}$$

The complete form of Eq. (12b) for the K-matrix is as follows:

$$\langle i'j' | \, K \, | ij \rangle = \int d\mathbf{r}_1 \, d\mathbf{r}_2 \, d\mathbf{r}_1' \, d\mathbf{r}_2' \phi^*_{i'j'}(\mathbf{r}_1', \mathbf{r}_2')\langle \mathbf{r}_1', \mathbf{r}_2' | \, K \, | \mathbf{r}_1, \mathbf{r}_2 \rangle \phi_{ij}(\mathbf{r}_1, \mathbf{r}_2) \tag{15a}$$

$$= \int d\mathbf{r}_1 \, d\mathbf{r}_2 \, d\mathbf{r}_1' \, d\mathbf{r}_2' \phi^*_{i'j'}(\mathbf{r}_1', \mathbf{r}_2')\langle \mathbf{r}_1', \mathbf{r}_2' | \, v \, | \mathbf{r}_1, \mathbf{r}_2 \rangle \psi_{ij}(\mathbf{r}_1, \mathbf{r}_2) \tag{15b}$$

and

$$\langle \mathbf{r}_1'\mathbf{r}_2' | \, K \, | \mathbf{r}_1\mathbf{r}_2 \rangle = \sum_{i'j',ij} \phi^*_{i'j'}(\mathbf{r}_1', \mathbf{r}_2')\langle i'j' | \, K \, | ij \rangle \phi_{ij}(\mathbf{r}_1, \mathbf{r}_2) \tag{15c}$$

$$= \sum_{i'j',ij} \phi^*_{i'j'}(\mathbf{r}_1', \mathbf{r}_2')\langle i'j' | \, v \, | ij \rangle \psi_{ij}(\mathbf{r}_1, \mathbf{r}_2) \tag{15d}$$

Under the approximation of Eqs. (13d) and (14a), for both v and K, Eqs. (15) reduce to the following

$$\langle i'j' | \, K \, | ij \rangle = \int d\mathbf{r} \, d\mathbf{r}' \phi^*_{i'j'}(\mathbf{r}')\langle \mathbf{r}' | \, K \, | \mathbf{r} \rangle \phi_{ij}(\mathbf{r}) \tag{16a}$$

$$= \int d\mathbf{r} \, d\mathbf{r}' \phi^*_{i'j'}(\mathbf{r}')\langle \mathbf{r}' | \, v \, | \mathbf{r} \rangle \psi_{ij}(\mathbf{r}) \tag{16b}$$

and

$$\langle \mathbf{r}' | \, K \, | \mathbf{r} \rangle = \sum_{i'j',ij} \phi^*_{i'j'}(\mathbf{r}')\langle i'j' | \, K \, | ij \rangle \phi_{ij}(\mathbf{r}) \tag{16c}$$

$$= \sum_{i'j',ij} \phi^*_{i'j'}(\mathbf{r}')\langle i'j' | \, v \, | ij \rangle \psi_{ij}(\mathbf{r}) \tag{16d}$$

The integral in Eq. (14b) for ψ can be rendered into a different form. We denote by H_0 the unperturbed Hamiltonian operator for the two nucleons. Then

$$H_0\phi_{ij}(\mathbf{r}) = (E_i + E_j)\phi_{ij}(\mathbf{r})$$
$$= \mathscr{E}_{ij}\phi_{ij}(\mathbf{r}) \tag{17a}$$

Operating with H_0 on Eq. (14b), we obtain

$$H_0\psi_{ij}(\mathbf{r}) = \mathscr{E}_{ij}\phi_{ij}(\mathbf{r}) + \int d\mathbf{r}' \sum_{i'j'} \frac{\mathscr{E}_{i'j'}\phi_{i'j'}(\mathbf{r})\phi^*_{i'j'}(\mathbf{r}')}{\mathscr{E}_{i'j';ij}} v(\mathbf{r}')\psi_{ij}(\mathbf{r}') \tag{17b}$$

Multiplying Eq. (14b) by $\mathscr{E}_{ij}$ and subtracting from Eq. (17b), we have

$$(H_0 - \mathscr{E}_{ij})\psi_{ij}(\mathbf{r}) = \int d\mathbf{r}' Q(\mathbf{r}, \mathbf{r}')v(\mathbf{r}')\psi_{ij}(\mathbf{r}') \qquad (17c)$$

where

$$Q(\mathbf{r}, \mathbf{r}') = \sum_{i'j' \neq ij} \frac{\mathscr{E}_{i'j'} - \mathscr{E}_{ij}}{\mathscr{E}_{i'j',ij}} \phi_{i'j'}(\mathbf{r})\phi^*_{i'j'}(\mathbf{r}') \qquad (17d)$$

Equation (17c) is the Bethe-Goldstone[12] (B-G) equation. $Q(\mathbf{r}, \mathbf{r}')$ is a projection operator which takes into account the Pauli exclusion principle. In the limit where we neglect the presence of the other nucleons in the nucleus, that is, ignoring the Pauli exclusion principle, and therefore taking

$$\delta\mathscr{E}_{i'j';ij} = 0,$$

we have

$$Q(\mathbf{r}, \mathbf{r}') = \sum_{i'j'} \phi_{i'j'}(\mathbf{r})\phi^*_{i'j'}(\mathbf{r}') = \delta(\mathbf{r} - \mathbf{r}')$$

and Eqs. (14b) and (17c) become the usual two-body Schrödinger equation in the relative coordinate $\mathbf{r}$.

9.5 Partial Wave Analysis

Green's Function

In the plane wave approximation, the Green's function $\mathscr{G}(\mathbf{r}, \mathbf{r}')$, Eqs. (11b) and (14c), is given by

$$\mathscr{G}(\mathbf{r}, \mathbf{r}', \mathbf{P}) = \sum_{\mathbf{p}''} \frac{e^{i\mathbf{p}''\cdot(\mathbf{r}-\mathbf{r}')}}{\mathscr{E}(\mathbf{p}'', \mathbf{p}, \mathbf{P})} f(\mathbf{p}'', \mathbf{P}) \qquad (18a)$$

where

$$\mathscr{E}(\mathbf{p}'', \mathbf{p}, \mathbf{P}) = E(\tfrac{1}{2}\mathbf{P} + \mathbf{p}'') + E(\tfrac{1}{2}\mathbf{P} - \mathbf{p}'') - E(\tfrac{1}{2}\mathbf{P} + \mathbf{p}) - E(\tfrac{1}{2}\mathbf{P} - \mathbf{p})$$
$$- \delta\mathscr{E}(\mathbf{p}'', \mathbf{p}, \mathbf{P}) \qquad (18b)$$

and the labels ij have been specified by the momenta. The E's are defined by Eq. (8d). For the two-body problem

$$f(\mathbf{p}'', \mathbf{P}) = 1 \qquad \delta\mathscr{E} = 0 \qquad E(\mathbf{p}) = \frac{\mathbf{p}^2}{2M}$$

so that the energy denominator

$$\mathscr{E}(\mathbf{p}'', \mathbf{p}, \mathbf{P}) = \frac{\mathbf{p}''^2 - \mathbf{p}^2}{M}$$

which is independent of the angles between $\mathbf{p}''$ and $\mathbf{P}$ and between $\mathbf{p}$ and $\mathbf{P}$. In the nuclear matter problem, the Green's function depends on these angles through the energy denominator and $f(\mathbf{p}'', \mathbf{P})$. Brueckner and

Gammel[4] have suggested two approximations whereby the angular dependent functions are replaced by their angular averages.

1. Replace

$$f(\mathbf{p}'', \mathbf{P}) \to \frac{1}{4\pi} \int d\Omega_P f(\mathbf{p}'', \mathbf{P}) = 0 \qquad \text{for} \quad (p''^2 + \tfrac{1}{4}P^2)^{\frac{1}{2}} < p_F$$

$$= 1 \qquad \text{for} \quad p'' - \tfrac{1}{2}P > p_F \qquad (18c)$$

$$= \frac{p''^2 + \tfrac{1}{4}P^2 - p_F^2}{p''P} \qquad \text{otherwise}$$

2. Expand the energy denominator as follows:

$$\mathscr{E}(\mathbf{p}'', \mathbf{p}, \mathbf{P}) = A + B_1(p_+''^2 + p_-''^2) - B_2(p_+^2 + p_-^2) + C_1(p_+''^4 + p_-''^4)$$
$$- C_2(p_+^4 + p_-^4) + \cdots \qquad (18d)$$

where $\mathbf{p}_\pm = \tfrac{1}{2}\mathbf{P} \pm \mathbf{p}$. The approximation in Eq. (18d) involves the replacement

$$(\mathbf{p}'' \cdot \mathbf{P})^2 \to \frac{1}{4\pi} \int d\Omega_P (\mathbf{p}'' \cdot \mathbf{P})^2 f(\mathbf{p}'', \mathbf{P}) \qquad (18e)$$

which is equivalent to the replacements

$$\mathbf{p}_\pm''^2 \to \tfrac{1}{4}P^2 + p''^2 \pm \frac{1}{\sqrt{3}} f^2(\mathbf{p}'', \mathbf{P}) p'' P \qquad (18f)$$

The energy denominator $\mathscr{E}$ [Eq. (18d)] is approximated by the first three terms which are independent of the angle $(\mathbf{p}'' \cdot \mathbf{P})$. The higher order terms C_1, C_2, etc., involve the angle but are expected to be important only for $p'' \gg P$, in which case $p_\pm$ will be large, so that we can approximate

$$\mathscr{E}(\mathbf{p}'', \mathbf{p}, \mathbf{P}) \simeq \frac{1}{M}(\tfrac{1}{4}P^2 + p''^2) - E(\tfrac{1}{2}\mathbf{P} + \mathbf{p}) - E(\tfrac{1}{2}\mathbf{P} - \mathbf{p}) \qquad \text{for} \quad p'' \gg P$$

$$(18g)$$

Using Eqs. (18c), (18d), and (18g), the angular momentum expansion of the Green's function $\mathscr{G}(\mathbf{r}, \mathbf{r}', \mathbf{P})$ [Eq. (18a)] is readily carried out.

$$\mathscr{G}(\mathbf{r}, \mathbf{r}', \mathbf{P}) = \sum_{l=0}^{\infty} (2l + 1) \sqrt{\frac{4\pi}{2l + 1}} \mathscr{G}_l(r, r') Y_l^0(\hat{r} \cdot \hat{r}') \qquad (19a)$$

where

$$\mathscr{G}_l(r, r') = \int_0^{\infty} dp'' p''^2 \frac{j_l(p''r) j_l(p''r')}{\mathscr{E}(p'', p, P)} f(p'', P) \qquad (19b)$$

and we have used the partial wave expansion of the plane wave

$$e^{i\mathbf{p}\cdot\mathbf{r}} = \sum_{l=0}^{\infty} (2l + 1)i^l j_l(pr)\sqrt{\frac{4\pi}{2l + 1}}\, Y_l^0(\hat{p}\cdot\hat{r}), \tag{19c}$$

$\hat{p}, \hat{r}$ being unit vectors in the direction of $\mathbf{p}$ and $\mathbf{r}$.

Two-Particle Wave Function

The unperturbed wave function (including spin) represented by the plane wave is given by

$$e^{i\mathbf{p}\cdot\mathbf{r}}\chi_S^{m_s} = \sum_{l=0}^{\infty} (2l + 1)i^l j_l(pr)\sqrt{\frac{4\pi}{2l + 1}}\, Y_l^0(\hat{p}\cdot\hat{r})\chi_S^{m_s}$$

$$= \sum_{l=0}^{\infty}\sum_J (2l + 1)i^l j_l(pr)\sqrt{\frac{4\pi}{2l + 1}}\, \langle lS0m_s \mid Jm_s\rangle \mathscr{Y}_{lSJ}^{m_s}(\hat{p}\cdot\hat{r}) \tag{20a}$$

where $\langle lSm_l m_s \mid JM\rangle$ is the Clebsch-Gordan coefficient and $\mathscr{Y}_{lSJ}^M(\hat{p}\cdot\hat{r})$ is an eigenstate corresponding to orbital angular momentum l and total angular momentum J. The spin of the two nucleons $\mathbf{S} = \mathbf{s}_1 + \mathbf{s}_2 = 0$ or 1 and $\mathbf{J} = \mathbf{l} + \mathbf{S}$. For the singlet state of the two nucleons, $J = l$ and the summation over J in Eq. (20a) drops out. For the triplet state, the summation over J extends over the three values $J = l \pm 1, l$. The perturbed wave function cannot be written so simply because of the two-nucleon tensor part of the interaction which is diagonal in l only for $J = l$; but for $l = J \pm 1$, it has both diagonal and nondiagonal elements. Thus the $l = J \pm 1$ state is coupled to $l' = J \pm 1$ and $l' = J \mp 1$ states. Following Brueckner and Gammel,[4] we obtain for the perturbed wave function pertaining to orbital angular momentum l the following expression

$$(\psi(\mathbf{r}))_l^{m_l}\chi_S^{m_s} = \sum_J \langle lSm_l m_s \mid JM\rangle \sum_{l'} u_{ll'}^{JS}(r)\mathscr{Y}_{l'SJ}^M(\hat{r}) \tag{20b}$$

where for $J = l$, $l' = l$, and for $J = l \pm 1$, l' takes the two values $l' = l$ and $l \pm 2$, and $u_{ll'}^{JS}(r)$ are the solutions of the radial Schrödinger equations which for $J = l \pm 1$ are coupled equations. The complete perturbed wave function (labeling it with subscript p) is given by

$$\psi_p(\mathbf{r})\chi_S^{m_s} = \sum_{l=0}^{\infty}\sum_J (2l + 1)i^l \sqrt{\frac{4\pi}{2l + 1}}\, \langle lS0m_s \mid Jm_s\rangle \sum_{l'} u_{ll'}^{JS}(r)\mathscr{Y}_{l'SJ}^{m_s}(\hat{p}\cdot\hat{r}) \tag{20c}$$

where we have chosen the z-axis along $\hat{p}$ so that $m_l = 0$. For the general two-body interaction involving the central, spin-orbit, and tensor potential, the total angular momentum J, its z-component M, and the spin S are constants of motion.

Substituting Eqs. (19a), (20a), and (20c) in the integral equation (14b) for $\psi(\mathbf{r})$, we have

$$\sum_{l=0}^{\infty}(2l+1)i^l\sqrt{\frac{4\pi}{2l+1}}\langle lS0m_s\mid Jm_s\rangle\sum_{l'}u_{ll'}^{JS}(r)\mathcal{Y}_{l'SJ}^{m_s}(\hat{p}\cdot\hat{r})$$

$$=\sum_{l=0}^{\infty}(2l+1)i^lj_l(pr)\sqrt{\frac{4\pi}{2l+1}}\langle lS0m_s\mid Jm_s\rangle\mathcal{Y}_{lSJ}^{m_s}(\hat{p}\cdot\hat{r})$$

$$+\int d\mathbf{r'}\sum_{l''=0}^{\infty}(2l''+1)\sqrt{\frac{4\pi}{2l''+1}}\,\mathcal{G}_{l''}(r,r')Y_{l''}^0(\hat{r}\cdot\hat{r}')v(\mathbf{r}')$$

$$\cdot\sum_{l_1=0}^{\infty}(2l_1+1)i^{l_1}\sqrt{\frac{4\pi}{2l_1+1}}\langle l_1S0m_{s_1}\mid Jm_{s_1}\rangle\sum_{l_1'}u_{l_1l_1'}^{JS}(r')\mathcal{Y}_{l_1'SJ}^{m_{s_1}}(\hat{p}\cdot\hat{r}')$$

$$\tag{21a}$$

where the summation over J has been dropped since it is a constant of motion. In order to eliminate the angular dependence from Eq. (21a), we multiply by $\mathcal{Y}_{L'SJ}^{m_s*}(\hat{p}\cdot\hat{r})$ on the left and integrate over the solid angle $d\hat{r}$.

$$\sum_{l=0}^{\infty}(2l+1)i^l\sqrt{\frac{4\pi}{2l+1}}\langle lS0m_s\mid Jm_s\rangle\sum_{l'}u_{ll'}^{JS}(r)\,\delta_{l'L'}$$

$$=\sum_{l=0}^{\infty}(2l+1)i^lj_l(pr)\sqrt{\frac{4\pi}{2l+1}}\langle lS0m_s\mid Jm_s\rangle\delta_{lL'}$$

$$+\int dr'r'^2\sum_{l''=0}^{\infty}(2l''+1)\sqrt{\frac{4\pi}{2l''+1}}\,\mathcal{G}_{l''}(r,r')$$

$$\cdot\sum_{l_1=0}^{\infty}(2l_1+1)i^{l_1}\sqrt{\frac{4\pi}{2l_1+1}}\langle l_1S0m_{s_1}\mid Jm_{s_1}\rangle\sum_{l_1'}\bar{v}_{L'l_1'l''}^{JS}(r)u_{l_1l_1'}^{JS}(r')\tag{21b}$$

where

$$\bar{v}_{Ll_1l''}^{JS}(\mathbf{r}')=\int d\hat{r}\,d\hat{r}'\mathcal{Y}_{LSJ}^{m_s*}(\hat{p}\cdot\hat{r})Y_{l''}^0(\hat{r}\cdot\hat{r}')v(\mathbf{r}')\mathcal{Y}_{l_1SJ}^{m_s}(\hat{p}\cdot\hat{r}')\tag{21c}$$

But

$$\int d\hat{r}\,\mathcal{Y}_{LSJ}^{m_s*}(\hat{p}\cdot\hat{r})Y_{l''}^0(\hat{r}\cdot\hat{r}')$$

$$=\int d\hat{r}\sum_{m_L}\langle LSm_L\;m_s-m_L\mid Jm_s\rangle Y_L^{m_L*}(\hat{p}\cdot\hat{r})\chi_S^{m_s-m_L}$$

$$\cdot\left[\sum_{m''}\sqrt{\frac{4\pi}{2l''+1}}\,Y_{l''}^{m''*}(\hat{p}\cdot\hat{r}')Y_{l''}^{m''}(\hat{p}\cdot\hat{r})\right]$$

$$=\sum_{m_L}\sqrt{\frac{4\pi}{2L+1}}\langle LSm_L\;m_s-m_L\mid Jm_s\rangle Y_L^{m_L*}(\hat{p}\cdot\hat{r}')\chi_S^{m_s-m_L}\delta_{l''L}$$

$$=\sqrt{\frac{4\pi}{2L+1}}\,\mathcal{Y}_{LSJ}^{m_s*}(\hat{p}\cdot\hat{r}')\delta_{l''L}\tag{21d}$$

so that

$$\bar{v}^{JS}_{Ll_1'l'}(r') = \sqrt{\frac{4\pi}{2L+1}} \ v^{JS}_{Ll_1}(r') \ \delta_{l''L} \tag{21e}$$

where

$$v^{JS}_{ll'}(r') = \int d\hat{r}' \mathscr{Y}_{lSJ}^{m_s*}(\hat{p}\cdot\hat{r}')v(\mathbf{r}')\mathscr{Y}_{l'SJ}^{m_s}(\hat{p}\cdot\hat{r}') \tag{21f}$$

Multiplying Eq. (21b) by $\langle LS0m_s \,|\, Jm_s\rangle$, summing over m_s and using

$$\sum_{m_s=-1}^{1} \langle LS0m_s \,|\, Jm_s\rangle\langle lS0m_s \,|\, Jm_s\rangle = \delta_{Ll}\frac{2J+1}{2l+1} \tag{21g}$$

we obtain

$$u^{JS}_{ll'}(r) = j_l(pr)\,\delta_{ll'} + 4\pi \sum_{l''} \int dr' r'^2 \mathscr{G}_{l'}(r,\,r')v^{JS}_{l'l''}(r')u^{JS}_{ll''}(r') \tag{22}$$

where we have relabelled L, L', l_1' by l, l', l'' respectively.

Equation (22) represents an integral equation for the perturbed wave function $u^{JS}_{ll'}(r)$; a single integral equation for the states $J = l$, $S = 0$ or 1, and coupled integral equations in $u^{JS}_{J\pm1,J\pm1}(r)$ and $u^{JS}_{J\pm1,J\mp1}(r)$ for l equals $J \pm 1$. For $S = 1$, Eq. (22) can be written in a matrix form.

9.6   Treatment of the Problem with a Hard Core in the Two-Nucleon Potential

We define the two-nucleon potential as follows

$$v(\mathbf{r}') = \infty \qquad \text{for} \quad r' \le r_c$$
$$= \text{analytic function for } r' > r_c. \tag{23a}$$

The boundary condition imposed on the radial solution of the Schrödinger equation is

$$[u(r)]_{r=r_c} = 0 \tag{23b}$$

For convenience we consider only the $J = l$ state; the general case can be considered similarly. The integral equation to be solved is

$$u^{lS}_{ll}(r) = \phi_l(r) + 4\pi \int_0^\infty dr' r'^2 \mathscr{G}_l(r,\,r')v^{lS}_{ll}(r')u^{lS}_{ll}(r') \tag{24a}$$

where $\phi_l(r)$ is the unperturbed solution.

In view of Eqs. (23a) and (23b), the integral in Eq. (24a) is not well defined from $0 \le r \le r_c$. In this region, $v(r') = \infty$ and $u(r') = 0$ for hard cores, but the product $v(r')u(r')$ is indeterminate. Brueckner and Gammel[4] suggest the following replacement:

$$v(r')u(r') = \lambda\delta(r' - r_c) \qquad \text{for} \quad r' \le r_c \tag{24b}$$

where the constant λ is determined from Eqs. (23b) and (24a). By splitting the integral in Eq. (24a) into two parts, the integral equation becomes

$$u_{ll}^{lS}(r) = \phi_l(r) + 4\pi\left[\int_0^{r_c} + \int_{r_c}^{\infty}\right] dr' r'^2 \mathscr{G}_l(r, r')v_{ll}^{lS}(r')u_{ll}^{lS}(r')$$

$$= \phi_l(r) + 4\pi r_c^2 \lambda \mathscr{G}_l(r, r_c) + 4\pi\int_{r_c}^{\infty} dr' r'^2 \mathscr{G}_l(r, r')v_{ll}^{lS}(r')u_{ll}^{lS}(r') \tag{24c}$$

From Eqs. (24b), (24c), and (23b), we obtain

$$\lambda = -\left[\phi_l(r_c) + 4\pi\int_{r_c}^{\infty} dr' r'^2 \mathscr{G}_l(r_c, r')v_{ll}^{lS}(r')u_{ll}^{lS}(r')\right]\bigg/ 4\pi r_c^2 \mathscr{G}_l(r_c, r_c) \tag{24d}$$

Substituting the expression in Eq. (24d) for λ in Eq. (24c), we have

$$u_{ll}^{lS}(r) = S_{ll}^{lS}(r) + 4\pi\int_{r_c}^{\infty} dr' r'^2 F_l(r, r')v_{ll}^{lS}(r')u_{ll}^{lS}(r') \tag{25a}$$

where

$$S_{ll}^{lS}(r) = \phi_l(r) - \phi_l(r_c)\frac{\mathscr{G}_l(r, r_c)}{\mathscr{G}_l(r_c, r_c)} \tag{25b}$$

$$F_l(r, r') = \mathscr{G}_l(r, r') - \frac{\mathscr{G}_l(r, r_c)\mathscr{G}_l(r_c, r')}{\mathscr{G}_l(r_c, r_c)} \tag{25c}$$

For the scattering problem

$$\phi_l(r) = j_l(pr) \tag{26a}$$

$$\mathscr{G}_l(r, r') = -\frac{Mp}{4\pi} j_l(pr_<)n_l(pr_>) \tag{26b}$$

where

$$\begin{aligned} r_< = r' \qquad r_> = r \qquad \text{for} \quad r' < r \\ r_< = r \qquad r_> = r' \qquad \text{for} \quad r' > r \end{aligned} \tag{26c}$$

From Eqs. (25a) and (26) we observe that $u_{ll}^{lS}(r) = 0$ for $r < r_c$.

The expressions for the K-matrix can be worked out using Eqs. (16), (20a), and (20d). It is easy to show that

$$\sum_{m_s} \langle p, S, m_s| \, K \, |p, S, m_s\rangle = 4\pi \sum_{l=J-1}^{J+1} (2J + 1)\int_0^{\infty} dr r^2 j_l(pr) \sum_{l'=J-1}^{J+1} v_{ll'}^{JS}(r)u_{ll'}^{JS}(r) \tag{27a}$$

In the presence of a hard core the K-matrix is given by

$$\sum_{m_s} \langle p, S, m_s | K | p, S, m_s \rangle$$

$$= 4\pi \sum_J (2J + 1) \sum_{l=J-1}^{J+1} \left[-\frac{j_l^2(pr_c)}{\mathscr{G}_l(r_c, r_c)} + \int_{r_c}^{\infty} dr\, r^2 S_l(pr) \sum_{l'=J-1}^{J+1} v_{ll'}^{JS}(r) u_{ll'}^{JS}(r) \right]$$

$$(27b)$$

where

$$S_l(pr) = j_l(pr) - j_l(pr_c) \frac{\mathscr{G}_l(r, r_c)}{\mathscr{G}_l(r_c, r_c)} \tag{27c}$$

9.7   Bethe-Goldstone's Treatment of the Repulsive Core

Bethe and Goldstone[12] consider the solution of the integral equation

$$\psi(\mathbf{x}) = e^{i\mathbf{p}_0 \cdot \mathbf{x}} - \int d^3 y\, v(\mathbf{y}) \psi(\mathbf{y}) \Gamma(\mathbf{x}, \mathbf{y}) \tag{28a}$$

where the nonlocal operator Γ is defined by

$$\Gamma(\mathbf{x}, \mathbf{y}) = (2\pi)^{-3} \int_{P_F} \frac{d^3 p}{e(p)}\, e^{i\mathbf{p} \cdot (\mathbf{x} - \mathbf{y})} \tag{28b}$$

and the energy denominator, in the effective mass approximation, is taken to be

$$e(p) = E(\tfrac{1}{2}\mathbf{P} + \mathbf{p}) + E(\tfrac{1}{2}\mathbf{P} - \mathbf{p}) - E(\tfrac{1}{2}\mathbf{P} + \mathbf{p}_0) - E(\tfrac{1}{2}\mathbf{P} - \mathbf{p}_0) \quad (28c)$$

$$= \frac{p^2 - p_0^2}{M^*} \quad \text{with} \quad E(k) = \frac{k^2}{2M^*} \tag{28d}$$

which is independent of $\mathbf{P}$ and where M^* is the effective mass†. The integration in Eq. (28b) is restricted to $p \geq p_F$ since the Pauli exclusion principle does not allow excitation to momentum states already occupied. The integral equation (28a) can easily be transformed into the following differential equation:

$$\frac{1}{M^*} (\nabla^2 + p_0^2) \psi(\mathbf{x}) = v(\mathbf{x}) \psi(\mathbf{x}) - \int d^3 y\, v(\mathbf{y}) \psi(\mathbf{y}) g(\mathbf{x} - \mathbf{y}) \tag{29a}$$

---

† The effective mass approximation is possible provided it is a good approximation to treat the potential $V(p) = V_0 + ap^2$ for momenta up to p_F and somewhat larger. Then in the Schrödinger equation the ap^2 term can be absorbed in the kinetic energy term so that the effective mass is given by $1/M^* = 1/M + 2a$. The physical basis of this approximation follows from the fact that the two-nucleon motion in nuclear matter is essentially that of free particles except when their separation distance $\leqslant 10^{-13}$ cm; the average separation distance is $\simeq 1.66 \times 10^{-13}$ cm. Thus, although the effect of the two-nucleon interaction is not entirely negligible it is not yet too great and can be incorporated by the introduction of an effective mass.

where

$$g(\mathbf{x}) = \frac{1}{(2\pi)^3} \int_0^{P_F} d\mathbf{p} e^{i\mathbf{p} \cdot \mathbf{x}}$$

$$= \frac{\sin p_F x - p_F x \cos p_F x}{2\pi^2 x^3} \qquad \text{for} \quad \mathbf{P} = 0 \qquad (29b)$$

The second term on the right-hand side of Eq. (29a) represents the effect of the Pauli principle. In arriving at Eq. (29a), the integral over the momentum has been split into an integral from 0 to ∞ which yields $\delta(\mathbf{x} - \mathbf{y})$ minus an integral from 0 to p_F.

Bethe and Goldstone[12] consider the solutions of Eq. (29a) for the case of a spherically symmetric potential $v(x)$ and for the S state. Eliminating the angular coordinates, Eq. (29a) becomes

$$\frac{d^2 u}{dr^2} + K_0^2 u(r) = w(r) - \int ds w(s) \chi(r, s) \qquad (30a)$$

where

$$\mathbf{r} = p_F \mathbf{x} \qquad \mathbf{s} = p_F \mathbf{y} \qquad K = \frac{p}{p_F} \qquad (30b)$$

$$\psi(\mathbf{x}) = \frac{u(r)}{r} \qquad w(r) = \frac{M^*}{p_F^2} u(r) v(r) \qquad (30c)$$

and

$$\int ds w(s) \chi(r, s) = \frac{M^*}{p_F^2} r \int \frac{d\mathbf{s}}{p_F^3} v(s) \frac{u(s)}{s} g(\mathbf{r} - \mathbf{s})$$

$$= \frac{M^* r}{p_F^5} \int 2\pi s \, ds \frac{z \, dz}{r} \frac{u(s) v(s)}{s} g(\mathbf{z}) \qquad (30d)$$

so that

$$\chi(r, s) = \frac{1}{\pi} \int_0^1 dK \{\cos K |r - s| - \cos K(r + s)\}$$

$$= \frac{1}{\pi} \left[\frac{\sin |r - s|}{|r - s|} - \frac{\sin (r + s)}{r + s} \right] \qquad (30e)$$

The second term on the right-hand side of Eq. (30a) represents the effect of the Pauli principle.

We specify the potential as follows

$$v(x) = \infty \qquad \text{for} \quad x \leq r_c$$

$$= 0 \qquad \text{for} \quad x > r_c \qquad (31a)$$

The boundary condition for the solution of Eq. (30a) is therefore

$$u(r) = 0 \quad \text{for} \quad r < c = p_F r_c$$
$$\neq 0 \quad \text{for} \quad r > c \tag{31b}$$

and at large r, $u(r)$ should go over into the free-particle wave function.

From Eqs. (31b) and (30a), we find that w satisfies the integral equation

$$w(r) = \int ds w(s) \chi(r, s) \quad \text{for} \quad r < c \tag{31c}$$

At $r = c$, u must be continuous, but du/dr may be discontinuous, that is,

$$u'(c + \epsilon) = A \tag{31d}$$

where A has to be determined by the condition

$$\lim_{r \to \infty} u(r) = \frac{1}{K_0} \sin K_0 r \tag{31e}$$

From Eqs. (31d) and (30a), it follows that

$$w(r) = A \, \delta(r - c) + w_1(r) \tag{32a}$$

and thus from Eq. (31c), we have

$$w_1(r) = A \chi(r, c) + \int_0^c ds w_1(s) \chi(r, s) \tag{32b}$$

with

$$w_1(r) = 0 \quad \text{for} \quad r > c \big\rbrace$$
$$= \text{finite} \quad \text{for} \quad r < c \big\rbrace \tag{32c}$$

From Eqs. (32a) and (30a), we find that

$$\frac{d^2u}{dr^2} + K_0^2 u = A \, \delta(r - c) - \int ds w(s) \chi(r, s) \Big\rbrace$$
$$= A \, \delta(r - c) - A \chi(r, c) - \int_0^c ds w_1(s) \chi(r, s) \Big\rbrace r > c \tag{32d}$$

The second term on the right-hand side, being negative, indicates that the correction to the repulsive core due to the Pauli principle is equivalent to an attractive potential.

For small core radius ($c = 0.77$), we can expand $\chi(r, s)$ in Eq. (30e) in powers of r and s and use Eq. (32b) to calculate $w_1(r)$. We find

$$\chi(r, s) = \frac{2rs}{3\pi} [1 - \tfrac{1}{10}(r^2 + s^2) + \cdots] \tag{33a}$$

$$w_1(r) = A \frac{2rc}{3\pi} \left[1 - \tfrac{1}{10}(r^2 + c^2) + \frac{2c^3}{9\pi} + \cdots \right]$$
$$\simeq A \chi(r, c) + \text{terms } O(c^4) \tag{33b}$$

where the term of the order of c^4 may be neglected. To this order of approximation, we can neglect the integral on the right-hand side of Eq. (32d), and the solution is given by

$$u(r) = \frac{1}{K_0} \int_0^r ds f(s) \sin K_0(r - s) \tag{34a}$$

where

$$f(r) \simeq A \, \delta(r - c) - A\chi(r, c) \tag{34b}$$

From Eqs. (34), we obtain

$$u(r) = B \sin K_0 r + C \cos K_0 r \tag{34c}$$

$$B = \frac{A}{2\pi K_0}\left\{ [2\pi - Si(1 + K_0)2c - Si(1 - K_0)2c] \cos K_0 c \right.$$
$$\left. + \left[\ln \frac{1 + K_0}{1 - K_0} + Ci(1 + K_0)2c - Ci(1 - K_0)2c \right] \sin K_0 c \right\} \tag{34d}$$

$$C = \frac{A}{2\pi K_0}\left\{ \left[\ln \frac{1 + K_0}{1 - K_0} - Ci(1 + K_0)2c + Ci(1 - K_0)2c \right] \cos K_0 c \right.$$
$$\left. - [Si(1 + K_0)2c + Si(1 - K_0)2c] \sin K_0 c \right\} \tag{34e}$$

where

$$Si(z) = \int_0^z \frac{\sin t}{t}\, dt$$

$$Ci(z) = \gamma + \ln z + \int_0^z \frac{\cos t - 1}{t}\, dt \qquad (|\arg z| < \pi)$$

$$\gamma = 0.577\,216 \qquad \text{is Euler's constant}$$

The constant A is determined by the condition

$$\lim_{r \to \infty} u(r) = \frac{\sin K_0 r}{K_0} \tag{34f}$$

so that

$$A^{-1} = \left[1 - \frac{c}{\pi}\left(2 - K_0 \ln \frac{1 + K_0}{1 - K_0} \right) - \cdots \right] \tag{34g}$$

Figure 9-1 shows a plot of the wave function $u(r)$ against r. The Pauli principle which has an effect equivalent to an attractive potential, causes a downward curve of the wave function. In Fig. 9-2, the wave function is plotted for an attractive potential (no repulsive core) for $K_0 = 0$. The curve for $0 < r < b$ is dominated by the potential term [first term on

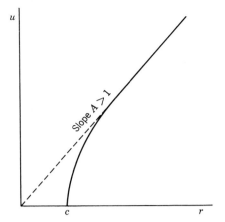

Fig. 9-1 Wave function with a pure repulsive core (radius c) and the exclusion principle (Bethe et al.[12]).

the right of Eq. (30a)]. For $r > b$, the first and the second terms (quasi-repulsive Pauli exclusion term from the attractive potential) have opposite contributions and make the wave function close to the free-particle wave function $u = r$; the Born approximation gives good results. The wave function for a repulsive core and an attractive potential is indicated in Fig. 9-3. In the region $c < r < b$, the attractive potential and the

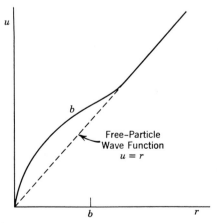

Fig. 9-2 Wave function for pure attractive potential of range b (Bethe et al.[12]).

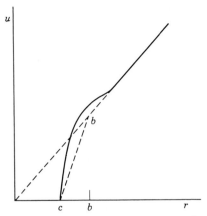

Fig. 9-3   Wave function for a repulsive core (radius c) plus attractive potential (range b) with exclusion principle (Bethe et al.[12]).

quasi-attractive Pauli term due to the core are important. For

$$r_c < r \lesssim b, \quad u(r) < r \quad \text{(the free wave function)}$$

but

$$u(r) > \frac{b}{b-c}(r-c)$$

Calculation of the K-matrix

The diagonal element of the K-matrix gives the potential energy. Thus we have

$$\langle p_0| \, K \, |p_0 \rangle = \int d^3x v(\mathbf{x})\psi(\mathbf{x})e^{-i\mathbf{p}_0 \cdot \mathbf{x}}$$

$$= \frac{4\pi}{M^* p_F} \int dr r \, \frac{\sin K_0 r}{K_0 r} \, w(r) \tag{35a}$$

$$= \frac{4\pi}{M^*} A \, \frac{\sin p_0 c}{p_0} \tag{35b}$$

where in Eq. (35b), we have used Eq. (32a) after neglecting w_1. The result of Eq. (35b) for a repulsive core includes the effect of the Pauli exclusion principle. We can compare it with the case of scattering of two free nucleons, keeping M^* as the effective mass. For a repulsive core, the phase shift $\delta_0 = -p_0 r_c$ and the K-matrix elements are given by

$$\langle k_0| \, K \, |k_0 \rangle_{\text{free}} = \frac{4\pi \tan p_0 r_c}{M^* p_0} \quad \text{(without exclusion principle)} \tag{35c}$$

Comparing Eqs. (35b) and (35c), we find

$$\frac{\langle k_0| \; K \; |k_0\rangle_{\text{excl. princ}}}{\langle k_0| \; K \; |k_0\rangle_{\text{no excl. princ}}} = A \cos k_0 r_c$$

$$= \frac{1}{1 - \dfrac{Si2c}{\pi}} \qquad [\text{for } p_0 = 0, \text{ Eq. (34d)}]$$

$$\simeq 1 + \frac{2c}{\pi} \qquad (\text{for } c < 1) \tag{35d}$$

so that the $p_0 = 0$ level is shifted upward due to the Pauli principle.

Bethe and Goldstone[12] have developed a calculation to test the effective-mass approximation at large values of p, namely that the energy is quadratic in p. Brueckner and Wada[14] have obtained the effective mass $M^* = 0.60M$ at low energy. Bethe and Goldstone find that at large momenta the effective mass

$$M^* = M\left(1 - \frac{2r_c^3}{r_0^3}\right)$$

where r_0 is the nuclear radius parameter. For $r_c = 0.5 \times 10^{-13}$ cm, the effective mass is $M^* = 0.85M$, which is considerably larger than the value of Brueckner and Wada.[14]

Bauer and Moshinsky,[15] and Moshinsky[15] have considered the problem when the common nuclear potential is a harmonic-oscillator potential and the two-nucleon potential is a central Yukawa form with a hard core. They carried out a perturbation expansion taking the core radius as the expansion parameter. Nigam[16] considered the two-nucleon interaction in a common harmonic-oscillator potential when the two-nucleon potential includes repulsive hard core plus central, spin-orbit, and tensor parts.

9.8   Theory of the Finite Nucleus

In the nuclear matter problem (infinite nucleus), the eigenstates are known to be plane waves, and the so-called Hartree-Fock self-consistency problem does not arise. However, the self-consistency problem appears through the energy denominators (Green's function) in the integral equation for the K-matrix in Eq. (1a) and those resulting through the use of Eqs. (2c) and (2d) in Eqs. (6a) to (6c). This problem has been considered by Brueckner,[3] Brueckner and Wada,[14] and Brueckner and Gammel,[4] in the effective mass approximation and by an iteration process.

For the case of a finite nucleus the procedure suggested by Bethe[2] and by Brueckner, Gammel, and Weitzner[5] is as follows. Starting from a given set of single-particle eigenfunctions $\phi_i^{(n)}$ (the nth iteration), we calculate the single-particle potential $V^{(n)}(\mathbf{r}, \mathbf{r}')$ from Eq. (2d) and then solve for the new set $\phi_i^{(n+1)}$ from the Schrödinger Eq. (2c). In general, the $(n + 1)$th and the nth iterations of ϕ_i and $V(\mathbf{r}, \mathbf{r}')$ will not agree. The Hartree-Fock self-consistency problem must therefore be solved by an iteration-interpolation procedure, starting with a trial guess and improving the wave functions at each successive iteration until self consistency results. Added to this, there is also the self consistency of the energy denominators since the change of the single-particle wave function $\phi_i^{(n)} \to \phi_i^{(n+1)}$ also changes the single-particle energy spectrum. The magnitude of the problem involved in solving the coupled self-consistency is so great (beyond the presently available computing facilities) that Brueckner, Gammel, and Weitzner[5] suggested the following approximation.

The energy denominators in the integral equation of the K-matrix involve excitation of a bound pair to momenta higher than the Fermi momentum p_F. This corresponds to large energy differences of the order of 150 to 250 Mev. Therefore, what is of interest is to predict them correctly. The momenta of the excited nucleons are $p \sim 1.5 p_F$ which, at normal density, correspond to wavelengths $\lambda \sim 0.5 \times 10^{-13}$ cm. Assuming that the nuclear density varies slowly over distances $r \sim \lambda$, we can treat the finite nucleus as a uniform medium (Fermi gas) at the local density $\rho(\mathbf{r}) = \sum_i |\phi_i(\mathbf{r})|^2$, and the energies in the Green's functions can be calculated in this approximation. This approximation is supported by the evidence that the wave function for relative particle motion approaches rapidly its unperturbed form for distances $\geqslant 10^{-13}$ cm with marked departures occurring only for smaller separation distances. Thus correlation distances in the wave function are quite small, and $K \simeq v$ for $r \geqslant 10^{-13}$ cm, so that the correlation-dependent effects in the K-matrix can be determined by the local density provided density variations over distances $\sim 10^{-13}$ cm are small.

The calculation of the K-matrix for the finite nucleus can be carried out using the results obtained for nuclear matter. We next calculate the elements of the K-matrix, $\langle ij| K(\rho) |kl \rangle$ in the plane-wave representation at the local density ρ. In the coordinate space, we have

$$\langle \mathbf{r}_1, \mathbf{r}_2| K(\rho) |\mathbf{r}_1', \mathbf{r}_2' \rangle = \sum_{ij,kl} \phi_i^*(\mathbf{r}_1)\phi_j^*(\mathbf{r}_2)\langle ij \mid K(\rho) \mid kl \rangle \phi_k(\mathbf{r}_1')\phi_l(\mathbf{r}_2') \quad (36)$$

which in general will turn out to be a nonlocal operator.

The calculations of the reaction matrix K have been developed by Brueckner, Gammel, and Weitzner[5] using the two-nucleon interaction $v(r)$ given by

$$v(r) = v_c(r) + v_T(r)S_{12} + v_{LS}(r)\mathbf{L} \cdot \mathbf{S} \tag{37a}$$

where

$$S_{12} = \frac{3(\boldsymbol{\sigma}_1 \cdot \mathbf{r})(\boldsymbol{\sigma}_2 \cdot \mathbf{r})}{r^2} - \boldsymbol{\sigma}_1 \cdot \boldsymbol{\sigma}_2 \tag{37b}$$

The parameters used are those of the Gammel-Thaler potentials given in Table 9-1.

The qualitative form of the K-matrix can be written as follows:

$$\langle \mathbf{r}' | \, K \, | \mathbf{r} \rangle = \langle \mathbf{r}' | \, K \, | \mathbf{r} \rangle_{\text{core}} + \langle \mathbf{r}' | \, K \, | \mathbf{r} \rangle_{\text{attr}} \tag{38a}$$

where the contributions from the repulsive core and the attractive potential have been separated. For the singlet S states, it can be shown[5] that

$$\langle \mathbf{r}' | \, K \, | \mathbf{r} \rangle_{\text{core}} = \frac{4\pi}{(2\pi)^3} \int dk k^2 j_0(kr') \, \delta(r - r_c) \lambda_{0k}^{00}$$

$$= -\frac{\delta(r' - r_c)\,\delta(r - r_c)}{(4\pi r_c^2)^2 G_0(r_c, r_c)} - \frac{\mathcal{G}(r_c, r')}{4\pi r_c^2 \mathcal{G}(r_c, r_c)} \, v_{\text{attr}}(r') \, \delta(r - r_c) \tag{38b}$$

$$\langle \mathbf{r}' | \, K \, | \mathbf{r} \rangle_{\text{attr}} = \frac{4\pi}{(2\pi)^3} \int dk k^2 j_0(kr') v_a(r') u_{0k}^{00}(r')$$

$$= \frac{\delta(r - r')}{4\pi r^2} \, v_{\text{attr}} - \delta(r - r_c) v_{\text{attr}}(r') \, \frac{\mathcal{G}_0(r', r_c)}{4\pi r_c^2 \mathcal{G}_0(r_c, r_c)} \tag{38c}$$

Table 9-1 Constants of the Gammel-Thaler Potentials. The Potentials Have the Yukawa Form and Repulsive Cores with $r_c = 0.40 \times 10^{-13}$ cm (Brueckner et al.[5])

State	Strength (Mev)	Inverse Range (10^{13} cm^{-1})
Triplet central even	−877.39	2.0908
Tensor even	−159.40	1.0494
Spin-orbit even	−5000	3.70
Singlet even	−434.0	1.45
Triplet central odd	−14.0	1.00
Tensor odd	22.0	0.80
Spin-orbit odd	−7315	3.70
Singlet odd	130.0	1.00

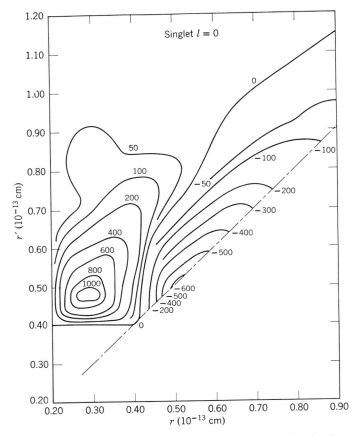

Fig. 9-4   Contour plot of constant values of $2\pi^2\langle\mathbf{r}|\,K\,|\mathbf{r}'\rangle$ for $l = 0$, singlet. Since $\langle\mathbf{r}|\,K\,|\mathbf{r}'\rangle$ is symmetric in r and r', the function is plotted only for $r < r'$. The contribution from the core alone has not been included in this plot; it would occur as a very high repulsive-core spike at $r = r' = 0.4 \times 10^{-13}$ cm (Brueckner et al.[5]).

The results of numerical calculations are shown in Figs. 9-4 to 9-6 as contours of constant values of $2\pi^2\langle\mathbf{r}|\,K\,|\mathbf{r}'\rangle$ in the r–r' plot for $l = 0$ singlet and triplet states and the spin-orbit part of the K-matrix for even states. The nonlocal nature of the K-matrix is apparent, but it approaches the local potential for r and r' greater than 10^{-13} cm. We observe that along the line $r = r'$—the "local line"—at large distances the potential is attractive while at short distances $\leqslant 0.5 \times 10^{-13}$ cm the potential is repulsive, becoming infinitely repulsive at $r = r_c$.

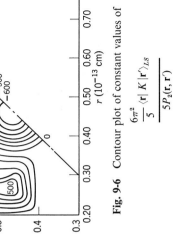

Fig. 9-6 Contour plot of constant values of

$$\frac{6\pi^2}{5} \langle \mathbf{r} | K | \mathbf{r}' \rangle_{LS}$$

$$5P_2(\mathbf{r}, \mathbf{r}')$$

for even states (Brueckner et al.[5]).

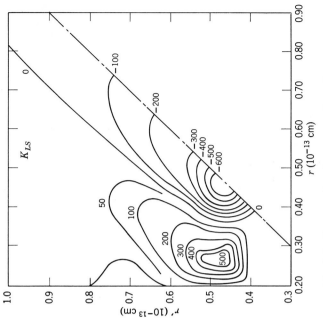

Fig. 9-5 Contour plot of constant values of $2\pi^2 \langle \mathbf{r} | K | \mathbf{r}' \rangle$ for $l = 0$, triplet. The core contribution is omitted here as in Fig. 9-4 (Brueckner et al.[5]).

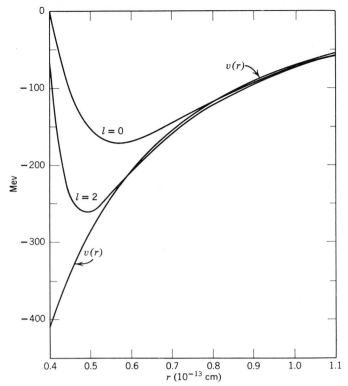

Fig. 9-7 Integral of $\langle \mathbf{r} | K | \mathbf{r}' \rangle$ normalized to the correct asymptotic behavior, for singlet $l = 0$ and $l = 2$. Also included is the local singlet potential with parameters shown in Table 9-1 (Brueckner et al.[5]).

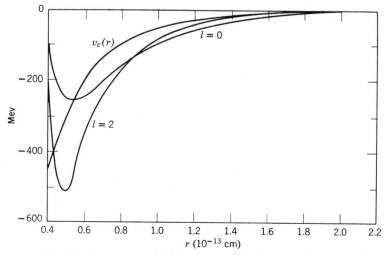

Fig. 9-8 Integral of $\langle \mathbf{r} | K | \mathbf{r}' \rangle$ for triplet $l = 0$ and $l = 2$ together with the central part of the triplet even-state potential (Brueckner et al.[5]).

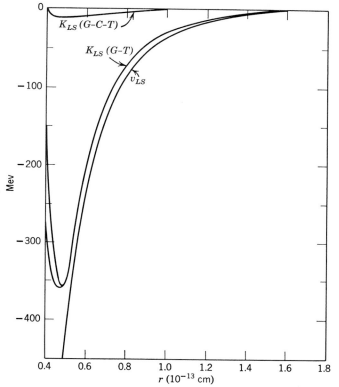

Fig. 9-9 Integral of $\langle \mathbf{r}| \, K \, |\mathbf{r}'\rangle_{LS}$ from tensor forces in the Gammel-Christian-Thaler potential compared with the same integral for the Gammel-Thaler potential. Also included are the Gammel-Thaler spin-orbit potentials for even and odd states (Brueckner et al.[5]).

To compare the K-matrix with the two-nucleon potential $v(r)$, Brueckner et al. considered the function

$$f(r) = \int dr' \langle \mathbf{r}| \, K \, |\mathbf{r}'\rangle \tag{38d}$$

Their plot of $f(r)$ for singlet and triplet $l = 0$ and $l = 2$ is shown in Figs. 9-7 and 9-8 respectively, and $f(r)$ for the spin-orbit matrix $\langle \mathbf{r}| \, K \, |\mathbf{r}'\rangle_{LS}$ is represented in Fig. 9-9 from the Gammel-Thaler spin-orbit potentials for even and odd states. For the sake of comparison $\int dr' \langle \mathbf{r}| \, K \, |\mathbf{r}'\rangle_{LS}$ obtained from the tensor part of the potential due to Gammel-Christian-Thaler is also included. The even-state tensor part of the two-body interaction gives a negligible contribution to the spin-orbit K-matrix.

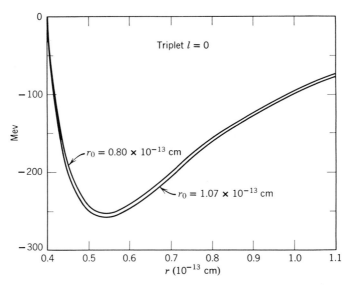

Fig. 9-10 Integral of $\langle \mathbf{r} | K | \mathbf{r}' \rangle$ for triplet $l = 0$, at densities corresponding to $r_0 = 0.80 \times 10^{-13}$ cm and $r_0 = 1.07 \times 10^{-13}$ cm. The core contribution is omitted (Brueckner et al.[5]).

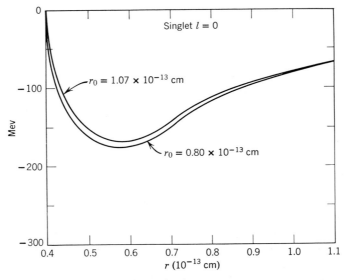

Fig. 9-11 Integral of $\langle \mathbf{r} | K | \mathbf{r}' \rangle$ for singlet $l = 0$, at densities corresponding to $r_0 = 0.80 \times 10^{-13}$ cm and $r_0 = 1.07 \times 10^{-13}$ cm. The core contribution is omitted (Brueckner et al.[5]).

Furthermore, for $r > 10^{-13}$ cm there is little difference between the integral of $\langle \mathbf{r} | K | \mathbf{r}' \rangle$ and the two-body potential $v(r)$.

Another property of the K-matrix investigated by Brueckner et al. is its variation with nuclear density in the range of $r_0 = 0.80 \times 10^{-13}$ cm to $r_0 = 1.07 \times 10^{-13}$ cm (normal), corresponding to a density ratio of 2.39 (nuclear radius $R = r_0 A^{1/3}$). The integral of $\langle \mathbf{r} | K | \mathbf{r}' \rangle$ is plotted for triplet and singlet $l = 0$ at these two densities in Figs. 9-10 and 9-11. An increase in repulsion of 35 to 40% at the higher density ($r_0 = 0.80 \times 10^{-13}$ cm) has been obtained. The rapid increase in the repulsion with increasing density has been indicated as being the principal origin of the saturation of the nuclear forces; the pronounced minimum in energy for nuclear matter was at -15.2 Mev per particle at $r_0 = 1.02 \times 10^{-13}$ cm. Without the density dependence of the K-matrix, the system will not show saturation.

The density dependence of the repulsive core term in the K-matrix has been found[7] to behave as follows for 0.80×10^{-13} cm $\leqslant r_0 \leqslant 1.6 \times 10^{-13}$ cm:

$$\frac{K_{\text{core}}(r_0)}{K_{\text{core}}(1.07 \times 10^{-13} \text{ cm})} = \frac{0.544}{\left(1 - \dfrac{0.488 \times 10^{-13}}{r_0}\right)} \quad \text{singlet}$$

$$= \frac{0.472}{\left(1 - \dfrac{0.459 \times 10^{-13}}{r_0}\right)} \quad \text{triplet} \quad (38e)$$

Brueckner, Lockett, and Rotenberg[6] studied the properties of O^{16}, Ca^{40}, and Zr^{90} using the Brueckner-Gammel-Weitzner[5] theory of finite nuclei. They have obtained self-consistent solutions of the Hartree-Fock equations as modified by Brueckner and Goldman.[17] They computed the following properties: binding energy, mean proton and neutron radii, separation energies, spin-orbit splittings, nonlocal and state-dependent single-particle potentials, surface depth of density and potentials, and potential-density relation. Some of the results of their calculations are given in Tables 9-2 to 9-4. Comparing the predictions of the theory with experimental results indicates that the agreement is of a semiquantitative nature.

Calculations of the spin-orbit doublet separations in nuclei, following the procedures of Brueckner theory, have been carried out by Kisslinger,[18] Jancovici,[19] Nigam and Sundaresan,[20] and others.[21] They considered a two-nucleon potential which includes central and tensor parts. The tensor interaction generates a spin-orbit term for the nucleus. Evidence shows that the tensor potential gives an incorrect sign of the spin-orbit splitting and is of too small a magnitude. However, Nigam and

Table 9-2 Calculated and Experimental Energies for O^{16}, Ca^{40}, and Zr^{90}. The Core Strength Has Been Reduced to 0.825 of the Normal Value for O^{16}, and to 0.90 of the Normal Value for Ca^{40} and Zr^{90}. The Energies Are in Mev (Brueckner et al.[6]).

Element	State	Potential Energy		Eigenvalue		Experimental Separation Energy		Total Energy per Particle	
		Neutron	Proton	Neutron	Proton	Neutron	Proton	Calc.	Exptl.
O^{16}	$1s_{1/2}$	−58.0	−53.0	−44.3	−39.6				
	$1p_{3/2}$	−40.1	−35.2	−19.0	−14.6				
	$1p_{1/2}$	−34.4	−29.7	−14.9	−10.7	−15.60	−12.11	−4.41	−7.98
Ca^{40}	$1s_{1/2}$	−82.4	−72.1	−70.1	−60.0				
	$1p_{3/2}$	−65.2	−55.1	−44.7	−35.1				
	$1p_{1/2}$	−59.2	−49.3	−38.6	−29.2				
	$1d_{5/2}$	−48.3	−38.2	−20.6	−11.6			−6.12	−8.55
	$2s_{1/2}$	−40.5	−30.0	−16.0	−7.3				
	$1d_{3/2}$	−39.6	−29.6	−13.4	−4.9	−15.98	−8.34		
Zr^{90}	$1s_{1/2}$	−87.7	−72.0	−79.5	−64.0				
	$1p_{3/2}$	−77.8	−62.3	−62.8	−47.7				
	$1p_{1/2}$	−75.5	−60.2	−59.8	−44.9				
	$1d_{5/2}$	−66.6	−51.4	−44.5	−29.9				
	$2s_{1/2}$	−62.2	−46.5	−38.6	−23.8			−5.80	−8.67
	$1d_{3/2}$	−63.7	−48.6	−40.2	−25.7				
	$1f_{7/2}$	−55.4	−40.2	−26.2	−12.0				
	$1f_{5/2}$	−51.2	−36.0	−20.5	−6.6				
	$2p_{1/2}$	−47.5	−31.0	−17.0	−3.2		−8.80		
	$1g_{9/2}$	−44.1		−8.5		−12.37			

Table 9-3 Difference in Separation Energy for Neutrons and Protons (Brueckner et al.[6])

Element	Separation Energy (Mev)	
	Calculated	Experimental
O^{16}	4.2	3.49
Ca^{40}	8.5	7.64
Zr^{90}	5.3	3.57

Table 9-4 Spin-Orbit Splitting in Mev (Brueckner et al.[6])

	O^{16}		Ca^{40}		Zr^{90}	
	Neutron	Proton	Neutron	Proton	Neutron	Proton
$1p_{1/2}-1p_{3/2}$	4.1	3.9	6.1	5.9	3.0	2.8
$1d_{3/2}-1d_{5/2}$			7.2	6.7	4.3	4.2
$1f_{5/2}-1f_{7/2}$					5.7	5.4

Sundaresan,[22] Moshinsky,[23] and Sawicki and Folk[24] obtained the correct sign and order of magnitude of the splitting by using the two-nucleon potentials given by Signell and Marshak,[8] and Gammel and Thaler.[9] These two-nucleon potentials explicitly contain spin-orbit interaction, which is mainly responsible for the spin-orbit splitting in nuclei.

References

1. Brueckner, K. A., R. J. Eden, and N. Francis, *Phys. Rev.* **98**, 1445, 1955.
2. Bethe, H. A., *Phys. Rev.* **103**, 1353, 1956; Bethe, H. A., B. H. Brandow, and A. G. Petschek, *Phys. Rev.* **129**, 225, 1963.
3. Brueckner, K. A., and C. A. Levinson, *Phys. Rev.* **97**, 1344, 1955; Brueckner, K. A., *Phys. Rev.* **97**, 1353, 1955; Brueckner, K. A., C. A. Levinson, and H. Mahmoud, *Phys. Rev.* **95**, 217, 1954; Brueckner, K. A., *Phys. Rev.* **96**, 508, 1954.
4. Brueckner, K. A., and J. L. Gammel, *Phys. Rev.* **109**, 1023, 1958.
5. Brueckner, K. A., J. L. Gammel, and H. Weitzner, *Phys. Rev.* **110**, 431, 1958; also list of references quoted therein.
6. Brueckner, K. A., A. M. Lockett, and M. Rotenberg, *Phys. Rev.* **121**, 255, 1961.
7. Watson, K. M., *Phys. Rev.* **89**, 575, 1953; Francis, N. C., and K. M. Watson, *Phys. Rev.* **92**, 291, 1953.
8. Signell, P. S., and R. E. Marshak, *Phys. Rev.* **106**, 832, 1957; *ibid.*, **109**, 1229, 1958; Signell, P. S., R. Zinn, and R. E. Marshak, *Phys. Rev. Letters* **1**, 416, 1958.
9. Gammel, J. L., and R. M. Thaler, *Phys. Rev.* **107**, 291 and 1337, 1957.
10. Gomes, L. C., J. D. Walecka, and V. F. Weisskopf, *Ann. Phys.* (N.Y.). **3**, 241, 1958.
11. Eden, R. J., *Proc. Roy. Soc.* (*London*) **A235**, 408, 1956.
12. Bethe, H. A., and J. Goldstone, *Proc. Roy. Soc.* (*London*) **A239**, 551, 1957.

13. Brueckner, K. A., *Phys. Rev.* **100**, 36, 1955.
14. Brueckner, K. A., and W. W. Wada, *Phys. Rev.* **103**, 1008, 1956.
15. Bauer, M., and M. Moshinsky, *Nuclear Phys.* **4**, 615, 1957; Moshinsky, M., *Rev. Mex. Fis.* **6**, 185, 1957.
16. Nigam, B. P., *Phys. Rev.* **133**, B1381, 1964.
17. Brueckner, K. A., and D. T. Goldman, *Phys. Rev.* **117**, 207, 1960.
18. Kisslinger, L., *Phys. Rev.* **104**, 1077, 1956.
19. Jancovici, B., *Phys. Rev.* **107**, 631, 1957.
20. Nigam, B. P., and M. K. Sundaresan, *Can. J. Phys.* **36**, 571, 1958.
21. Hughes, J., and K. J. LeCouteur, *Proc. Phys. Soc.* (*London*) **A63**, 1219, 1950; Blin-Stoyle, R. J., *Phil. Mag.* [7] **46**, 973, 1955; Bell, J. S., and T. H. R. Skyrme, *Phil. Mag.* [8] **1**, 1055, 1956; Clark, J. W., *Ann. Phys.* (N.Y.) **11**, 483, 1960; Tauber, G. E., and T. Y. Wu, *Nuclear Phys.* **22**, 339, 1961.
22. Nigam, B. P., and M. K., Sundaresan, *Phys. Rev.* **111**, 284, 1958.
23. Moshinsky, M., *Rev. Mex. Fis.* **7**, 95, 1958.
24. Sawicki, J., and R. Folk, *Nuclear Phys.* **11**, 368, 1959; Sawicki, J., *Nuclear Phys.* **13**, 350, 1959.

10

NUCLEAR REACTION II:
OPTICAL MODEL

10.1   Introduction

The strong interaction model of Bohr successfully explains the existence of sharp, narrow resonances noted in the elastic scattering of slow neutrons by nuclei. This model, known as the compound-nucleus model, was discussed in Chapter 6. We know that the mean life of the compound state is long; consequently the width of the level is sharp. The cross section in the neighborhood of a compound state is given by the Breit-Wigner one-level formula. However, observation of giant resonances with both slow[1] and fast neutrons[2] indicates that the concept of the compound nucleus is not adequate to explain them. These resonances were observed to have cross sections with a broad peak and a large width ~ 1 Mev which varies regularly with energy and the mass number A. This dependence of the cross section is in contradiction to the compound-nucleus type of reaction.

An adequate explanation regarding both the existence and location of these giant resonances is based on the optical model, which is used to describe both low- and high-energy phenomena. At low energies, however, it is not concerned with the fine structure resonances, but rather deals with the energy average of the cross section. It is hard to obtain mono-energetic neutrons; consequently, it is easier to average a larger number of individual resonances caused by the energy dispersion in the neutron beam. The average cross section can then be studied as a function of the incident energy and the mass number.

In the optical model a nucleus is represented by a complex potential. The imaginary part of the potential describes inelastic processes permitted by the Pauli principle and by the law of conservation of energy. The Schrödinger equation when solved for the optical potential, which is

$\Gamma \tau = \hbar$

a function of space coordinates and energy of the bombarding particle, gives the scattering and reaction cross sections.

Both the real and imaginary part of the complex potential are energy dependent. At low energies the real part of the potential is similar to the potential used in the nuclear-shell model. The imaginary part of the potential interacts with the incident wave and attenuates it. In addition, its value is so chosen as to produce the required mean free path of the incident particle in the target nucleus at various incident energies. A small value of the imaginary part of the potential is connected with the long mean free path. At low energies, we may expect that the attenuation of the incident beam is predominant near the nuclear surface. This may be due to the fact that the imaginary part of the potential may be larger near the nuclear surface than it is deeper inside the nucleus. However, as the incident energy increases, this effect may become less important and the absorption of the incident wave may take place uniformly throughout the whole volume of the nucleus. In the optical-model analysis of experimental results, both the surface- and volume-absorption terms are used quite often.

The simplest form of optical potential is the square-well potential used by earlier workers:

$$V(r) = -V_0 - iW_0 \qquad \text{for} \quad r < a \qquad (1)$$

This form of potential gives too large a cross section for the elastic scattering process in backward directions. However, a modified form of potential has been proposed by Woods and Saxon[3] which replaces the square-well potential by a smoothed-out potential with a much better agreement with the experimental results. It explains angular distribution, reaction, and total cross sections. The form of the potential is

$$V = -(V_0 + iW_0)\left[1 + \exp\left(\frac{r - R}{a}\right)\right]^{-1} \qquad (2)$$

where V_0, W_0, R, and a are optical-model parameters. In recent years other forms of optical potentials have been introduced to take into account the deformation of the nuclei, the spin-orbit coupling, and also the energy region at which the experiments are being performed. All nuclei are not spherically symmetric; therefore, for deformed nuclei, the optical potential should be modified to include terms which represent the deviation of the nucleus from spherical symmetry. In addition, the coupling of the incident particle spin to the target-nucleus spin can also be of significant importance. Hence additional terms are required to take into account these effects.

A more general form of potential than the Woods-Saxon type is given by[4]

$$V(r) = V_c(r) + U_c b_1(r) - iW_c[\xi b_2(r) + (1 - \xi)b_0(r)]$$
$$+ \lambda_\pi^2 \frac{1}{r}\left[U_{so}\frac{db_3(r)}{dr} - iW_{so}\frac{db_4(r)}{dr}\right]\mathbf{l}\cdot\boldsymbol{\sigma} \tag{3}$$

where $\mathbf{l}$ is the angular momentum of the incident nucleon and $\frac{1}{2}\boldsymbol{\sigma}$ is its spin. The form factors b_0, b_1, b_2, b_3, and b_4 are taken to be Gaussian and of the Woods-Saxon form. The derivative form factor of the potential is analogous to the Thomas spin-orbit potential for an electron interacting with a Coulomb field. The coupling of spin and orbital angular momentum is needed, for the elastically scattered nucleon is found to be polarized after scattering. The potential form in Eq. (3) should by no means be considered as the most general and may even be inadequate to explain the cross section very accurately since several effects have not been taken into account. This potential form contains 19 adjustable parameters. Simplified forms, with reduced numbers of parameters, have, however, been used by many workers.

Recently, Rosen, Beery, Goldhaber, and Auerbach[5] arrived at a spin-dependent optical potential by analyzing and measuring 80 separate angular distribution data between 14.5 and 10.5 Mev. Their potential has the form

$$V(r) = V_{\text{coulomb}} - Vf(r, R, a) - iWg(r, R, b) - V_s\lambda_\pi^2\left(\frac{1}{r}\right)\left|\frac{df(r)}{dr}\right|\mathbf{l}\cdot\boldsymbol{\sigma}$$
$$\tag{4a}$$

where

$$f(r, R, a) = \left[1 + \exp\left(\frac{r - R}{a}\right)\right]^{-1} \tag{4b}$$

$$g(r, R, b) = -4b\left(\frac{d}{dr}\right)\left[1 + \exp\left(r - \frac{R}{b}\right)\right]^{-1} \tag{4c}$$

and λ_π is the pion Compton wavelength. They have published a unique set of parameters for both protons and neutrons which is applicable for a large number of elements in the periodic table. These parameters are the following:

Protons	Neutrons
$V = (53.35 - 0.33E)$ Mev	$V = (49.3 - 0.33E)$ Mev
$W = 7.5$ Mev	$W = 5.75$ Mev

$$V_s = 5.5 \text{ Mev}$$
$$R = 1.25\, A^{\frac{1}{3}}\text{F}$$
$$a = 0.65 \text{ F}$$
$$b = 0.70 \text{ F} \tag{5}$$

The comparison between the predictions of this potential and the experimental data will be given in a later section.

10.2 Optical Model at Low Energies

The concept of the optical model applies to the cross sections averaged over energy ranges Δ which are larger than the separation D between the energy levels (that is, the cross section is averaged over several energy levels). The actual cross sections may fluctuate considerably with energy because of resonances. However, the process of averaging leads to cross sections that vary smoothly with energy. In the following, we shall neglect the spin of the incident nucleon.

The average of a function $f(E)$ is defined as follows:

$$\langle f(E) \rangle = \int_{-\infty}^{\infty} \rho(E - E') f(E') \, dE' \tag{5a}$$

where ρ is a weighting function. Feshbach, Porter, and Weisskopf[6] used the following square function for ρ

$$\rho(x) = \begin{cases} 0 & x < -\Delta/2 \\ \Delta^{-1} & -\Delta/2 < x < \Delta/2 \\ 0 & x > \Delta/2 \end{cases} \tag{6a}$$

so that

$$\langle f(E) \rangle = \frac{1}{\Delta} \int_{E-\Delta/2}^{E+\Delta/2} f(E') \, dE' \tag{6b}$$

Another convenient form usually used is

$$\rho(x) = \frac{1}{\pi} \frac{1}{x^2 + \Delta^2} \tag{7}$$

The final result of averaging should not depend on the exact value of Δ for the result to have physical sense. This is why Δ is taken to be large compared to D, the energy separation between levels.

We next define the various cross sections. If σ_T is the total cross section, and σ_{el} and σ_r the elastic and reaction cross sections, then

$$\sigma_T = \sigma_{el} + \sigma_r \tag{8}$$

We note that the solution of the Schrödinger equation for the scattering problem, in the asymptotic region, is given by

$$\psi(\mathbf{r}) \xrightarrow[r \to \infty]{} \frac{\sqrt{\pi}}{kr} \sum_{l=0}^{\infty} (2l + 1)^{1/2} i^{l+1} [e^{-i(kr - l\pi/2)} - S_l e^{i(kr - l\pi/2)}] Y_{l,0}(\theta, \phi) \tag{9a}$$

where the first term represents an ingoing spherical wave, the second term corresponds to the outgoing wave modified by a factor S_l due to the scattering, and $\hbar k$ is the momentum in the center of mass. S_l, which is the amplitude of the outgoing scattered wave, is related to the phase shifts (complex) δ_l as

$$S_l = \exp{(i2\delta_l)} \tag{9b}$$

The differential cross section for elastic scattering is

$$\frac{d\sigma_{\text{el}}}{d\Omega} = \frac{\pi}{k^2} | \sum_l (2l + 1)^{1/2}(1 - S_l)Y_{l,0}(\theta)|^2 \tag{10}$$

and the cross sections are given by

$$\sigma_{\text{el}} = \frac{\pi}{k^2} \sum_l (2l + 1) |1 - S_l|^2 = \sum_l \sigma_{\text{el}}^{(l)} \tag{11a}$$

$$\sigma_r = \frac{\pi}{k^2} \sum_l (2l + 1)[1 - |S_l|^2] = \sum_l \sigma_r^{(l)} \tag{11b}$$

$$\sigma_T = \frac{\pi}{k^2} \sum_l (2l + 1)[2 \, \text{Re} \, (1 - S_l)] = \sum_l \sigma_T^{(l)} \tag{11c}$$

Carrying out the average of each term in Eqs. (11), we obtain

$$\langle \sigma_{\text{el}} \rangle = \frac{\pi}{k^2} \sum (2l + 1)[1 - \langle S_l \rangle - \langle S_l^* \rangle + \langle |S_l|^2 \rangle] \qquad \bar{\sigma} \equiv \langle \sigma \rangle$$

$$= \frac{\pi}{k^2} \sum (2l + 1)[|1 - \langle S_l \rangle|^2 + (\langle |S_l|^2 \rangle - |\langle S_l \rangle|^2)] \tag{12a} = \bar{\sigma}_{se} + \bar{\sigma}_{ce}$$

$$\langle \sigma_r \rangle = \frac{\pi}{k^2} \sum (2l + 1)[1 - |\langle S_l \rangle|^2 - (\langle |S_l|^2 \rangle - |\langle S_l \rangle|^2)] \tag{12b} = \bar{\sigma}_c - \bar{\sigma}_{ce}$$

$$\langle \sigma_T \rangle = \frac{\pi}{k^2} \sum (2l + 1)[|1 - \langle S_l \rangle|^2 + 1 - |\langle S_l \rangle|^2] \tag{12c}$$

It is usual to define the shape elastic cross section σ_{se} which depends on the averaged $\langle S_l \rangle$ and the compound elastic fluctuation cross section σ_{ce} as

$$\bar{\sigma}_{\text{se}} = \frac{\pi}{k^2} \sum (2l + 1) |1 - \langle S_l \rangle|^2 \tag{13a}$$

$$\bar{\sigma}_{\text{ce}} = \frac{\pi}{k^2} \sum (2l + 1)[\langle |S_l|^2 \rangle - |\langle S_l \rangle|^2] \rightarrow \text{FLUCTUATION (13b)} \\ \text{TERM}$$

The shape elastic cross section corresponds to direct elastic scattering without the formation of the compound nucleus. The cross section σ_c for the formation of the compound nucleus is defined as

$$\bar{\sigma}_c = \frac{\pi}{k^2} \sum (2l + 1)[1 - |\langle S_l \rangle|^2] \tag{13c}$$

We therefore have

$$\langle \sigma_{el} \rangle = \sigma_{se} + \sigma_{ce} \tag{14a}$$

$$\langle \sigma_r \rangle = \sigma_c - \sigma_{ce} \tag{14b}$$

$$\langle \sigma_T \rangle = \sigma_{se} + \sigma_c \tag{14c}$$

The interaction of the incident wave with the real part of the optical potential leads to shape elastic scattering. A part of the incident wave is also absorbed in interaction with the imaginary part of the optical potential leading to the formation of a compound system which may exhibit itself in the form of a compound nucleus. The compound nucleus, when it decays, may yield some compound elastic scattering. The compound elastic scattering is not predictable in detail by the optical model. If its cross section is small, then various types of nuclear reactions can be analyzed in terms of the optical model.

Because of the averaging process involved in the calculations of the optical model, the averaged phase shifts obtained from the complex potential give $\langle S_l \rangle$. Comparing Eqs. (13a) to (13c) with Eqs. (11a) to (11c), it is clear that the optical-model calculations predict (1) the shape-elastic cross section σ_{se}, instead of the elastic cross section $\langle \sigma_{el} \rangle$ which is the experimentally measured quantity, and (2) the cross section σ_c for the formation of the compound nucleus, instead of the reaction cross section $\langle \sigma_r \rangle$. From Eqs. (14) we find that $\langle \sigma_{el} \rangle \simeq \sigma_{se}$ and $\langle \sigma_r \rangle \simeq \sigma_c$, provided $\sigma_{ce} \ll \sigma_{se}$ and $\sigma_{ce} \ll \sigma_c$. This occurs for nucleon scattering from medium to heavy nuclei for energies greater than 10 Mev. At these high energies, since the widths Γ of the compound nucleus become much larger than the spacing D ($\Gamma \gg D$ at high energies), S_l varies slowly with momentum so that $|\langle S_l \rangle|^2 \simeq \langle |S_l|^2 \rangle$ and $\sigma_{ce} \to 0$. At energies lower than 10 Mev, σ_{ce} should be taken into account.

10.3   Kapur-Peierls Dispersion Formulas for Potential Scattering

The purpose of the optical model is to describe the scattering of particles of energies in the range of Kev to Mev by complex nuclei; this is done in terms of a complex potential. Since in the energy range Kev-Mev (low-energy range) many nuclear levels participate in the scattering, it is more convenient to use the formalism of Kapur and Peierls,[7] in which the sum over the many levels enters linearly into the scattering amplitude. In our derivations we shall follow closely the articles by Brown[8] and by Jones.[4]

We first consider the two-body problem and treat only an S-wave scattering of a neutron by a potential $V(r)$ by using the Kapur-Peierls method and later extending it to the many-particle case.

The radial Schrödinger equation describing the scattering of a neutron of mass M and energy E is

$$\left\{\frac{\hbar^2}{2M}\frac{d^2}{dr^2} + [E - V(r)]\right\}[r\psi(r)] = 0 \tag{15a}$$

If we define a radius R such that for $r > R$, the potential $V(r) = 0$, we have

$$\frac{d^2\phi}{dr^2} + k^2\phi = 0 \qquad \text{for} \quad r > R \tag{15b}$$

where

$$\phi(r) = r\psi(r) \qquad \text{and} \quad k = \sqrt{\frac{2ME}{\hbar^2}} \tag{15c}$$

The solution of Eq. (15b) in the asymptotic region $r \to \infty$ follows from Eq. (9a) and is given by

$$\phi(r) \simeq i\frac{\sqrt{\pi}}{k}[e^{-ikr} - Se^{ikr}] \tag{15d}$$

where S is the amplitude of the outgoing scattered wave. We now introduce the Kapur-Peierls eigenfunctions $\phi_\mu(r)$ which satisfy the equation

$$\frac{\hbar^2}{2M}\frac{d^2\phi_\mu}{dr^2} + (E_\mu - V)\phi_\mu = 0 \tag{16a}$$

where the boundary condition satisfied by ϕ_μ is

$$\frac{d\phi_\mu}{dr}\bigg]_{r=R} = ik\phi_\mu(r)\bigg]_{r=R} \tag{16b}$$

Equation (16b) depends explicitly on k and hence the energy eigenvalues E_μ. For $k > 0$, the eigenvalues E_μ are complex on account of the imaginary boundary condition, Eq. (16b). The complex energies imply a finite width of the state, the width being related to the imaginary part.

As an example, we consider $k = 0$ and take the special case when $V(r)$ is a square-well real potential $V(r) = U$ for $r < R$, and $V(r) = 0$ for $r > R$. The solution of Eq. (16a) is then

$$\phi_\mu^{(0)}(r) = \sqrt{\frac{2}{R}}\sin k_\mu r \tag{17a}$$

where

$$k_\mu = \frac{1}{\hbar}\sqrt{2M(E_\mu - U)} \tag{17b}$$

and the eigenvalues are given by

$$k_\mu R = (\mu + \tfrac{1}{2})\pi \tag{17c}$$

with $\mu = 0, 1, 2, \ldots$. Hence μ signifies the number of radial nodes in the square well. It thus follows that for the particular case $k = 0$, the eigenvalues E_μ are real, but for $k > 0$ they will be complex.

The eigenfunctions $\phi_\mu(r)$ form a complete set[9] in the region 0 to R, which can be shown as follows. Multiplying Eq. (16a) on the left by ϕ_ν and the corresponding equation for ϕ_ν by ϕ_μ on the left and subtracting, we obtain

$$\frac{\hbar^2}{2M}\left(\phi_\nu \frac{d^2\phi_\mu}{dr^2} - \phi_\mu \frac{d^2\phi_\nu}{dr^2}\right) + (E_\mu - E_\nu)\phi_\nu\phi_\mu = 0 \tag{18}$$

By integrating Eq. (18) from 0 to R and using Green's theorem,

$$\frac{\hbar^2}{2M}\left[\phi_\nu \frac{d\phi_\mu}{dr} - \phi_\mu \frac{d\phi_\nu}{dr}\right]_{r=R} = (E_\nu - E_\mu)\int_0^R \phi_\mu\phi_\nu \, dr \tag{19a}$$

Using Eq. (16b), the left-hand side vanishes, and since $E_\mu \neq E_\nu$, we have

$$\int_0^R \phi_\mu\phi_\nu \, dr = 0 \qquad \text{for} \quad E_\mu \neq E_\nu \tag{19b}$$

For $\mu = \nu$, we can suitably normalize ϕ_μ's, and therefore

$$\int_0^R \phi_\mu^2 \, dr = 1 \tag{19c}$$

The orthogonality condition is between ϕ_μ and ϕ_ν and not between ϕ_ν^* and ϕ_μ. Furthermore, the boundary condition, Eq. (16b), has been explicitly made use of in establishing the orthogonality.

Since the Kapur-Peierls eigenfunctions $\phi_\mu(r)$ satisfying Eqs. (16a) and (16b) form a complete set in the inside region $0 < r < R$, we can expand the wave function $\phi(r)$ for the problem involved, Eqs. (15), in terms of $\phi_\mu(r)$. Thus

$$\phi(r) = \sum_\mu a_\mu\phi_\mu(r) \tag{20}$$

where the expansion coefficients a_μ can be determined as follows. From Eqs. (15a) and (16a), following the steps involved in the derivation of Eq. (19a), we obtain

$$\frac{\hbar^2}{2M}\left[\phi \frac{d\phi_\mu}{dr} - \frac{d\phi}{dr}\phi_\mu\right]_{r=R} = (E - E_\mu)\int_0^R \phi_\mu\phi \, dr \tag{21a}$$

Using Eqs. (16b), (20), (19b), and (19c), we find that Eq. (21a) reduces to

$$(E - E_\mu)a_\mu = -\frac{\hbar^2}{2M}\left[\left(\frac{d\phi}{dr} - ik\phi\right)\phi_\mu\right]_{r=R}$$

$$= -\frac{\hbar^2}{M}\sqrt{\pi}e^{-ikR}\phi_\mu(R) \tag{21b}$$

where in the last step Eq. (15d) has been used. We therefore have

$$a_\mu = - \frac{\hbar^2}{M} \frac{\sqrt{\pi}}{E - E_\mu} e^{-ikR} \phi_\mu(R) \tag{22}$$

The scattering amplitude S can be determined by joining the inside and the outside solutions at $r = R$.

$$\sum a_\mu \phi_\mu(R) = \frac{i\sqrt{\pi}}{k} [e^{-ikR} - Se^{ikR}]$$

which gives

$$S = e^{-i2kR} \left[1 - i \sum_\mu \frac{\Gamma_\mu}{E - E_\mu} \right] \tag{23a}$$

where the width Γ_μ is defined by

$$\Gamma_\mu = \frac{\hbar^2 k}{M} [\phi_\mu(R)]^2 \tag{23b}$$

Equations (23a) and (23b) are the Kapur-Peierls dispersion formulas which express the scattering amplitude S in terms of the Kapur-Peierls eigenfunctions ϕ_μ without any approximation. The first term in Eq. (23a) corresponds to scattering by a hard sphere of radius R (phase shift $\delta = -kR$).

We write the complex energy eigenvalues E_μ in the form

$$E_\mu = \mathscr{E}_\mu - \frac{i}{2} \epsilon_\mu \tag{24}$$

The imaginary part ϵ_μ can be expressed in terms of the eigenfunctions ϕ_μ. Corresponding to Eq. (19a), we can write

$$(E_\mu^* - E_\mu) \int_0^R \phi_\mu \phi_\mu^* \, dr = \frac{\hbar^2}{2M} \left[\phi_\mu^* \frac{d\phi_\mu}{dr} - \phi_\mu \frac{d\phi_\mu^*}{dr} \right]_{r=R}$$

$$= \frac{\hbar^2}{2M} 2ik \phi_\mu^*(R) \phi_\mu(R)$$

so that

$$\epsilon_\mu = \frac{\hbar^2 k}{M} \frac{|\phi_\mu(R)|^2}{\int_0^R |\phi_\mu(r)|^2 \, dr}$$

$$= \hbar v \frac{\text{probability of the particle being on the surface}}{\text{probability of the particle being in the nucleus}} \tag{25a}$$

where the velocity $v = \hbar k/M$. At low energies

$$\phi_\mu \simeq \text{real} \quad \text{and} \quad \int_0^R |\phi_\mu(r)|^2 \, dr \simeq 1$$

so that, comparing Eqs. (25a) and (23b), we find that

$$\epsilon_\mu \simeq \Gamma_\mu \quad \text{(at low energies)} \tag{25b}$$

To make an estimate of the values of ϵ_μ and Γ_μ at low energies, we approximate $\phi_\mu \to \phi_\mu^{(0)}$ and replace the boundary condition (16b) by

$$\left[\frac{d\phi_\mu^{(0)}}{dr}\right]_{r=R} = 0 \tag{26a}$$

This is the boundary condition used by Wigner and Eisenbud[10] and leads to real $\phi_\mu^{(0)}$. As a first approximation, we may take $\phi_\mu^{(0)}(r)$ to be given by Eq. (17a), namely, $\phi_\mu^{(0)}(r) \simeq \sqrt{2/R} \sin k_\mu r$, so that from Eqs. (25a) and (25b) we obtain

$$\epsilon_\mu \simeq \Gamma_\mu \simeq \frac{2\hbar^2 k}{MR} \tag{26b}$$

If the Schrödinger equation can be rewritten in the form

$$\frac{\hbar^2}{2M} \frac{d^2\phi_\mu}{dr^2} + [(E_\mu - iW) - (U - iW)]\phi_\mu = 0, \tag{27}$$

interpreting $U - iW$ as a complex potential $V(r)$, the energy eigenvalues are $E_\mu - iW$, with the eigenfunctions ϕ_μ unchanged, for a square well. The scattering amplitude S is now given by [see Eq. (23a)]

$$S = e^{-i2kR}\left[1 - i \sum_\mu \frac{\Gamma_\mu}{E - \epsilon_\mu + i(\frac{1}{2}\mathscr{E}_\mu + W)}\right] \tag{28}$$

and from Eqs. (11c) and (28), in the energy range $E \simeq \mathscr{E}_\mu$, the scattering cross section is given by

$$\sigma \simeq \frac{2\pi}{k^2} \frac{\epsilon_\mu(\frac{1}{2}\epsilon_\mu + W)}{(E - \mathscr{E}_\mu)^2 + (\frac{1}{2}\epsilon_\mu + W)^2} \tag{29}$$

Equation (29) shows that adding an imaginary part W to the potential U results in the broadening of the resonance level.

We shall not carry out the generalization of the above for nonzero angular momentum. This is indicated by Brown,[8] to whose paper the reader is referred. If the incident particle is charged (proton), the outgoing part of the wave function, [Eq. (9a)], in the asymptotic region, namely, $\exp[ikr - (l\pi/2)]$ should be replaced by $\exp[ikr - \eta\ln 2kr - (l\pi/2) + \sigma_l]$ where σ_l is the Coulomb phase shift, $\eta = (Ze^2)/(\hbar v)$, and v the velocity of the incident proton.

10.4   Dispersion Formula for the Many-Body Case

In this section we discuss the scattering of a nucleon (neutron) by a target nucleus which will be treated as a many-particle system. We investigate whether it is qualitatively possible to explain the experimentally observed giant resonances which occur at low neutron energies on the basis of an extension of the two-body dispersion formula, developed in Section 10.3, to the many-body case. For simplicity we assume the incident particle to be distinguishable from the particles in the nucleus, and both the incident particle and the target nucleus to have zero spin. Since the nature of the final results does not depend on these approximations, appropriate generalizations can be made.

We define a radius R such that for distances larger than R the interaction between the incident particle and the target nucleus vanishes. The wave function of the system is denoted by $\Psi(\mathbf{r}, \boldsymbol{\eta})$ and that of the compound states by $\Phi^{(c)}(\mathbf{r}, \boldsymbol{\eta})$, where $\mathbf{r}$ is the coordinate of the incident particle and $\boldsymbol{\eta}$ the coordinates of the A particles inside the nucleus. The compound states $\Phi^{(c)}(\mathbf{r}, \boldsymbol{\eta})$ are chosen to form an orthonormal set:

$$\int_0^R \Phi^{(c)\star}\Phi^{(c')} \, d^3\eta \, d^3r = \delta_{cc'} \tag{30}$$

where the star indicates complex conjugation.

The total Hamiltonian is

$$H = H_\eta + H_r + V(\mathbf{r}, \boldsymbol{\eta}) \tag{31a}$$

where H_η is the Hamiltonian for the A particles in the nucleus, H_r is the Hamiltonian (kinetic energy) of the incident particle, and $V(\mathbf{r}, \boldsymbol{\eta})$ is the interaction between the incident particle and the particles in the nucleus. In terms of the nucleon-nucleon interaction $V(\mathbf{r}_i, \mathbf{r}_j)$ between two nucleons at $\mathbf{r}_i$ and $\mathbf{r}_j$, we have

$$V(\mathbf{r}, \boldsymbol{\eta}) = \sum_{i=1}^{A} V(\mathbf{r}, \mathbf{r}_i) \tag{31b}$$

If E is the energy of the incident particle and W_c are the complex* (with negative imaginary parts) energy eigenvalues of the compound nucleus, the Schrödinger equations for $\Psi(\mathbf{r}, \boldsymbol{\eta})$ and $\Phi^{(c)}(\mathbf{r}, \boldsymbol{\eta})$ are

$$H\Psi(\mathbf{r}, \boldsymbol{\eta}) = E\Psi(\mathbf{r}, \boldsymbol{\eta}) \tag{32a}$$

$$H\Phi^{(c)}(\mathbf{r}, \boldsymbol{\eta}) = W_c\Phi^{(c)}(\mathbf{r}, \boldsymbol{\eta}) \tag{32b}$$

---

* The complex energy $E - iW$ implies a wave function of the form

$$\exp -i(E - iW)t/\hbar = e^{-Wt/\hbar} \exp -iEt/\hbar$$

which represents a decaying state with the mean life $\tau = \hbar/W$ and a width $\Gamma = \hbar/\tau$.

The compound-nucleus wave functions $\Phi^{(c)}$ can be expanded in terms of the product of the complete set of states $\chi_t(\eta)$ of the target nucleus and a complete set of single-particle Kapur-Peierls eigenfunctions $\phi_{\mu t}(\mathbf{r})$ for every state t of the target nucleus; the ground state of the target nucleus is denoted by t_0 with energy $E_1(t_0)$, which is taken to be the zero of energy.

$$\Phi^{(c)}(\mathbf{r}, \boldsymbol{\eta}) = \sum_{t,\mu} a_{t\mu}^{(c)} \chi_t(\boldsymbol{\eta}) \phi_{\mu t}(\mathbf{r}) \tag{33}$$

The single-particle Kapur-Peierls eigenfunctions $\phi_{\mu t}(\mathbf{r})$ can be separated into the radial eigenfunctions $\phi_{\mu t}(r)$ and the angular part $Y_l^m(\theta, \phi)$, which is the usual spherical harmonic signifying an angular momentum state l with z-component m.

$$\phi_{\mu t}(\mathbf{r}) = \frac{1}{r} \phi_{\mu t}(r) Y_l^m(\theta, \phi) \tag{34a}$$

where $\phi_{\mu t}$ satisfies the boundary condition

$$\frac{d\phi_{\mu t}(r)}{dr}\bigg]_{r=R} = ik_t \phi_{\mu t}(R) \tag{34b}$$

and k_t is defined by

$$k_t = \frac{1}{\hbar} [2M(E - E_1(t))]^{\frac{1}{2}} \tag{34c}$$

k_t corresponds to an energy equal to the energy excess $E - E_1(t)$ of the incident particle energy E over the excitation energy $E_1(t)$ of the target nucleus.

In the inside region $r < R$, the wave function $\Psi(\mathbf{r}, \boldsymbol{\eta})$ can be expanded in terms of the complete set of states $\Phi^{(c)}(\mathbf{r}, \boldsymbol{\eta})$ of the compound nucleus. In the outside region $r > R$, a scattering solution for $\Psi(\mathbf{r}, \boldsymbol{\eta})$ can be written. Thus

$$\Psi(\mathbf{r}, \boldsymbol{\eta}) = \sum_c a_c \Phi^{(c)}(\mathbf{r}, \boldsymbol{\eta}) \qquad \text{for} \quad r < R \tag{35a}$$

and

$$\Psi(\mathbf{r}, \boldsymbol{\eta}) = \sqrt{\pi} \, \frac{i^{l+1}(2l + 1)^{\frac{1}{2}}}{2k}$$

$$\times \left[\{\phi_\alpha^-(\mathbf{r}) - S_\alpha \phi_\alpha^+(\mathbf{r})\} \chi_{t_0}(\boldsymbol{\eta}) + \sum_{\alpha \neq \alpha'} S_{\alpha\alpha',t'} \phi_{\alpha't'}^+(\mathbf{r}) \chi_{t'}(\boldsymbol{\eta}) \right] \quad \text{for} \quad r > R \tag{35b}$$

where α specifies the channel variables μ, t, and l; S_α is the amplitude for elastic scattering and $S_{\alpha\alpha',t'}$ is the amplitude for inelastic scattering for channel $\alpha \rightarrow \alpha'$, with the target nucleus left in an excited state $\chi_{t'}$. ϕ_α^+ and ϕ_α^- represent outgoing and ingoing waves whose radial parts $\phi_\alpha^+(r)$ and $\phi_\alpha^-(r)$ have the asymptotic behavior [see Eqs. (9a) and (34a)] given by

$$\phi^{(\pm)}(r) \xrightarrow[r \to \infty]{} e^{\pm i(kr - l\pi/2)} \tag{35c}$$

The expansion coefficients a_c in Eq. (35a) can be determined by using Green's theorem. From Eqs. (32a), (32b), and (35a),

$$\int_0^R [\Phi^{(c)} H \Psi - \Psi H \Phi^{(c)}] \, d^3r \, d^3\eta = (E - W_c) a_c \tag{36a}$$

By using Eqs. (33) and (34), the left-hand side becomes equal to

$$-\frac{\hbar^2}{2M} \sum_{t,\mu} a_{t\mu}^{(c)} \int_0^R d^3\eta \chi_t(\eta) \int d\Omega_r \left[R\phi_{\mu t}(\mathbf{R}) \frac{d}{dr} (r\Psi(\mathbf{r}, \boldsymbol{\eta})) \right.$$
$$\left. - R\Psi(\mathbf{R}, \boldsymbol{\eta}) \frac{d}{dr} (r\phi_{\mu t}(\mathbf{r})) \right]_{r=R} \tag{36b}$$

so that

$$a_c = \frac{\hbar^2}{2M(W_c - E)} \sum_{t,\mu} a_{t\mu}^{(c)} \int_0^R d^3\eta \chi_t(\eta) \int d\Omega_r \left[R\phi_{\mu t}(\mathbf{R}) \left\{ \frac{d}{dr} - ik_t \right\} \right.$$
$$\left. \times (r\Psi(\mathbf{r}, \boldsymbol{\eta})) \right]_{r=R} \tag{37a}$$

To evaluate the right-hand side it is necessary to use the scattering solution, Eq. (35b), for $r\Psi$. Since $[(d/dr) - ik_t] \phi_t^+ = 0$, only the $\phi_\alpha^- \chi_{t_0}$ term in Eq. (35b) contributes to Eq. (37a). Using the orthogonality of the χ's and the fact that $k_t = k$ for $t = t_0$, and carrying out the angular integration $d\Omega_r$ (which results in restricting the angular dependence of ϕ_μ to the same as that of the incident channel α), we have

$$a_c = -\sqrt{\pi} i^l \frac{(2l+1)^{1/2} \hbar^2}{2M(E - W_c)} \phi_\alpha^-(R) \sum_\mu a_{t_0,\mu}^{(c)} \phi_{\mu,t_0}(R) \tag{37b}$$

The scattering amplitudes S_α and $S_{\alpha\alpha',t'}$ can now be determined by equating the expressions (35a) and (35b) for Ψ at $r = R$.

$$(\Psi_{\text{in}})_{r=R} = (\Psi_{\text{out}})_{r=R} \tag{38a}$$

Multiplying Eq. (38a) by $\chi_{t_0}(\boldsymbol{\eta})$ and RY_l^m and integrating over $d^3\eta$ and $d\Omega_r$, we obtain

$$-S_\alpha \phi_\alpha^+(R) = \left[\frac{\sqrt{\pi} i^{l+1} (2l+1)^{1/2}}{2k} \right]^{-1} \sum_c a_c \sum_{\mu'} a_{t_0,\mu'}^{(c)} \phi_{\mu',t_0}(R) - \phi^-(R) \tag{38b}$$

From Eqs. (37b) and (38b), we obtain

$$S_\alpha = \frac{\phi^-(R)}{\phi^+(R)} \left[1 - i \sum_c \frac{\gamma_c}{E - W_c} \right] \tag{39a}$$

where the complex width γ_c is defined by

$$\gamma_c = \frac{\hbar^2 k}{M} \sum_{\mu,\mu'} a_{t_0,\mu}^{(c)} a_{t_0,\mu'}^{(c)} \phi_{\mu,t_0}(R) \phi_{\mu',t_0}(R) \tag{39b}$$

Equations (39a) and (39b) are the many-particle analogues of Eqs. (28) and (23b). From Eq. (11a), we find that the cross section for elastic scattering $\sigma_{el}^{(l)}$ in the angular momentum state l is given by

$$\sigma_{el}^{(l)} = \frac{\pi}{k^2}(2l+1)\left|\left(1 - \frac{\phi^-(R)}{\phi^+(R)}\right) + i\frac{\phi^-(R)}{\phi^+(R)}\sum_c \frac{\gamma_c}{E - W_c}\right|^2 \tag{40}$$

Similarly, one can obtain expressions for $S_{\alpha\alpha't}$ and $\sigma_{\alpha\alpha't}$.

The energy W_c is complex and can be written as

$$W_c = \mathscr{E}_c - \frac{i}{2}w_c \tag{41a}$$

where $\mathscr{E}_c$ and w_c are real. The width w_c can be calculated from Eq. (32b) and its complex conjugate equation. By multiplying Eq. (32b) on the left by $\Phi^{(c)*}$ and the complex conjugate equation by $\Phi^{(c)}$, and subtracting and integrating over $d^3\eta$ and d^3r, it can be shown that

$$w_c = \frac{\hbar^2}{M}\sum_{t,\mu,\mu'} \frac{k_t a_{t\mu}^{(c)*} a_{t\mu'}^{(c)}\phi_{\mu t}^*(R)\phi_{\mu't}(R)/\phi_{\alpha't}^+(R)\phi_{\alpha't}^-(R)}{\int_0^R \Phi^{(c)*}(\mathbf{r},\boldsymbol{\eta})\Phi^{(c)}(\mathbf{r},\boldsymbol{\eta})\,d^3\eta\,d^3r} \tag{41b}$$

In the region of low energies it turns out that $w_c \simeq \sum_t \gamma_{ct}$, which implies that the total width is equal to the sum of the partial widths for the various processes.

10.5   Lane, Thomas, and Wigner Model: Giant Resonances

To explain the experimentally observed giant resonances in the total cross section for neutron scattering in the energy range 0 to 3 Mev, Lane, Thomas, and Wigner[11] introduced a complex (optical) potential $V = U - iW$, Eq. (27), such that S calculated from it would reproduce the average scattering amplitude $\langle S \rangle$. Therefore $\langle S \rangle$ corresponds to the scattering amplitude in Eq. (23a). The compound elastic scattering amplitude S_{ce} is then the difference of S given by Eq. (39a) and $\langle S \rangle$ given by (23a) (we restrict our discussion to $l = 0$)

$$S_{ce} = S - \langle S \rangle \tag{42a}$$

$$= -ie^{-2ikR}\left\{\sum_c \frac{\gamma_c}{E - W_c} - \sum_\mu \frac{\Gamma_\mu}{E - E_\mu}\right\} \tag{42b}$$

with

$$E_\mu = \mathscr{E}_\mu - \frac{i}{2}\epsilon_\mu - iW \tag{42c}$$

By definition $\langle S_{ce} \rangle = 0$, so that taking the average of Eq. (42b), we have

$$\left\langle \sum_c \frac{\gamma_c}{E - W_c} \right\rangle = \sum_\mu \frac{\Gamma_\mu}{E - E_\mu} \tag{43a}$$

where an average of the terms on the right is unnecessary since in the energy range 0 to 3 Mev the intervals over which averages are to be taken are small compared to the widths of single-particle resonances. Using the weighting function in Eq. (7), we have for the left-hand side of Eq. (43a)

$$\left\langle \sum_c \frac{\gamma_c}{E - W_c} \right\rangle = \frac{1}{\pi} \int_{-\infty}^{\infty} \sum_c \frac{\gamma_c}{E' - W_c} \frac{1}{(E - E')^2 + \Delta^2} \, dE'$$

$$= \sum_c \frac{\gamma_c}{E + i\Delta - W_c}$$

$$\simeq \frac{1}{D} \int_{-\infty}^{\infty} \frac{\bar{\gamma}}{(E - \mathscr{E}_c) + i\left(\Delta + \dfrac{w_c}{2}\right)} \, d\mathscr{E}_c \tag{43b}$$

where in the last step we have substituted $W_c = \mathscr{E}_c - \dfrac{i}{2} w_c$, Eq. (41a), and replaced the summation $\sum_c$ by an integration. $1/D$ is the density of levels, that is, the number of levels per unit interval which is assumed to be large in the region of interest. $\bar{\gamma}$ is the average width. The imaginary part of Eq. (43b) is $-\pi(\bar{\gamma}/D)$ which is called the "strength function". Assuming that Γ_μ is real at low energies, Eqs. (25), and noting that $E_\mu = \mathscr{E}_\mu - i(W + \frac{1}{2}\epsilon_\mu)$, we have by equating the imaginary parts of Eq. (43a) the values of the strength function

$$\frac{\pi\bar{\gamma}}{D} = \sum_\mu \frac{\Gamma_\mu(W + \frac{1}{2}\epsilon_\mu)}{(E - \mathscr{E}_\mu)^2 + (W + \frac{1}{2}\epsilon_\mu)^2} \tag{44a}$$

In the special case that the incident energy E is in the neighborhood of the resonant energy $\mathscr{E}_n$ of the complex optical potential, the summation $\sum_\mu$ on the right-hand side of Eq. (44a) can be replaced by a single term $\mu = n$, provided that the single-particle resonances are sufficiently separated. The strength function can then be approximated by the following formula

$$\frac{\pi\bar{\gamma}}{D} \simeq \frac{\Gamma_n(W + \frac{1}{2}\epsilon_n)}{(E - \mathscr{E}_n)^2 + (W + \frac{1}{2}\epsilon_n)^2}, \qquad E \simeq \mathscr{E}_n \tag{44b}$$

which has the Lorentz shape.

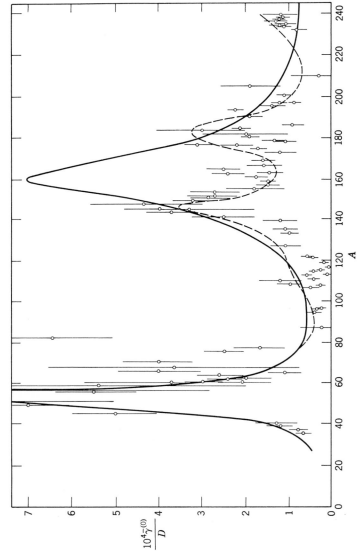

Fig. 10-1 Measured *S*-wave neutron strength functions, referred to an energy of 1 ev and multiplied by a factor of 10^4, are compared with the predictions of the optical models described in the text. The effect of increasing the imaginary central potential is to decrease the height of the giant resonances (Campbell, Feshbach, Porter, and Weisskopf[12]).

To calculate the total cross section σ_T, (Eq. (11c)), it is necessary to determine Re $\langle S \rangle$. At low energies $kR \ll 1$, and if the incident energy E is in the neighborhood of $\mathscr{E}_n$, we have from Eq. (28)

$$\text{Re } \langle S \rangle \simeq 1 + \text{Im } \frac{\Gamma_n}{E - E_n}, \qquad E \simeq \mathscr{E}_n$$

$$\simeq 1 - \frac{\pi \bar{\gamma}}{D} \tag{45a}$$

so that the total cross section

$$\langle \sigma_T \rangle = \frac{2\pi}{k^2} [1 - \text{Re } \langle S \rangle]$$

$$\sim \frac{2\pi}{k^2} \frac{\pi \bar{\gamma}}{D}$$

$$\simeq \frac{2\pi}{k^2} \frac{\Gamma_n (W + \frac{1}{2}\epsilon_n)}{(E - \mathscr{E}_n)^2 + (W + \frac{1}{2}\epsilon_n)^2} \tag{45b}$$

It is clear from Eq. (45b) that the energy-averaged total cross section $\langle \sigma_T \rangle$ has a giant resonance for incident energy E which is small ($kR \ll 1$) and in the neighborhood of the resonant energy $\mathscr{E}_n$.

From Eqs. (44b) and (26b), it is clear that the strength function $\pi \bar{\gamma}/D$ is proportional to the wave vector k and (implicitly) depends on the mass number A through the radius R. One of the successes of the optical model at low energies has been the prediction of the dependence of the strength function $\pi \bar{\gamma}/D$, which determines the average ratio of the (neutron) energy-level width to level spacing, on the mass number A. To factor out the energy dependence of the strength function, it is usual to define

$$\frac{\bar{\gamma}^{(0)}}{D} = \sqrt{\frac{E_0}{E}} \frac{\bar{\gamma}}{D} \tag{46}$$

where E_0 is taken to be 1 ev. In Fig. 10-1 (Jones[4]) the solid curve shows the variation of $\bar{\gamma}^{(0)}/D$ with A as obtained by Campbell, Feshbach, Porter, and Weisskopf[12] using an optical potential of the Woods-Saxon form with parameters $U = -52$ Mev, $W = 3.1$ Mev, $R = (1.15A^{\frac{1}{3}} + 0.4) \times 10^{-13}$ cm, and $a = 0.52 \times 10^{-13}$ cm. The experimental points are due to Hughes, Zimmerman, and Chrien.[13]

10.6 Optical Model, Experimental

The optical model is phenomenological in its origin. The potential used in the model to describe the interaction of a nucleon with a nucleus is complex. The real part accounts for refraction and the imaginary part for absorption of the incident nucleons. The potential usually includes a spin-orbit term which describes changes in spin orientations through the coupling of spin and angular momenta. This orientation, which is known as polarization, is a sensitive probe for search of nuclear potential.

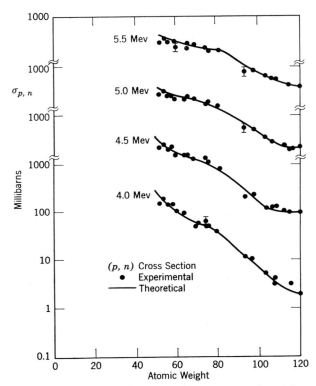

Fig. 10-2 (p, n) cross section versus atomic weight for protons of 5.5, 5.0, 4.5, and 4.0 Mev (Albert[14]).

The model has been useful in interpreting nuclear scattering from low energies up to relatively high energies. In particular, the occurrence of giant resonances, the total elastic scattering cross section of neutrons, the total reaction cross section, polarization cross section, and the angular distribution of elastically scattered protons can be understood in terms of the optical model. We shall give some examples of experimental results which have been satisfactorily analyzed in terms of the optical model. Albert[14] has measured (p, n) cross sections in some eighteen medium-weight nuclei between the energy range 4 to 5.5 Mev. He has used the

Table 10-1 Parameters Adopted as Giving the Best Fits to Experimental Data of Fig. 10-2: $a = 0.65$ F; $r_0 = 1.25$ F; $b = 0.98$ F (Albert[14])

E (Mev)	V (Mev)	W (Mev)
5.5	44	8.7
5.0	45	8.25
4.5	45	7.7
4.0	47	7.0

Bjorklund and Fernbach[15] optical potential which has the form

$$U(r) = V\rho(r) + iWq(r) + \frac{\lambda\hbar^2}{4m_0^2c^2}\frac{V}{r}\frac{d\rho}{dr}(\mathbf{\sigma} \cdot \mathbf{l}) \tag{47a}$$

where

$$\rho(r) = \left[1 + \exp\left(\frac{r - R_0}{a}\right)\right]^{-1} \tag{47b}$$

$$q(r) = \exp\left[-\left(\frac{r - R_0}{b}\right)^2\right] \tag{47c}$$

$$R_0 = r_0 A^{1/3}, \quad m_0 = \text{mass of the electron}$$

The third term is spin-orbit potential times a constant term λ. Figure 10-2 gives the results of the measurements made by Albert and also the theoretical curves, Eq. (47a), obtained with parameters of Table 10-1. The agreement between the theory and experiment is excellent.

The Bjorklund and Fernbach form of optical potential has also been used by Shore, Wall, and Irvine[16] to analyze angular distribution of 7.5 Mev protons elastically scattered by vanadium. They used two sets of parameters corresponding to surface absorption and to volume absorption. Their results are given in Fig. 10-3.

The radial dependence of the imaginary part of the potential can be calculated[4] using the Thomas-Fermi approximation which assumes that a Fermi energy can be defined as a function of nucleon density (hence of radial position). Because of the exclusion principle, the imaginary part of the potential is not proportional to the nucleon density but decreases more slowly. These calculations give a maximum for the imaginary part of the potential at the nuclear surface. The effectiveness of the exclusion principle diminishes as the energy of the incident particle increases, with the result that the maximum at the surface disappears.

The recent analysis by Rosen, Beery, Goldhaber, and Auerbach[5] indicates excellent agreement with the potential proposed by them. The

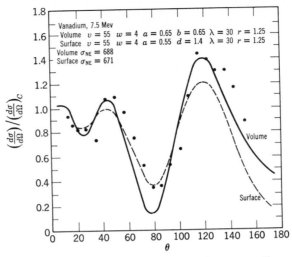

Fig. 10-3 Elastic scattering from vanadium. The curves show typical best fits for volume-absorption (solid line) and surface-absorption (broken line) type potentials to the experiments (solid circles). Here v and w are in Mev; a, b, d, and r are in Fermis, and σ_{NE} are in millibarns. The σ_{NE} are the nonelastic cross sections predicted by the model, and d is the imaginary potential-well surface parameter (Shore et al.[16]).

fit is over a wide range of elements and energy with a unique set of parameters for neutrons and for protons. They have used a spin-dependent optical potential. The values of the parameters have been given in Section 10-1. Some of their results are given in Figs. 10-4 and 10-5.

Halbert, Bassel, and Satchler[17] have carried out an optical-model analysis of the $(d\text{-}d)$ scattering data at 11 Mev[18] and at 11.8 Mev.[19] They obtained an excellent fit for the target nuclei Ni, Zr, Ag, and Sn and a reasonably good fit for Ca and Ti, assuming nuclear potentials of the form

$$V\left[1 + \exp\left(\frac{r - r_0 A^{1/3}}{a}\right)\right]^{-1} + iW[1 + \exp(r - r_W A^{1/3})/a_W]^{-1} \quad (48a)$$

for volume absorption, and

$$V\left[1 + \exp\left(\frac{r - r_0 A^{1/3}}{a}\right)\right]^{-1} - ia_W W_0 \frac{d}{dr}[1 + \exp(r - r_W A^{1/3})/a_W]^{-1}$$

$$(48b)$$

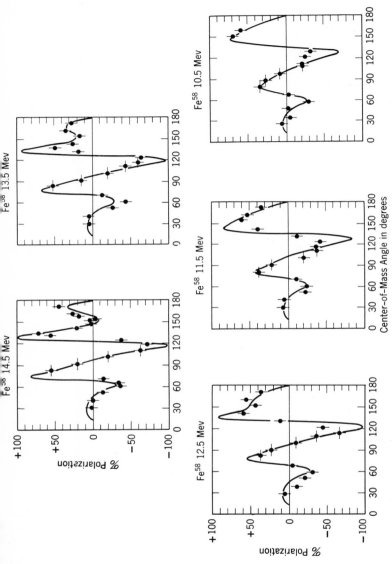

Fig. 10-4 Experimental points ($+$) are compared with curves calculated from optical model parameters: $V = (53.8\text{--}33E)$ Mev; $V_s = 5.5$ Mev; $W = 7.5$ Mev; $a = 0.65$ F; $b = 0.70$ F; $r_0 = 1.25$ F; (Rosen et al.[5]).

373

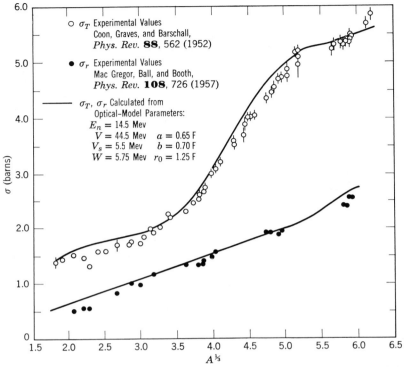

Fig. 10-5 Variation of cross section σ as a function of A. The parameters used are also given in the figure. The analysis indicates excellent agreement between experimental results and theory (Rosen et al.[5]).

for surface absorption. For the Coulomb potential, uniform charge distribution of radius $1.3A^{1/3}F$ was assumed in each case. The results are given in Fig. 10-6. The peaks observed for 11.8 Mev data for Zr, Ag, and Sn between 20 and 30 degrees are not shown. Table 10-2 gives the parameters for some of the potentials with which fits were obtained. D represents the root-mean-square percentage deviation of the theoretical from the experimental cross section and D^* is the improved value of D, obtained for an optimum value of r_0.

The case of the deuteron is complicated because, due to polarization or stripping of the deuteron by the Coulomb interaction, nonelastic channels may couple strongly to the elastic channel and may make the optical model inadequate, or the optical-model parameters may change from element to element.

An investigation was made by Brockman[20] to see if the optical-model parameters for deuteron scattering may be obtained from those for

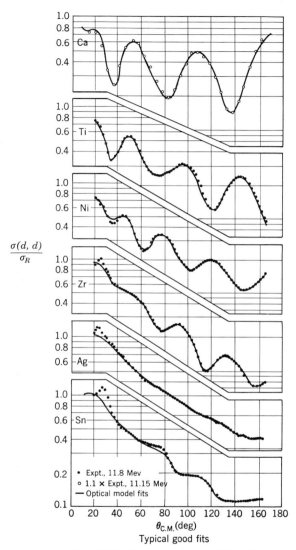

Fig. 10-6 Comparison of (*d-d*)-scattering cross section as a function of the angle in the center-of-mass system in various elements. The parameters are given in Table 10-2 (Halbert et al.[17]).

The figure axes and labels read:

$$\frac{\sigma(d,\,d)}{\sigma_R}$$

- Expt., 11.8 Mev
- 1.1 × Expt., 11.15 Mev
- Optical model fits

$\theta_{\text{C.M.}}$(deg)

Typical good fits

375

Table 10-2 Samples of Optical-Model Potentials Found (Halbert et al.[17])

	E_d (Mev)	V (Mev)	r_0 (F)	a (F)	W (Mev)	W_D (Mev)	r_W (F)	a_W (F)	D (%)	D^* (%)
Ca*	11.15	32.7	0.880	1.233		25.1	1.731	0.639	4.5	
Ti	11.8	53.3	1.133	0.840		48.1	1.433	0.680	3.9	3.6
Ti[49]	21.6†	50.9	1.131	0.868		41.2	1.465	0.690	3.3	
Cr	11.15	40.9	1.341	0.922		66.8	1.476	0.550	12.2	
Fe	11.8	56.0	1.133	0.819		53.3	1.351	0.732	4.3	4.3
Ni	11.8	58.9	1.133	0.879		56.4	1.422	0.671	3.3	3.3
Ni	11.8	60.5	1.121	0.860			1.834	0.537	3.5	
Ni	11.8	79.5	1.274	0.739	7.58	81.5	1.389	0.625	2.8	
Ni	11.8	85.1	1.233	0.735	11.25		1.717	0.567	4.0	
Cu	11.8	60.6	1.133	0.868		52.6	1.414	0.716	3.4	3.7
Zn	11.8	62.6	1.133	0.800		56.4	1.341	0.772	3.7	3.7
Kr	10.95	59.6	1.133	0.402		18.6	2.216	0.986	9.7	9.7
Zr	11.8	67.5	1.133	0.764		34.9	1.361	0.857	3.0	2.8
Nb	11.8	71.0	1.133	0.712		40.4	1.278	0.804	2.9	2.9
Ag	11.8	67.8	1.133	0.777		71.6	1.220	0.816	2.8	2.7
Ag	11.8	114.2	1.035	0.791		85.2	1.186	0.817	2.7	
Sn	11.8	63.6	1.133	0.690		28.6	1.810	0.855	5.9	5.5
Sn	11.8	69.2	0.825	1.033		30.4	1.808	0.858	3.4	

* The experimental cross sections were multiplied by 1.1 for this search.
† J. L. Yntema, private communication.

376

Table 10-3 Optical-Model Parameters (Brockman[20])

		V	W_0	W_s	r_0	a
9.4 Mev	p-Cu	47	0	8.2	1.3	0.65
21.6 Mev	d-Ni	71.74	4.22	14.50	1.29	0.71

nucleon scattering. The concept used was that the deuteron optical potential for a given energy E can be obtained by folding a deuteron wave function into the nucleon optical potential appropriate to scattering at $E/2$. This would involve doubling the strength of the potentials. It implies a greater diffuseness parameter for the deuteron and the nucleon potentials. To take into account the stripping of the deuteron, the deuteron optical model must have a strong surface-absorption term. Assuming the Woods-Saxon volume and derivative surface forms, the data of Yntema[21] for 21.6 Mev d-Ni have been analyzed by Brockman, and for a comparison with the nucleon-nucleus scattering potential, the data of Robbins, Grotowski, and Greenlees[22] have been used. Table 10-3 gives the optical parameters used for the analysis. The resultant comparisons are shown in Fig. 10-7. The agreement appears to be reasonably good. The value of r_0 is practically the same in both cases, whereas a is larger for deuterons. The surface-absorption potential W_s and the potential V are both large for the deuteron, although the value of V is not twice as large as it is for nucleon-nucleus scattering.

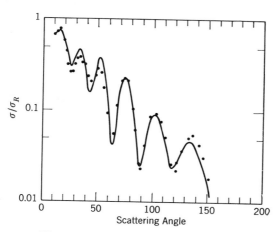

Fig. 10-7 Ratio of cross section to Rutherford cross section for 21.6 Mev d-Ni scattering. Solid curve is optical-model fit and dots are experimental points (Brockman[20]).

Another interesting analysis of proton-scattering data has been made by Olkowsky, Melkanoff, and Nodvik[23] for p-Cu scattering[24] in the energy range from 7 to 17 Mev. The investigation was undertaken to determine to what extent the experimental data permit us to ascertain the surface-absorption parameters b and W of the optical model. The standard optical-model potential with gaussian surface absorption and the spin-orbit term of Thomas form[25] have been used for the analysis. The results are shown in Table 10-4. The optical parameters given in this table represent the optimal values which led to the best agreement with experimental results. The results indicate that the parameter b depends upon energy and also r_0. Both b and W appear to vary ambiguously.

Table 10-4 Optical-Model Parameters Yielding Acceptable Fits to the Experimental Data (Olkowsky et al.[23])

E (Mev)	r_0 (F)	b (F)	V (Mev)	W (Mev)	a (F)	V_s (Mev)	σ_R (mb)
	1.3	0.5	54	21	0.56	−3	400
	1.3	1.0	51	9.5	0.50	−1	470
7.34	1.3	1.5	51	5.3	0.41	−4	490
	1.3	2.0	52	3.2	0.36	−5	520
	1.3	2.5	52	2.2	0.33	−5	570
	1.3	1.0	50	14.0	0.63	−2	810
	1.3	1.5	48	8.3	0.62	−2	890
10.20	1.3	2.0	47	5.2	0.58	−4	950
	1.3	2.5	47	3.6	0.53	−5	1020
	1.3	0.5	51	37.0	0.61	−5	790
	1.3	1.0	48	15.0	0.63	−1	920
	1.3	1.5	46	7.7	0.65	−6	1030
12.29	1.2	1.0	58	17.0	0.60	−2	810
	1.2	1.5	56	9.4	0.62	−2	910
	1.2	2.0	55	5.9	0.61	−5	990
	1.2	2.5	55	4.2	0.56	−5	1060
	1.3	0.75	46	20.0	0.67	−7	1010
	1.3	1.0	43	12.0	0.70	−9	1080
17.27	1.2	1.0	54	13.0	0.63	−8	910
	1.2	1.25	53	9.5	0.65	−8	960
	1.2	1.50	52	7.7	0.64	−8	1010

Perey and Buck[26] have shown that the study of elastic scattering of 7 Mev neutrons in the lead region can help determine nonlocal optical potential* parameters. The parameters thus determined can be of great use in fitting a wider range of data on neutron scattering and reaction. A precise experiment has been performed by Zafiratos, Oliphant, Levin, and Cranberg.[27] The data were obtained from measurements of the scattered neutrons using a pulsed beam time-of-flight spectrometer together with an electrostatic generator. The source of neutrons was D(d, n) He³ and the target was Bi²⁰⁹. The Woods-Saxon real well with derivative absorption and spin-orbit potential of the following form was used for analysis.

$$
V \frac{1}{1 + \exp\left[(r - R_0 A^{1/3})/a_0\right]} + iW \frac{4 \exp\left[(r - R_i A^{1/3})/a_i\right]}{[1 + \exp\{(r - R_i A^{1/3})/a^i\}]^2}
$$

$$
+ U \frac{\mathbf{I} \cdot \boldsymbol{\sigma}}{r_s} \left(\frac{\hbar}{2M_p c}\right)^{1/2} \frac{d}{dr} \frac{1}{1 + \exp\left[(r - R_s A^{1/3})/a_s\right]} \quad (49)
$$

The parameters used for fitting the experimental results were $V = 45.93$ Mev, $R_0 = 1.23$ F, $a = 0.69$ F, $W = 5.16$ Mev, $R_i = 1.34$ F, $a_i = 0.48$ F, $U = 995.1$ Mev, $R_s = 1.23$ F, $a_s = 0.69$ F. Figure 10-8 gives the results. We can see the excellent fit obtained at all angles. The results of the fit are in better agreement than those of Perey and Buck, who used values of the parameters given by $V = 45.31$ Mev, $R_0 = 1.25$ F, $a = 0.65$ F, $W = 6.57$ Mev, $R_i = 1.25$ F, $a_i = 0.47$ F, $U = 1202$ Mev, $R_s = 1.25$ F, and $a_s = 0.65$ F.

The nonlocal potential of Perey and Buck which described the scattering of neutrons by nuclei is given by

$$
V \psi(r) = \int V(r, r') \psi(r') \, dr' \quad (50a)
$$

$$
V(r, r') = V(r', r) \quad (50b)
$$

$$
V(r, r') = U(\tfrac{1}{2} |r + r'|) H(|r - r'|) \quad (50c)
$$

$$
H(|r - r'|) = \frac{\exp\left[-\left(\frac{r - r'}{\beta}\right)^2\right]}{\pi^{3/2} \beta^3}, \quad (50d)
$$

* In a nonlocal potential the energy of a particle at point **r** depends not only on **r** but also on the wave function at $\mathbf{r}' \neq \mathbf{r}$. The Schrödinger equation in a nonlocal potential takes the form

$$
-\frac{\hbar^2}{2M} \nabla^2 \psi(\mathbf{r}) + \int d\mathbf{r}' V(\mathbf{r}, \mathbf{r}') \psi(\mathbf{r}') = E \psi(\mathbf{r}).
$$

where U is the complex optical potential and β is the range of nonlocality. With a single set of parameters and a nonlocality range of 0.85 F, they were able to fit neutron elastic scattering data up to 24 Mev.

Perey[28] has extended his calculations to analyze 35 angular distribution measurements in various elements at different proton energies.[29] The results of 9.4 and 14.3 Mev data are reproduced in Fig. 10-9.

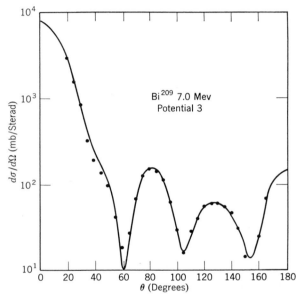

Fig. 10-8 The best fit to the data obtained with all parameters free to vary (Zafiratos et al.[27]).

The proton data have also been studied using a local potential with the same parameters, $U = 44$ Mev, $W = 11$ Mev, $U_s = 16.6$ Mev, $W_s = 0$, $r_0 = 1.25$ F, $a = 0.65$ F, $b = 0.98$ F, as used by Bjorklund and Fernbach[15] for neutron analysis data. The Thomas spin-orbit potential was set at 7.5 Mev for the 9.4 and 14.3 Mev results. The agreement is satisfactory.

Since a large amount of data was investigated, some systematic trends of parameters as a function of mass number and energy were obtained. It was observed that the real-well depth increased as a function of Z at a given incident energy. Figure 10-10 gives the V versus $Z/A^{1/3}$; the slope of the line at each bombarding energy is unity. This value is too large to account for the variation of well depth due to the increased Coulomb potential for increased Z. If one supposes, for the real-well depth, an

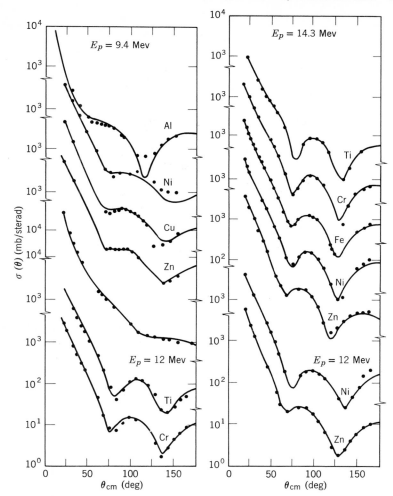

Fig. 10-9 The angular distribution cross sections at 9.4 and 14.3 Mev in various elements (Perey[28]).

energy variation of 0.3 E, then the correction for increased Z is 0.3 times the average Coulomb potential inside the well.

Figure 10-11 gives the energy dependence of the real-well depth after it has been corrected for Coulomb effects and symmetry energy. The slope is about 0.55 E. This value is higher than 0.3 E, used to correct for the Coulomb potential effect.

Deuterons elastically scattered by different elements and at different energies have been analyzed through the optical-model potential by

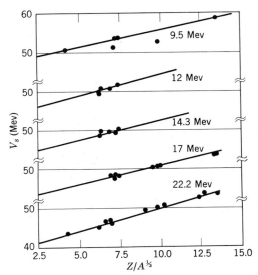

Fig. 10-10 A plot of V_s as a function of $Z/A^{1/3}$ at different energies (Perey[28]).

many workers. Good fits with experimental data have been obtained by Halbert.[30] It is known that a different set of parameters can be used to explain the same observed distribution. Perey and Perey[31] noted in analyzing scattering of deuterons in several elements that more than one set of parameters can explain the same results and that the optical potential V and the nuclear radius R_N satisfy the relationship $VR_N^n = \text{const}$, where n can have more than one value.

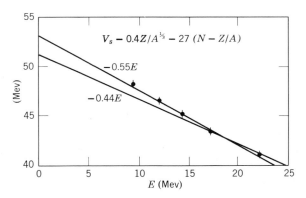

Fig. 10-11 The variation of real-well depth as a function of energy (Perey[28]).

El-Nadi and Rabie[32] have analyzed the angular distribution of elastically scattered deuterons by Y^{89}, Nb^{93}, Mo^{96}, Ag^{107}, and Er^{166}. The experimental results were due to Jolly, Lin, and Cohen.[33] El-Nadi and Rabie took a volume absorption potential. The spin-orbit term was not taken into account since the deuteron energy and mass number of the target nuclei are both relatively high. The form of the potential used is

$$V(r) = V_C(r) + V_N(r) \tag{51a}$$

where the Coulomb potential $V_C(r)$ is given by

$$V_C(r) = \frac{Ze^2}{2R_c}\left(3 - \frac{r^2}{R_c^2}\right) \qquad \text{for} \quad r \le R_c \tag{51b}$$

$$= \frac{Ze^2}{r} \qquad \text{for} \quad r \ge R_c \tag{51c}$$

with R_c the charge radius, given by $R_c = r_{0c}A^{\frac{1}{3}}F$. The nuclear potential has the form

$$V_N(r) = -Vf(r, r_0, a) - iWg(r, r_0', a') \tag{51d}$$

where $f(r, r_0, a)$ and $g(r, r_0', a')$ are the form factors of the real and imaginary well depths. The f and g used have the Woods-Saxon form

$$f(r, r_0, a) = g(r, r_0, a) = \frac{1}{1 + \exp\left[\dfrac{r - R_N}{a}\right]} \tag{52}$$

where $R_N = r_0 A^{\frac{1}{3}}F$ is the radius of the target nucleus and a is the diffuseness parameter of the potential. Using different sets of optical parameters, the differential cross sections were calculated. The optimum fit chosen was the one which corresponded with the set of parameters that gave minimum value of the quantity

$$\chi^2 = \frac{1}{N}\sum_{i=1}^{N}\left[\frac{\sigma_{\text{th}}(\theta_i) - \sigma_{\text{exp}}(\theta_i)}{\Delta\sigma_{\text{exp}}(\theta_i)}\right]^2 \tag{53}$$

where $\sigma_{\text{th}}(\theta_i)$ and $\sigma_{\text{exp}}(\theta_i)$ were the theoretical and experimental differential cross sections at angle θ_i, whereas $\Delta\sigma_{\text{exp}}(\theta_i)$ is the error in the experimental differential cross section at θ_i. The parameters are given in Table 10-5 whereas the results are shown in Fig. 10-12.

Good fitting of the experimental curves has been obtained with different sets of parameters. It was also noted that if a is decreased, the differential cross section increases, especially at higher angles, and if W diminishes, the amplitude of the oscillation in the differential cross section increases.

El-Nadi and Riad[34] investigated the elastic scattering of α-particles by silver at 18.7 Mev[35] and 40 Mev.[37] They have considered a two-body

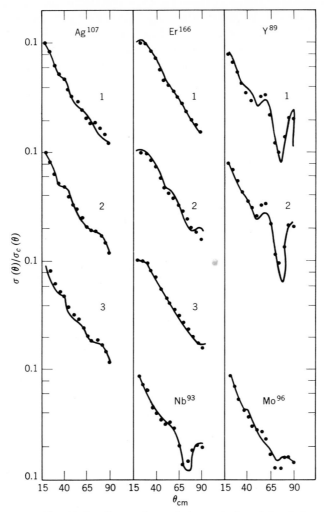

Fig. 10-12 Comparison of the optical-model calculations for 15-Mev deuterons elastically scattered from Ag^{107}, Er^{166}, Y^{89}, Nb^{93}, and Mo^{96}, with the parameters given in Table 10-5. The solid curves represent the theoretical curves while dashed curves represent the experimental data (El-Nadi and Rabie[32]).

Table 10-5 Parameters Used in Fig. 10-12 (El-Nadi and Rabie[32])

Element	E_d (Mev)	Set No.	V (Mev)	W (Mev)	a (F)	r_0 (F)	σ_R (mb)	χ^2
Ag[107]	15	1	110	68.7	0.70	1.17	136.4	0.69
		2	85	13	0.60	1.33	130.6	0.66
		3	50	20	0.58	1.6	176.2	0.68
Er[166]	15	1	100	55	0.78	1.17	132.5	0.43
		2	79	11	0.64	1.33	130.2	0.70
		3	35	9	0.56	1.60	164.0	0.30
Y[89]	15	1	80	12	0.56	1.33	131.5	1.42
		2	55	9	0.57	1.33	124.5	1.40
Mo[96]	15	1	85	14	0.60	1.33	139.9	1.90
Nb[93]	15	1	85	12	0.56	1.30	126.0	0.86

interaction $V(r)$ between the incident particle and target nucleus

$$V(r) = V_N(r) + V_C(r) \tag{54a}$$
$$V_N(r) = -(V + iW)f(r) \tag{54b}$$

where the Woods-Saxon form factor $f(r)$ is

$$f(r) = \{1 + \exp [(r - R_0)/a]\}^{-1} \tag{54c}$$

the nuclear radius $R_0 = r_0 A^{1/3}$ and a is the width of the surface layer. The parameters are given in Table 10-6; Figs. 10-13, 10-14, and 10-15 show the

Table 10-6 Potential Parameters (El-Nadi and Riad[34])

E (Mev)	Set No.	V (Mev)	W (Mev)	a (F)	R_0(F)	χ^2
18.7	1	35	7.5	0.52	7.709	0.92
	2	50	20	0.55	7.500	0.83
	3	75	27	0.55	7.244	0.89
	4	150	44	0.57	6.683	1
	5	110	68	0.76	5.554	2.3
22	1	35	7.5	0.55	7.709	0.63
	2	50	20	0.60	7.500	0.97
	3	75	27	0.60	7.244	0.94
	4	150	43	0.59	6.683	0.94
	5	110	68	0.79	5.554	1.86
40	1	35	22	0.61	7.709	3.74
	2	50	29	0.61	7.500	3.81
	3	75	37	0.60	7.244	4.07
	4	150	70	0.60	6.683	3.43

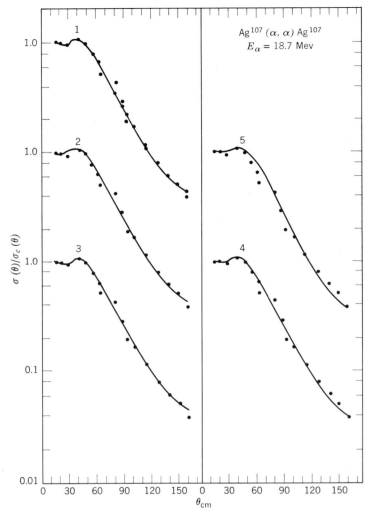

Fig. 10-13 Comparison of the experimental data (represented by the dotted curve) at incident alpha particle energy of 18.7 Mev, with the theoretical angular distribution (represented by the solid curves) for the various sets of Table 10-6 (El-Nadi and Riad[34]).

386

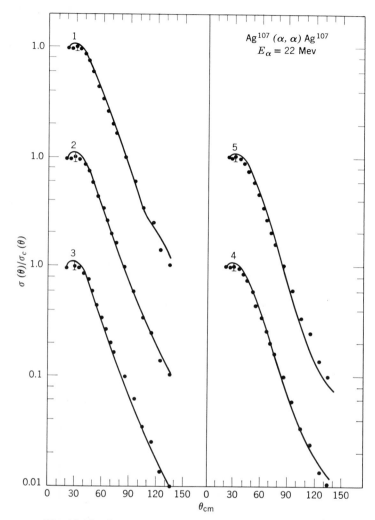

Fig. 10-14 Comparison of the experimental data (represented by the dotted curve) at incident alpha particle energy of 22 Mev, with the theoretical angular distribution (represented by the solid curves) for the various sets of Table 10-6 (El-Nadi and Riad[34]).

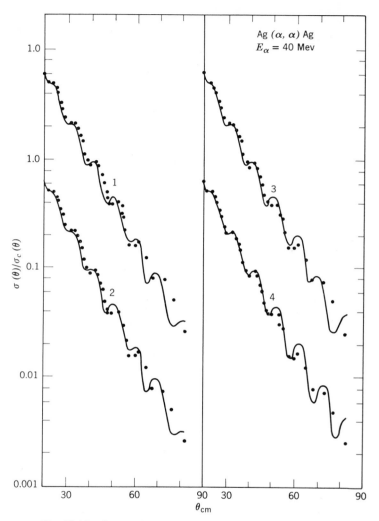

Fig. 10-15 Comparison of the experimental data (represented by the dotted curve) at incident alpha energy of 40 Mev, with the theoretical angular distribution (represented by the solid curves) for the various sets of Table 10-6 (El-Nadi and Riad[34]).

comparison between the experimental and theoretical results. Again it was noted that very good agreement could be obtained with different sets of parameters as is apparent from Table 10-5. From the study of the variations of the parameters it was observed that the shape and magnitude of the angular distribution are insensitive to large changes in V and W, but the shape is very sensitive to the diffuseness parameter a. As R_0 increases, an increase in the amplitude of oscillation is noted.

10.7   Conclusion

We shall briefly summarize some of the features of the optical model. One of the important factors to be considered before the analysis can be made is the energy of the incident particle. The energy of the incident particle should be large enough to overcome the Coulomb barrier of the target nucleus so that the incoming and outgoing waves are distorted by the nuclear potential. If the energy of the incident particle is above the barrier height but below, say, 50 Mev, then a potential containing a surface-absorption term is sufficient to explain the observed scattering. The scattering of heavier particles such as He^3 and He^4 is essentially from the nuclear surface.

There are several adjustable parameters, U, W, r_0, and a, which define the two distorting potentials. These parameters are varied systematically to obtain the best fit to the experimental data. For this reason it is hard to find a unique set of parameters for all elements and energies. The optical-model parameters are found to vary considerably as a function of energy and to a certain extent as a function of mass number. The reasons for this variation are complex and sometimes are not fully understood. They may be traced to experimental inaccuracies, inapplicability of the optical model for the analysis, different forms of potential used, or even some peculiarities of the nucleus to which the optical model is not applicable. Sometimes the parameters have been determined from elastic scattering and they have then been used in optical potentials for the analysis of experimental data.[38]

Hodgson[39] has indicated that the values of the radius parameters r_0 and the diffuseness parameters a and b can be fixed for all nuclei at all energies. The value of the radius parameter r_0 according to Hodgson is $r_0 = 1.25$ F for neutrons and protons; $r_0 = 1.50$ F for deuterons; $r_0 = 1.60$ F for tritons and He^3; $r_0 = 1.70$ F for alpha particles. The values of the diffuseness parameters for all particles are $a = 0.65$ F and $b = 0.98$ F. The optical potential may contain spin-orbit terms when the incident particle has a spin other than zero. The strength of the spin-orbit potential is adjusted to fit the measured polarization of the scattered particles.

The radial variation of the spin-orbit term is introduced in analogy with the Thomas term in atomic physics and is chosen proportional to the derivative of the real potential. It should be remarked that the spin-orbit term is stronger and of the opposite sense, compared to the atomic case.

The basic idea of the shell model is present in the optical-model analysis of nuclear reactions. The incident particle in the optical model is subjected to a potential similar to that used in the shell model; in addition, an imaginary potential is added (in the optical model) to the real potential to take into account the energy loss of the incident particle in the nucleus. Without the imaginary part of the potential, the Schrödinger equation, when solved, gives the stationary orbits.

Lane[40] has introduced a term in the real part of the nuclear optical potential, depending upon the isotopic spins $\mathbf{t}$ of the incident particle and $\mathbf{T}$ of the final nucleus. The inclusion of the isotopic spin term in the real potential is useful, for it makes it possible to calculate the potential appropriate to one isotope of a nucleus when that for another is known. In particular, the advantage is more noticeable for calculating the potential of an unstable nucleus. For our discussion we shall give the analysis made by Hodgson.[39] An isospin potential U_1 is included in the real part of the optical nuclear potential so that

$$U = U_0 + (\mathbf{t} \cdot \mathbf{T})U_1 \tag{55a}$$

For elastic scattering, the two potentials are $U^+ = U_0 + \frac{1}{2}TU_1$, $U^- = U_0 - \frac{1}{2}(T + 1)U_1$ for two possible isospin states with total isospins $T \pm \frac{1}{2}$. For nuclei whose total isospin state $T \neq 0$, the scattering of protons from such nuclei will allow both isospin states. The average potential may be obtained by multiplying with the appropriate weight factors $(2T + 1)^{-1}$ and $2T(2T + 1)^{-1}$ and averaging, thus yielding the average potential

$$U_p = U_0 - \frac{1}{2}U_1 T \tag{55b}$$

Lane and Soper[41] have shown that nuclei are predominantly in the state of minimum isospin and hence $T = \frac{1}{2}(N - Z)$. Using this relationship, we may write

$$U_p = U_0 - \frac{1}{4}(N - Z)U_1 \tag{55c}$$

Since only the $T + \frac{1}{2}$ state is allowed in neutron scattering, the corresponding neutron potential is

$$U_n = U_0 + \frac{1}{4}(N - Z)U_1 \tag{55d}$$

From these expressions it is possible to calculate the optical potential of an unstable final nucleus formed in a direct reaction process, provided the optical potential is known for a stable isotope of the same element from the elastic scattering analysis.

References

1. Ford, K. W., and D. Bohm, *Phys. Rev.* **79**, 745, 1950.
2. Barschall, H. H., *Phys. Rev.* **86**, 431, 1952. Miller, D. W., R. K. Adair, C. K. Bockelman, and S. E. Darden, *Phys. Rev.* **88**, 83, 1952.
3. Woods, R. D., and D. S. Saxon, *Phys. Rev.* **95**, 577, 1954.
4. Jones, P. B., *The Optical Model in Nuclear and Particle Physics*, John Wiley and Sons, N.Y. 1963.
5. Rosen, L., J. G. Beery, A. S. Goldhaber, and E. H. Auerbach (Private Communication by L. Rosen).
6. Feshbach, H., C. E. Porter, and V. F. Weisskopf, *Phys. Rev.* **96**, 488, 1954.
7. Kapur, P. L., and R. E. Peierls, *Proc. Roy. Soc. (London)* **A166**, 277, 1938.
8. Brown, G. E., *Rev. Mod. Phys.* **31**, 893, 1959.
9. Peierls, R. E., *Proc. Cambridge Phil. Soc.* **44**, 242, 1948.
10. Wigner, E. P., and L. Eisenbud, *Phys. Rev.* **72**, 29, 1947.
11. Lane, A. M., R. G. Thomas, and E. Wigner, *Phys. Rev.* **98**, 693, 1955.
12. Campbell, E. J., H. Feshbach, C. E. Porter, and V. F. Weisskopf, Laboratory for Nuclear Sci. Tech. Rep. No. 73, p. 132, M.I.T., 1960.
13. Hughes, D. J., R. L. Zimmerman, and R. E. Chrien, *Phys. Rev. Letters*, **1**, 461, 1958.
14. Albert, R. D., *Phys. Rev.* **115**, 925, 1959.
15. Bjorklund, F., and S. Fernbach, *Phys. Rev.* **109**, 1295, 1958.
16. Shore, B. W., N. S. Wall, and J. W. Irvine, *Phys. Rev.* **123**, 276, 1961.
17. Halbert, E. C., R. H. Bassel, and G. R. Satchler, *Proc. Conf. Direct Interaction Nucl. Reaction Mech.*, p. 167. Gordon and Breach, Science Publishers, Inc. New York 1962.
18. Takeda, M., *J. Phys. Soc. Japan* **15**, 557, 1960.
19. Igo, G., W. Lorenz, and U. Schmidt-Rohr, *Phys. Rev.* **124**, 832, 1961.
20. Brockman, K. W., *Proc. Conf. Direct Interaction Nucl. Reaction Mech.*, p. 159, 1962. Gordon and Breach, Science Publishers Inc., New York, 1962.
21. Yntema, J. L., *Phys. Rev.* **113**, 261, 1959.
22. Robbins, A. B., K. A. Grotowski, and G. W. Greenlees, *Proc. Rutherford Jubilee Intern. Conf. Manchester*, 1961, p. 419, Heywood and Co., 1962.
23. Olkowsky, J., M. A. Melkanoff, and J. S. Nodvik, *Proc. Conf. Direct Interaction Nucl. Reaction Mech.*, p. 192, Gordon and Breach, Science Publishers Inc. New York, 1962.
24. Benveniste, J., R. Booth, and A. Mitchell, *Phys. Rev.* **123**, 1818, 1961; Dayton, I. E., and G. Schrank, *Phys. Rev.* **106**, 4, 1956; Rosen, L., J. E. Brolley, and L. Stewart, *Phys. Rev.* **121**, 1423, 1961; Blampied, W. A., *Phys. Rev.* **113**, 1099, 1959.
25. Nodvik, J. S., C. B. Duke, and M. A. Melkanoff, *Phys. Rev.* **125**, 975, 1962.
26. Perey, F. G., and B. Buck, *Nucl. Phys.* **32**, 353, 1962.
27. Zafiratos, C. D., T. A. Oliphant, J. S. Levin, and L. Cranberg, *Phys. Rev. Letters*, **14**, 913, 1965.
28. Perey, F. G., *Proc. Conf. Direct Interaction Nucl. Reaction Mech.*, p. 125, Gordon and Breach, Science Publishers Inc., New York, 1962.
29. Greenlees, G. W., L. G. Kuo, and M. Petranie, *Proc. Roy. Soc.* **A243**, 206, 1957; Dayton, I. E., and G. Schrank, *Phys. Rev.* **101**, 1358, 1956; Fulmer, C. B., *Phys. Rev.* **125**, 631, 1962; Hu, C., et al., *J. Phys. Soc. Japan* **14**, 861, 1959.
30. Halbert, E. C., *Nuclear Phys.* **50**, 353, 1964.
31. Perey, C. M., and F. G. Perey, *Phys. Rev.* **132**, 755, 1963.

32. El-Nadi, M., and A. Rabie, *Nucl. Phys.* **65**, 90, 1965.
33. Jolly, R. R., E. K. Lin, and B. L. Cohen, *Phys. Rev.* **130**, 2391, 1963.
34. El-Nadi, M., and F. Riad, *Nucl. Phys.* **65**, 99, 1965.
35. Gailer, O. H., E. Bleuler, and D. J. Tandem, *Phys. Rev.* **112**, 1889, 1958.
36. Wall, N. S., J. R. Rees, and K. W. Ford, *Phys. Rev.* **97**, 726, 1955.
37. Igo, G., H. E. Wegner, and R. H. Eisberg, *Phys. Rev.* **101**, 1508, 1956.
38. Tobocman, W., and M. H. Kalos, *Phys. Rev.* **97**, 132, 1955; Buck, B., and P. E. Hodgson, *Nuclear Phys.* **29**, 496, 1962.
39. Hodgson, P. E., *Proc. Conf. Direct Interactions Nucl. Reaction Mech.*, p. 103, Gordon and Breach, Science Publishers, Inc., New York, 1962.
40. Lane, A. M., *Phys. Rev. Letters* **8**, 171, 1962; *Nucl. Phys.* **35**, 676, 1962.
41. Lane, A. M., and J. M. Soper, Quoted in Ref. 39.

Problems

1. In the optical model, the nuclear matter is sometimes assigned a complex refractive index $N = n + i\tau$. Identify n and τ in this context.

2. Find an expression for inelastic scattering cross section assuming a uniform-sphere model (that is, the refractive index is constant within the nuclear sphere and unity outside).

3. The angular distribution of the diffraction scattering can be obtained by summing the contributions reaching a given image point, far behind the sphere, from every source point in a plane wave front of amplitude $(a - 1)$ within the geometrical shadow. Then the Kirchhoff integral (of optics) can be written as

$$a_{sc} = \frac{\text{constant}}{R} \int\int d\phi \, \rho \, d\rho \, e^{ik_0\mathbf{R} \cdot \mathbf{\rho}/|R|}[1 - a(s)]$$

Integrate this using polar coordinates and arrive at a form similar to the one obtained by the W.K.B. approximation to the phase shifts of the Rayleigh partial wave procedure.

4. What is the effect on the scattered wave amplitude as a result of the introduction of a complex potential? Consider the problem from the standpoint of elementary partial wave analysis.

5. Discuss the consequences of the Kapur-Peierls boundary conditions

$$\frac{d\phi_\mu}{dr}\bigg|_{r=R} = ik\,\phi_\mu(R)$$

6. Examine the scattering amplitude, Eq. (23a), at low energies, and determine the reaction cross section for this approximation.

7. Taking the scattering amplitude of Prob. 6, determine the elastic scattering cross section for this low-energy approximation for neutrons.

8. Using different experimental results discussed in the text, discuss the extent to which the nuclear radius is dependent upon the optical model potentials.

11

NUCLEAR REACTIONS III: DIRECT REACTIONS

11.1 Introduction

The term, direct reaction, is used for a variety of nuclear processes including inelastic nuclear collisions, stripping, and its inverse, the pick-up reaction. A direct reaction is one which proceeds without the formation of a compound nucleus. The time during which the incident and target nucleus interact is very much shorter than the life of a corresponding compound nucleus. Because of this, the reaction products exhibit certain characteristics which are entirely different from those seen if the reaction has proceeded through a compound-nucleus formation.

These two processes represent extreme views of the mechanism of nuclear reactions. In the direct-reaction process, the target nucleus and the incident projectile system have a lifetime of the order of 10^{-22} sec, assuming an interaction-potential depth of some tens of Mev. On the other hand, the compound nucleus has a lifetime of the order of 10^{-14} sec for an energy width of the order of a fraction of an electron volt. Thus the time scales of the two mechanisms for the reaction are quite different. It is very difficult to say at what energy a given reaction will proceed according to either one or the other reaction mechanism. One can argue qualitatively that with increasing energy of incident particles, the partial widths as well as the number of reaction channels increase, thereby resulting in a progressively shorter time that the system spends as a compound nucleus. At low energies, formation of the compound nucleus is more likely, whereas the direct reaction mechanism will prevail at higher energies.[1]

The direct reaction is a one-step process. This was first recognized by Oppenheimer and Phillips[2] in analyzing the low-energy (d, p) reactions.[3] It was observed experimentally that (d, p) reactions were more frequent than (d, n) reactions. This is completely opposite from what would be expected if the reaction had proceeded through the formation of the compound nucleus. Because of the absence of the Coulomb barrier, there would be a preponderance of the (d, n) reactions over the (d, p) reactions.

Oppenheimer and Phillips explained the reaction by stating that the deuteron is a loosely bound system, and when it approaches the target nucleus the proton is detached from the deuteron due to the Coulomb field, whereas the neutron is captured. At low energies this is known as the Oppenheimer and Phillips process, although it is now more commonly known as the stripping process, at both low and high energies. In the high-energy region, the (d, p) and (d, n) reactions are equally probable. But what distinguishes the direct reaction from other nuclear-reaction mechanisms is that the angular distribution of disintegration products is peaked in the forward direction with a very small intensity in the backward direction.

The theoretical work of Butler[4] has very successfully demonstrated that the angular distribution of the forward peak is given by the square of the spherical Bessel function of order l, where l is the angular momentum of the state in which the neutron [in the case of the (d, p) reaction] or proton [for the (d, n) reaction] is captured. It is a single-step process, without the formation of a compound nucleus. At short distances, due to the strong interaction between the bombarded nucleus and either of the two nucleons of the deuteron, either neutron or proton is captured. The uncaptured nucleon proceeds in the forward direction giving a forward peak. Eventually, it was found that a large number of nuclear reactions[5], such as $P^{31}(\alpha, p)S^{34}$, $Na^{23}(d, p)Na^{24}$, $Li^7(p, d)Li^6$, $C^{13}(He^3, \alpha)C^{12}$, and many others, showed characteristics of "stripping" or the inverse "pick-up" reaction by the forward peaking. The reactions (p, d) and (n, d) are known as the pick-up reactions and are the inverse of the (d, p) and (d, n) reactions. The process of the pick-up reaction is as follows. When the incident proton approaches very closely to the target nucleus, there is a strong interaction between the proton and an outer neutron, resulting in the formation of a deuteron which is then emitted. A similar explanation holds for the (n, d) reaction.

To explain the forward peaking of an (α, p) reaction, it is considered as the stripping of a triton from the alpha particle. The (p, α) reaction on the other hand is the reverse reaction, that is, the pick-up of a triton by the proton from the target to form an alpha particle. The reactions such as (α, p) and (n, p) are known as knock-on reactions, in which the incident particle strikes a particle of another kind and ejects it.

Reactions of types (p, p'), (α, α'), and (d, d') can also be analyzed according to the direct-reaction process. When the incident projectile enters the nucleus, it is subjected to the optical potential. It interacts with a surface nucleon, losing some of its energy, and then escapes from the nucleus. If the nucleon that is hit is of the same kind as the incident particle, it may be ejected through an exchange inelastic reaction. These types of reactions are also known as surface reactions.

Nuclear-level structure is often obtained from the study of Coulomb excitation and can be interpreted through the direct reaction mechanism. Inelastic scattering, such as the (p, p'), (α, α'), and others, can be used to excite collective levels (Chapter 8). Studies of γ-rays emitted in transitions between states can provide information on the collective levels. The stripping and pick-up reactions throw light on the structure of the nucleus. In the early stage of the theory the reaction mechanism was treated using a plane-wave approximation, in which $\psi(\mathbf{r})$ can be written as $\exp(i\mathbf{k} \cdot \mathbf{r})$. This approximation did not accurately describe the process. However, for completeness, we have included these calculations. It is now recognized that the incident wave is indeed distorted by the nuclear inter-action. The direct-reaction theories based upon the distorted-wave Born approximation (DWBA) have been developed and give more accurate descriptions of direct reactions such as stripping, the pick-up process, inelastic scattering, and perhaps more complex reactions such as the (d, t) and (He^3, α). We have given some calculations of the DWBA method together with suitable experimental results to substantiate them.

11.2 Kinematics of the Stripping and Pick-up Reactions

The stripping and pick-up reactions can in general be written in the following form

$$(1 + 2) + 3 \rightarrow 1 + (2 + 3) \tag{1}$$

The parentheses in the first term denote the bound state of nucleus 1 and nucleus 2. Similarly on the right, we have the bound state of nuclei 2 and 3; any one of them may be a single nucleon, proton or neutron. Nucleus 3 is initially free, and nucleus 1 is free in the final state. Thus, in a stripping (d, p) reaction $d + X^A \rightarrow p + X^{A+1}$, we use $1 \equiv p$, $2 \equiv n$, and $3 \equiv X^A$. Similarly, in a pick-up (p, d) reaction $p + X^A \rightarrow d + X^{A-1}$ we have $1 \equiv X^{A-1}$, $2 \equiv n$, $3 \equiv p$. As another example of the pick-up reaction we consider the (p, α) reaction $p + X^A \rightarrow \alpha + X^{A-3}$, in which case $1 \equiv X^{A-3}$, $2 \equiv \text{H}^3$, and $3 \equiv p$.

Consider the reaction in the center-of-mass system, Fig. 11-1. Initially, the momentum of particle 3 is $\mathbf{P}_i$ and that of the bound nucleus $(1 + 2)$ is $-\mathbf{P}_i$. Finally the momentum of the free particle 1 is $\mathbf{P}_f$ and that of the bound nucleus $(2 + 3)$ is $-\mathbf{P}_f$. Since the initial momentum $-\mathbf{P}_i$ of

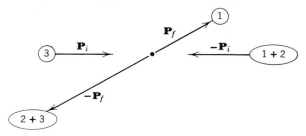

Fig. 11-1 Scattering in the center-of-mass system.

$(1 + 2)$ is shared between particles 1 and 2, the initial momenta which can be ascribed to 1 and 2 are

$$- \frac{m_1}{m_1 + m_2} \mathbf{P}_i \quad \text{and} \quad - \frac{m_2}{m_1 + m_2} \mathbf{P}_i$$

respectively. Similarly, the final momenta of 2 and 3 are

$$- \frac{m_2}{m_2 + m_3} \mathbf{P}_f \quad \text{and} \quad - \frac{m_3}{m_2 + m_3} \mathbf{P}_f$$

respectively. If we denote the momentum transfer, which is the difference between the final and initial momenta, by $\mathbf{q}_k$ for the kth particle where $k = 1, 2, 3$, we have

$$\mathbf{q}_1 = \mathbf{P}_f + \frac{m_1}{m_1 + m_2} \mathbf{P}_i \tag{2a}$$

$$\mathbf{q}_2 = - \frac{m_2}{m_2 + m_3} \mathbf{P}_f + \frac{m_2}{m_1 + m_2} \mathbf{P}_i \tag{2b}$$

$$\mathbf{q}_3 = - \frac{m_3}{m_2 + m_3} \mathbf{P}_f - \mathbf{P}_i \tag{2c}$$

Because the mass arrangements are not the same in the initial and the final states, the reduced masses μ_i and μ_f to be associated with the initial and the final momenta are different. μ_i and μ_f are given by

$$\frac{1}{\mu_i} = \frac{1}{m_1 + m_2} + \frac{1}{m_3} \tag{3a}$$

$$\frac{1}{\mu_f} = \frac{1}{m_1} + \frac{1}{m_2 + m_3} \tag{3b}$$

The total energy E is given by

$$E = \frac{\mathbf{P}_i^2}{2\mu_i} - \epsilon_{12} = \frac{\mathbf{P}_f^2}{2\mu_f} - \epsilon_{23} \tag{4a}$$

where* $P_i^2/2\mu_i$ and $P_f^2/2\mu_f$ are the initial and final kinetic energies and ϵ_{12} and ϵ_{23} are, respectively, the binding energies of the initially and finally bound systems, $(1 + 2)$ and $(2 + 3)$. The Q-value for the reaction is given by

$$Q = \frac{P_f^2}{2\mu_f} - \frac{P_i^2}{2\mu_i}$$

$$= \epsilon_{23} - \epsilon_{12} \tag{4b}$$

If the coordinates of particles 1, 2, and 3 are specified by $\mathbf{r}_1$, $\mathbf{r}_2$, and $\mathbf{r}_3$, then the centers of mass of $(1 + 2)$ and $(2 + 3)$ are at

$$\mathbf{R}_{12} = \frac{m_1\mathbf{r}_1 + m_2\mathbf{r}_2}{m_1 + m_2} \quad \text{and} \quad \mathbf{R}_{23} = \frac{m_2\mathbf{r}_2 + m_3\mathbf{r}_3}{m_2 + m_3}$$

respectively. Since the center-of-mass remains fixed, the independent sets of coordinates are both the relative coordinates of the particles in the bound system and the difference between the coordinates of the free particle and the center of mass of these particles. Thus

Initially

$$\mathbf{r}_{12} = \mathbf{r}_1 - \mathbf{r}_2 \qquad \mathbf{r}_i = \mathbf{r}_3 - \mathbf{R}_{12} \tag{5a}$$

Finally

$$\mathbf{r}_{23} = \mathbf{r}_2 - \mathbf{r}_3 \qquad \mathbf{r}_f = \mathbf{r}_1 - \mathbf{R}_{23} \tag{5b}$$

are the set of independent coordinates initially and finally, with the condition

$$m_1\mathbf{r}_1 + m_2\mathbf{r}_2 + m_3\mathbf{r}_3 = 0 \tag{5c}$$

that is, the center-of-mass of the whole system is at rest. We can determine the momenta $\mathbf{p}_{12}$ and $\mathbf{p}_i$ ($\mathbf{p}_{23}$ and $\mathbf{p}_f$) which are canonically conjugate to the coordinates $\mathbf{r}_{12}$ and $\mathbf{r}_i$ ($\mathbf{r}_{23}$ and $\mathbf{r}_f$), respectively, in terms of the momenta $\mathbf{p}_1$, $\mathbf{p}_2$, and $\mathbf{p}_3$ which are canonically conjugate to $\mathbf{r}_1$, $\mathbf{r}_2$, and $\mathbf{r}_3$, respectively. From Eq. (5), we can express $\mathbf{r}_1$, $\mathbf{r}_2$, and $\mathbf{r}_3$ in terms of $\mathbf{r}_{12}$ and $\mathbf{r}_i$, or $\mathbf{r}_{23}$ and $\mathbf{r}_f$, and then obtain $\mathbf{p}_{12}$ and $\mathbf{p}_i$ from the relations ($\hbar = 1$)

$$\mathbf{p}_{12} = \frac{1}{i}\frac{\partial}{\partial\mathbf{r}_{12}} = \sum_{k=1,2}\mathbf{p}_k\frac{\partial\mathbf{r}_k}{\partial\mathbf{r}_{12}} \tag{6a}$$

$$\mathbf{p}_i = \frac{1}{i}\frac{\partial}{\partial\mathbf{r}_i} = \sum_{k=1,2,3}\mathbf{p}_k\frac{\partial\mathbf{r}_k}{\partial\mathbf{r}_i} \tag{6b}$$

* For a three vector, say $\mathbf{A}$, we are using $\mathbf{A}^2$ and A^2 interchangeably.

Following this procedure, we obtain

$$\mathbf{p}_{12} = \mu_{12}\left(\frac{\mathbf{p}_1}{m_1} - \frac{\mathbf{p}_2}{m_2}\right) \tag{7a}$$

$$\mathbf{p}_i = \mu_i\left(-\frac{\mathbf{p}_1 + \mathbf{p}_2}{m_1 + m_2} + \frac{\mathbf{p}_3}{m_3}\right) \tag{7b}$$

$$\mathbf{p}_{23} = \mu_{23}\left(\frac{\mathbf{p}_2}{m_2} - \frac{\mathbf{p}_3}{m_3}\right) \tag{7c}$$

$$\mathbf{p}_f = \mu_f\left(\frac{\mathbf{p}_1}{m_1} - \frac{\mathbf{p}_2 + \mathbf{p}_3}{m_2 + m_3}\right) \tag{7d}$$

where μ_{12} and μ_{23} are the reduced masses for $(1 + 2)$ and $(2 + 3)$, respectively, and are given by

$$\frac{1}{\mu_{12}} = \frac{1}{m_1} + \frac{1}{m_2} \tag{8a}$$

$$\frac{1}{\mu_{23}} = \frac{1}{m_2} + \frac{1}{m_3} \tag{8b}$$

The kinetic energy operator T_c in the center-of-mass system is therefore

$$T_c = \frac{\mathbf{p}_{12}^2}{2\mu_{12}} + \frac{\mathbf{p}_i^2}{2\mu_i} = \frac{\mathbf{p}_{23}^2}{2\mu_{23}} + \frac{\mathbf{p}_f^2}{2\mu_f} \tag{9}$$

11.3 Theory of the Stripping and Pick-up Reactions

The total Hamiltonian for the system is given by

$$H = T_c + V_{12} + V_{13} + V_{23} \tag{10}$$

where V is the interaction potential between the particles indicated by the subscripts. If E is the total energy of the three particles in the center-of-mass system and ψ is the wave function of the system, then

$$H\psi = E\psi \tag{11}$$

is the Schrödinger equation satisfied by ψ. If ϕ_{12} and ϕ_{23} represent the wave functions of the initial and final bound states $(1 + 2)$ and $(2 + 3)$, respectively, then the Schrödinger equations satisfied by ϕ_{12} and ϕ_{23} are

$$\left(\frac{\mathbf{p}_{12}^2}{2\mu_{12}} + V_{12}\right)\phi_{12}(\mathbf{r}_{12}) = -\epsilon_{12}\phi_{12}(\mathbf{r}_{12}) \tag{12a}$$

$$\left(\frac{\mathbf{p}_{23}^2}{2\mu_{23}} + V_{23}\right)\phi_{23}(\mathbf{r}_{23}) = -\epsilon_{23}\phi_{23}(\mathbf{r}_{23}) \tag{12b}$$

We denote by $\chi_i(\mathbf{r}_i)$ and $\chi_f(\mathbf{r}_f)$ the wave functions of the free particle 3 with respect to the center-of-mass of $(1 + 2)$ in the initial state, and of 1 with respect to the center of mass of $(2 + 3)$ in the final state, respectively. The wave functions $\psi(\mathbf{r}_{1\,2}, \mathbf{r}_i)$ and $\psi(\mathbf{r}_{23}, \mathbf{r}_f)$ can be expanded as follows

$$\psi(\mathbf{r}_{1\,2}, \mathbf{r}_i) = \sum_\alpha \phi_\alpha(\mathbf{r}_{12})\chi_\alpha(\mathbf{r}_i) \tag{13a}$$

$$\psi(\mathbf{r}_{23}, \mathbf{r}_f) = \sum_\alpha \phi_\alpha(\mathbf{r}_{23})\chi_\alpha(\mathbf{r}_f) \tag{13b}$$

where α signifies a complete set of states of the bound system and the free particle. From Eqs. (13) we obtain

$$\chi_i(\mathbf{r}_i) = \int \phi_{12}^*(\mathbf{r}_{12})\psi(\mathbf{r}_{12}, \mathbf{r}_i)\, d^3 r_{12} \tag{14a}$$

$$\chi_f(\mathbf{r}_f) = \int \phi_{23}^*(\mathbf{r}_{23})\psi(\mathbf{r}_{23}, \mathbf{r}_f)\, d^3 r_{23} \tag{14b}$$

To obtain the differential equation satisfied by $\chi_f(\mathbf{r}_f)$, we note that $p_f^2 = -\nabla_f^2$, since $\mathbf{p}_f$ is the momentum canonically conjugate to the coordinate $\mathbf{r}_f$, and from Eqs. (4a), (9), (10), and (11) we have

$$H\psi(\mathbf{r}_{23}, \mathbf{r}_f) = \left(\frac{\mathbf{p}_{23}^2}{2\mu_{23}} + \frac{\mathbf{p}_f^2}{2\mu_f} + V_{12} + V_{13} + V_{23}\right)\psi(\mathbf{r}_{23}, \mathbf{r}_f)$$

$$= \left(\frac{P_f^2}{2\mu_f} - \epsilon_{23}\right)\psi(\mathbf{r}_{23}, \mathbf{r}_f)$$

or

$$\frac{1}{2\mu_f}(\nabla_f^2 + P_f^2)\psi(\mathbf{r}_{23}, \mathbf{r}_f) = \left(\frac{\mathbf{p}_{23}^2}{2\mu_{23}} + V_{12} + V_{13} + V_{23} + \epsilon_{23}\right)\psi(\mathbf{r}_{23}, \mathbf{r}_f) \tag{15a}$$

Applying the operator $(\nabla_f^2 + P_f^2)$ to $\chi_f(\mathbf{r}_f)$ in Eq. (14b) and using Eqs. (12) and (15a), we obtain

$$(\nabla_f^2 + P_f^2)\chi_f(\mathbf{r}_f) = 2\mu_f \int \phi_{23}^*(\mathbf{r}_{23})[V_{12} + V_{13}]\psi(\mathbf{r}_{23}, \mathbf{r}_f)\, d^3 r_{23} \tag{15b}$$

The solution for $\chi_f(\mathbf{r}_f)$ can be obtained by using the outgoing Green function

$$-\frac{\exp iP_f\,|\mathbf{r}_f - \mathbf{r}|}{4\pi\,|\mathbf{r}_f - \mathbf{r}|}$$

Thus

$$\chi_f(\mathbf{r}_f) = -\frac{\mu_f}{2\pi} \int \frac{\exp iP_f\,|\mathbf{r}_f - \mathbf{r}|}{|\mathbf{r}_f - \mathbf{r}|}\, \phi_{23}^*(\mathbf{r}_{23})[V_{12} + V_{13}]\psi d^3 r_{23}\, d^3 r \tag{16}$$

In order that the total wave function ψ describe the reaction process $(1 + 2) + 3 \rightarrow 1 + (2 + 3)$, the boundary condition imposed on $\chi_f(\mathbf{r}_f)$ is

$$\chi_f(\mathbf{r}_f) \xrightarrow[r_f \to \infty]{} f(\theta, \phi) \frac{e^{iP_f r_f}}{r_f} \tag{17a}$$

where $f(\theta, \phi)$ is the reaction amplitude. Comparing Eqs. (17a) and (16), we obtain

$$f(\theta, \phi) = -\frac{\mu_f}{2\pi} \int \phi_{23}^*(\mathbf{r}_{23}) e^{-i\mathbf{P}_f \cdot \mathbf{r}_f} [V_{12} + V_{13}] \psi \, d^3 r_{23} \, d^3 r_f \tag{17b}$$

Born Approximation: (Butler Theory)

In the Born approximation, we can replace ψ by

$$\phi_{12}(\mathbf{r}_{12}) \exp (-i\mathbf{P}_i \cdot \mathbf{R}_{12} + i\mathbf{P}_i \cdot \mathbf{r}_3) = \phi_{12}(\mathbf{r}_{12}) \exp (i\mathbf{P}_i \cdot \mathbf{r}_i)$$

and then the reaction amplitude $f(\theta, \phi)$ is given by

$$f(\theta, \phi) \simeq -\frac{\mu_f}{2\pi} \int \phi_{23}^*(\mathbf{r}_{23}) e^{-i\mathbf{P}_f \cdot \mathbf{r}_f} [V_{12} + V_{13}] e^{i\mathbf{P}_i \cdot \mathbf{r}_i} \phi_{12}(\mathbf{r}_{12}) \, d^3 r_{23} \, d^3 r_f$$

$$= -\frac{\mu_f}{2\pi} \int \phi_{23}^*(\mathbf{r}_{23}) e^{i(\mathbf{q}_3 \cdot \mathbf{r}_{23} - \mathbf{q}_1 \cdot \mathbf{r}_{12})} [V_{12} + V_{13}] \phi_{12}(\mathbf{r}_{12}) \, d^3 r_{12} \, d^3 r_{23}$$

$$\tag{18}$$

where we have made use of the equalities

$$-\mathbf{P}_f \cdot \mathbf{r}_f + \mathbf{P}_i \cdot \mathbf{r}_i = \mathbf{q}_3 \cdot \mathbf{r}_{23} - \mathbf{q}_1 \cdot \mathbf{r}_{12} \quad \text{and} \quad d^3 r_{23} \, d^3 r_f = d^3 r_{23} \, d^3 r_{12}$$

Also the potentials are assumed to be independent of the momenta. It should be noted that the Born approximation ignores the interaction between the incident particle and the target nucleus in expressing ψ as the product of the incident plane wave and the wave function of the target nucleus. This approximation is not too unreasonable if the mechanism of reaction is the direct interaction which is assumed to take place as a single encounter near the surface of the target nucleus. If the reaction occurs through the formation of a compound nucleus however, this will not be true.

If the reaction takes place through the formation of a compound nucleus, then the compound-nuclear eigenfunctions describe the wave function ψ. The properties of these eigenfunctions are such that they describe the strong interaction between the incident particle and the struck nucleus. If ψ overlaps with a single compound-nuclear eigenfunction, then the compound-nucleus model gives the appropriate description of the nuclear reaction. Thus we see that in the direct-interaction model the value of the wave function ψ is approximate as it ignores the strong interaction between the incident particle and the struck nucleus. This model is applicable when the contribution from the compound-nuclear reaction can be neglected.

The reaction cross section $\sigma(\theta, \phi)$ is given by the outgoing current divided by the incident current density P_i/μ_i, that is,

$$
\begin{aligned}
\sigma(\theta, \phi) \atop {\scriptstyle (1+2)3 \to 1(2+3)} &= \lim_{R \to \infty} \frac{1}{2i\mu_f} \left(\chi_f^* \frac{\partial \chi_f}{\partial r_f} - \frac{\partial \chi_f^*}{\partial r_f} \chi_f \right)_{r_f = R} \frac{R^2}{P_i/\mu_i} \\
&= \frac{\mu_i P_f}{\mu_f P_i} |f(\theta, \phi)|^2 \\
&= \frac{\mu_i \mu_f}{(2\pi)^2} \frac{P_f}{P_i} \\
&\quad \times \left| \int \phi_{23}^*(\mathbf{r}_{23}) e^{i(\mathbf{q}_3 \cdot \mathbf{r}_{23} - \mathbf{q}_1 \cdot \mathbf{r}_{12})} [V_{12} + V_{13}] \phi_{12}(\mathbf{r}_{12}) \, d^3 r_{12} \, d^3 r_{23} \right|^2
\end{aligned}
$$

(19a)

Equations (18) and (19a) can be simplified further by neglecting the interaction V_{13} between particles 1 and 3. This is done because in the reaction $(1 + 2) + 3 \to 1 + (2 + 3)$ particles 1 and 3 never appear in a bound state. In the stripping reaction $X^A(d, p)X^{A+1}$, $V_{13} = V_{p,A}$, and in the pick-up reaction $X^A(p, d)X^{A-1}$, $V_{13} = V_{p,A-1}$. The interaction V_{12} equals V_{np} for both the stripping reaction (d, p) and the pick-up reaction (p, d) if the latter is considered as a process inverse to that of the former. In Eq. (19a), the V_{12} term contributes a nonvanishing result provided the final state contains components of the core, the target nucleus, left in its ground state. On the other hand, the contribution arising from the interaction $V_{13} (= V_{pA})$ will be nonvanishing if the final state corresponds to excitation of the core. Generally, in a stripping reaction the contribution of the V_{13} interaction is much less than that of V_{12} unless the final state involves almost purely the excitation of the core. Hence in the following we shall drop V_{13}. In this approximation the cross section is given by

$$
\sigma(\theta, \phi) \simeq \frac{\mu_i \mu_f}{(2\pi)^2} \frac{P_f}{P_i} \left| \int \phi_{23}^* e^{i\mathbf{q}_3 \cdot \mathbf{r}_{23}} \, d^3 r_{23} \int e^{-i\mathbf{q}_i \cdot \mathbf{r}_{12}} V_{12}(\mathbf{r}_{12}) \phi_{12}(\mathbf{r}_{12}) \, d^3 r_{12} \right|^2
$$

(19b)

Equation (12a) is satisfied by the bound-state wave function $\phi_{12}(\mathbf{r}_{12})$. It can be written as

$$
\left[-\frac{\nabla_{12}^2}{2\mu_{12}} + V_{12}(\mathbf{r}_{12}) + \epsilon_{12} \right] \phi_{12}(\mathbf{r}_{12}) = 0
$$

(20a)

Also

$$\left(-\frac{\nabla_{12}^2}{2\mu_{12}} - \frac{q_1^2}{2\mu_{12}}\right)e^{-i\mathbf{q}_1\cdot\mathbf{r}_{12}} = 0 \tag{20b}$$

Multiplying Eq. (20a) on the left by $e^{-i\mathbf{q}_1\cdot\mathbf{r}_{12}}$ and Eq. (20b) on the left by $\phi_{12}(\mathbf{r}_{12})$, and then subtracting and integrating over $\mathbf{r}_{12}$, we obtain

$$\int e^{-i\mathbf{q}_1\cdot\mathbf{r}_{12}}\left[V_{12}(\mathbf{r}_{12}) + \epsilon_{12} + \frac{q_1^2}{2\mu_{12}}\right]\phi_{12}(\mathbf{r}_{12})\,d^3r_{12}$$

$$= \frac{1}{2\mu_{12}}\int [e^{-i\mathbf{q}_1\cdot\mathbf{r}_{12}}\nabla_{12}^2\phi_{12}(\mathbf{r}_{12}) - \phi_{12}(\mathbf{r}_{12})\nabla_{12}^2 e^{-i\mathbf{q}_1\cdot\mathbf{r}_{12}}]\,d^3r_{12} = 0 \tag{21a}$$

where we have used the property that surface contributions vanish. Therefore

$$\int e^{-i\mathbf{q}_1\cdot\mathbf{r}_{12}}V_{12}(\mathbf{r}_{12})\phi_{12}(\mathbf{r}_{12})\,d^3r_{12} = -\left(\epsilon_{12} + \frac{q_1^2}{2\mu_{12}}\right)\int e^{-i\mathbf{q}_1\cdot\mathbf{r}_{12}}\phi_{12}(\mathbf{r}_{12})\,d^3r_{12} \tag{21b}$$

From Eqs. (21b), (18), and (19b) we obtain (after neglecting the interaction V_{13})

$$f(\theta, \phi) \simeq \frac{\mu_f}{2\pi}\left(\epsilon_{12} + \frac{q_1^2}{2\mu_{12}}\right)\mathscr{G}_1(\mathbf{q}_1)\mathscr{G}_3(\mathbf{q}_3) \tag{22a}$$

Thus

$$\sigma(\theta, \phi) \simeq \frac{\mu_i\mu_f}{(2\pi)^2}\frac{P_f}{P_i}\left(\epsilon_{12} + \frac{q_1^2}{2\mu_{12}}\right)^2 |\mathscr{G}_1(\mathbf{q}_1)\mathscr{G}_3(\mathbf{q}_3)|^2, \tag{22b}$$

where

$$\mathscr{G}_1(\mathbf{q}_1) = \int e^{-i\mathbf{q}_1\cdot\mathbf{r}_{12}}\phi_{12}(\mathbf{r}_{12})\,d^3r_{12} \tag{23a}$$

$$\mathscr{G}_3(\mathbf{q}_3) = \int \phi_{23}^*(\mathbf{r}_{23})e^{i\mathbf{q}_3\cdot\mathbf{r}_{23}}\,d^3r_{23} \tag{23b}$$

If the bound nuclei $(1 + 2)$ and $(2 + 3)$ are in definite orbital-angular momentum states (l_{12}, m_{12}) and (l_{23}, m_{23}) respectively, we can write

$$\phi_{12}(\mathbf{r}_{12}) = \phi_{12}(r_{12})Y_{l_{12}m_{12}}(\hat{r}_{12}) \tag{24a}$$

$$\phi_{23}(\mathbf{r}_{23}) = \phi_{23}(r_{23})Y_{l_{23}m_{23}}(\hat{r}_{23}) \tag{24b}$$

where $Y_{lm}(\hat{r})$ are the usual spherical harmonics, $\hat{r} = (\theta, \phi)$ is the unit vector specifying the direction, and $\phi(r)$ are the radial wave functions. In both Eqs. (24a) and (24b), the spins of the bound states are ignored. Using the formula for the expansion of a plane wave in terms of spherical harmonics

$$e^{i\mathbf{k}\cdot\mathbf{r}} = 4\pi \sum_{l=0}^{\infty} \sum_{m=-l}^{l} i^l j_l(kr)Y_{lm}(\hat{r})Y_{lm}^*(\hat{k}) \tag{25a}$$

we have

$$\int e^{i\mathbf{k}\cdot\mathbf{r}} Y^*_{lm}(\hat{r})\, d\hat{r} = 4\pi i^l j_l(kr) Y^*_{lm}(\hat{k}) \tag{25b}$$

Therefore from Eqs. (23a), (23b) and (24a), (24b) we obtain

$$\mathscr{G}_1(\mathbf{q}_1) = 4\pi(-i)^{l_{12}} Y_{l_{12}m_{12}}(\hat{q}_1) \int r_{12}^2 \phi_{12}(r_{12}) j_{l_{12}}(q_1 r_{12})\, dr_{12} \tag{26a}$$

$$\mathscr{G}_3(\mathbf{q}_3) = 4\pi(i)^{l_{23}} Y^*_{l_{23}m_{23}}(\hat{q}_3) \int r_{23}^2 \phi^*_{23}(r_{23}) j_{l_{23}}(q_3 r_{23})\, dr_{23} \tag{26b}$$

Substituting Eqs. (26a) and (26b) in Eqs. (22a) and (22b) and using the usual procedure of evaluating the cross section by averaging over the initial magnetic quantum number m_{12} and summing over the final magnetic quantum number m_{23}, we obtain

$$\underset{(1+2)3\to1(2+3)}{f(\theta,\phi)} = 8\pi(i)^{l_{23}-l_{12}}\mu_f\left(\epsilon_{12} + \frac{q_1^2}{2\mu_{12}}\right) Y_{l_{12}m_{12}}(\hat{q}_1) Y^*_{l_{23}m_{23}}(\hat{q}_3) R_1(q_1) R_3(q_3) \tag{27a}$$

and

$$\begin{aligned}
\underset{(1+2)3\to1(2+3)}{\sigma(\theta,\phi)} &= 4(4\pi)^2 \mu_i \mu_f \frac{P_f}{P_i}\left(\epsilon_{12} + \frac{q_1^2}{2\mu_{12}}\right)^2 \frac{1}{2l_{12}+1} \\
&\quad \times \sum_{m_{12}, m_{13}} |Y_{l_{12}m_{12}}(\hat{q}_1) Y^*_{l_{23}m_{23}}(\hat{q}_3)|^2\, R_1^2(q_1) R_3^2(q_3) \\
&= 4\mu_i\mu_f \frac{P_f}{P_i}\left(\epsilon_{12} + \frac{q_1^2}{2\mu_{12}}\right)^2 (2l_{23}+1) R_1^2(q_1) R_3^2(q_3) \tag{27b}
\end{aligned}$$

where

$$R_1(q_1) = \int_0^\infty r_{12}^2 \phi_{12}(r_{12}) j_{l_{12}}(q_1 r_{12})\, dr_{12} \tag{28a}$$

$$R_3(q_3) = \int_0^\infty r_{23}^2 \phi_{23}(r_{23}) j_{l_{23}}(q_3 r_{23})\, dr_{23} \tag{28b}$$

with

$$\mathbf{q}_1 = \mathbf{P}_f + \frac{m_1}{m_1 + m_2}\mathbf{P}_i \tag{29a}$$

$$\mathbf{q}_3 = -\frac{m_3}{m_2 + m_3}\mathbf{P}_f - \mathbf{P}_i \tag{29b}$$

In Eq. (27b) we have used the identity

$$\sum_{m=-l}^{l} |Y_{lm}|^2 = \frac{(2l+1)}{4\pi} \tag{29c}$$

The angular dependence of the differential cross section $\sigma(\theta, \phi)$ [Eq. (27b)] occurs in the momentum transfers $\mathbf{q}_1$ and $\mathbf{q}_3$ which, according to Eqs. (29a) and (29b), depend on the angle θ between the vectors $\mathbf{P}_i$ and $\mathbf{P}_f$ and not on the azimuthal angle of $\mathbf{P}_f$ and $\mathbf{P}_i$.

In the (d, p) reaction, the notation of Eq. (1) and Fig. 11-1 have the interpretation $1 = p$, $2 = n$, $3 = X^A$, and the experimentally observed quantities are the momentum $-\mathbf{P}_i$ of the lighter incident particle $d \equiv (2 + 3)$ and the momentum $\mathbf{P}_f$ of the lighter outgoing particle. When the proton is emitted in the forward direction, that is, in the direction of the incident deuteron, the values of the two momentum transfers $\mathbf{q}_1$ and $\mathbf{q}_3$ are at a minimum. The maximum values occur when the proton is emitted in the backward direction. The integrals $R_1(q_1)$ and $R_3(q_3)$ are the Fourier transforms and $R_1^2(q_1)$ indicates the probability that the internal momentum of particle 1 will have the value q_1 when it is in a bound state with particle 2. The Fourier transform could be calculated from Eqs. (28) if the nuclear wave functions ϕ_{12} and ϕ_{23} were known. Since they are not, we assume certain forms for the wave functions with appropriate angular momentum from which we can deduce the nuclear size.

11.4   Reverse Reaction

The reaction amplitude for the reaction $1 + (2 + 3) \rightarrow (1 + 2) + 3$ can readily be shown to be

$$
\underset{1(2+3) \rightarrow (1+2)3}{f(\theta, \phi)} \simeq -\frac{\mu_i}{2\pi} \int d^3 r_{23} e^{-i\mathbf{q}_3 \cdot \mathbf{r}_{23}} V_{23}(\mathbf{r}_{23}) \phi_{23}(\mathbf{r}_{23}) \int d^3 r_{12} e^{i\mathbf{q}_1 \cdot \mathbf{r}_{12}} \phi_{12}^*(\mathbf{r}_{12})
$$

$$
= \frac{\mu_i}{2\pi} \left(\epsilon_{23} + \frac{q_3^2}{2\mu_{23}} \right) \mathscr{G}_3^*(\mathbf{q}_3) \mathscr{G}_1^*(\mathbf{q}_1) \tag{30a}
$$

where we note that

$$
\epsilon_{23} + \frac{q_3^2}{2\mu_{23}} = \epsilon_{12} + \frac{q_1^2}{2\mu_{12}} \tag{30b}
$$

so that

$$
\underset{1(2+3) \rightarrow (1+2)3}{f(\theta, \phi)} = \frac{\mu_i}{\mu_f} \underset{(1+2)3 \rightarrow 1(2+3)}{f^*(\theta, \phi)} \tag{31a}
$$

Hence, or using the principle of detailed balancing, we find

$$
\sigma_{1(2+3) \rightarrow (1+2)3} = \frac{P_f^2}{P_i^2} \sigma_{(1+2)3 \rightarrow 1(2+3)} \tag{31b}
$$

We note that if the process $1(2 + 3) \rightarrow (1 + 2)3$ describes a stripping reaction, then $(1 + 2)3 \rightarrow 1(2 + 3)$ describes a pick-up reaction. It is necessary to consider only one of these. The reverse or pick-up reactions such as (p, d) and (p, t) are similar to the stripping processes such as (d, p) and (t, p), and their mathematical treatments are alike. We expect, and in fact obtain, similar angular distributions of disintegration products.

We shall first consider some examples of the reverse reaction. Legg[6] studied the (p, d) reaction in elements B^{11}, C^{14}, O^{16}, and O^{18} with proton

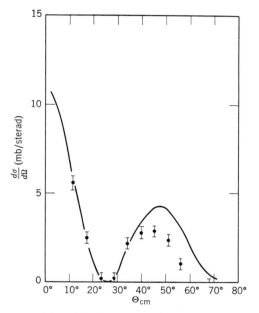

Fig. 11-2 Angular distribution of tritons from $C^{14}(p, t)C^{12}$ ground state. The solid line is a $Cj_0^2(qr_0)$ curve with C chosen to give fit on the side of the first maximum; $l = 0$, $r_0 = 5.1$ F. Proton energy was 18.5 Mev (Legg[6]).

energies between 17.6 Mev and 20 Mev and also (p, t) reactions in C^{14} and O^{18} over the same energy range. Some of the results are shown in Figs. 11-2 and 11-3.

For the reaction $O^{16}(p, d)O^{15}$ (Fig. 11-3) a comparison has been made with Butler's plane-wave theory. The position of the maximum is well reproduced by the theory. On the other hand, at higher angles, the theoretical curve falls much faster than do the experimental points. It appears that Butler's theory as given in Eq. (27b) is able to explain, at least in a

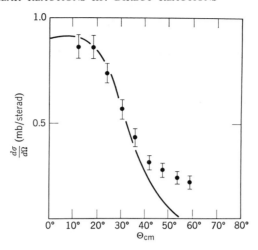

Fig. 11-3 Angular distribution of deuterons from $O^{16}(p, d)O^{15}$ ground state. The solid line is a plane-wave Butler curve with $l = 1, r_0 = 5.2$ F. Proton energy was 18.5 Mev (Legg[6]).

semiqualitative way, the observed angular distribution. The same conclusion can be drawn for the reaction $C^{14}(p, t)C^{12}$ shown in Fig. 11-2.

11.5 Stripping Reaction

In the stripping reaction, the incident nucleus is $(1 + 2)$, which is light compared to the target nucleus 3. To calculate the cross section for the process, it is essential to estimate the integrals $R_1(q_1)$ and $R_3(q_3)$ [Eqs. (28a) and (28b)]. The evaluation of $R_1(q_1)$ depends upon the wave function ϕ_{12} of the incident particle $(1 + 2)$ and its orbital angular momentum l_{12}. If the incident particle is a deuteron, $\phi_{12}(r_{12})$ will be an appropriate deuteron wave function, and $R_1(q_1)$ can be calculated. To evaluate $R_3(q_3)$, use is usually made of the specific approximations of the direct interaction model, that is, that the interaction between the incident particle and target nucleus 3 takes place in the outer region of nucleus 3 and not through the formation of the compound nucleus; if the compound nucleus was formed, the incident particle $(1 + 2)$ would be absorbed into the inner regions of heavy nucleus 3. If the direct interactions are assumed to occur only for values of $r_{23} > R_0$, then the limits of integration in Eq. (28b) should extend from R_0 to ∞. The Schrödinger equation for $\phi_{23}(r_{23})$ involves the interaction potential V_{23}. However, if the range of the potential V_{23}

is less than R_0, we have

$$\left[\frac{d^2}{dr^2} - \frac{l(l+1)}{r^2} - 2\mu\epsilon\right](r\phi_l(r)) = 0 \qquad \text{for} \quad r > R_0 \qquad (32a)$$

where the subscripts 23 have been dropped. The equation satisfied by $j_l(q_3 r)$ is

$$\left[\frac{d^2}{dr^2} - \frac{l(l+1)}{r^2} + q_3^2\right](rj_l(q_3 r)) = 0 \qquad (32b)$$

From Eqs. (32a) and (32b), we can readily show that

$$R_3(q_3) = \int_{R_0}^{\infty} r^2 \phi_l(r) j_l(q_3 r) \, dr$$

$$= \left[2\mu\left(\epsilon + \frac{q_3^2}{2\mu}\right)\right]^{-1} R_0^2 \left[\phi_l(R_0)\left\{\frac{d}{dr} j_l(q_3 r)\right\}_{r=R_0}\right.$$

$$\left. - \left\{\frac{d}{dr}\phi_l(r)\right\}_{r=R_0} j_l(q_3 R_0)\right] \qquad (33a)$$

which may be further simplified by using the recursion relation

$$r\frac{d}{dr}j_l(qr) = qrj_{l-1}(qr) - (l+1)j_l(qr) \qquad (33b)$$

The result, Eq. (33a), can be made more explicit by approximating $\frac{d}{dr}[\ln \phi_l(r)]$ in the second term on the right-hand side by the logarithmic derivative of the Hankel function of the first kind $h_l^{(1)}(i\sqrt{2\mu\epsilon}\, r)$ which satisfies Eq. (32a) and has the bound-state boundary condition, namely, that it vanishes at infinity. Thus

$$R_3(q_3) = (2\mu_{23}\epsilon_{23} + q_3^2)^{-1} R_0^2 \phi_{23}(R_0)$$

$$\times \left[\frac{d}{dr}j_l(q_3 r) - \frac{j_l(q_3 r)}{h_l^{(1)}(i\sqrt{2\mu_{23}\epsilon_{23}}\, r)} \frac{d}{dr} h_l^{(1)}(i\sqrt{2\mu_{23}\epsilon_{23}}\, r)\right]_{r=R_0} \qquad (33c)$$

The cross section $\sigma(\theta, \phi)$ is given by Eq. (27b) after substituting Eq. (33c) for $R_3(q_3)$.

$$\sigma(\theta, \phi) = \frac{\mu_i \mu_f}{\mu_{23}^2} \frac{P_f}{P_i} (2l_{23} + 1) \left(\frac{\epsilon_{12} + q_1^2/2\mu_{12}}{\epsilon_{23} + q_3^2/2\mu_{23}}\right)^2 \left| R_0^2 \phi_{23}(R_0) \right.$$

$$\times \left[\frac{d}{dr}j_l(q_3 r) - \frac{j_l(q_3 r)}{h_l^{(1)}(i\sqrt{2\mu_{23}\epsilon_{23}}\, r)} \frac{d}{dr} h_l^{(1)}(i\sqrt{2\mu_{23}\epsilon_{23}}\, r)\right]_{r=R_0}\Bigg|^2$$

$$\times \int_0^{\infty} r_{12}^2 \phi_{12}(r_{12}) j_{l_{12}}(q_1 r_{12}) \, dr_{12} \qquad (34)$$

where $\phi_{12}(r_{12})$, l_{12}, ϵ_{12}, μ_{12}, and r_{12} are the wave-function, orbital angular momentum, binding energy, reduced mass, and relative coordinate, respectively, of the initially bound nucleus $(1 + 2)$, and the same quantities with subscript 2 3 for the finally bound nucleus $(2 + 3)$.

The nuclear wave function $\phi_{23}(R_0)$, which describes the formation of the nucleus with 2 and 3 as its components, can be estimated from a knowledge of the potential. The radius R_0 is not the nuclear radius but extends somewhat beyond the nuclear surface to take into account the tail of the Fermi density distribution. It can be used as the limit up to which the nuclear potential extends. The expression within the bracket of Eqs. (33c) and (34), which is the logarithmic derivative of the wave function expressed in terms of the logarithmic derivative of the Hankel function, gives the angular distribution of the disintegration products. It has the properties of damped oscillations, passing through several maxima of diminishing amplitude corresponding to different values of the angular momentum l.

Inclusion of Spin

In this section we treat the effect of introducing spins of the three particles in the reaction $(1 + 2) + 3 \rightarrow 1 + (2 + 3)$. We denote the spin-wave functions of particles 1, 2, and 3 by $|j_1m_1\rangle$, $|j_2m_2\rangle$, and $|j_3m_3\rangle$. The orbital angular momenta of $(1 + 2)$ and $(2 + 3)$ are l_{12}, m_{12} and l_{23}, m_{23} respectively. According to the vector coupling scheme indicated in Fig. 11-4a,

$$|j_{12}\mu_{12}\rangle = \sum_{\substack{m_2,m_{12} \\ \mu_{12}=m_2+m_{12}}} \langle j_2l_{12}m_2m_{12} \,|\, j_{12}\mu_{12}\rangle |j_2m_2\rangle |l_{12}m_{12}\rangle \qquad (35a)$$

$$|J_{12}M_{12}\rangle = \sum_{\substack{\mu_{12},m_1 \\ M_{12}=\mu_{12}+m_1}} \langle j_{12}j_1\mu_{12}m_1 \,|\, J_{12}M_{12}\rangle |j_{12}\mu_{12}\rangle |j_1m_1\rangle \qquad (35b)$$

where $\langle j_2l_{12}m_2m_{12} \,|\, j_{12}\mu_{12}\rangle$ etc., are the Clebsch-Gordan coefficients and where

$$\sum_{\substack{m_2,m_{12} \\ \mu_{12}=m_2+m_{12}}}$$

means the sum over all allowable values of m_2, m_{12} such that $m_2 + m_{12} = \mu_{12}$. Combining Eqs. (35a) and (35b) we obtain the wave function for the nucleus $(1 + 2)$

$$|(j_2l_{12})j_{12}j_1J_{12}M_{12}\rangle$$
$$= \sum_{\substack{m_1,m_2,m_{12} \\ \mu_{12}=m_2+m_{12} \\ M_{12}=\mu_{12}+m_2}} \langle j_2l_{12}m_2m_{12} \,|\, j_{12}\mu_{12}\rangle\langle j_{12}j_1\mu_{12}m_1 \,|\, J_{12}M_{12}\rangle$$
$$\times |j_1m_1\rangle |j_2m_2\rangle Y_{l_{12}}^{m_{12}}\phi_{12}(r_{12})$$

$$(36a)$$

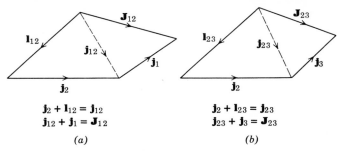

$$\mathbf{j}_2 + \mathbf{l}_{12} = \mathbf{j}_{12} \qquad\qquad \mathbf{j}_2 + \mathbf{l}_{23} = \mathbf{j}_{23}$$
$$\mathbf{j}_{12} + \mathbf{j}_1 = \mathbf{J}_{12} \qquad\qquad \mathbf{j}_{23} + \mathbf{j}_3 = \mathbf{J}_{23}$$

(a) $\qquad\qquad\qquad\qquad$ (b)

Fig. 11-4 Angular momentum coupling.

Similarly, using Fig. 11-4b, the wave function for the nucleus $(2 + 3)$ is

$$
\begin{aligned}
|(j_2 l_{23}) j_{23} j_3 J_{23} M_{23}\rangle
&= \sum_{m_2, m_3, m_{23}} \langle j_2 l_{23} m_2 m_{23} \,|\, j_{23}\mu_{23}\rangle\langle j_{23} j_3 \mu_{23} m_3 \,|\, J_{23} M_{23}\rangle \\
&\qquad\qquad \times |j_2 m_2\rangle\,|j_3 m_3\rangle Y^{m_{23}}_{l_{23}}\phi_{23}(r_{23}) \quad (36b)
\end{aligned}
$$

To obtain the wave function $\psi_{J_{12} M_{12}}(r_{12})$ for the nucleus $(1 + 2)$ formed as a compound of particles 1 and 2, instead of say $1'$ and $2'$ or $1''$ and $2''$ etc., which pairs also form the same final nucleus as that formed by 1 and 2, that is,

$$N_1 + N_2 + Z_1 + Z_2 = N_1' + N_2' + Z_1' + Z_2', \qquad \text{etc.},$$

we should multiply Eq. (36a) by the fractional parentage coefficient $\langle(j_2 l_{12}) j_{12} j_1 \,|\, J_{12}\rangle$ which determines the probability amplitude for the formation of the nucleus $(1 + 2)$ from particles 1 and 2. Thus the wave functions $\psi_{J_{12} M_{12}}(r_{12})$ and $\psi_{J_{23} M_{23}}(r_{23})$ for the nucleus $(1 + 2)$ and nucleus $(2 + 3)$ are given by

$$\phi_{J_{12} M_{12}}(r_{12}) \sim \langle(j_2 l_{12}) j_{12} j_1 \,|\, J_{12}\rangle\,|(j_2 l_{12}) j_{12} j_1 J_{12} M_{12}\rangle \qquad (37a)$$

$$\phi_{J_{23} M_{23}}(r_{23}) \sim \langle(j_2 l_{23}) j_{23} j_3 \,|\, J_{23}\rangle\,|(j_2 l_{23}) j_{23} j_3 J_{23} M_{23}\rangle \qquad (37b)$$

If we now take the spins of the nuclei into account, then, by using Eqs. (36) to (37), the expression for the reaction amplitude $f(\theta, \phi)$ [Eq. (27a)] becomes

$$
\begin{aligned}
\underset{(1+2)3\to1(2+3)}{f(\theta, \phi)} &= 8\pi(i)^{l_{23}-l_{12}}\mu_f\left(\epsilon_{12} + \frac{q_1^2}{2\mu_{12}^2}\right)R_1(q_1)R_3(q_3) \\
\sum_{m_{12}m_{23}} Y_{l_{12}m_{12}}(\hat{q}_1)Y^*_{l_{23}m_{23}}(\hat{q}_3) &\,\langle(j_2 l_{12}) j_{12} j_1 \,|\, J_{12}\rangle\langle(j_2 l_{23}) j_{23} j_3 \,|\, J_{23}\rangle \\
&\langle j_2 l_{12} m_2 m_{12} \,|\, j_{12}\mu_{12}\rangle\langle j_{12} j_1 \mu_{12} m_1 \,|\, J_{12} M_{12}\rangle \\
&\langle j_2 l_{23} m_2 m_{23} \,|\, j_{23}\mu_{23}\rangle\langle j_{23} j_3 \mu_{23} m_3 \,|\, J_{23} M_{23}\rangle \quad (38)
\end{aligned}
$$

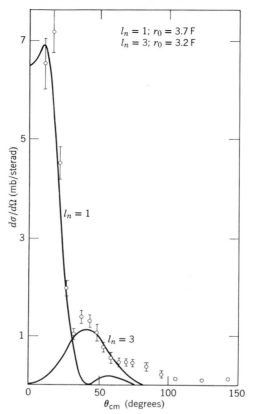

Fig. 11-5 Angular distribution of protons from the reaction $N^{14}(d, p)N^{15}$ (Erramuspe and Slobodrian[7]).

The best-known examples of direct interaction come from the analysis of the angular distributions of the (d, p) type of stripping reactions. The angular distributions observed in the stripping process are peaked quite sharply in the forward direction, which is in contrast with those in the compound-nuclear reactions where there are none in evidence. In addition, the compound nucleus predicts sharp resonances which are not characteristic of the direct-interaction process.

Erramuspe and Slobodrian[7] studied experimentally the angular distribution of the $N^{14}(d, p)N^{15}$ reaction with the incident energy of the deuteron $E_d = 27.0$ Mev. They analyzed their results by applying Butler's theory with undistorted plane-wave calculations. To obtain good fit with the experimental results they superimposed the theoretical curves of $l_n = 1$

and $l_n = 3$ for the captured neutrons (Fig. 11-5). The r_0 referred to in the figure are the interaction radii.

The (d, p) reaction can be considered as a single stripping reaction and the analysis of the angular distribution is not too difficult. However, in a double pick-up reaction such as (d, α) the data are more complex to analyze because one has to take into account the vector addition of the orbital angular momenta of the extra proton and neutron. Consequently, it may be necessary to consider many of its values in the analysis of the angular distribution data. Theoretical calculations of the double stripping process such as the (d, α) reaction have been done by using the plane-wave Born approximation.[8] The direct interaction process in (d, α) reactions has been studied by Micheletti and Mead[9] in a large number of elements. Figure 11-6 represents the results of Micheletti and Mead for

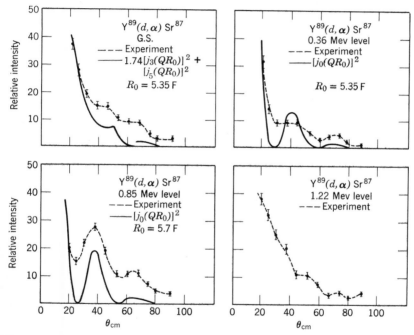

Fig. 11-6 Angular distributions of alpha particles from the formation of the first four levels of Sr^{87}. Dashed lines only connect the experimental points. The solid lines are the theoretical curves for ground-state, 0.36-Mev, and 0.85-Mev levels, as calculated from Glendenning.[8] For the transition to the ground state $j_n = \frac{8}{2}$ and $j_p = \frac{1}{2}$ have been used, the allowed l-values then being 3 and 5. The curve for the 0.36-Mev level is a tentative fit obtained using only an $l = 0$ spherical Bessel function. The curve which is compared with the angular distribution for the 0.85-Mev level is the spherical Bessel function for $l = 0$ (Micheletti and Mead[9]).

the reaction $Y^{89}(d, \alpha)Sr^{87}$ for the first four states of Sr^{87} together with the predictions of Glendenning's theory.[8] Glendenning has given an expression for the angular distribution of the (α, d) reaction in the plane-wave Born approximation. The angular distribution is of the form

$$\frac{d\sigma}{d\Omega} \propto \exp\left[-\frac{K^2}{8\gamma^2}\right] \sum_L \frac{1}{2L+1} C_L |B_L(Q)|^2 \quad \text{where} \quad \mathbf{K} = \mathbf{K}_d - \tfrac{1}{2}\mathbf{K}_\alpha$$

is the momentum transferred to the outgoing deuteron and

$$\mathbf{Q} = \mathbf{K}_\alpha - \frac{M_i}{M_f} \mathbf{K}_d$$

is the momentum carried into the nucleus by the stripped pair. The angular-momentum coupling coefficient C_L depends upon the coupling scheme. The term $B_L(Q) \propto \langle l_n l_p 00 | L0 \rangle j_L(QR_0)$ for a point α-particle. The r.m.s. radius of the α-particle charge density is represented by γ. It has been assumed that the α-particle is stripped of a neutron and proton at the nuclear surface rather than in the interior of the nucleus. In the latter case the outgoing deuteron would probably be absorbed by the nucleus. The selection rules on the angular momentum L which characterizes the angular distribution for two-nucleon stripping reactions are

$$\pi_i \pi_f = (-)^{l_n + l_p} \qquad \mathbf{L} = \mathbf{l}_n + \mathbf{l}_p, \qquad \mathbf{J}_f = \mathbf{J}_i + \mathbf{L} + \mathbf{S}, \qquad \mathbf{S} = \mathbf{s}_n + \mathbf{s}_p$$

In the analysis of Micheletti and Mead, it has been assumed that in the target nucleus the odd neutron occupies a state j'_n outside an even core with $\mathbf{J}_c = 0$ so that the initial spin is $\mathbf{J}_i = \mathbf{j}'_n$. In the residual nucleus the odd neutron and the stripped neutron couple to spin $\mathbf{J}$ which is coupled to the spin $\mathbf{j}_p$ of the stripped proton to give the final spin $\mathbf{J}_f$:

$$\mathbf{j}'_n + \mathbf{j}_n = \mathbf{J}, \qquad \mathbf{J} + \mathbf{j}_p = \mathbf{J}_f.$$

The agreement between the theory and the experimental results is approximate. Reactions of the type (t, p), (t, n), (He^3, p), (He^3, n), and (α, d) show evidence of double-stripping reactions. These start to be evident as the energy of the incident particle increases. This is seen from Fig. 11-7 compiled by Middleton[10] from the experimental results of various workers[11] at different energies for the reaction $Be^9(He^3, p)B^{11}$. It is evident from the figure that the angular distribution of protons shows strong energy dependence at the two lower energies; forward peaking, a characteristic of stripping reaction, is not observed. However, as the energy of the incident particle increases, we see that forward peaking is noticeable from 4.5 Mev and becomes increasingly pronounced as the energy increases. At lower energies, there is competition between the direct-reaction mechanism and the compound-nucleus reaction. The interference

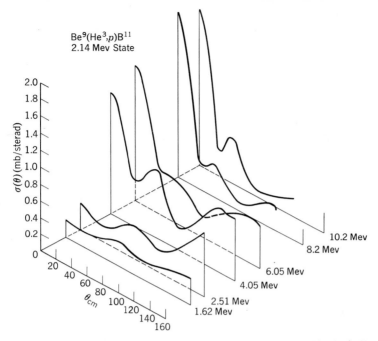

Fig. 11-7 Angular distributions of the protons from the Be⁹(He³, p)B¹¹ reaction corresponding to the first excited state. Data at 1.62 and 2.51 Mev from Almqvist et al.,[11] at 4.50 Mev from Holmgren et al.,[11] at 6.05 Mev from Sweetman,[11] and at 8.82 and 10.2 Mev, from Hinds and Middleton[11] (Middleton[10]).

between the two mechanisms makes the reaction strongly energy dependent. However, as the energy increases, the number of decay channels from the compound nucleus increases, and thereby the decay through any particular reaction channel decreases. Therefore, direct-reaction mechanism dominates, for its cross section is not so dependent upon the number of available channels. This begins to occur around 5 Mev. One clear example[10] of the double-stripping process is provided by the reaction $Mg^{26}(t, p)Mg^{28}$, shown in Fig. 11-8.

The experimental results of Middleton have been compared with an approximate expression for the double-stripping process given by Newns[8] which is

$$\sigma(\theta) \sim \sum_L |A(L)j_L(kR)|^2 \tag{39}$$

This expression has been derived by assuming that the two nucleons are captured in one unit, and is similar to the calculations done by Bhatia, Huang, Huby, and Newns[12] for deuteron stripping.

The selection rules for double-stripping reactions are:

$$S = 1 \qquad T = 0 \qquad \text{for} \quad (t, n), (He^3, p), \text{ and } (d, \alpha) \text{ reactions}$$
$$S = 0 \qquad T = 1 \qquad \text{for} \quad (t, p), (He^3, p), \text{ and } (He^3, n) \text{ reactions}$$
$$\Delta \pi = (-1)^L \qquad J_i = J_f + J$$

where T is the isotopic spin, L is the orbital angular momentum of the captured nucleons, and J_i and J_f are the initial and final nuclear spins. These selection rules are valid if the double-stripping process is considered as a transfer of two nucleons in one unit.

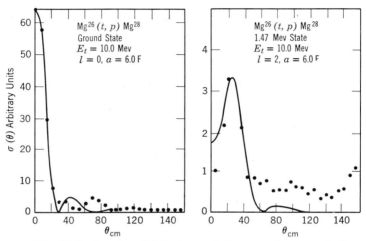

Fig. 11-8 Angular distributions of the ground-state and first-excited-state proton groups from the $Mg^{26}(t, p)Mg^{28}$ reaction measured at an energy of 10 Mev. The unbroken-line curves were calculated from an approximate expression for double stripping by Newns[8] (Middleton[10]).

The reactions (He^3, p) and (He^3, n) on light odd-mass nuclei can be used to distinguish the direct-reaction mechanism from the compound-nuclear process.[13]

Weil, Din, Kuan, and Almond[14] studied the reaction $Be^9(He^3, n)C^{11}$ with the energy of the incident He^3 varying from 1.5 to 5 Mev. If the reaction proceeds through the compound-nuclear formation, then the cross section of the processes $Be^9(He^3, n)C^{11}$ and $Be^9(He^3, p)B^{11}$ should be identical since the final nuclei C^{11} and B^{11} in the two reactions are mirror nuclei. This was found to be the case at low energies, but at higher energies the cross section differed. This is to be expected, if the reactions proceed through direct-reaction mechanism, since the reaction (He^3, p) is allowed only when $T = 1$. The inverse double pick-up reactions of the type (d, α) and (p, He^3) may give information concerning the neutron-proton forces and their correlations since the (d, α) reactions must have $S = 1$ and (p, He^3) involves $S = 0$ correlations.

From the examples cited above, it is evident that angular distribution data on double-stripping reactions can be well fitted by using the plane-wave Born approximation calculations.

One of the main distinguishing features of the stripping reactions, as mentioned earlier, is the forward peaking of the angular distribution of the disintegration product. However, it has been observed that in some cases the peaking may occur in the backward direction. This backward peaking has been explained in terms of the exchange effect in the stripping reaction. The mechanism of the reaction has been explained on the assumption that the incident stripped nucleon is captured by the final nucleus, whereas a similar nucleon is emitted through exchange interaction from the target nucleus. Consider the reaction $O^{16}(d, p)O^{17}$ in which the proton from the stripped deuteron can be captured by the final nucleus O^{17} while a proton from the target nucleus can be emitted through the exchange process. Owen and Madansky[15] [see Fig. 11-9 for $B^{11}(d, n)C^{12}$ reaction] were the first to interpret the exchange effect in the direct-interaction process.

Detailed calculations on the relative phases and magnitudes of the direct and exchange amplitudes have been performed[15,16] by Owen and Madansky.[15] Figure 11-9 shows that the exchange-stripping amplitude corresponds to the heavy particle stripping. The backward peaking can be understood even in terms of the plane-wave Born approximation (PWBA) method. This technique has been successful in the analysis of a large number of stripping and pick-up reactions. The mechanism can be used in analyzing[17] the pick-up reaction $F^{19}(p, \alpha)O^{16}$. In the pick-up process F^{19} can be thought of as an O^{16} cluster plus a triton cluster. The incident proton picks up the triton to form the α-particle. The forward peaking results from the fact that the incident proton will have the smallest momentum change if it comes out in the forward direction as a constituent of the α-particle. In the exchange pick-up mode, on the other hand, F^{19} can be considered as an N^{15} cluster plus an α-cluster. The incident proton picks up an N^{15} cluster to form the ejected O^{16} nucleus as a heavy particle pick-up. Once again the proton will have its minimum momentum change if it emerges in the forward direction as a part of O^{16}, and then the α-particle will demonstrate backward peaking. In this latter case the total wave function of the system must be antisymmetric under exchange of the impinging proton with the protons in the outer shell of F^{19}.

The relative proportion of the two processes will depend upon the relative probabilities of F^{19} in the respective clusters and whether F^{19}

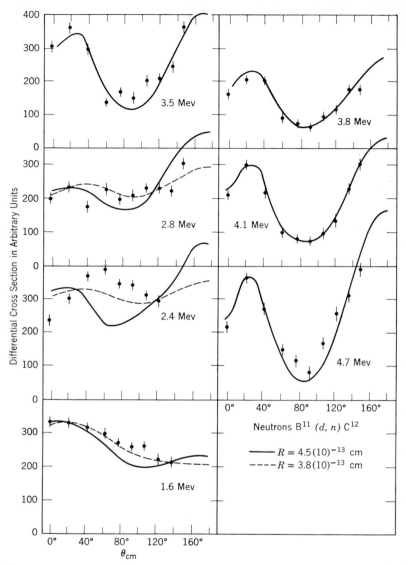

Fig. 11-9 Angular distributions of the ground-state neutrons from the reaction $B^{11}(d, n)C^{12}$ for bombarding energies from 1.6 to 4.7 Mev. The curves are derived from nuclear-stripping theory. The solid curve corresponds to an interaction radius of $R = 4.5 \times 10^{-13}$ cm. The dashed curve is for $R = 3.8 \times 10^{-13}$ cm (Owen and Madansky[15]).

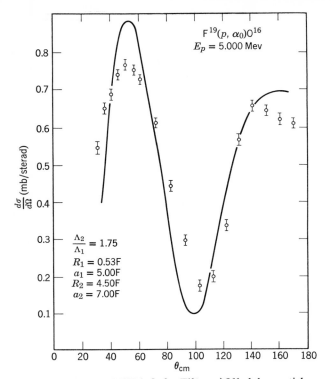

Fig. 11-10 PWBA fit for $F^{19}(p, \alpha_0)O^{16}$ alpha-particle angular distribution for incident proton energy $E_p = 5$ Mev (Warsh et al.[18]).

can be represented by the cluster model. Figures 11-10 and 11-11 give the angular distributions of the reaction $F^{19}(p, \alpha_0)O^{16}$ at $E_p = 5.0$ Mev and 8.0 Mev. The experimental results were fitted with the PWBA theory using square-well wave functions for the cluster and radial cutoffs for all four of the momentum transforms.

11.6 Distorted-Wave Method

The plane-wave approximation discussed in preceding Section 11.5 ignores two interactions: (1) the long-range repulsive Coulomb force, and (2) the short-range nuclear interaction. Both these interactions give rise to a distortion of the wave function, and in order to obtain detailed agreement between theory and the experimental results for stripping (and pick-up) reactions, it is essential to take these into account, especially if the energies of the incident particles are high enough to enable them to

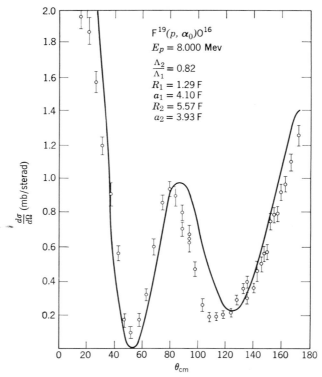

Fig. 11-11 PWBA fit for $F^{19}(p, \alpha_0)O^{16}$ angular distribution for $E_p = 8$ Mev (Warsh et al.[18]).

penetrate the Coulomb barrier ($E_c \sim ZZ'r_0^{-1}A^{-1/3}$) and approach within the region of the nuclear range. Assuming the interactions to be central, the radial equation satisfied by the wave function $\phi_{ijl}(k_{ij}r_{ij})$ for the relative motion of particles i and j in the orbital angular momentum state l is

$$\left[-\frac{d^2}{dr_{ij}^2} + \frac{l(l+1)}{r_{ij}^2} + \frac{2\mu_{ij}}{\hbar^2}\left(V_{ij}(r_{ij}) + \frac{Z_iZ_je^2}{r_{ij}} \right) - k_{ij}^2 \right] r_{ij}\phi_{ijl}(k_{ij}r_{ij}) = 0 \quad (40)$$

where μ_{ij} and k_{ij} are the reduced mass and the wave number and V_{ij} is the nuclear interaction potential. Equation (40) is solved by numerical integration. All the steps and integrations following Eq. (17b) are then carried out numerically. Practically all calculations based on the distorted-wave method of stripping employ the zero-range force approximation, that is,

$$V_{ij}(r_{ij})\phi_{ij}(r_{ij}) = -V_0r_0^{3/2}\,\delta(\mathbf{r}_{ij}) \quad (41)$$

Calculations using a finite-range force involve considerable numerical computation.

Butler's theory has been useful in explaining many experimental data in the energy region where the Coulomb effect can be neglected and where the distortion due to the optical potential is small. However, if the energy of the incident particle is such that the Coulomb effects cannot be neglected, then the solution is obtained by the method of distorted-wave Born approximation introduced by Tobocman[19] and Huby, Refai, and

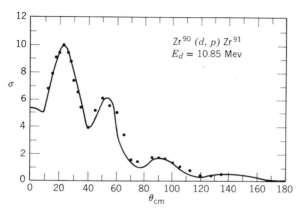

Fig. 11-12 Comparison of experimental and theoretical angular distributions for the $Zr^{90}(d, p)Zr^{91}$ ground-state reaction, $E_d = 10.85$ Mev, $l_n = 2$, and $Q = 5.02$ Mev (Smith and Ivash[21]).

Satchler.[20] Some recent calculations for the (d, p) reactions have been performed assuming potentials similar to the optical-model type, taking into account the Coulomb effects, and extending the radial integral up to the origin. The form of the Schrödinger equation used by Smith and Ivash[21] for the (d, p) reaction is

$$\psi''(r) - \frac{2\mu}{\hbar^2}\left[E + VF_R + iWF_I + V_C - \frac{\hbar^2 l(l + 1)}{2\mu r^2}\right]\psi(r) = 0 \quad (42)$$

where V and W are the real and imaginary potential-well depths, F_R and F_I are the optical-well form factors, and V_C is the Coulomb potential. Calculations have been performed with the computers using suitable optical-model parameters fitting a large number of angular distributions for (d, p) processes in different elements. The agreement between theoretical and experimental results is excellent as is indicated by Figs. 11-12 and 11-13. The optical parameters used for the fitting of data in Fig.

11-12 are: $R = 1.48$ F, $a = 0.70$ F, $V = 60$ Mev, and $W = 16$ Mev. The parameters used for Fig. 11-13 are: $R = 1.48$ F, $a = 0.75$ F, $V = 48$ Mev, and $W = 12$ Mev. The good agreement obtained indicates the validity of both the distorted-wave Born approximation and the optical model.

The direct-reaction theory in stripping processes can be put to a rigorous test if one measures the polarization of deuteron-stripping reactions. If the neutron stripped from the deuteron is captured in an S-state ($l_n = 0$),

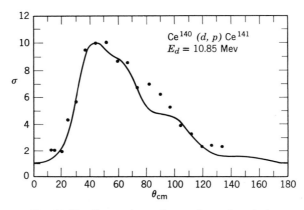

Fig. 11-13 Comparison of experimental and theoretical angular distributions for the $Ce^{140}(d, p)Ce^{141}$ ground-state reaction $E_d = 10.85$ Mev, $l_n = 3$, and $Q = 3.21$ Mev (Smith and Ivash[21]).

then the distorted wave Born approximation (DWBA) theory predicts zero polarization for the outgoing nucleon if no spin-dependent term is taken into account in the distorting optical potentials of the proton or the deuteron or both. Saladin and Reber[22] have measured the angular dependence of the proton polarization, using a 15 Mev deuteron beam, from the reactions $C^{12}(d, p)C^{*13}$ (3.09 Mev excited state), $Mg^{24}(d, p)Mg^{25}*$ (0.58-Mev excited state), and the ground state of the reactions $Be^9(d, p)Be^{10}$ and $Mg^{24}(d, p)Mg^{25}$. Figure 11-14 reproduces the results for the above reactions including reactions $Al^{27}(d, p)Al^{28}$ and $Si^{28}(d, p)Si^{29}$ investigated by Isoya and Marrone[23] for $l_n = 0$. The results of the first-excited-state reactions of C^{13} and Mg^{25} correspond to zero orbital angular momentum transfer. For $l_n = 0$, the DWBA calculation predicts zero polarization if there are no spin-orbit terms in the distorting optical potentials of the proton or the deuteron. The observed polarization in these experiments points out the necessity of including spin-orbit terms. The results of the

$Al^{27}(d, p)Al^{28}$ and $Si^{28}(d, p)Si^{29}$ reactions are similar to those of the previous two examples.

Robson[24] has calculated the S-wave capture for the reaction $Si^{28}(d, p)Si^{29}$ and compared it with the experimental results of Isoya, Micheletti, Marrone, and Reber.[25] For distorting potential, he assumed Woods-Saxon optical-model potentials

$$V(r) = V_C - (V + iW)g(r) + \left(\frac{\hbar}{m_\pi c}\right)^2 V_{S0} \frac{1}{r} \frac{dg}{dr} (\boldsymbol{\sigma} \cdot \mathbf{L}) \qquad (43a)$$

$$g(r) = \left\{1 + \exp \frac{(r - R)}{a}\right\}^{-1} \qquad (43b)$$

The optical-model parameters used for the deuteron were:

$$V_d = 55 \text{ Mev} \qquad W_d = 25 \text{ Mev} \qquad R_d = 4.5 \text{ F} \qquad (44a)$$
$$a_d = 0.6 \text{ F} \qquad V_{S0_d} = 8 \text{ Mev}$$

and for the proton

$$V_p = 45 \text{ Mev} \qquad W_p = 12 \text{ Mev} \qquad R_p = 3.9 \text{ F} \qquad (44b)$$
$$a_p = 0.6 \text{ F} \qquad V_{S0_p} = 8 \text{ Mev}$$

The numerical calculations for polarization $P(\theta)$ together with the experimental results are given in Fig. 11-15. Curve a gives the polarization allowing for spin-orbit distortion in both channels, deuteron and proton; curve b is for protons alone; and curve c is for spin-orbit distortion in the deuteron channel alone. Curves b and c are similar and approximately additive. The agreement with the experimental result is only qualitative.

11.7 Direct Processes (Inelastic Scattering or Surface Reaction)

In considering inelastic scattering of particles, the reaction can take place by the formation of the compound nucleus and/or by direct interaction. At sufficiently high energies of the incident particle, the final nucleus can be left in any of its excited states. For highly excited states of the final nucleus, the calculations of the cross section using the statistical theory based on the compound nucleus are in satisfactory agreement with experimental results. But for low excited states the experimental cross sections are much larger than those predicted by the statistical theory. The direct-interaction theory can, however, explain these larger cross sections.

In direct-interaction processes involving inelastic scattering, the incident particle (wave) suffers an inelastic collision with (some degree of freedom of) the target nucleus (interaction with one or more nucleons,

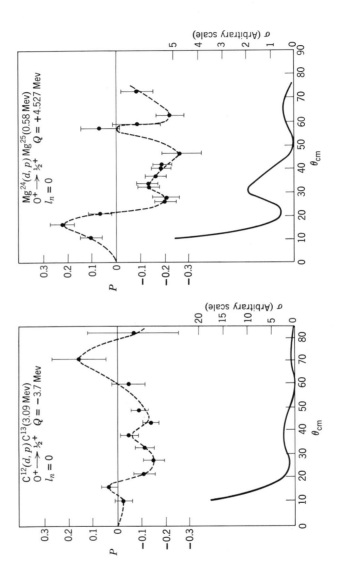

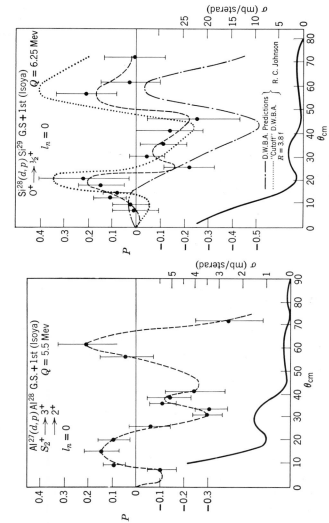

Fig. 11-14 Angular distributions of the polarization and the differential cross section for (d, p) reactions with $l_n = 0$, $E_d^{(lab)} = 15$ Mev. The dashed curves have no theoretical significance (Saladin and Reber[22]).

vibrational or rotational modes, etc., of the target nucleus) without the formation of a compound nucleus. The direct-interaction model for inelastic scattering is similar to the optical model for elastic scattering. In the optical-model calculation, the scattering amplitude is an averaged amplitude over several resonant compound-nucleus states. If the inelastic scattering occurs with the formation of resonant compound-nucleus

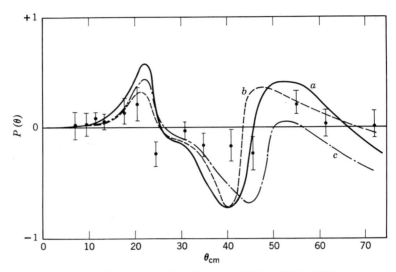

Fig. 11-15 Numerical calculations of $P(\theta)$ for $Si^{28}(d, p)Si^{29}*$ compared to the experimental points of Ref. (25). Curve a is the calculated polarization allowing for spin-orbit distortion in both initial and final channels. Curves b and c are the corresponding results but with $V_{so_d} = 0$ and $V_{so_p} = 0$ respectively (Robson[24]).

states, the statistical theory is applicable. On the other hand, the reaction is direct if there is no formation of the compound nucleus and the times of interaction are of the order of nuclear times (time the incident particle takes to travel the nuclear dimension) $\sim 10^{-22}$ sec instead of the times ($\sim 10^{-14}$ sec) involved in reactions occurring via compound-nucleus formation. Such short times are not measurable, but since the differential cross sections predicted by the two models are different, the experimental results can provide evidence of the applicability of one model or the other. For energies higher than 10 Mev, the direct-interaction model has been found to be in agreement with the experimental results.

As an example, we consider the inelastic scattering

$$(1 + 2) + 3 \rightarrow 1 + (2 + 3)$$

where the incident particle 3 (proton) interacts directly with particle 1 (neutron) in the outer shell of the initial nucleus $(1 + 2)$. In the center-of-mass system, we take $\mathbf{P}_i$ as the momentum of the incident particle 3 and $\mathbf{P}_f$ as the momentum of the outgoing particle 1. In the (p, n) reaction, assuming that the only interaction which is of importance is that between the incident particle 3 (proton) and the outgoing particle 1 (neutron), in Eq. (17b) the interaction V_{13} $(=V_{np})$ contributes much more than the interaction V_{12} $(=V_{nA})$. Thus in the approximation of direct interaction, the amplitude for inelastic scattering is given by

$$f(\theta, \varphi) \simeq - \frac{\mu_f}{2\pi} \int \phi_{23}^*(\mathbf{r}_{23}) e^{-i\mathbf{P}_f \cdot \mathbf{r}_f} V_{13} e^{i\mathbf{P}_i \cdot \mathbf{r}_i} \phi_{12}(\mathbf{r}_{12}) \, d^3 r_{23} \, d^3 r_f \qquad (45)$$

For the interaction V_{13}, we take the zero-range interaction

$$V_{13}(\mathbf{r}_{13}) = V_0 \, \delta(\mathbf{r}_{13}) \qquad (46a)$$

From Eqs. (45) and (46a), we obtain

$$f(\theta, \varphi) = - \frac{\mu_f}{2\pi} V_0 \int \phi_{23}^*(\mathbf{r}_{12}) \phi_{12}(\mathbf{r}_{12}) e^{i\mathbf{Q} \cdot \mathbf{r}_{12}} \, d^3 r_{12} \qquad (46b)$$

where

$$\mathbf{Q} = \frac{m_2}{m_1 + m_2} \mathbf{P}_i - \frac{m_2}{m_2 + m_3} \mathbf{P}_f$$

The spin-dependence of the scattering amplitude can be obtained as in Eqs. (36)–(38). Denoting the intrinsic spins of particles 1, 2, and 3 by $\mathbf{s}_1$, $\mathbf{s}_2$, and $\mathbf{s}_3$, and the angular momenta of the free particles 1 and 3, with respect to the core particle 2, by $\mathbf{l}_{12}$ and $\mathbf{l}_{23}$, we can couple the angular momenta as follows.

Initially:

$$\mathbf{l}_{23} + \mathbf{s}_3 = \mathbf{j}_{23} \qquad \mathbf{j}_{23} + \mathbf{s}_2 = \mathbf{J}_{23} \qquad (47a)$$

Finally:

$$\mathbf{l}_{12} + \mathbf{s}_1 = \mathbf{j}_{12} \qquad \mathbf{j}_{12} + \mathbf{s}_2 = \mathbf{J}_{12} \qquad (47b)$$

so that

$$\phi_{23}(\mathbf{r}_{12}) \sim \sum_{m_2, m_3, m_{23}, j_{23}} \langle l_{23} s_3 m_{23} m_3 | j_{23} m_3 + m_{23} \rangle \langle j_{23} s_2 m_3 + m_{23} m_2 | J_{23} M_{23} \rangle$$
$$\times \, Y_{l_{23} m_{23}}(\hat{r}_{12}) |s_3 m_3\rangle |s_2 m_2\rangle \phi_{23}(r_{12} l_{23}) \qquad (48a)$$

$$\phi_{12}(\mathbf{r}_{12}) \sim \sum_{m_1, m_2, m_{12}, j_{12}} \langle l_{12} s_1 m_{21} m_1 | j_{12} m_1 + m_{12} \rangle \langle j_{12} s_2 m_1 + m_{12} m_2 | J_{12} M_{12} \rangle$$
$$\times \, Y_{l_{12} m_{12}}(\hat{r}_{12}) |s_1 m_1\rangle |s_2 m_2\rangle \phi_{12}(r_{12} l_{12}) \qquad (48b)$$

with

$$M_{23} = m_2 + m_3 + m_{23} \qquad M_{12} = m_1 + m_2 + m_{12} \qquad (49a)$$

and the over-all conservation law for the z-component of angular momentum

$$m_1 + M_{23} = M_{12} + m_3 \qquad (49b)$$

We expand $\exp(i\mathbf{Q} \cdot \mathbf{r}_{12})$ into spherical harmonics,

$$e^{i\mathbf{Q}\cdot\mathbf{r}_{12}} = 4\pi \sum_{l,m} i^l j_l(Qr_{12}) Y_l^m(\hat{r}_{12}) Y_{lm}^*(\hat{Q}), \tag{50a}$$

and using the formula

$$\int Y_{l_1 m_1}(\Omega) Y_{l_2 m_2}(\Omega) Y_{l_3 m_3}^*(\Omega)\, d\Omega$$
$$= \left[\frac{(2l_1 + 1)(2l_2 + 1)}{4\pi(2l_3 + 1)}\right]^{1/2} \langle l_1 l_2 m_1 m_2 \mid l_3 m_3 \rangle \langle l_1 l_2 00 \mid l_3 0 \rangle, \tag{50b}$$

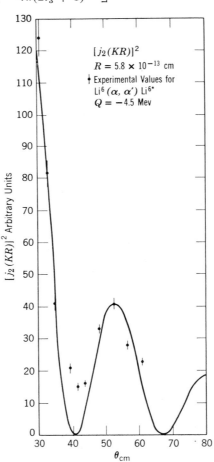

Fig. 11-16 Experimental data for the interaction Li^6(α, α')Li^{6*}, $Q = -4.5$ Mev compared with the theoretical angular distribution (Watters[26]).

after substituting Eqs. (48a)–(50b) in Eq. (46b), (taking the z-axis along $\hat{Q}$) we obtain

$$f(\theta, \phi) = -\frac{\mu_f}{2\pi} V_0 \sum \int dr_{12} r_{12}^2 \phi_{23}^*(r_{12}, l_{23}) \phi_{12}(r_{12}, l_{12}) j_l(Qr_{12})$$

$$\times C(s_2, M_{23}, M_{12}, m_3, l_{23}, l_{12}, j_{23}, j_{12}, l) \quad (51a)$$

where

$$C(s_2, M_{23}, M_{12}, m_3, l_{23}, l_{12}, j_{23}, j_{12}, l) = i^l \sqrt{\frac{(2l_{12} + 1)}{(2l_{23} + 1)}} (2l + 1)\, \delta(m_{12}, m_{23})$$

$$(-1)^l \langle l_{12} l m_{12} 0 \mid l_{23} m_{12} \rangle \langle l_{12} l 00 \mid l_{23} 0 \rangle$$

$$\langle l_{23} s_3 m_{23} m_3 \mid j_{23}\, m_3 + m_{23} \rangle \langle j_{23} s_2\, m_3 + m_{23}\, m_2 \mid J_{23} M_{23} \rangle$$

$$\langle l_{12} s_1 m_{12} m_1 \mid j_{12}\, m_1 + m_{12} \rangle \langle j_{12} s_2\, m_1 + m_{12}\, m_2 \mid J_{12} M_{12} \rangle \quad (51b)$$

The selection rules which follow from Eq. (51b) are

$$\mathbf{l}_{12} + \mathbf{l} = \mathbf{l}_{23} \quad (52)$$

The surface reactions or direct processes have been evident in a large number of measurements in the inelastic scattering processes. Consider the experiments of Watters,[26] in which the inelastically scattered 31.5 Mev alpha particles in Li^6, C^{12}, and Mg^{24} were studied. The observed angular distributions, reproduced in Figs. 11-16 and 11-17, could not be interpreted as results of compound nuclear interactions, for the angular distribution is mostly confined to the forward direction and is asymmetric in the center-of-mass system. Instead, the experimental results have been compared with the predictions of the direct surface-interaction theory of Austern, Butler, and McManus.[27] For the reaction $Li^6(\alpha, \alpha')Li^{6*}$, where the star indicates that the final nucleus Li is left in an excited state, the J values of the ground state, and the 4.5 Mev state are, respectively, 1^+ and 2^+. The theory predicts the angular distribution of the inelastically scattered alpha particles with respect to the direction of incident alpha particles to be given by the square of the spherical Bessel function $|j_L(kR)|^2$ where $R = r_0 A^{1/3}$ and $\hbar k$ is the momentum. For the $Mg^{24}(\alpha, \alpha')Mg^{24*}$ reaction, the theory predicts with success an angular distribution $|j_L(kR)|^2$ for the ground-state, spin $J = 0^+$, and also for the excited state corresponding to the level 1.37 Mev, $J = 2^+$.

The reaction $Li^6(\alpha, \alpha')Li^{6*}$ can be interpreted according to the shell model in the following way. The configuration of Li^6 is $1s_{1/2}^4\, 2s_{1/2}^2$. The ground-state spin of Li^6 is $J = 1$ and of even parity. The spin of the 4.5-Mev level of Li^6 is $J = 2$ and is also of even parity. Hence a $2s_{1/2}$ nucleon is raised to $1d_{5/2}$ giving an excitation of 4.5 Mev which can then de-excite by emitting a γ-ray of 4.5 Mev with $J = 2^+$.

For the reaction $Mg^{24}(\alpha, \alpha')Mg^{24*}$, the configuration of Mg^{24} is $|s_{1/2}^4|\,p_{3/2}^8$ $|p_{1/2}^4|d_{3/2}^8$. The ground state of Mg^{24} has spin $J = 0^+$ and the 1.37Mev excited level has $J = 2^+$. Therefore, we may say a $d_{5/2}$ nucleon when excited goes to $1g_{7/2}$ state which can then de-excite giving a γ-ray of 1.37 Mev with $J = 2^+$. Thus we see that the direct-interaction mechanism is consistent with the prediction of the shell model.

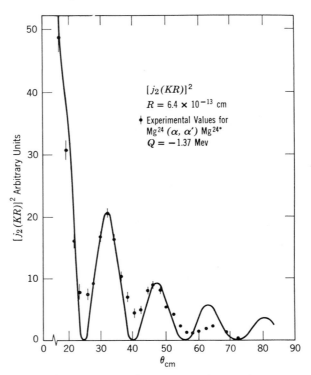

Fig. 11-17 Experimental data for the interaction $Mg^{24}(\alpha, \alpha')Mg^{24*}$, $Q = -1.37$ Mev compared with the theoretical angular distribution (Watters[26]).

Cohen and Rubin[28] were first to indicate that inelastic scattering processes preferentially excite collective states. Since then, a large number of experiments have been performed with (α, α'), (p, p'), (d, d'), and (e, e') type of reactions and the results have been analyzed quite often according to the direct-reaction mechanism. There are several theories available for comparison with experimental results. There are the diffraction theories[29] and the plane-wave theories.[30] Niewodniczanski, Nurzynski, and Wilczynski[31] have made interesting comparisons with these theories by studying the inelastic scattering of 2.8 Mev deuterons on Al^{27}. Their results are reproduced in Fig. 11-18.

In the shell-model calculation, the initial and final states correspond to definite values of l_{23}, s_2, j_{23} and l_{12}, s_2, j_{12}; the spin s_2 of the core nucleus remains unchanged. The scattering amplitude can be calculated using Eqs. (51a) and (51b), and hence the cross section from Eq. (19a). The angular distribution is contained in the Bessel function $j_l(Qr_{12})$, where

$$\mathbf{Q} = \frac{m_2}{m_1 + m_2} \mathbf{P}_i - \frac{m_3}{m_1 + m_3} \mathbf{P}_f,$$

and therefore involves the angle between the incident particle 3 and the outgoing particle 1. If the inelastic scattering occurs as a surface reaction, the range of integration over r_{12} extends from a value close to the surface radius R_0 to ∞. Since the bound-state wave functions ϕ_{23} and ϕ_{12} fall off sharply outside the nuclear surface, the main contribution of the integration is given by its value at $r_{12} = R_0$ and is therefore determined by the slowly varying Bessel function $j_l(QR_0)$. The cross section has the form

$$\sigma = |B_l j_l(QR_0)|^2 \tag{53}$$

where the values of l are $l_n + l_p \geq l \geq |l_n - l_p|$. The conservation of parity requires that only odd or even values can be taken in the above limit. For an allowed value of l, the spherical Bessel function gives a peak, as we found in the case of the stripping reaction. Austern, Butler, and McManus introduced the above formula to explain the angular distribution pattern of surface reactions of the types (α, α'), (p, p'), and others.

Another type of direct interaction possible is one in which the incident particle 3 interacts with a collective mode of the target nucleus $(1 + 2)$. Thus the scattering amplitude for the $(3, 3')$ reaction will be given by

$$f(\theta, \phi) \simeq \int \phi_f^*(\eta_{12}) V_{2\eta} \phi_i(\eta_{12}) e^{i(\mathbf{p}_i - \mathbf{p}_f') \cdot \mathbf{r}_3} \, d^3\eta_{12} \, d^3r_3 \tag{54}$$

where η_{12} describes the coordinate of collective motion (rotation or vibration) of nucleus $(1 + 2)$.

Direct-interaction analysis can be made with reactions such as $(p, 2p)$ and (p, dp). These reactions can also be used to obtain information regarding shell structure. Experiments[32] using protons of 340 Mev on carbon and lithium showed that the angular correlations and energy spectra of high-energy outgoing protons corresponded to a quasi-free scattering of the incident protons on protons of the target nucleus.

Further experiments of this nature by Tyren, Hillman, and Maris[33] demonstrated proton-energy peaks corresponding to the binding energies

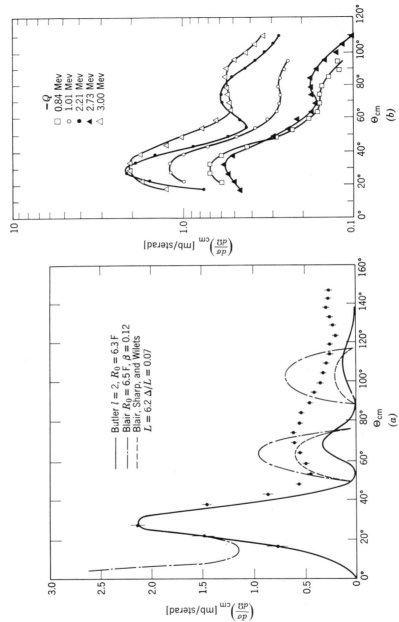

Fig. 11-18 Angular distributions for the inelastic scattering of 12.8-Mev deuterons on Al²⁷ nuclei. (*a*) Theoretical fits for excitation of the 2.21-Mev level. (*b*) Experimental results (Niewodniczanski et al.[31]).

of the protons in the outer and inner shells. When the protons were ejected from the inner shell, leaving a hole, the final nuclei were left in high-excitation energy states. These results gave information about the shell structure:

$$2^1S_{\frac{1}{2}}(Z-2)^1p_{\frac{3}{2}} \quad \text{for} \quad Z \leq 6$$

$$\text{and} \quad 2^1S_{\frac{1}{2}}4^1p_{\frac{3}{2}}, \quad 1 \quad \text{or} \quad 2^1p_{\frac{3}{2}} \quad \text{for} \quad Z = 7 \quad \text{or} \quad 8$$

Experiments to deduce momentum distributions of the protons in the various shells have also been performed[34] to gain knowledge on structure of light nuclei ($Z \leq 40$).

References

1. Feshbach, H., *Proc. Conf. Direct Interactions Nucl. Reaction Mech.*, 1962 p. 215, Gordon and Breach, Science Publishers Inc., New York, 1963.
2. Oppenheimer, J. R., and M. Phillips, *Phys. Rev.* **48**, 500, 1935.
3. Lawrence, E. O., E. McMillan, and R. L. Thornton, *Phys. Rev* **48**, 493, 1935.
4. Butler, S. T., *Phys. Rev.* **80**, 1095, 1950; *Nature*, **166**, 709, 1950; *Proc. Roy. Soc. (London)* **208A**, 559, 1951.
5. Hunting, C. E., and N. S. Wall, *Phys. Rev.* **108**, 901, 1957; Vogelsang, W. F., and J. N. McGruer, *Phys. Rev.* **109**, 1663, 1958; Reynolds, J. B., and J. G. Standing, *Phys. Rev.* **101**, 158, 1956; Holmgren, H. D., *Phys. Rev.* **106**, 100, 1957.
6. Legg, J. C., *Phys. Rev.* **129**, 272, 1963.
7. Erramuspe, H. J., and R. J. Slobodrian, *Nucl. Phys.* **34**, 532, 1962.
8. El-Nadi, M., *Phys. Rev.* **119**, 242, 1960; Newns, H. C., *Proc. Phys. Soc.* **76**, 489, 1960; Seth, K., *Nuclear Phys.* **25**, 169, 1961; Glendenning, N. K., *Nuclear Phys.* **29**, 109, 1962.
9. Micheletti, S., and J. B. Mead, *Nuclear Phys.* **37**, 201, 1962.
10. Middleton, R., *Proc. Conf. Direct Interactions Nucl. Reaction Mech.*, 1962, p. 435. Gordon and Breach, Science Publishers Inc., New York, 1963.
11. Almqvist, E., D. A. Bromley, H. E. Gove, A. E. Litherland, and E. B. Paul, *Bull. Am. Phys. Soc.* **1**, 195, 1956; Holmgren, H. D., W. E. Kunz, and L. Bullock, *Bull. Am. Phys. Soc.* **30**, 26, 1955; Sweetman, D. R., *Bull. Am. Phys. Soc.* **3**, 186, 1958; Hinds, S., and R. Middleton, *Proc. Phys. Soc. (London)* **75**, 754, 1960.
12. Bhatia, A. B., K. Huang, R. Huby, and H. C. Newns, *Phil. Mag.* [7] **43**, 485, 1952.
13. Clement, C. F., *Proc. Conf. Direct Interactions Nucl. Reaction Mech.*, 1962, p. 457. Gordon and Breach Science Publishers Inc. New York, 1963.
14. Weil, J. L., G. U. Din, H. M. Kuan, and P. R. Almond, *Bull. Am. Phys. Soc.* **11**, 759, 1962.
15. Owen, G. E., and L. Madansky, *Phys. Rev.* **105**, 1766, 1957; *ibid, Phys. Rev.* **99**, 1608, 1955.
16. French, A. P., *Phys. Rev.* **107**, 1655, 1957; M. A. Nagarajan and M. K. Banerjee, *Commun. Congr. Intern. Phys. Nucl., Paris*, 1959, p. 506.
17. Edwards, S., *Proc. Conf. Direct Interactions Nucl. Reaction Mech.* 1962, p. 469, Gordon and Breach Science Publishers Inc., New York, 1963.
18. Warsh, K. L., G. M. Temmer, and H. R. Blieden, Experimental Results quoted in Ref. 17.

19. Tobocman, W., *Phys. Rev.* **94**, 1655, 1954.
20. Huby, R., M. Y. Refai, and G. R. Satchler, *Nucl. Phys.* **9**, 94, 1958.
21. Smith, W. R., and E. V. Ivash, *Phys. Rev.* **128**, 1175, 1962; *ibid.*, *Phys. Rev.* **131**, 304, 1963.
22. Saladin, J. X., and L. H. Reber, *Proc. Conf. Direct Interactions Nucl. Reaction Mech.*, 1962, p. 625. Gordon and Breach Science Publishers Inc., New York, 1963.
23. Isoya, A., and M. T. Marrone, Quoted in Ref. 22.
24. Robson, D., *Proc. Conf. Direct Interactions Nucl. Reaction Mech.* 1962, p. 654. Gordon and Breach, Science Publishers Inc., New York, 1963.
25. Isoya, A., S. Micheletti, M. J. Marrone, and L. H. Reber, *Proc. Rutherford Jubilee Intern. Conf. Manchester*, 1961, p. 595, Heywood and Co., London, 1961.
26. Watters, H. J., *Phys. Rev.* **103**, 1763, 1956.
27. Austern, N., S. T. Butler, and H. McManus, *Phys. Rev.* **92**, 350, 1953.
28. Cohen, B. L., and A. G. Rubin, *Phys. Rev.* **111**, 1568, 1958.
29. Blair, J. S., *Phys. Rev.* **115**, 928, 1959; Blair, J. S., D. Sharp, and L. Wilets, *Phys. Rev.* **125**, 1625, 1962.
30. Sawicki, J., *Nucl. Phys.* **6**, 613, 1958.
31. Niewodniczanski, H., J. Nurzynski, and J. Wilczynski, *Proc. Conf. Direct Interactions Nucl. Reaction Mech*, 1962, p. 824. Gordon and Breach Science Publishers, Inc. New York, 1963.
32. Chamberlain, O., and E. Segre, *Phys. Rev.* **87**, 81, 1952; Wilcox, J. M., and B. J. Moyer, *Phys. Rev.* **99**, 875, 1955.
33. Tyren, H., P. Hillman, and Th. A. J. Maris, *Nucl. Phys.*, **7**, 1 and 10, 1958.
34. Gottschalk, B., and K. Strauch, *Phys. Rev.*, **120**, 1005, 1960; Gottschalk, B., Harvard University Thesis, 1962; Gooding, T. J., and H. G. Pugh, *Nucl. Phys.*, **18**, 46, 1960; Pugh, H. G., and K. F. Riley, *Proc. Rutherford Jubilee Intern, Conf.*, *Manchester*, 1961. Hillman, P., H. Tyren and Th. A. J. Maris, *Phys. Rev. Letters*, **5**, 107, 1960.

Problems

1. In the case of direct interaction, an incident particle with energy comparable to single-particle kinetic energies inside a nucleus may have a motion with respect to which the collective motion can be treated adiabatically. This is because in the case of some collective motions, the variable describing the excitations may vary slowly compared to changes in the projectile coordinates.

Give a quantitative analysis of the situation using adiabatic approximation. (See D. M. Chase, *Phys. Rev.* **104**, 833, 1956; for adiabatic approximation: L. Schiff, *Quantum Mechanics*, 2nd edition, McGraw-Hill Book Co., New York, 1955.)

2. Derive Eq. (18) from Eq. (17b).

3. Work out the details involved in the derivation of Eq. (16) from Eqs. (12b) and (15a).

4. Derive the "outgoing" Green's function

$$G(\mathbf{x}, \mathbf{x}') = \frac{-e^{ik|\mathbf{x}-\mathbf{x}'|}}{4\pi|\mathbf{x} - \mathbf{x}'|}$$

(See Mathews and Walker, *Mathematical Methods of Physics*, pp. 255–268, Benjamin, New York, 1964.)

5. It was first pointed out by Bethe and Butler (*Phys. Rev.* **85**, 1045, 1952) that one can verify and determine the shell-model single-particle-level spectrum through the study of stripping reactions. Using appropriate selection rules, illustrate this in the case of the reaction $B^{10}(d, p) B^{11}$ and compare with the actual experimental data. (See *Nuclear Spectroscopy* Part B, ed. F. Ajzenberg-Selove, Academic Press, New York, 1960, article by M. K. Banerjee.)

6. A typical reaction is $Ca^{44}(d, p) Ca^{45}$. Assuming the Q-value of the reaction to be 3.30 Mev and the energy of the incident deuteron to be 7.0 Mev, calculate the momentum transfer and cross section using expressions given in the text.

12

ELECTROMAGNETIC INTERACTIONS WITH NUCLEI

12.1 The Multipole Expansion

In this section we first show how to express an arbitrary electromagnetic field in terms of an infinite series of vector spherical harmonics multiplied by appropriate spherical Hankel functions. These are related to radiation quanta having definite angular momentum. Next it is shown that, for small sources, each component of the field is related to a definite multipole moment in the source; that is, the multipole field with quantum numbers (l, m) is caused by a specific oscillating 2^l-pole of charge (or of magnetization) density. These oscillating sources of definite l (the 2^l-poles) result from transitions within the nucleus in which the total angular momentum of the nucleus changes by $\pm l$ (or less with $J_i + J_f \geq l$), and the z-component changes by exactly $\pm m$; that is, the multipolarity l of the γ-transition between two states of specified angular momenta J_i and J_f of the nucleus, satisfies $|J_i - J_f| \leq l \leq J_i + J_f$.

The derivations are carried out in a hybrid notation which can be read either in the Gaussian cgs system or in the mks system, whichever the reader prefers. To read the formulas in the Gaussian system it is necessary only to set μ_0 and ϵ_0 equal to unity. If the mks units are preferred, we have only to omit the factors of $[4\pi]$ and $[c]$ which are in brackets. It should be kept in mind that in the mks system, $\sqrt{\mu\epsilon} = 1/v$, where v is the speed of light in a medium having permittivity ϵ and permeability μ. (In the vacuum this is $\sqrt{\mu_0\epsilon_0} = 1/c$.) In the Gaussian system, it follows that the corresponding equation is $\sqrt{\mu\epsilon} = c/v$.

We first consider the electromagnetic field in a uniform, isotropic, lossless medium (such as free space), that is, in a region free of sources

434

of radiation. Here, Maxwell's equations are

$$\nabla \cdot \mathbf{E} = 0 \tag{1a}$$

$$\nabla \cdot \mathbf{B} = 0 \tag{1b}$$

$$\nabla \times \mathbf{E} = -\left[\frac{1}{c}\right]\frac{\partial \mathbf{B}}{\partial t} \tag{1c}$$

$$\nabla \times \mathbf{B} = \frac{\mu\epsilon}{[c]}\frac{\partial \mathbf{E}}{\partial t} \tag{1d}$$

where the electric and magnetic fields, $\mathbf{E}(\mathbf{r}, t)$ and $\mathbf{B}(\mathbf{r}, t)$, are continuous vector functions of both position and time. Since we are dealing with radiation having definite energy, and since the frequency is proportional to energy in the quantized case, we may consider the frequency to have a definite value. Thus the time dependence is sinusoidal, and we may introduce the complex vector-amplitudes $\mathbf{E}(\mathbf{r})$ and $\mathbf{B}(\mathbf{r})$ as follows:

$$\begin{aligned}
\mathbf{E}(\mathbf{r}, t) &= \mathrm{Re}\,\{\mathbf{E}(\mathbf{r})e^{-i\omega t}\} \\
\mathbf{B}(\mathbf{r}, t) &= \mathrm{Re}\,\{\mathbf{B}(\mathbf{r})e^{-i\omega t}\}
\end{aligned} \tag{2}$$

where ω is the angular frequency related to the magnitude of the propagation vector $k = (2\pi)/\lambda$ by the relation $\omega = vk$, where $v = [c]/\sqrt{\mu\epsilon}$.

To solve for the fields, it is usual to eliminate one of them from Eq. (1) by substitution. Using Eq. (2) and then eliminating $\mathbf{B}$ between Eqs. (1c) and (1d) yields the following set of equations which are fully equivalent to Maxwell's equations.

$$(\nabla^2 + k^2)\mathbf{E} = 0 \tag{3a}$$

$$\nabla \cdot \mathbf{E} = 0 \tag{3b}$$

$$\mathbf{B} = -\frac{i\sqrt{\mu\epsilon}}{k}\nabla \times \mathbf{E} \tag{3c}$$

Alternatively, $\mathbf{E}$ can be eliminated, and Maxwell's equations then become

$$(\nabla^2 + k^2)\mathbf{B} = 0 \tag{4a}$$

$$\nabla \cdot \mathbf{B} = 0 \tag{4b}$$

$$\mathbf{E} = \frac{i}{\sqrt{\mu\epsilon}\,k}\nabla \times \mathbf{B} \tag{4c}$$

Clearly, any pair of vector fields $\mathbf{E}(\mathbf{r})$ and $\mathbf{B}(\mathbf{r})$ that satisfy the set of Eqs. (3) automatically satisfy the set of Eqs. (4) and vice versa. However, if to these sets of equations the transversality conditions

$$\mathbf{r} \cdot \mathbf{E} = 0 \tag{3d}$$

$$\mathbf{r} \cdot \mathbf{B} = 0 \tag{4d}$$

are added, then the solutions of the two sets are linearly independent. Any solution of Maxwell's equations can be expressed as a linear combination of two subfields, one a solution of the extended set of Eqs. (3) and the other of Eqs. (4). That is,

$$E(r) = E^E(r) + E^M(r)$$

$$B(r) = B^E(r) + B^M(r)$$

where E^E, B^E satisfy Eqs. (4) and E^M, B^M satisfy Eqs. (3). These are, respectively, the "transverse magnetic" (or "electric") and the "transverse electric" (or "magnetic") parts of the total field. As will be seen later, they are caused by oscillating electric and magnetic multipole distributions, respectively (hence the superscripts E and M). In view of Eq. (4d) we observe that an electric multipole field has nonvanishing radial components of the electric field but vanishing radial components of the magnetic field B. Similarly from Eq. (3d) we find that a magnetic multipole field has nonvanishing radial components of B but vanishing radial components of E.

Since each component of each of the vector fields E and B is a solution of the well-known scalar Helmholtz wave equation, the general solutions can be given in terms of spherical Hankel functions, $h_l^{(1,2)}(kr)$, multiplied by the spherical harmonics $Y_{lm}(\theta, \phi)$. Any electric and magnetic fields satisfying Eqs. (3a) and (4a) therefore have the following general form.

$$E^M(r) = \sum_{l=0}^{\infty} \sum_{m=-l}^{l} [e_{lm}^{(1)} h_l^{(1)}(kr) + e_{lm}^{(2)} h_l^{(2)}(kr)] Y_{lm}(\theta, \phi) \qquad (5a)$$

$$B^E(r) = \sum_{l=0}^{\infty} \sum_{m=-l}^{l} [b_{lm}^{(1)} h_l^{(1)}(kr) + b_{lm}^{(2)} h_l^{(2)}(kr)] Y_{lm}(\theta, \phi) \qquad (5b)$$

where

and

$$h_l^{(1)}(x) = j_l(x) + i n_l(x)$$

$$h_l^{(2)}(x) = j_l(x) - i n_l(x) \qquad (5c)$$

represent outgoing and incoming waves, respectively, and $e_{lm}^{(1,2)}$ and $b_{lm}^{(1,2)}$ are vectors to be determined by the boundary conditions.

We still have to impose the divergence restrictions, Eqs. (3b) and (4b), which give

$$\nabla \cdot E^M(r) = \sum_{l,m} \sum_{i=1}^{2} \nabla \cdot [e_{lm}^{(i)} h_l^{(i)}(kr) Y_{lm}(\theta, \phi)] = 0 \qquad (6a)$$

$$\nabla \cdot B^E(r) = \sum_{l,m} \sum_{i=1}^{2} \nabla \cdot [b_{lm}^{(i)} h_l^{(i)}(kr) Y_{lm}(\theta, \phi)] = 0 \qquad (6b)$$

The gradient operator, however, can be expressed in terms of orbital angular momentum operator

$$\mathbf{l} = \frac{1}{\hbar} (\mathbf{r} \times \mathbf{p}) = -i(\mathbf{r} \times \nabla)$$

as follows:

$$\nabla = \mathbf{r} \frac{1}{r} \frac{\partial}{\partial r} - \frac{i}{r^2} \mathbf{r} \times \mathbf{l} \tag{7}$$

(Note that $\mathbf{l}F(r) = 0$ for any function of the radius r only.)

The transversality conditions, Eqs. (3d) and (4d), give

$$\mathbf{r} \cdot \sum_m \mathbf{e}_{lm}^{(i)} Y_{lm} = 0 \tag{8a}$$

$$\mathbf{r} \cdot \sum_m \mathbf{b}_{lm}^{(i)} Y_{lm} = 0 \tag{8b}$$

Using Eqs. (7) and (6b),

$$\left[\mathbf{r} \cdot \sum_{l,m} \frac{\partial h_l^{(i)}}{\partial r} \mathbf{b}_{lm}^{(i)} Y_{lm} - \sum_{l,m} \frac{i}{r} h_l^{(i)} \mathbf{r} \cdot \mathbf{l} \times \mathbf{b}_{lm}^{(i)} Y_{lm} \right] = 0$$

Consequently, from Eqs. (6) to (8) we have

$$\mathbf{r} \cdot [\mathbf{l} \times \sum_m \mathbf{e}_{lm}^{(i)} Y_{lm}] h_l^{(i)}(kr) = 0 \tag{9a}$$

$$\mathbf{r} \cdot [\mathbf{l} \times \sum_m \mathbf{b}_{lm}^{(i)} Y_{lm}] h_l^{(i)}(kr) = 0 \tag{9b}$$

We can readily see that the following solutions satisfy Eqs. (8) and (9).

$$\sum_m \mathbf{e}_{lm}^{(i)} Y_{lm} = \sum_m c_{lm}^{(i)} \mathbf{l} Y_{lm} \tag{10a}$$

$$\sum_m \mathbf{b}_{lm}^{(i)} Y_{lm} = \sum_m d_{lm}^{(i)} \mathbf{l} Y_{lm} \tag{10b}$$

where we have made use of the fact that $\mathbf{r} \cdot \mathbf{l} = 0$ and of the commutation relation $\mathbf{l} \times \mathbf{l} = i\mathbf{l}$. The sum over m is required since l_x and l_y operating on the function Y_{lm} give linear combinations of $Y_{l,m+1}$ and $Y_{l,m-1}$.

Substituting Eq. (10) in Eqs. (5), we obtain

$$\mathbf{E}^{\mathrm{M}}(\mathbf{r}) = \sum_{l,m} \mathbf{E}_{lm}^{\mathrm{M}} = \sum_{l,m,i} c_{lm}^{(i)} h_l^{(i)} \mathbf{l} Y_{lm}(\theta, \phi) \tag{11a}$$

$$\mathbf{B}^{\mathrm{E}}(\mathbf{r}) = \sum_{l,m} \mathbf{B}_{lm}^{\mathrm{E}} = \sum_{l,m,i} d_{lm}^{(i)} h_l^{(i)} \mathbf{l} Y_{lm}(\theta, \phi) \tag{11b}$$

Equations (11a) and (11b) are the general solutions for the sets of Eqs. (3a, 3b, 3d) and (4a, 4b, 4d), and thus are the most general expressions for $\mathbf{E}^{\mathrm{M}}$ and $\mathbf{B}^{\mathrm{E}}$. The corresponding fields $\mathbf{B}^{\mathrm{M}}$ and $\mathbf{E}^{\mathrm{E}}$ are defined by Eqs. (3c) and (4c).

Summarizing, any electromagnetic field in a source-free region can be written as the sum of a transverse magnetic (E-type) and a transverse electric (M-type) component. These, in turn, can be expanded as an infinite series of multipole radiations. These are usually labeled only by their l value (although the m value is also needed for complete specification). For example, "transverse electric" radiation with $l = 2$ is called magnetic quadrupole radiation or M2 radiation for short. The explicit expressions are the following:

Electric 2^l-pole radiation or (El) radiation

$$\mathbf{B}_l^E(\mathbf{r}) = \sum_m f_{lm}^E(kr)\mathbf{X}_{lm}(\theta, \phi) \tag{12a}$$

$$\mathbf{E}_l^E(\mathbf{r}) = \frac{i}{\sqrt{\mu\epsilon}\, k}(\nabla \times \mathbf{B}_l^E) \tag{12b}$$

Magnetic 2^l-pole or (Ml) radiation

$$\mathbf{E}_l^M(\mathbf{r}) = \sum_m f_{lm}^M(kr)\mathbf{X}_{lm}(\theta, \phi) \tag{13a}$$

$$\mathbf{B}_l^M(\mathbf{r}) = -\frac{i\sqrt{\mu\epsilon}}{k}(\nabla \times \mathbf{E}_l^M) \tag{13b}$$

where

$$\mathbf{X}_{lm} = \frac{1}{\sqrt{l(l+1)}}\, l Y_{lm}(\theta, \phi) \tag{14a}$$

are the "transverse" vector spherical harmonics, and the $f_{lm}^{(E,M)}(kr)$ have the form

$$f_{lm}(kr) = a_{lm}^{(1)}h_l^{(1)}(kr) + a_{lm}^{(2)}h_l^{(2)}(kr) \tag{14b}$$

The factor $[1/\sqrt{l(l+1)}]$ in the definition of the $\mathbf{X}_{lm}$ has been inserted so that it satisfies the orthonormality condition

$$\int [\mathbf{X}_{lm}(\theta, \phi)]^* \cdot [\mathbf{X}_{l'm'}(\theta, \phi)]\, d\Omega = \delta_{ll'}\delta_{mm'} \tag{14c}$$

Alternative Procedure

From another point of view, one can characterize the electromagnetic field using only the single divergenceless vector field $\mathbf{A}(\mathbf{r}, t)$, in terms of which $\mathbf{E}$ and $\mathbf{B}$ are defined as

$$\mathbf{E}(\mathbf{r}, t) = -\frac{1}{[c]}\frac{\partial \mathbf{A}}{\partial t}(\mathbf{r}, t) \tag{15a}$$

$$\mathbf{B}(\mathbf{r}, t) = \nabla \times \mathbf{A}(\mathbf{r}, t)$$

After extracting the sinusoidal time dependence, the complex amplitudes are

$$\mathbf{E}(\mathbf{r}) = \frac{ik}{\sqrt{\mu\epsilon}} \mathbf{A}(\mathbf{r}) \tag{15b}$$

$$\mathbf{B}(\mathbf{r}) = \nabla \times \mathbf{A}(\mathbf{r})$$

Thus, from the first set of Eq. (15b) and Eqs. (12b) and (13a) we obtain

$$\mathbf{A}_{lm}^{\mathrm{E}}(\mathbf{r}) = \frac{1}{k^2} \operatorname{curl} \{f_{lm}^{\mathrm{E}}(kr)\mathbf{X}_{lm}(\theta, \phi)\}$$

$$\mathbf{A}_{lm}^{\mathrm{M}}(\mathbf{r}) = -\frac{i\sqrt{\mu\epsilon}}{k} f_{lm}^{\mathrm{M}}(kr)\mathbf{X}_{lm}(\theta, \phi) \tag{15c}$$

The fact that the electromagnetic field can be described mathematically by a vector field $\mathbf{A}$ leads to the assignment of spin $\mathbf{S} = 1$ to the electromagnetic field due to its transformation properties as a vector. The eigenvalues of the S_z operator are, of course, ± 1 and 0, and the three normalized eigenvectors of S_z (regarded as a 3×3 matrix operator, operating on the vectors of physical space) are

$$\chi_1^{\pm 1} = \mp \frac{1}{\sqrt{2}} (\hat{x} \pm i\hat{y})$$

$$\chi_1^0 = \hat{z} \tag{16}$$

where $\hat{x}$, $\hat{y}$, and $\hat{z}$ are the unit vectors along the x, y, and z axes.

As a result of the unit spin of the photon field, the total angular momentum $\mathbf{J}$ of a photon emitted in a 2^l-pole mode is the vector sum of the orbital angular momentum and the spin, that is, $\mathbf{J} = \mathbf{l} + \mathbf{S}$, and the eigenstates of the radiation field are given by the vector spherical harmonics $\mathscr{Y}_{lSJ}^M(\theta, \phi)$ obtained by coupling the usual spherical harmonics $Y_{lm}(\theta, \phi)$ with the $\chi_1^{m'}$ as follows:

$$\mathscr{Y}_{l1J}^M(\theta, \phi) = \sum_{\substack{m=-l \\ M=m+m'}}^{l} \sum_{m'=-1}^{1} \langle l1mm' \mid JM \rangle Y_{lm}(\theta, \phi)\chi_1^{m'} \tag{17}$$

where $\langle l1mm' \mid JM \rangle$ are the Clebsch-Gordan coefficients. For a given value of $J \geq 1$, there are three values of l ($J \pm 1$ and J). For $J = 0$, l will take only one value, $l = 1$. The vector spherical harmonics are eigenstates of the operators J^2 and J_z with eigenvalues $J(J + 1)$ and M, respectively,

$$J^2 \mathscr{Y}_{l1J}^M = J(J + 1)\mathscr{Y}_{l1J}^M \tag{18a}$$

$$J_z \mathscr{Y}_{l1J}^M = M\mathscr{Y}_{l1J}^M \tag{18b}$$

and satisfy the orthonormality relation

$$\int [\mathscr{Y}_{l1J}^{M}]^* \cdot [\mathscr{Y}_{l'1J'}^{M'}] \, d\Omega = \delta_{ll'}\delta_{JJ'}\delta_{MM'} \tag{18c}$$

The angular dependence of the vector potential $\mathbf{A}_{lm}(\mathbf{r})$ (and thus that of the fields $\mathbf{E}_{lm}(\mathbf{r})$ and $\mathbf{B}_{lm}(\mathbf{r})$) is expressed by the $\mathscr{Y}_{l1J}^{M}(\theta, \phi)$, Eq. (17), and since $\mathscr{Y}_{l1J}^{M}$ form a complete set, $\mathbf{A}_{lm}(\mathbf{r})$, $\mathbf{E}_{lm}(\mathbf{r})$, and $\mathbf{B}_{lm}(\mathbf{r})$ can be expanded in terms of it multiplied by suitable radial functions. In particular, we note that for $l = J$, we have

$$\mathscr{Y}_{J1J}^{M}(\theta, \phi) = \frac{\mathbf{l}Y_{JM}(\theta, \phi)}{\sqrt{J(J + 1)}} = \mathbf{X}_{JM}(\theta, \phi) \tag{19}$$

which corresponds to the solutions (12a) and (13a); the factor $1/\sqrt{J(J + 1)}$ arises from normalization. In Eqs. (12b) and (13b) we have a linear superposition of $\mathscr{Y}_{J+1,1,J}^{M}$ and $\mathscr{Y}_{J-1,1,J}^{M}$, which follows from parity considerations. The vector spherical harmonics $\mathscr{Y}_{lSJ}^{M}$ have the parity $\pi = (-1)^l$ so that $\mathscr{Y}_{J1J}^{M}$ has the parity $(-1)^J$ and $\mathscr{Y}_{J\pm1,1,J}^{M}$ has the parity $-(-1)^J$. The curl operator acting on a state of definite parity changes the parity of the state. It therefore follows from Eqs. (15a) and (15b) that the parity of the electric field $\mathbf{E}(\mathbf{r})$ is opposite to that of the magnetic field $\mathbf{B}(\mathbf{r})$. So, if the electric (magnetic) multipole radiation $\mathbf{B}_{lm}^{E}(\mathbf{E}_{lm}^{M})$ is given by Eq. (19), the corresponding $\mathbf{E}_{lm}^{E}(\mathbf{B}_{lm}^{M})$ has the following form

$$\nabla \times [f_{J,m}(kr)\mathscr{Y}_{J1J}^{M}(\theta, \phi)]$$
$$= f_{J+1,m}(kr)\mathscr{Y}_{J+1,1,J}^{M}(\theta, \phi) + f_{J-1,m}(kr)\mathscr{Y}_{J-1,1,J}^{M}(\theta, \phi) \tag{20}$$

where the radial functions $f_{J\pm1,m}(kr)$ are derivable from $f_{Jm}(kr)$.

It is clear from Eqs. (12) and (13) that for a light wave carrying angular momentum $\mathbf{l}$, two different waves can be realized, the *electric* or the *magnetic* multipole radiations which are solutions of Eqs. (4) and (3), respectively. There are two different solutions (the E- and the M-solutions) of opposite parity for each value of l because the restricted set of Eqs. (4a, b, c) [as also Eqs. (3a, b, c)] is invariant under the operation of parity transformation, and therefore $\mathbf{B}(r)$ and $\mathbf{E}(r)$ consist of an odd part and an even part, each of which satisfies Eqs. (4) [Eqs. (3)]. The transversality conditions, Eqs. (3d) and (4d), eliminate one of these parts, so that the parity of $\mathbf{E}(r)$ for either set (3) or set (4) is determined uniquely by the value of l.

Since the vector spherical harmonics $\mathscr{Y}_{lSJ}^{M}(\theta, \phi)$ form a complete set, the electric and magnetic multipoles, Eqs. (12) and (13), form a complete set. It is therefore possible to expand any arbitrary fields $E(r)$ and $B(r)$ which satisfy Maxwell equations in free space in terms of the multipoles.

$$E(r) = \sum_{l=1}^{\infty} \sum_{m=-l}^{l} [C_{lm}^E E_{lm}^E(r) + C_{lm}^M E_{lm}^M(r)] \qquad (21a)$$

$$B(r) = \sum_{l=1}^{\infty} \sum_{m=-l}^{l} [C_{lm}^E B_{lm}^E(r) + C_{lm}^M B_{lm}^M(r)] \qquad (21b)$$

where the coefficients C_{lm}^E and C_{lm}^M are the amplitudes of the electric and the magnetic 2^l-poles, respectively. The summation over l extends from 1 to ∞ since, according to Eqs. (12a) and (13a), the monopole ($l=0$) fields vanish identically. The coefficients C_{lm}^E and C_{lm}^M are related to the strength of the sources and the boundary conditions as will be shown in the next section.

The time average of two harmonically varying quantities, $V(t)$ and $U(t)$, where

$$V(t) = Ve^{-i\omega t} \quad \text{and} \quad U(t) = Ue^{-i\omega t},$$

is given in terms of the complex amplitudes V and U by

$$\langle \text{Re } U(t) \text{ Re } V(t) \rangle_t = \tfrac{1}{2} \text{ Re } [U^*V] = \tfrac{1}{2} \text{ Re } [U^*(t)V(t)]$$

Thus the time average of energy of the electromagnetic field is given in terms of the complex amplitudes by

$$\langle \text{energy} \rangle_t = \frac{1}{2[4\pi]} \int d^3r \langle \{ \text{Re } E(t) \cdot \text{Re } D(t) + \text{Re } B(t) \cdot \text{Re } H(t) \} \rangle_t$$

$$= \frac{1}{4[4\pi]} \int d^3r \, \text{Re } \{ E^* \cdot D + B^* \cdot H \} \qquad (22a)$$

$$= \frac{1}{4[4\pi]} \int d^3r \left\{ \epsilon \, |E|^2 + \frac{1}{\mu} |B|^2 \right\}$$

and the angular momentum of the electromagnetic field in free space is given by

$$J = \frac{\epsilon}{2[4\pi c]} \int d^3r \quad r \times (E^* \times B) \qquad (22b)$$

where we have used the fact that the momentum density is $1/v^2$ times the Poynting vector, which is the power density, given by

$$S(t) = \left(\frac{c}{4\pi} \right) (E(t) \times H(t)). \qquad (22c)$$

For a pure multipole of order (l, m), we have

$$J_z E_{lm}^{(E,M)} = m E_{lm}^{(E,M)}$$

and

$$J_z \mathbf{B}_{lm}^{(E,M)} = m \mathbf{B}_{lm}^{(E,M)}$$

It can be shown from Eqs. (22a) and (22b) that if the field is normalized in some volume so that it has energy $\hbar\omega$, then the z component of the angular momentum is $\hbar m$ and the square of the angular momentum is $\hbar^2 l(l+1)$.

12.2   Sources of Multipole Radiation

We now consider the sources of radiation. We assume that the radiation is generated by a localized charge and current density, $\rho(\mathbf{r}, t)$ and $\mathbf{j}(\mathbf{r}, t)$, and a magnetization density, $\mathbf{M}(\mathbf{r}, t)$, each having a time dependence given by $\exp(-ickt)$. Maxwell's equations in vacuum, for the complex amplitudes in the presence of these sources, are given by

$$\mathbf{\nabla} \cdot \mathbf{E} = \frac{[4\pi]\rho}{\epsilon_0} \tag{23a}$$

$$\mathbf{\nabla} \cdot \mathbf{B} = 0 \tag{23b}$$

$$\mathbf{\nabla} \times \mathbf{E} = \frac{ik}{\sqrt{\mu_0\epsilon_0}} \mathbf{B} \equiv ik\sqrt{\frac{\mu_0}{\epsilon_0}}\,(\mathbf{H} + [4\pi]\mathbf{M}) \tag{23c}$$

$$\mathbf{\nabla} \times \mathbf{H} = \mathbf{\nabla} \times \left[\frac{1}{\mu_0}\mathbf{B} - [4\pi]\mathbf{M}\right] = \left[\frac{4\pi}{c}\right]\mathbf{j} - ik\sqrt{\frac{\epsilon_0}{\mu_0}}\,\mathbf{E} \tag{23d}$$

and the continuity equation

$$\mathbf{\nabla} \cdot \mathbf{j} - i\omega\rho = 0 \tag{23e}$$

where

$$\omega = \frac{[c]}{\sqrt{\mu_0\epsilon_0}}\,k \tag{23f}$$

Substituting for ρ from Eq. (23e) into Eq. (23a), we have

$$\mathbf{\nabla} \cdot \mathscr{E} = 0 \tag{24a}$$

where

$$\mathscr{E} = \mathbf{E} + \frac{i[4\pi]}{\omega\epsilon_0}\mathbf{j} = \mathbf{E} + \frac{i}{k}\sqrt{\frac{\mu_0}{\epsilon_0}}\left[\frac{4\pi}{c}\right]\mathbf{j} \tag{24b}$$

Since $\mathscr{E}$ and $\mathbf{B}$ have vanishing divergence, it is appropriate to rewrite Eqs. (23a) and (23b) in terms of $\mathscr{E}$ and $\mathbf{B}$ so that the solution of $\mathscr{E}$ and $\mathbf{B}$ has the general form of the solution, Eqs. (12) and (13), of the free-space case. We then have the following equations corresponding to the sets of Eqs. (4) and (3).

E-Radiation

$$(\nabla^2 + k^2)\mathbf{B} = -\left[\frac{4\pi}{c}\right]\mu_0(\nabla \times \mathbf{j} + [c]\,\nabla \times \nabla \times \mathbf{M}) \tag{25a}$$

$$\nabla \cdot \mathbf{B} = 0 \tag{25b}$$

$$\mathscr{E} = \frac{i}{\sqrt{\mu_0\epsilon_0}\,k}(\nabla \times \mathbf{B} - [4\pi]\mu_0\nabla \times \mathbf{M}) \tag{25c}$$

M-Radiation

$$(\nabla^2 + k^2)\mathscr{E} = -\left[\frac{4\pi}{c}\right]ik\sqrt{\frac{\mu_0}{\epsilon_0}}\left(\frac{1}{k^2}\nabla \times \nabla \times \mathbf{j} + [c]\nabla \times \mathbf{M}\right) \tag{26a}$$

$$\nabla \cdot \mathscr{E} = 0 \tag{26b}$$

$$\mathbf{B} = -\frac{\sqrt{\mu_0\epsilon_0}}{k}\left(i\nabla \times \mathscr{E} + \frac{[4\pi]}{\omega\epsilon_0}\nabla \times \mathbf{j}\right) \tag{26c}$$

As before, the (l, m)-order multipole solutions of Eqs (25a) and (26a), which also satisfy Eqs. (25b) and (26b), are

$$\mathbf{B}_{lm}^{E}(\mathbf{r}) = r^{-1}\chi_{lm}^{ES}(r)\mathbf{X}_{lm}(\theta, \phi) \qquad \text{(E-radiation)} \tag{27a}$$

$$\mathscr{E}_{lm}^{M}(\mathbf{r}) = r^{-1}\chi_{lm}^{MS}(r)\mathbf{X}_{lm}(\theta, \phi) \qquad \text{(M-radiation)} \tag{27b}$$

where the superscript S on χ signifies the radial function when sources are present. The solution for $\mathbf{B}_{lm}^{M}$ can be obtained from Eqs. (27b) and (26c), and the solution for $\mathscr{E}_{lm}^{E}$ follows from Eqs. (27a) and (25c). Outside the region of the sources

$$r^{-1}\chi_{lm}^{(E,M)S} \rightarrow f_{lm}^{(E,M)}$$

given by Eq. (14b). The differential equations satisfied by $\chi_{lm}^{(E,M)S}(r)$ can be obtained quite readily by making use of the orthogonality relation, Eq. (14c), satisfied by $\mathbf{X}_{lm}(\theta, \phi)$. For example, by substituting Eq. (27a) in Eq. (25a), multiplying on the left by $\mathbf{X}_{lm}^{*}(\theta, \phi)$, and integrating over $d\Omega$, we obtain

$$\left[\frac{d^2}{dr^2} + k^2 - \frac{l(l+1)}{r^2}\right]\chi_{lm}^{E,S}(r) = -F_{lm}^{E,S}(r) \tag{28a}$$

where

$$F_{lm}^{E,S}(r) = [4\pi]\mu_0 r \int d\Omega \mathbf{X}_{lm}^{*}(\theta, \phi) \cdot \left(\left[\frac{1}{c}\right]\nabla \times \mathbf{j} + \nabla \times \nabla \times \mathbf{M}\right) \tag{28b}$$

To solve the inhomogeneous differential equation (28a), we make use of the Green's function technique. The Green's function $\mathscr{G}_l(r, r')$ satisfies the differential equation

$$\left[\frac{d^2}{dr^2} + k^2 - \frac{l(l+1)}{r^2}\right]\mathscr{G}_l(r, r') = -\frac{1}{r}\delta(r - r') \tag{29}$$

The solution of Eq. (29) which satisfies the condition that $r^{-1}\mathscr{G}_l(r, r')$ is finite at the origin and which leads to an outgoing wave at large distances is

$$\mathscr{G}_l(r, r') = ikr j_l(kr_<)h_l^{(1)}(kr_>) \qquad (30)$$

Using Eqs. (29) and (30), we obtain the following solution of Eq. (28a):

$$\chi_{lm}^{E,S}(r) = \int_0^\infty \mathscr{G}_l(r, r')F_{lm}^{E,S}(r')r'\,dr'$$

$$= ikr \int_0^\infty r' j_l(kr_<)h_l^{(1)}(kr_>)F_{lm}^{E,S}(r')\,dr' \qquad (31)$$

In the asymptotic region outside the source, we should identify $r_< = r'$ and $r_> = r$ so that

$$\chi_{lm}^{E,S}(r) \rightarrow ikr h_l^{(1)}(kr) \int_0^\infty r' j_l(kr')F_{lm}^{E,S}(r')\,dr' \qquad (32)$$

It is now possible to determine the amplitude C_{lm}^E of electric multipole of order (l, m) outside the source [Eqs. (21)]. From Eqs. (21b), (14b), (27a), (28b), and (32), we obtain

$$C_{lm}^E = [4\pi]ik\mu_0 \int j_l(kr)\mathbf{X}_{lm}^* \cdot \left(\left[\frac{1}{c}\right]\boldsymbol{\nabla} \times \mathbf{j} + \boldsymbol{\nabla} \times \boldsymbol{\nabla} \times \mathbf{M}\right) d^3r \qquad (33a)$$

Similarly we can show that the amplitude C_{lm}^M of magnetic multipole is

$$C_{lm}^M = -[4\pi]\sqrt{\frac{\mu_0}{\epsilon_0}} \int j_l(kr)\mathbf{X}_{lm}^* \cdot \left(\left[\frac{1}{c}\right]\boldsymbol{\nabla} \times \boldsymbol{\nabla} \times \mathbf{j} + k^2\boldsymbol{\nabla} \times \mathbf{M}\right) d^3r \qquad (33b)$$

These expressions can be written in terms of ordinary (scalar) spherical harmonics by remembering that

$$\sqrt{l(l+1)}\,\mathbf{X}_{lm}^* = (\mathbf{l}Y_{lm})^*$$

Since the sources $\boldsymbol{\nabla} \times \mathbf{j}$ and $\boldsymbol{\nabla} \times \mathbf{M}$ fall off faster than r^{-3} as $r \rightarrow \infty$, the Hermitian properties of $\mathbf{l}$ may be used. Equations (33a, b) then become

$$C_{lm}^E = \frac{[4\pi]ik\mu_0}{\sqrt{l(l+1)}} \int j_l(kr)Y_{lm}^*\mathbf{l} \cdot \left(\left[\frac{1}{c}\right]\boldsymbol{\nabla} \times \mathbf{j} + \boldsymbol{\nabla} \times \boldsymbol{\nabla} \times \mathbf{M}\right) d^3r \qquad (34a)$$

$$C_{lm}^M = -\frac{[4\pi]}{\sqrt{l(l+1)}}\sqrt{\frac{\mu_0}{\epsilon_0}} \int j_l(kr)Y_{lm}^*\mathbf{l} \cdot \left(\left[\frac{1}{c}\right]\boldsymbol{\nabla} \times \boldsymbol{\nabla} \times \mathbf{j} + k^2\boldsymbol{\nabla} \times \mathbf{M}\right) d^3r \qquad (34b)$$

Since $\mathbf{l} = -i(\mathbf{r} \times \boldsymbol{\nabla})$, the following identity holds for any vector field $\mathbf{V}$

$$\mathbf{l} \cdot \boldsymbol{\nabla} \times \mathbf{V} = -i[(\mathbf{r} \cdot \boldsymbol{\nabla})(\boldsymbol{\nabla} \cdot \mathbf{V}) - \nabla^2(\mathbf{r} \cdot \mathbf{V}) + \mathbf{V} \cdot (\nabla^2 \mathbf{r})] \qquad (35)$$

$$= -i[(r\partial_r)(\boldsymbol{\nabla} \cdot \mathbf{V}) - \nabla^2(\mathbf{r} \cdot \mathbf{V})]$$

This gives

$$
C_{lm}^{E} = -\frac{[4\pi]k\mu_0}{\sqrt{l(l+1)}} \int j_l(kr) Y_{lm}^{*}
$$
$$
\times \left\{ -\left[\frac{1}{c}\right] r\partial_r(\nabla \cdot \mathbf{j}) + \left[\frac{1}{c}\right]\nabla^2(\mathbf{r} \cdot \mathbf{j}) + \nabla^2(\mathbf{r} \cdot \nabla \times \mathbf{M}) \right\} d^3r \quad (36a)
$$

$$
C_{lm}^{M} = -\frac{[4\pi]i}{\sqrt{l(l+1)}} \sqrt{\frac{\mu_0}{\epsilon_0}} \int j_l(kr) Y_{lm}^{*}
$$
$$
\times \left\{ \left[\frac{1}{c}\right]\nabla^2(\mathbf{r} \cdot \nabla \times \mathbf{j}) + k^2\nabla^2(\mathbf{r} \cdot \mathbf{M}) - k^2 r\partial_r(\nabla \cdot \mathbf{M}) \right\} d^3r \quad (36b)
$$

Taking into account that the operators ∇^2 and $i\partial_r$ are Hermitian, they can be made to operate back to the left. Since ∇^2 has the eigenvalues k^2 when operating on $j_l(kr) Y_{lm}$, and since $\nabla \cdot \mathbf{j} = ick\rho$ and $\sqrt{\mu_0\epsilon_0} = [c]/c$, we have

$$
C_{lm}^{E} = -\frac{[4\pi]k^2\mu_0}{\sqrt{l(l+1)}} \int Y_{lm}^{*} \left\{ \frac{c}{[c]} \rho i\partial_r[rj_l(kr)] \right.
$$
$$
\left. + \left[\frac{-k}{[c]}\mathbf{r} \cdot \mathbf{j} + k\mathbf{r} \cdot \nabla \times \mathbf{M}\right] j_l(kr) \right\} d^3r
$$
$$
= -\frac{[4\pi]ik^2}{\sqrt{l(l+1)}} \sqrt{\frac{\mu_0}{\epsilon_0}} \int Y_{lm}^{*} \left\{ \rho\partial_r[rj_l(kr)] \right.
$$
$$
\left. - \left[\frac{-ik}{[c]}\mathbf{r} \cdot \mathbf{j} + i\sqrt{\mu_0\epsilon_0} k\nabla \cdot (\mathbf{r} \times \mathbf{M})\right] j_l(kr) \right\} d^3r \quad (37a)
$$

And similarly:

$$
C_{lm}^{M} = -\frac{[4\pi]ik^2}{\sqrt{l(l+1)}} \sqrt{\frac{\mu_0}{\epsilon_0}} \int Y_{lm}^{*} \left[\left\{ \left[\frac{1}{c}\right]\nabla \cdot (\mathbf{r} \times \mathbf{j}) \right. \right.
$$
$$
\left. \left. - k^2(\mathbf{r} \cdot \mathbf{M}) \right\} j_l(kr) + (\nabla \cdot \mathbf{M})\partial_r[rj_l(kr)] \right] d^3r \quad (37b)
$$

12.3 Multipole Moments

Approximation: $kr \ll 1$

For both the atomic and nuclear cases the wavelengths of the emitted light or γ-rays are large compared to the size of the source (an exception is found in nuclear giant resonances) so that $kr \ll 1$. For this limit, the asymptotic expression for the spherical Bessel function,

$$
j_l(kr) \simeq \frac{(kr)^l}{(2l+1)!!},
$$

can be used. We then have

$$C_{lm}^{E} \simeq \frac{-2i[4\pi]}{[2l+1]!!} \sqrt{\frac{\mu_0}{\epsilon_0}} k^{l+2} \sqrt{\frac{l+1}{l}} (Q_{lm} + Q_{lm}') \qquad (38a)$$

where the electric multipole moments are given by

$$Q_{lm} = \tfrac{1}{2} \int r^l Y_{lm}^*(\theta, \phi) \rho(\mathbf{r}) \, d^3r \qquad (38b)$$

$$Q_{lm}' = \frac{-ik\sqrt{\mu_0\epsilon_0}}{2(l+1)} \int r^l Y_{lm}^*(\theta, \phi) \left[\text{div } (\mathbf{r} \times \mathbf{M}) - \left[\frac{1}{c}\right] \mathbf{r} \cdot \mathbf{j} \right] d^3r \qquad (38c)$$

We note that the form of Q_{lm} is similar to that of the electric multipole moment defined in the static case and that, this represents an oscillating multipole in Eq. (38a), whereas Q_{lm}' depends on the magnetization density **M** and can be interpreted as an induced electric multipole moment. Note that $Q_{lm}'/Q_{lm} \sim kr \ll 1$ and thus Q_{lm}' is not important for sufficiently low energies.

Similarly, the expression for the magnetic multipole amplitude becomes

$$C_{lm}^{M} \simeq 2i \frac{[4\pi]}{(2l+1)!!} \sqrt{\frac{\mu_0}{\epsilon_0}} k^{l+2} \sqrt{\frac{l+1}{l}} (M_{lm} + M_{lm}') \qquad (39a)$$

where the magnetic multipole moments are

$$M_{lm} = -\frac{1}{2(l+1)[c]} \int r^l Y_{lm}^*(\theta, \phi) \text{ div } (\mathbf{r} \times \mathbf{j}) \, d^3r \qquad (39b)$$

$$M_{lm}' = -\tfrac{1}{2} \int r^l Y_{lm}^*(\theta, \phi) \left(\text{div } \mathbf{M} - \frac{k^2}{l+1} \mathbf{r} \cdot \mathbf{M} \right) d^3r \qquad (39c)$$

We note that $M_{lm} \sim M_{lm}'$ as far as k-dependence is concerned. The coefficients and signs of Q_{lm} and M_{lm} are chosen to agree with the conventional definitions of the static (spherical) moments.

Approximate Expressions for the Electric Multipole Fields

Near Zone: $kr \ll 1$. In this region we take $f_{lm}(kr) \simeq j_l(kr) \simeq \frac{(kr)^l}{(2l+1)!!}$. Then for the electric multipole radiation, from Eqs. (27a) and (25c) we have

$$\mathbf{B}_{lm}^{E}(\mathbf{r}) \simeq C_{lm}^{E} \frac{(kr)^l}{(2l+1)!!} \frac{1}{\sqrt{l(l+1)}} Y_{lm}(\theta, \phi) \qquad (40a)$$

$$\mathbf{E}_{lm}^{E}(\mathbf{r}) \simeq \frac{C_{lm}^{E}}{(2l+1)!!} \frac{i}{\sqrt{\mu_0\epsilon_0} \, k} \nabla \times \frac{1}{\sqrt{l(l+1)}} (kr)^l Y_{lm}(\theta, \phi) \qquad (40b)$$

But

$$\nabla \times \mathbf{l} = -i\mathbf{r}\nabla^2 + i\nabla \left(1 + r \frac{\partial}{\partial r} \right) \qquad (41)$$

and

$$\nabla^2[r^l Y_{lm}(\theta, \phi)] = 0$$

We have therefore

$$\mathbf{E}_{lm}^{\mathrm{E}}(\mathbf{r}) \simeq -\frac{C_{lm}^{\mathrm{E}}}{\sqrt{\mu_0 \epsilon_0}} \frac{k^{l-1}}{(2l+1)!!} \sqrt{\frac{l+1}{l}} \, \nabla(r^l Y_{lm}(\theta, \phi)) \qquad (40c)$$

We note that in the near zone

$$\frac{|\mathbf{B}_{lm}^{\mathrm{E}}|}{|\mathbf{E}_{lm}^{\mathrm{E}}|} \approx \sqrt{\mu_0 \epsilon_0} \, kr$$

Wave Zone: $kr \gg 1$.

In this region the appropriate radial function $f_{lm}(kr)$ would be the out-going spherical wave

$$h_l^{(1)}(kr) \simeq (-i)^{l+1} \frac{e^{ikr}}{kr}$$

We therefore have

$$\mathbf{B}_{lm}^{\mathrm{E}}(\mathbf{r}) \simeq C_{lm}^{\mathrm{E}}(-i)^{l+1} \frac{e^{ikr}}{kr} \frac{1}{\sqrt{l(l+1)}} \, Y_{lm} \qquad (42a)$$

$$\mathbf{E}_{lm}^{\mathrm{E}}(\mathbf{r}) \simeq C_{lm}^{\mathrm{E}} \frac{i(-i)^{l+1}}{k\sqrt{\mu_0\epsilon_0}} \, \nabla \times \left\{ \frac{e^{ikr}}{kr} \frac{1}{\sqrt{l(l+1)}} \, Y_{lm} \right\}$$

$$= \frac{C_{lm}^{\mathrm{E}}(-i)^l}{\sqrt{\mu_0\epsilon_0} \, k^2} \left\{ \nabla\left(\frac{e^{ikr}}{kr}\right) \times \frac{1}{\sqrt{l(l+1)}} \, Y_{lm} + \frac{e^{ikr}}{r} \nabla \times \frac{l Y_{lm}}{\sqrt{l(l+1)}} \right\}$$

$$\simeq \frac{1}{\sqrt{\mu_0\epsilon_0}} \, \mathbf{B}_{lm}^{\mathrm{E}} \times \hat{r} \qquad (42b)$$

where in the last step we have used Eq. (41) and dropped terms of higher order in $1/kr$. In the wave zone all the fields are proportional to $1/r$ and transverse to the radius vector.

Approximate expressions for the magnetic multipole fields are the following:

$kr \ll 1$ (Near zone):

$$\mathbf{E}_{lm}^{\mathrm{M}} \simeq C_{lm}^{\mathrm{M}} \frac{(kr)^l}{(2l+1)!!} \, \mathbf{X}_{lm} \qquad (40d)$$

$$\mathbf{B}_{lm}^{\mathrm{M}} \cong -C_{lm}^{\mathrm{M}} \frac{\sqrt{\mu_0\epsilon_0} \, k^{l-1}}{(2l+1)!!} \sqrt{\frac{l+1}{l}} \, \nabla(r^l Y_{lm}) \qquad (40e)$$

$kr \gg 1$ (Wave zone)

$$\mathbf{E}_{lm}^{\mathrm{M}} \simeq C_{lm}^{\mathrm{M}}(-i)^{l+1} \frac{e^{ikr}}{kr} \, \mathbf{X}_{lm} \qquad (42c)$$

$$\mathbf{B}_{lm}^{\mathrm{M}} \simeq \frac{-\sqrt{\mu_0\epsilon_0} \, (-i)^l}{k^2} \left[\left(\nabla \frac{e^{ikr}}{r}\right) \times \mathbf{X}_{lm} + \frac{e^{ikr}}{r} \nabla \times \mathbf{X}_{lm} \right]$$

$$\cong -\sqrt{\mu_0\epsilon_0} \, \mathbf{E}_{lm}^{\mathrm{M}} \times \hat{r} \qquad (42d)$$

The results of the near-zone (approximation $kr \ll 1$) are applicable while treating interaction with sources of small sizes, for example in the calculation of transition probabilities for emission and absorption of radiation by atoms and nuclei. The results of the wave-zone (approximation $kr \gg 1$) are useful in discussing the behavior of fields far from the source such as in the calculation of angular distributions and polarizations.

12.4   Angular Distribution of the Multipole Radiation

The angular distribution of the energy emitted per second (power) in the multipole radiation is obtained from the Poynting vector

$$\mathbf{S} = \left[\frac{c}{4\pi} \right] [\mathbf{E}(t) \times \mathbf{H}(t)].$$

The region of interest is the wave zone, where $|\mathbf{E}| \simeq (\mu/\epsilon)^{1/2} |\mathbf{H}|$ and they are perpendicular to each other and to the radius vector $\mathbf{r}$. Therefore we have, since the velocity is $v = [c]/\sqrt{\mu_0 \epsilon_0} = c$,

$$\text{wave zone:} \ |\mathbf{S}| \simeq \frac{c\epsilon_0}{[4\pi]} |\mathbf{E}(t)|^2 \simeq \frac{c\mu_0}{[4\pi]} |\mathbf{H}(t)|^2 = \frac{c}{[4\pi]\mu_0} |\mathbf{B}(t)|^2 \quad (43)$$

The time dependence of the $\mathbf{E}(t)$ and $\mathbf{B}(t)$ fields is e^{-ickt}. Inserting this time dependence of the fields, we have from Eqs. (42a)–(42d), (21a), and (21b) that the time-averaged power radiated within the solid angle $d\Omega$ is given by

$$dP = \frac{1}{2} \frac{c}{[4\pi]k^2\mu_0} \left| \sum_{l,m} (-i)^{l+1} \{ C_{lm}^{\text{E}} \mathbf{X}_{lm} - \sqrt{\mu_0 \epsilon_0}\, C_{lm}^{\text{E}} \mathbf{X}_{lm} \times \hat{r} \} \right|^2 d\Omega \quad (44)$$

The polarizations of the electric and the magnetic multipoles of order (l, m) are specified by $\mathbf{X}_{lm}(\theta, \phi)$ and $\mathbf{X}_{lm}(\theta, \phi) \times \hat{r}$, respectively. Note that these differ only in polarization. For pure electric or magnetic multipole (l, m), the angular distribution is given by a single term

$$dP_{lm}^{\text{E}} = \frac{1}{2} \frac{c}{[4\pi]k^2\mu_0} |C_{lm}^{\text{E}}|^2 |\mathbf{X}_{lm}(\theta, \phi)|^2 d\Omega \quad (45a)$$

$$dP_{lm}^{\text{M}} = \frac{1}{2} \frac{c\epsilon_0}{[4\pi]k^2} |C_{lm}^{\text{M}}|^2 |\mathbf{X}_{lm}(\theta, \phi)|^2 d\Omega \quad (45b)$$

where, using Eqs. (14b), (19), and (17), we have

$$\mathbf{X}_{lm}(\theta, \phi) = -\left[\frac{(l + m)(l - m + 1)}{2l(l + 1)}\right]^{\frac{1}{2}} Y_{l,m-1}(\theta, \phi)\chi_1^{+1}$$

$$+ \frac{m}{\sqrt{l(l + 1)}} Y_{lm}(\theta, \phi)\chi_1^0$$

$$+ \left[\frac{(l - m)(l + m + 1)}{2l(l + 1)}\right]^{\frac{1}{2}} Y_{l,m+1}(\theta, \phi)\chi_1^{-1} \qquad (46a)$$

$$\mathbf{X}_{lm}^* \cdot \mathbf{X}_{lm} = \frac{1}{2}\left[1 - \frac{m(m + 1)}{l(l + 1)}\right] |Y_{l,m+1}|^2 + \frac{1}{2}\left[1 - \frac{m(m - 1)}{l(l + 1)}\right] |Y_{l,m-1}|^2$$

$$+ \frac{m^2}{l(l + 1)} |Y_{lm}|^2 \qquad (46b)$$

and $\chi_1^{\pm 1}$, χ_0^1 are given by Eq. (16).

For reference we give the values of $\mathbf{X}_{lm}(\theta, \phi)$ for dipole ($l = 1$) and quadrupole ($l = 2$).

$$\mathbf{X}_{1,0} = -i\sqrt{\frac{3}{8\pi}} \sin\theta[\sin\phi\hat{x} - \cos\phi\hat{y}] \qquad (47a)$$

$$\mathbf{X}_{1,\pm 1} = \sqrt{\frac{3}{16\pi}} \{\cos\theta(\hat{x} \pm i\hat{y}) - \sin\theta e^{\pm i\phi}\hat{z}\} \qquad (47b)$$

$$\mathbf{X}_{2,0} = -i\sqrt{\frac{15}{8\pi}} \sin\theta\cos\theta[\sin\phi\hat{x} - \cos\phi\hat{y}] \qquad (48a)$$

$$\mathbf{X}_{2,\pm 1} = \sqrt{\frac{5}{16\pi}} \{\tfrac{1}{2}(3\cos^2\theta - 1 + \sin^2\theta e^{\pm 2i\phi})\hat{x}$$

$$\pm \tfrac{1}{2}(3\cos^2\theta - 1 - \sin^2\theta e^{\pm 2i\phi})\hat{y} - \sin\theta\cos\theta e^{\pm i\phi}\hat{z}\} \qquad (48b)$$

$$\mathbf{X}_{2,\pm 2} = \mp\sqrt{\frac{5}{16\pi}} \sin\theta[\cos\theta e^{\pm i\phi}(\hat{x} \pm i\hat{y}) - \sin\theta e^{\pm 2i\phi}\hat{z}] \qquad (48c)$$

The angular distributions for these two cases are given as follows:
Dipole ($l = 1$)

$$|\mathbf{X}_{1,0}(\theta, \phi)|^2 = \frac{3}{8\pi} \sin^2\theta \qquad (49a)$$

$$|\mathbf{X}_{1,\pm 1}(\theta, \phi)|^2 = \frac{3}{16\pi}(1 + \cos^2\theta) \qquad (49b)$$

Quadrupole ($l = 2$)

$$|\mathbf{X}_{2,0}(\theta, \phi)|^2 = \frac{15}{8\pi} \sin^2 \theta \cos^2 \theta \tag{50a}$$

$$|\mathbf{X}_{2,\pm1}(\theta, \phi)|^2 = \frac{5}{16\pi} (1 - 3 \cos^2 \theta + 4 \cos^4 \theta) \tag{50b}$$

$$|\mathbf{X}_{2,\pm2}(\theta, \phi)|^2 = \frac{5}{16\pi} (1 - \cos^4 \theta) \tag{50c}$$

The total power P which is radiated in all directions is obtained by integrating Eq. (44) over the solid angle $d\Omega$. Using Eq. (14c), we obtain

$$P = \frac{c}{2[4\pi]k^2} \sum_{l,m} \left\{ \epsilon_0 |C_{lm}^{\mathrm{M}}|^2 + \frac{1}{\mu_0} |C_{lm}^E|^2 \right\} \tag{51}$$

where $C_{lm}^{(\mathrm{E,M})}$ are given in terms of the sources by Eqs. (33) and (34).

For nuclear and atomic systems, $kr \ll 1$, and from Eqs. (38a) and (39a) we have

$$P_{lm}^E = \frac{1}{\epsilon_0} \frac{2[4\pi]c}{\{(2l+1)!!\}^2} \left(\frac{l+1}{l}\right) k^{2l+2} |Q_{lm} + Q'_{lm}|^2 \tag{51a}$$

$$P_{lm}^{\mathrm{M}} = \mu_0 \frac{2[4\pi]c}{\{(2l+1)!!\}^2} \left(\frac{l+1}{l}\right) k^{2l+2} |M_{lm} + M'_{lm}|^2 \tag{51b}$$

12.5 Parity Considerations and Selection Rules

The parity of the multipole radiation is generally specified by the parity of the magnetic field $\mathbf{B}_{lm}^{(\mathrm{E,M})}$ which for the E-multipole radiation is $(-1)^l$ and for the M-multipole radiation is $-(-1)^l$. We chose this because the interaction Hamiltonian H_{int}, which is responsible for the electromagnetic transitions, given by

$$H_{\mathrm{int}} = \frac{1}{[c]} \mathbf{j} \cdot \mathbf{A}, \tag{52}$$

has the same parity as the parity of the $\mathbf{B}$ field. This follows because under the parity operation, the current operator $\mathbf{j}$ is odd and, since $\mathbf{B} = \mathrm{curl}\ \mathbf{A}$, the parity of $\mathbf{A}$ is opposite to that of $\mathbf{B}$. Therefore if the nucleus undergoes a transition from the initial state ψ_i to a final state ψ_f, from the conservation of parities, the parities π_i and π_f of the initial and the final nuclear states are related as follows

$$\pi_i = (-1)^l \pi_f \quad \text{for} \quad \text{E-radiation} \tag{53a}$$

$$\pi_i = -(-1)^l \pi_f \quad \text{for} \quad \text{M-radiation} \tag{53b}$$

except when the initial and final total angular momenta J_i and J_f are $J_i = J_f = 0$, in which case, from Eqs. (12a) and (13a), it follows that no multipole radiation exists and that the radiation transition between two states $J_i = J_f = 0$ is absolutely forbidden.

The law of conservation of total angular momentum gives us an additional vectorial relation between $\mathbf{J}_i$, $\mathbf{J}_f$, and $\mathbf{l}$, the angular momentum carried by the multipole radiation, and a relation between their z-components M_i, M_f, and m.

$$\mathbf{J}_i = \mathbf{J}_f + \mathbf{l} \tag{54a}$$

$$M_i = M_f + m \tag{54b}$$

Equation (54a) signifies

$$|J_i - J_f| \leq l \leq J_i + J_f \tag{54c}$$

12.6 γ-Decay Transition Probabilities in Nuclear Systems

The transition probability per unit time for the emission of a multipole of order (l, m) can be obtained from the total power radiated, Eqs. (51a) and (51b), by dividing by the energy $\hbar\omega = \hbar c k$ of the quantum. Denoting by w_{lm}^E and w_{lm}^M the transition probability for the electric and magnetic multipole radiations, we have

$$w_{lm}^E = \frac{2}{\epsilon_0} \frac{[4\pi]}{\hbar} \frac{(l+1)}{l[(2l+1)!!]^2} k^{2l+1} |Q_{lm} + Q'_{lm}|^2 \tag{55a}$$

$$w_{lm}^M = \frac{2\mu_0[4\pi]}{\hbar} \frac{(l+1)}{l\{(2l+1)!!\}^2} k^{2l+1} |M_{lm} + M'_{lm}|^2 \tag{55b}$$

where the moments Q_{lm}, Q'_{lm}, M_{lm}, and M'_{lm} are defined by Eqs. (38b), (38c), (39b), and (39c). [Results (55a) and (55b) differ from the results of Blatt and Weisskopf, *Theoretical Nuclear Physics*, Chapter XII, Eqs. (3.21) and (3.22), by a factor of 4, since our definitions of the moments differ from those of Blatt and Weisskopf by a factor of 2.] In the expressions for the multipole moments it is necessary to introduce the quantum mechanical quantities replacing the oscillating charge and current densities, $\rho(\mathbf{r})$ and $\mathbf{j}(\mathbf{r})$, for each proton in the nucleus as follows

$$\rho(\mathbf{r}) \to 2e\psi_f^*(\mathbf{r})\psi_i(\mathbf{r}) \tag{55c}$$

$$\mathbf{j}(\mathbf{r}) \to 2\frac{e}{M}\psi_f^*(\mathbf{r})\mathbf{p}\psi_i(\mathbf{r}) = -\frac{ie\hbar}{M}[\psi_f^*\boldsymbol{\nabla}\psi_i - (\boldsymbol{\nabla}\psi_f^*)\psi_i] \tag{55d}$$

where $\psi_i(\mathbf{r})$ and $\psi_f(\mathbf{r})$ are the initial and final states of the nucleon. The factor of 2 is required since $e\psi^*(\mathbf{r}, t)\psi(\mathbf{r}, t)$ represents the average charge density, which may have a time-varying part. However, $\rho(\mathbf{r})$ is the peak amplitude of the oscillation, not the rms, or average, value. Equations (55c) and (55d) involve the usual procedure for introducing quantum mechanical definitions, where the dynamic variables are operators, with matrix elements defined between the initial and final states.

The oscillating magnetization density term depends on the change in particle density as well as the change in spin:

$$\mathbf{M}(\mathbf{r}) = \mu_N \frac{eh}{2M[c]} 2\psi_f^*(\mathbf{r})\boldsymbol{\sigma}\psi_i(\mathbf{r}) \tag{55e}$$

where $eh/2M[c]$ is the Bohr-magneton for a nucleon, μ_N nuclear magnetons is the magnetic moment of the nucleon (neutron or proton), and both of the ψ's must now be regarded as two component spinors to take into account the spin orientation.

If these values are put in the Eqs. (38b), (38c), (39b), and (39c) for Q, Q', M, and M', the results are

$$Q_{lm} \equiv \frac{1}{2} \int d^3 r r^l Y_{lm}^*(\theta, \phi)\rho(\mathbf{r})$$

$$\rightarrow e \int d^3 r \psi_f^*(\mathbf{r}) r^l Y_{lm}^*(\theta, \phi)\psi_i(\mathbf{r})$$

$$= e\langle f| r^l Y_{lm}^* |i\rangle \tag{56a}$$

In addition, starting with

$$Q'_{lm} = -\frac{ik\sqrt{\mu_0\epsilon_0}}{2(l+1)} \frac{eh}{M[c]} \int d^3 r r^l Y_{lm}^* \{\mu_N \boldsymbol{\nabla} \cdot [\psi_f^*(\mathbf{r} \times \boldsymbol{\sigma})\psi_i] - 2i\psi_f^*(\mathbf{r} \cdot \boldsymbol{\nabla}\psi_i)\}$$

and using the identities

$$\boldsymbol{\nabla} \cdot (\phi\mathbf{V}) = \phi\boldsymbol{\nabla} \cdot \mathbf{V} + \mathbf{V} \cdot \boldsymbol{\nabla}\phi$$

$$\boldsymbol{\nabla} \times \mathbf{r} = 0$$

and the hermiticity of the operator $i\boldsymbol{\nabla}$, we obtain:

$$Q'_{lm} = -\frac{iekh\sqrt{\mu_0\varepsilon_0}}{2M[c](l+1)} \int d^3 r \psi_f^* [\mu_N \boldsymbol{\sigma} \times \mathbf{r} \cdot \boldsymbol{\nabla}(r^l Y_{lm}^*) - 2ir^l Y_{lm}^* \mathbf{r} \cdot \boldsymbol{\nabla}]\psi_i$$

That is,

$$Q'_{lm} \simeq -\frac{iekh\sqrt{\mu_0\varepsilon_0}}{2(l+1)M[c]} \langle f| \mu_N \boldsymbol{\sigma} \times \mathbf{r} \cdot \boldsymbol{\nabla}(r^l Y_{lm}^*) + 2r^l Y_{lm}^* \frac{\mathbf{r} \cdot \mathbf{p}}{\hbar} |i\rangle \tag{56b}$$

Similarly,

$$M_{lm} = -\frac{e}{[c](l+1)} \int d^3r \, r^l Y_{lm}^* \boldsymbol{\nabla} \cdot (\mathbf{r} \times \psi_f^* \mathbf{p}\psi_i)$$

$$= \frac{-1}{[c](l+1)} \frac{ie\hbar}{M} \int d^3r \, \boldsymbol{\nabla}(r^l Y_{lm}^*) \cdot \psi_f^*(\mathbf{r} \times \boldsymbol{\nabla})\psi_i$$

$$= \frac{e\hbar}{(l+1)M[c]} \langle f | \, \boldsymbol{\nabla}(r^l Y_{lm}^* \cdot \mathbf{l}) \, | i \rangle \tag{57a}$$

$$M'_{lm} = -\tfrac{1}{2}\mu_N \frac{e\hbar}{M[c]} \int d^3r \, r^l Y_{lm}^* \left[\boldsymbol{\nabla} \cdot \psi_f^* \boldsymbol{\sigma}\psi_i + \frac{k^2}{l+1} \psi_f^* \mathbf{r} \cdot \boldsymbol{\sigma}\psi_i \right]$$

$$= \tfrac{1}{2}\mu_N \frac{e\hbar}{M[c]} \int d^3r \, \psi_f^* \left[\boldsymbol{\sigma} \cdot \boldsymbol{\nabla}(r^l Y_{lm}^*) - \frac{k^2}{l+1} \mathbf{r} \cdot \boldsymbol{\sigma} r^l Y_{lm}^* \right] \psi_i$$

$$\simeq \tfrac{1}{2}\mu_N \frac{e\hbar}{M[c]} \langle f | \, \boldsymbol{\sigma} \cdot \boldsymbol{\nabla}(r^l Y_{lm}^*) \, | i \rangle \tag{57b}$$

(The second term can be dropped since it is of order $(kr)^2$ times the first term.)

When these matrix elements are evaluated between the initial and final nuclear states, they are zero unless certain selection rules are satisfied. For instance, Q_{lm} is zero unless $|l_f - l_i| \leq l \leq l_f + l_i$ and $m_f - m_i = m$. The transition probabilities are obtained by dividing these by $\hbar\omega$, as given in Eqs. (55a, b).

12.7 Quantum Mechanical Derivation of the Transition Probabilities

The results, Eqs. (55a) and (55b), for the transition probabilities have been derived from classical considerations which have then been rendered into quantum mechanics by the usual prescriptions given in Eqs. (55a)–(55c). In the following, we derive the transition probabilities for multipole radiation using the quantum mechanical approach from the beginning.

According to perturbation theory, the quantum mechanical transition probability per unit time for transition from an initial state ψ_i to a final state ψ_f is

$$w_{fi} = \frac{2\pi}{\hbar} \rho_f \, |\langle \psi_f | \, H' \, | \psi_i \rangle|^2 \tag{58}$$

where H' is the interaction Hamiltonian and ρ_f is the density (number of possible states per unit energy interval) of the final states. The non-relativistic interaction Hamiltonian between nucleons of charge e_j and of magnetic moment μ_j magnetons and the quantized electromagnetic field is

$$H' = - \sum_j \frac{e_j}{M[c]} \frac{\mathbf{p}_j \cdot \mathbf{A} + \mathbf{A} \cdot \mathbf{p}_j}{2} - \frac{e\hbar}{2M[c]} \sum_j \mu_j \boldsymbol{\sigma}_j \cdot \mathbf{B} \qquad (59)$$

where $e_j = +e$ or zero, for proton and neutron, respectively, the summation over j is over the nucleons, and $\mathbf{A}$ is the vector potential operator. The Hermitian operator $\mathbf{A}$ can be expanded into orthogonal waves.

$$\mathbf{A} = \sum_\mu \{ a_\mu \mathbf{A}_\mu(\mathbf{r}) + a_\mu^* \mathbf{A}_\mu^*(\mathbf{r}) \} \qquad (60)$$

where a_μ and a_μ^* are the annihilation and creation operators for the photon which respectively decrease and increase the number of photons in the system by one. They satisfy the following commutation relations

$$[a_\mu, a_{\mu'}^*] = a_\mu a_{\mu'}^* - a_{\mu'}^* a_\mu = \delta_{\mu\mu'}$$

$$[a_\mu, a_{\mu'}] = [a_\mu^*, a_{\mu'}^*] = 0 \qquad (60a)$$

The matrix elements of a_μ and a_μ^* between photon states $|n_1 \cdots n_\mu \cdots \rangle$ and $|n_1' \cdots n_\mu' \cdots \rangle$, where n_μ specifies the number of photons in the state μ, are given by

$$\langle n_1' \cdots n_\mu' \cdots | a_\mu | n_1 \cdots n_\mu \cdots \rangle = \delta_{n_1' n_1} \cdots \delta_{n_\mu', n_\mu - 1} \sqrt{n_\mu} \cdots$$

$$\langle n_1' \cdots n_\mu' \cdots | a_\mu^* | n_1 \cdots n_\mu \cdots \rangle = \delta_{n_1' n_1} \cdots \delta_{n_\mu', n_\mu + 1} \sqrt{n_\mu + 1} \cdots$$

The multipole solutions of the vector potential $\mathbf{A}$ are given by Eq. (15c), but we rewrite them as follows

$$\mathbf{A}_{lm}^{\mathrm{E}}(\mathbf{r}) = k^{-2} \operatorname{curl} [C^{\mathrm{E}} j_l(kr) \mathbf{X}_{lm}(\theta, \phi)] \qquad (61a)$$

$$\mathbf{A}_{lm}^{\mathrm{M}}(\mathbf{r}) = \frac{-i\sqrt{\mu\epsilon}}{k} C^{\mathrm{M}} j_l(kr) \mathbf{X}_{lm}(\theta, \phi) \qquad (61b)$$

where the coefficients C^{E}, C^{M} can be determined from the condition that the energy of a photon confined to a sphere of radius R is equal to $\hbar\omega = \hbar c k$. Using Eqs. (22a), (42a, b, c, d) and taking into account that a confined photon consists of ingoing as well as outgoing waves, we have

$$C^{\mathrm{E}} = \sqrt{[4\pi]\mu_0 c\hbar k^3 / R}$$

$$C^{\mathrm{M}} = k^2 \sqrt{[4\pi] c\hbar k^3 / \epsilon_0 R} \qquad (61c)$$

From Eqs. (59), (61a) to (61c), (12), and (13) we obtain

$$H'(A_{lm}^{\mathrm{E}}) = -\sqrt{\frac{[4\pi]\mu_0 c\hbar}{kR}} \sum_j \left[\frac{e_j}{M[c]} \mathbf{p}_j \cdot (\mathrm{curl}\, j_l \mathbf{X}_{lm})^* \right.$$
$$\left. + \frac{\hbar e k^2}{2M[c]} \mu_j \boldsymbol{\sigma}_j \cdot (j_l \mathbf{X}_{lm})^* \right] \tag{62a}$$

$$H'(A_{lm}^{\mathrm{M}}) = ik\sqrt{\frac{[4\pi]\mu_0 c\hbar}{kR}} \sum_j \left[\frac{e_j}{M[c]} \mathbf{p}_j \cdot (j_l \mathbf{X}_{lm})^* \right.$$
$$\left. + \frac{\hbar e}{2M[c]} \mu_j \boldsymbol{\sigma}_j \cdot (\mathrm{curl}\, j_l \mathbf{X}_{lm})^* \right] \tag{62b}$$

Since the radius of the nucleus is very much smaller than the wavelength of the radiation ($kr \ll 1$), we take

$$j_l(kr) \simeq \frac{(kr)^l}{[(2l+1)!!]}$$

We note that

$$(\mathrm{curl}\, \mathbf{1} j_l Y_{lm})^* = i[\mathbf{r}\, \nabla^2 j_l Y_{lm} - (\mathbf{r} \times \mathrm{grad} + 2)\, \mathrm{grad}\, j_l Y_{lm}]^*$$

$$(\mathrm{curl}\, j_l \mathbf{X}_{lm})^* \simeq i\sqrt{\frac{l+1}{l}}\, (\mathrm{grad}\, j_l Y_{lm})^*$$

and

$$\langle f|\, \mathbf{p}_j \cdot (\mathrm{grad}\, j_l Y_{lm})^*\, |i\rangle = -i\frac{M}{\hbar}\left\langle f\left| \frac{p^2}{2M} j_l Y_{lm}^* - j_l Y_{lm}^* \frac{p^2}{2M} \right| i\right\rangle$$
$$= -iMck\langle f|j_l Y_{lm}^*|i\rangle \tag{63}$$

Using Eqs. (63), we obtain from Eqs. (62)

$$\langle f|\, H'(A_{lm}^{(\mathrm{E,M})})\, |i\rangle = \sqrt{\frac{[4\pi]c\hbar}{\epsilon R}}\sqrt{\frac{l+1}{l}}\, \frac{k^{l+\frac{1}{2}}}{(2l+1)!!}\, \langle f|\, \mathcal{M}_{lm}^{\mathrm{E,M}}\, |i\rangle \tag{64}$$

where

$$\mathcal{M}_{lm}^{\mathrm{E}} = \sum_j \left\{ e_j r^l Y_{lm}^*(\theta, \phi) - \frac{ie\hbar k}{2M[c]}\frac{1}{(l+1)}\mu_j \boldsymbol{\sigma}_j \times \mathbf{r} \cdot [\mathrm{grad}\, (r^l Y_{lm})]^* \right\} \tag{64a}$$

$$\mathcal{M}_{lm}^{\mathrm{M}} = \sqrt{\mu_0 \epsilon_0} \sum_j \left\{ \frac{e_j \hbar}{M[c]}\frac{1}{l+1} \mathbf{1}_j \cdot [\mathrm{grad}\, (r^l Y_{lm})]^* \right.$$
$$\left. + \frac{e\hbar}{2M[c]}\mu_j \boldsymbol{\sigma}_j \cdot [\mathrm{grad}\, (r^l Y_{lm})]^* \right\} \tag{64b}$$

are the electric and magnetic moment operators corresponding to Q_{lm}, Q'_{lm} and M_{lm}, M'_{lm} defined earlier in Eqs. (38) and (39). The first term in each of Eqs. (64) arises from the orbital motion of the charges, whereas the second term is the contribution arising from the change in the distribution of the intrinsic magnetic moment. As examples, we give the dipole ($l = 1$) moment operators for a proton in the case $m = 0$.

$$\mathscr{M}^{E}_{10} = \sqrt{\frac{3}{4\pi}}\, ez - i\sqrt{\frac{3}{4\pi}}\, \mu_p \frac{e\hbar}{4Mc}\, k(\boldsymbol{\sigma}_p \times \mathbf{r})_z \tag{65a}$$

$$\mathscr{M}^{M}_{10} = \sqrt{\mu_0\epsilon_0}\sqrt{\frac{3}{4\pi}}\, \frac{e\hbar}{2M[c]}\, (l_{pz} + \mu_p\sigma_{pz}) \tag{65b}$$

where μ_p nuclear magnetons is the magnetic moment of the proton and l_z is its angular momentum projection.

To determine the density of final states we consider a sphere of radius R. The allowed values of k are given by the condition that there are standing multiple waves, that is, $k_n = n\pi/R$, where n are integers. We have therefore $dn = (R/\pi)\, dk$, and the number of final states per unit energy interval ρ_f is given by

$$\rho_f = \frac{dn}{d\mathrm{E}} = \frac{R}{\pi\hbar c} \tag{66}$$

From Eqs. (58), (64), and (66), we find that the transition probability for electric and magnetic multipoles of order (l, m) is

$$w^{(E,M)}_{fi} = \frac{2[4\pi]}{\epsilon_0\hbar}\, \frac{l+1}{l[(2l+1)!!]^2}\, k^{2l+1} |\langle f|\, \mathscr{M}^{(E,M)}_{lm}\, |i\rangle|^2 \tag{67}$$

where $\mathscr{M}^{(E,M)}_{lm}$ are given by Eqs. (64a) and (64b).

12.8   The Cross Section of $p + n \rightleftharpoons D + \gamma$

The cross section for the photodisintegration of a deuteron ($D + \gamma \rightarrow n + p$) has as its inverse reaction, the radiative capture of a neutron by a proton ($n + p \rightarrow D + \gamma$), so that calculation of one cross section will also yield the other by use of the principle of detailed balance. The photodisintegration can be calculated from the multipole expansion operators representing the transition from a free n-p .system to the bound state (D), with the emission of a γ-ray (primarily in the E2 and M1 modes). For the capture of a thermal neutron by a proton, the cross section is not too dependent on the exact shape of the wave function for the deuteron; thus exact knowledge of the nuclear forces is not needed. Instead, the experimental data on the effective range for n-p scattering can be used.

Radiative Capture of a Thermal Neutron

Suppose a thermal neutron (that is, one with kinetic energy less than 0.1 ev) is to be captured by a proton at rest. The relative wave function of this two-body system is a plane wave and can be decomposed into partial waves (see the section on scattering theory). Since the momentum $\hbar k$ is small, only the S-wave contribution is significant at such low energies. Therefore the parity of the relative wave function is even, and the total (relative) angular momentum is due only to the sum of the spins of the two particles, so that $J = 0$ or 1. The final state is the deuteron, which is known to have $J = 1$ and even parity. Hence, the emitted γ-ray must have even parity and $l = 1$ or 2. Hence the transition is either M1 or E2. In addition, since the n and p initially have negligible kinetic energy, the γ-ray energy can be found directly from the mass defect for a deuteron:

$$E_\gamma = (M_n + M_p - M_D)c^2 = 2.23 \text{ Mev}$$

and therefore the wave number of the γ-ray is

$$k = \frac{E_\gamma}{\hbar c} = 4.4 \frac{mc}{\hbar} = 4.4/\lambda_c$$

where λ_c is the Compton wavelength of an electron.

We shall determine first which terms in the expression for the transition probabilities are most important. To do this, we note that the radius of the deuteron is

$$R_D \simeq 4.3 \times 10^{-15} \text{ meters} = 4.3 \text{ F}$$

so that

$$kR_D \simeq 0.03 \ll 1$$

This validates the assumption made in the derivation of the multipole expansion (the replacement of the spherical Bessel functions by powers of r) and also shows that the radiation is primarily M1 rather than E2.

The reason for the dominance of the M1 mode can be seen as follows. Equations (55a, b) give the transition probabilities for the El and Ml modes. In particular

$$w^{\text{E}}_{2m} = \frac{4[4\pi]k^5}{300\epsilon_0\hbar} |Q_{2m} + Q'_{2m}|^2$$

$$\simeq \frac{4[4\pi]k^5}{300\epsilon_0\hbar} |2eR_D^2|^2 \tag{68a}$$

$$w^{\text{M}}_{1m} = \frac{4[4\pi]\mu_0 k^3}{9\hbar} |M_{1m} + M'_{1m}|^2$$

$$\simeq \frac{4[4\pi]\mu_0 k^3}{9\hbar} \left| \frac{eR_D p}{M[c]} \right|^2$$

$$\simeq \frac{4[4\pi]\mu_0 k^3}{9\hbar} \left| e \frac{v}{[c]} R_D \right|^2 \tag{68b}$$

The ratio is of the order

$$\frac{w_{2m}^{E}}{w_{1m}^{M}} \simeq \frac{0.12k^2 R_D^2}{\mu_0 \epsilon_0} \bigg/ \frac{v^2}{[c]^2} = 0.12(kR_D)^2 \bigg/ \left(\frac{v}{c}\right)^2 \qquad (69)$$

For an incoming neutron of energy 30 Mev, the *relative* v/c is

$$\frac{v}{c} = \frac{1}{2}\sqrt{\frac{2E_n}{M_n c^2}} = \frac{1}{2}\sqrt{\frac{60 \text{ Mev}}{938 \text{ Mev}}} \simeq 0.12.$$

The ratio w_{2m}^{E}/w_{1m}^{M} is thus small because $kR_D \simeq 0.03$. The cross section for radiative capture can therefore be adequately calculated using only the M1 term. In other words, emission of the photon results from the change in magnetic moment distribution of the *n-p* system in going from the free singlet or triplet state ($J = 0, 1$) to the bound triplet state ($J = 1$).

From Eqs. (57a, b), the magnetic dipole moments are given by

$$M_{1m} = \frac{e\hbar}{2M[c]} \langle f | \, \nabla(r Y_{1m}^{*}) \cdot \mathbf{l}_p \, |i\rangle \qquad (70a)$$

$$M'_{1m} = \frac{e\hbar}{2M[c]} \langle f | \, (\mu_n \boldsymbol{\sigma}_n + \mu_p \boldsymbol{\sigma}_p) \cdot \nabla(r Y_{1m}^{*}) \, |i\rangle \qquad (70b)$$

which, for $m = 0$, become:

$$M_{10} = \frac{e\hbar}{2M[c]}\sqrt{\frac{3}{4\pi}} \, \langle f | \, l_{pz} \, |i\rangle \qquad (71a)$$

$$M'_{10} = \frac{e\hbar}{2M[c]}\sqrt{\frac{3}{4\pi}} \, \langle f | \, \mu_n \sigma_{nz} + \mu_p \sigma_{pz} \, |i\rangle \qquad (71b)$$

However, M_{10} is zero since $\mathbf{l}_p \, |i\rangle = 0$ (the initial state is an S state), which leaves M'_{10} to be evaluated.

First of all, M'_{10} is zero if the initial state is a triplet ($J = 1$) because, in this case, the spin parts of the initial and final wave functions are identical; thus the initial free state and the deuteron are just two S states of the same *n-p* system, differing only in energy. Hence, the radial parts of the initial and final states are orthogonal, and M'_{10} vanishes.

In the singlet case, the space states need not be orthogonal since the spin states are different. We note that

$$\mu_n \boldsymbol{\sigma}_n + \mu_p \boldsymbol{\sigma}_p = (\mu_n + \mu_p)\mathbf{S} + \tfrac{1}{2}(\mu_n - \mu_p)(\boldsymbol{\sigma}_n - \boldsymbol{\sigma}_p) \qquad (72)$$

where $\mathbf{S}$ is the total spin $\mathbf{S} = \tfrac{1}{2}(\boldsymbol{\sigma}_n + \boldsymbol{\sigma}_p)$.

The first term is zero since the initial state is a singlet, so the matrix element becomes

$$M'_{10} = \frac{e\hbar}{2M[c]}\sqrt{\frac{3}{4\pi}}\left(\frac{\mu_n - \mu_p}{2}\right)\langle{}^3S|(\boldsymbol{\sigma}_n - \boldsymbol{\sigma}_p)_z|{}^1S \text{ (free)}\rangle \qquad (73)$$

The matrix element involved here is known as the magnetic dipole spin-flip transition.

Now, we need expressions for the initial and final wave functions to complete the calculation. The space part of the wave function has the asymptotic form

$$e^{i\mathbf{k}\cdot\mathbf{r}} + f(\theta, \phi)\frac{e^{ikr}}{r}$$

for large r. When this is expanded in partial waves, assuming that the S-wave contribution dominates, the asymptotic form becomes simply

$$\phi_i(\mathbf{r}) = \frac{\sin(Kr + \delta_0)}{Kr} \qquad (74a)$$

where K is the wave number of the n-p relative motion. In general, ϕ_i can be written

$$\phi_i(\mathbf{r}) = \frac{u_i(r)}{Kr} \qquad (74b)$$

where u_i goes to zero at $r = 0$ and depends on the details of the nuclear force. The wave function for the deuteron can be well represented by the form

$$\psi_D = \sqrt{1 - \delta^2}\,\phi_S + \delta\phi_D \qquad (75a)$$

where the state-mixing coefficient δ is about 0.26, and ϕ_S and ϕ_D are normalized wave functions representing the $l = 0$ and $l = 2$ parts of the deuteron wave function. (The tensor part of the two-nucleon force tends to mix states with l differing by 2.) The singlet wave function, ϕ_S, is written, for convenience, in the form

$$\phi_S(\mathbf{r}) = \frac{u_f(r)}{\sqrt{4\pi}\,r} \qquad (75b)$$

Since ψ_D is orthogonal to ϕ_i, it does not contribute to M'_{10}. Thus we have for the spin-flip matrix element:

$$\langle f|(\boldsymbol{\sigma}_n - \boldsymbol{\sigma}_p)_z|i\rangle$$

$$= [\chi_1^{0*}(\boldsymbol{\sigma}_n - \boldsymbol{\sigma}_p)_z\chi_0^0]\sqrt{1 - \delta^2}\int_0^\infty 4\pi r^2\,dr\,\frac{u_f^*(r)u_i(r)}{\sqrt{4\pi}\,rKr}$$

$$= C_S\sqrt{1 - \delta^2}\,\frac{\sqrt{4\pi}}{K}\,I \qquad (76a)$$

where the spin matrix element C_S is

$$C_S = \chi_1^{0*}(\boldsymbol{\sigma}_n - \boldsymbol{\sigma}_p)_z \chi_0^0$$

$$= \left(\frac{\alpha(n)\beta(p) + \beta(n)\alpha(p)}{\sqrt{2}}\right)^\dagger (\sigma_{nz} - \sigma_{pz})\left(\frac{\alpha(n)\beta(p) - \beta(n)\alpha(p)}{\sqrt{2}}\right)$$

$$= \tfrac{1}{2}[\alpha^\dagger(n)\beta^\dagger(p)(\sigma_{nz} - \sigma_{pz})\alpha(n)\beta(p) - \beta^\dagger(n)\alpha^\dagger(p)(\sigma_{nz} - \sigma_{pz})\beta(n)\alpha(p)]$$

$$= 2 \tag{76b}$$

and the spatial matrix element I is

$$I = \int_0^\infty u_f^*(r)u_i(r)\,dr \tag{76c}$$

The transition probability for $m = 0$ is thus

$$w_{10}^M = \frac{4[4\pi]\mu_0 k^3}{9\hbar}|M'_{10}|^2$$

$$= \frac{4[4\pi]\mu_0 k^3}{3\hbar K^2}\left(\frac{e\hbar}{M[c]}\right)^2(\mu_n - \mu_p)^2(1 - \delta^2)I^2 \tag{77}$$

The total transition probability from the singlet to the triplet state is three times this since there are three magnetic dipole modes with different m's. The contribution of all three must be the same by rotational symmetry. In addition, the probability that the initial n-p system is in the singlet state is $\tfrac{1}{4}$. Thus the total radiative capture transition probability is

$$w(^1S \text{ free} \to \text{Deutron}) = \frac{[4\pi]\mu_0 k^3}{\hbar K^2}\left(\frac{e\hbar}{M[c]}\right)^2(\mu_n - \mu_p)^2(1 - \delta^2)I^2 \tag{78}$$

The cross section for radiative capture.   This cross section is obtained from the transition probability by assuming an incoming beam (of neutrons) of unit density; thus the incident flux is $v = (p_n/M_n) = (2\hbar K/M)$ (the factor 2 occurs because K is the relative wave number). Thus the capture cross section is given by

$$\sigma_c = \frac{M}{2\hbar K} w(\text{free} \to D + \gamma) \tag{79}$$

since the transition probability w is really the transition probability *for unit neutron density* [cf. Eq. (74a)].

Since the deuteron is a loosely bound system, the cross section can be obtained from a knowledge of the asymptotic behavior of the relative wave functions only. Hence

$$u_f \sim Ne^{-\gamma r} \tag{80a}$$

where

$$\hbar \gamma = \sqrt{MW_D} \tag{80b}$$

and W_D is the deuteron binding energy. Writing the photon wave number in terms of the parameter γ gives

$$k = \frac{E_\gamma}{\hbar c} = \left[W_D + \frac{p^2}{2\left(\frac{M}{2}\right)} \right] \bigg/ \hbar c = \frac{\hbar^2 \gamma^2 + p^2}{M \hbar c}$$

$$= \frac{\hbar^2 \gamma^2 + \hbar^2 K^2}{M \hbar c} = \frac{\hbar}{Mc}(\gamma^2 + K^2) \tag{81}$$

We now have, for the cross section,

$$\sigma_c = \frac{4\pi}{2} \left(\frac{[4\pi]e^2}{4\pi\epsilon_0 \hbar c} \right) \left(\frac{\hbar}{Mc} \right)^4 \left(\frac{\gamma^2 + K^2}{K} \right)^3 (\mu_n - \mu_p)^2 (1 - \delta^2) I^2$$

$$= \frac{4\pi}{2} \alpha \left(\frac{\hbar}{Mc} \right)^4 \left(\frac{\gamma^2 + K^2}{K} \right)^3 (\mu_n - \mu_p)^2 (1 - \delta^2) I^2 \tag{82}$$

where α is the fine-structure constant. Actually, it is unnecessary to estimate wave functions very carefully since the values of μ_n and μ_p result largely from the motion of the meson cloud around each nucleon, and when the nucleons are close, the cloud changes shape. This changes the values of μ_n and μ_p part of the time, making the calculation unreliable at close approach. Fortunately, in the loosely bound deuteron, the correction is only a few percent. Thus we make the approximation

$$u_f(r) \simeq \sqrt{2\gamma} \, e^{-\gamma r} \tag{83a}$$

which is normalized according to

$$\int_0^\infty |u_f(r)|^2 \, dr = 1$$

Fig. 12-1 compares this function with a more reasonable solution of the radial wave equation (including nuclear forces).

The initial wave function is also approximated by its asymptotic form; that is,

$$u_i(r) \simeq \sin(Kr + \delta_{0s}) \tag{83b}$$

where δ_{0s} is the $l = 0$, the singlet phase shift. To this approximation,

$$I = \int_0^\infty u_f(r) u_i(r) \, dr = \int_0^\infty \sqrt{2\gamma} \, e^{-\gamma r} \sin(Kr + \delta_{0s}) \, dr$$

$$= \sqrt{2\gamma} \, \frac{K \cos \delta_{0s} + \gamma \sin \delta_{0s}}{K^2 + \gamma^2} \tag{84}$$

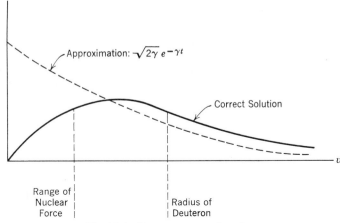

Fig. 12-1 Deuteron wave functions.

From low-energy scattering theory, we know that as $K \to 0$, we have, in terms of the "scattering length," a_s,

$$\cot \delta_{0s} \simeq -\frac{1}{a_s K} \tag{85a}$$

that is,

$$\delta_{0s} \simeq -a_s K \tag{85b}$$

Thus, using the small-angle approximations for the trigonometric functions,

$$I = \sqrt{2\gamma} \, \frac{K - \gamma a_s K}{K^2 + \gamma^2} \simeq \sqrt{\frac{2}{\gamma^3}} \, K(1 - \gamma a_s) \tag{86}$$

Putting this in Eq. (82) gives

$$\sigma_c = \frac{4\pi}{K} \alpha (\lambda_n)^4 \gamma^3 (\mu_n - \mu_p)^2 (1 - \delta^2)(1 - \gamma a_s)^2 \tag{87}$$

where

$$\alpha = \frac{[4\pi]}{4\pi} \frac{e^2}{\epsilon_0 \hbar c} \approx \frac{1}{137}$$

is the fine-structure constant, and λ_n is the Compton wavelength for a neutron. Remembering that

$$\gamma = \frac{\sqrt{W_D M}}{\hbar} \tag{88a}$$

and that

$$E_{\text{lab}} = 2E_{\text{CM}} = 2 \frac{\hbar^2 K^2}{2\left(\dfrac{M}{2}\right)} \tag{88b}$$

we have

$$\gamma^3 \frac{1}{K}\left(\frac{\hbar}{Mc}\right)^2 = \frac{W_D^{3/2}M^{3/2}}{\hbar^3} \frac{\hbar}{\sqrt{E_{\text{lab}}\left(\frac{M}{2}\right)}} \frac{\hbar^2}{M^2c^2} = \frac{W_D}{Mc^2}\sqrt{\frac{2W_D}{E_{\text{lab}}}} \qquad (88c)$$

Hence the cross section of $n + p \rightarrow D + \gamma$ can be written as

$$\sigma_c = 4\pi\alpha(\lambda_n)^2\left(\frac{W_D}{Mc^2}\right)\sqrt{\frac{2W_D}{E}}(\mu_n - \mu_p)^2(1 - \delta^2)(1 - \gamma a_s)^2$$

$$= \frac{4\pi}{137}(0.210\text{ F})^2\left(\frac{2.23\text{ Mev}}{938\text{ Mev}}\right)\sqrt{\frac{4.46\text{ Mev}}{E_{\text{lab}}}}(2.79 + 1.91)^2$$

$$\times (1 - \delta^2)\left(1 - \frac{a_s}{4.3\text{ F}}\right)^2 \qquad (89)$$

It is clear from Eq. (89) that $\sigma_c \sim (1/\sqrt{E}) \sim (1/v)$ for thermal neutrons, which means that the reaction yield is proportional to the density of neutrons present, not to the flux. Using the values $a_s = -23.7$ F and $\delta^2 = 0.07$ which are determined by scattering experiments, we get the value $\sigma_c = 0.292$ barn.

Experimental Results.   In evaluating the neutron-proton capture cross section, we have assumed that the deuteron wave function is known as well as the initial and final states of the interaction. Therefore we have used the effective range calculations to obtain the capture cross section. Any agreement with the experimentally determined cross section is a test of the validity of the method. Several different experimental methods have been used to obtain the neutron-proton capture cross sections. The variation between these results is small. The average value of these cross section measurements for thermal neutrons is found to be $\sigma_c = 0.332 \pm 0.002$ barn, which compares very favorably with the theoretically computed cross section $\sigma_c = 0.292$ barn. However, if we take the singlet scattering length $a_s = +23.7 \times 10^{-13}$ cm, then we get $\sigma_c = 0.140$ barn (the plus sign indicates the existence of a bound singlet state). Historically, this disagreement was the first proof that the *n-p* system does not have any singlet bound state. Finer considerations show that there is some disagreement both in the cross section and in the angular distribution. It has been attributed to the mesonic current[2,1] which we have neglected in our calculations.

Reverse Reaction: Photodisintegration

We shall now discuss the photodisintegration cross section $D + \gamma \rightarrow n + p$ which is the inverse of the capture process. As in the case of the capture, the magnetic dipole is the most important interaction in the photodisintegration process just above threshold. However, as the energy of the incident photon is increased, the electric quadrupole interaction predominates over the magnetic dipole. We shall confine ourselves to the low energy.

The calculation of the cross section is facilitated by the application of the theorem known as the reciprocity theorem. Consider a box of volume V containing neutrons, protons, deuterons, and γ-rays in equilibrium. We denote the state $n + p$ by "1" and the state $D + \gamma$ by "2." Using the ideas of statistical mechanics, we assume all possible states to have equal probabilities of occupancy. The number of states of kind 1 between momentum p_1 and $p_1 + dp_1$ is given by

$$dN_1 = g_n g_p \frac{V}{(2\pi\hbar)^3} 4\pi p_1^2 \, dp_1 \tag{90}$$

where g_n and g_p are the statistical weight factors for the neutron and proton, and p_1 is the momentum with respect to the center of mass. Since $E^2 = c^2 p^2 + m^2 c^4$, we have $dp = (E/c^2 p) \, dE$. Also, for zero rest mass, $(E/c^2 p) = (cp/c^2 p) = 1/c$, and for finite rest mass, we have $(E/c^2 p) = (M_{rel} c^2/c^2 p) = 1/v$. Therefore $(dp/dE) = 1/v$, a relationship which is good for relativistic or nonrelativistic velocities, zero or finite rest mass. Hence the density of states of type 1 is

$$\frac{dN_1}{V} = g_n g_p \frac{p_1^2}{2\pi^2 \hbar^3} \frac{dE}{v_1} \tag{91a}$$

Similarly, the number of states per unit volume of kind 2 in the energy interval dE is:

$$\frac{dN_2}{V} = g_D g_\gamma \frac{p_2^2}{2\pi^2 \hbar^3} \frac{dE}{v_2} \tag{91b}$$

where p_2 is the momentum of the photon with respect to the center of mass. Therefore,

$$\frac{dN_1}{dN_2} = \frac{(g_n g_p) p_1^2 / v_1}{(g_D g_\gamma) p_2^2 / v_2} \tag{91c}$$

For equilibrium, the number of transitions per second out of the state 1 would be equal to the number of transitions per second into the state 1. Therefore

$$dN_1 w_{1\to2} = dN_2 w_{2\to1}$$

or

$$\frac{w_{2\to1}}{w_{1\to2}} = \frac{(g_n g_p) p_1^2 / v_1}{(g_D g_\gamma) p_2^2 / v_2} \tag{92}$$

In order to obtain the cross section, we divide w by the flux for unit density of particles (which is just the velocity)

$$\sigma_{1\to2} = \frac{w_{1\to2}}{v_1} \tag{93a}$$

and

$$\sigma_{2 \to 1} = \frac{w_{2 \to 1}}{v_2} \tag{93b}$$

Thus

$$\frac{\sigma_{2 \to 1}}{\sigma_{1 \to 2}} = \frac{g_n g_p p_1^2}{g_D g_\gamma p_2^2} \tag{93c}$$

The values of the weight factors are the following:

$g_D = 3$ since for the $S = 1$ state there are three orientations of the spin

$g_\gamma = 2$ for two possible directions of polarization for the γ-ray

$g_n = 2$ for the two spin states of the neutron

$g_p = 2$ for the two spin states of the proton

From Eq. (93c) the cross section $\sigma_{2 \to 1}$ for absorbing a γ-ray of a particular polarization is $\frac{1}{2} \times \frac{4}{3}$ times the expression given in Eq. (82) or (89). Since we are considering the low-energy photodisintegration process, we cannot neglect K^2 in comparison with γ_t^2 and $1/a_s^2$. Therefore, we write for I, from Eq. (86), the expression

$$I = \frac{\sqrt{2\gamma_t}}{K^2 + \gamma_t^2} \frac{K(1 - \gamma_t a_s)}{\sqrt{1 + a_s^2 K^2}} \tag{94}$$

Putting all these together, we obtain the cross section for photodisintegration for an $m = 0$ deuteron. The $m = \pm 1$ gives the same result for the total cross section for photodisintegration of a deuteron. Therefore σ_{dis} is just σ_c as given in Eqs. (87) or (82) multiplied by

$$\frac{2}{3} \frac{K^2}{k^2} = \frac{2}{3} \frac{K^2}{(K^2 + \gamma_t^2)^2 \left(\frac{\hbar}{Mc}\right)^2} \tag{95}$$

The magnetic dipole cross section for the photodisintegration of a deuteron is then given by

$$\begin{aligned}
\sigma_{\text{dis,M1}} &= \frac{2}{3} \frac{K^2}{\left(\frac{\hbar}{Mc}\right)^2 (K^2 + \gamma_t^2)^2} 4\pi\alpha \left(\frac{\hbar}{Mc}\right)^4 \left(\frac{\gamma_t^2 + K^2}{K}\right)^3 \\
&\quad \times (\mu_n - \mu_p)^2 (1 - \delta^2) \frac{\gamma_t}{(K^2 + \gamma_t^2)^2} \frac{K^2(1 - \gamma_t a_s)^2}{1 + a_s^2 K^2} \\
&= \frac{8\pi\alpha}{3} \left(\frac{\hbar}{Mc}\right)^2 (\mu_n - \mu_p)^2 (1 - \delta^2) \frac{K\gamma_t(1 - \gamma_t a_s)^2}{(K^2 + \gamma_t^2)(1 + a_s^2 K^2)} \tag{96}
\end{aligned}$$

This M1 contribution dominates at very low energies.

As soon as there is enough energy to give an appreciable amount of P-state in the free n-p system, E1 begins contributing, since the parity can now be odd. We shall first obtain an expression for $\sigma(E1)$ and then discuss the numerical results for M1 and E1. We first need to show that Q'_{10} can be neglected

$$\frac{Q'_{10}}{Q_{10}} = \frac{ik}{2}\frac{\hbar}{2Mc}\frac{\int d\tau \phi_f^*(\mu_n \mathbf{r}_n \times \boldsymbol{\sigma}_n + \mu_p \mathbf{r}_p \times \boldsymbol{\sigma}_p)_z \phi_i}{\int d\tau(\phi_f^* z_p \phi_i)}$$

$$\simeq \frac{ck\hbar}{Mc^2} = \frac{\text{a few Mev}}{938 \text{ Mev}} \tag{97}$$

Hence we have only to consider Q_{10}.

The selection rules for E1 require $|J_f - J_i| \leq 1$, $\pi_i\pi_f = -1$. The initial state is $J_i = 1$, so that $J_f = 0$, 1, or 2. To change parity, the final state must have $l = 1, 3, 5, \ldots$. Since Q_{1m} does not contain any spin operator, the final state must be a triplet like the initial state and the spin cannot be flipped. Thus, this part of the problem would be the same as if there were no spin. If we neglect the few percent of the D-state in deuteron, the transition must therefore be ${}^3S \rightarrow {}^3P$. To this approximation, we may write, as before

$$\phi_i = \frac{u_D(r)}{\sqrt{4\pi}\, r} \tag{98a}$$

For the final state, we should have the p-wave part of $e^{iKz} + [f(\theta)e^{iKr}]/r$. However, since the n-p interaction in the few Mev region is small in the p state, we can neglect the scattering term and obtain

$$\phi_f^* = e^{-iKz} \tag{98b}$$

We know $z_p = \frac{1}{2}z = \frac{1}{2}r \cos\theta$, so that

$$Q_{10} = e\sqrt{\frac{3}{4\pi}} \int d\tau[\phi_f^* z_p \phi_i]$$

$$= \frac{e\sqrt{3}}{8\pi} \int d\tau e^{-iKz} r \cos\theta \frac{u_D(r)}{r}$$

$$= \frac{e\sqrt{3}}{8\pi} \int_0^\infty dr r^2 u_D(r) 2\pi \int_0^\pi d\theta \sin\theta \cos\theta e^{-iKr\cos\theta}$$

$$= \frac{e\sqrt{3}}{4} \int_0^\infty dr r^2 u_D(r) \int_{-1}^{+1} du u e^{-iKru}$$

$$= \frac{e\sqrt{3}}{4} \int_0^\infty r^2\, dr u_D(r) \left[\frac{e^{-iKru}}{(-iKr)^2}(-iKru - 1)\right]_{-1}^{+1}$$

$$= \frac{-ie\sqrt{3}}{2} \int_0^\infty r^2\, dr u_D(r) \left[\frac{\sin Kr}{(Kr)^2} - \frac{\cos Kr}{Kr}\right] \tag{99}$$

Therefore

$$Q_{10} = \frac{-i\sqrt{3}\,e}{2K} I_{E1} \tag{100a}$$

where

$$I_{E1} = \int_0^\infty r\,dr u_D(r)\left(\frac{\sin Kr}{Kr} - \cos Kr\right) \tag{100b}$$

We note that

$$Q_{1,\pm 1} \equiv e \int d\tau r Y_{1,\pm 1}^* \phi_f^* \phi_i = 0 \tag{101}$$

because ϕ_f^* and ϕ_i contain only $m = 0$. Keeping in mind that only one-half of the photons have useful polarization, we have

$$\sigma_{dis,E1} = \frac{1}{2}\frac{K^2}{k^2}\left(\frac{\hbar K}{M/2}\right)^{-1} w_{10}^E$$

$$= \frac{1}{2}\frac{K^2}{k^2}\frac{M}{2\hbar K}\frac{4[4\pi]}{9\epsilon_0}\frac{k^3}{\hbar}\left|\frac{-ie\sqrt{3}}{2K}I_{E1}\right|^2 \tag{102a}$$

where from Eq. (67), w_{10}^E is the transition probability per unit time for emission of $E1$ γ-rays in $n + p \to D + \gamma$. We know that

$$k = \frac{\hbar}{Mc}(K^2 + \gamma_t^2)$$

Therefore

$$\sigma_{dis,E1} = \frac{\pi}{3}\alpha\left(\frac{K^2 + \gamma_t^2}{K}\right)|I_{E1}|^2 \tag{102b}$$

where

$$I_{E1} = \int_0^\infty r\,dr u_D(r)\left(\frac{Kr - K^3 r^3/6}{Kr} - 1 + \frac{K^2 r^2}{2} + \cdots\right)$$

$$= \int_0^\infty dr\left(\frac{K^2 r^2}{3} + \cdots\right) u_D(r) \tag{102c}$$

The value of I_{E1} is very insensitive to the behavior of u_D near the origin so we can take $u_D(r) \simeq Ne^{-\gamma_t r}$. For M1, we had fair cancellation of errors by simply normalizing the $e^{-\gamma_t r}$ form and using $\sqrt{2\gamma_t}\,e^{-\gamma_t r}$. Here, however, since we see only the outside part, there is no cancellation of the overestimate inside the range of the force and the underestimate outside, and we must look at the normalization more carefully. From the effective-range argument we choose $\int_0^\infty u_D^2\, dr = 1$, where u_D is a wave function that matches $e^{-\gamma_t r}$ outside the range of forces. The exterior wave function we want is then $Ne^{-\gamma_t r}$. We recall that the triplet effective range is

$$r_{0t} = 2\int_0^\infty dr\left[e^{-2\gamma_t r} - \frac{u_D^2(r)}{N^2}\right] \tag{103}$$

By multiplying this equation by N^2, rearranging terms, and taking into account the normalization of u_D, we get

$$1 = \int_0^\infty u_D^2\, dr = \frac{-r_{0t}}{2}N^2 + N^2\int_0^\infty e^{-2\gamma_t r}\, dr$$

$$= N^2\left[\frac{-r_{0t}}{2} + \frac{1}{2\gamma_t}\right] \tag{104a}$$

so that N can be expressed in terms of the effective range

$$N = \sqrt{\frac{2\gamma_t}{1 - \gamma_t r_{0t}}} \tag{104b}$$

with $\gamma_t = (4.3\ \text{F})^{-1}$ and the triplet effective range $r_{0t} = 1.7\ \text{F}$. Therefore

$$I_{E1} = \int_0^\infty r\, dr\left(\sqrt{\frac{2\gamma_t}{1 - \gamma_t r_{0t}}}\, e^{-\gamma_t r}\right)\left(\frac{\sin Kr}{Kr} - \cos Kr\right)$$

$$= \sqrt{\frac{2\gamma_t}{1 - \gamma_t r_{0t}}}\frac{2K^2}{(K^2 + \gamma_t^2)^2} \tag{105}$$

and

$$\sigma_{dis,E1} = \frac{8\pi}{3}\left(\frac{[4\pi]}{4\pi}\frac{e^2}{\epsilon_0\hbar c}\right)\left(\frac{\gamma_t}{1 - \gamma_t r_{0t}}\right)\left(\frac{K}{K^2 + \gamma_t^2}\right)^3$$

$$= \frac{8\pi}{3}\alpha\left(\frac{\gamma_t}{1 - \gamma_t r_{0t}}\right)\left(\frac{K}{K^2 + \gamma_t^2}\right)^3 \tag{106}$$

We note that the range correction

$$\frac{1}{1 - \gamma_t r_{0t}} = 1.65$$

is thus quite an important consideration.

The simple theory which we have discussed is subject to the same conditions as the neutron-proton capture process, in which it was assumed that the state of the deuteron and the initial and final states of the reaction are well known. Once again we note good agreement between theory and experiment in the "low-energy" region, as is indicated in Fig. 12-2.

It is reasonable to say, then, that at moderately low gamma energies, the photodisintegration proceeds primarily through an E1 transition. This kind of calculation has been useful to obtain and compare the

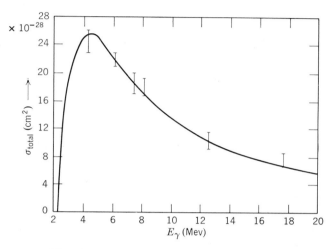

Fig. 12-2 Cross section for the photodisintegration of the deuteron from 4 to 20 Mev; the theoretical results are those of the low-energy theory discussed in the text (Bishop and Wilson[1]).

triplet-state parameter r_{0t}. However, the situation changes as the energy of the incident photon increases. In addition to the E1 transition one has to consider the contributions of M1 spin-flips and the E2 transition.

At higher energies, in addition one may expect contributions from still higher multipoles. Such calculations have been performed by several authors, assuming sometimes Gammel and Thaler potential and other times the Signell-Marshak potential. In the medium-energy range, DeSwart and Marshak,[2] have calculated the photodisintegration cross section at six different energies from 9 to 80 Mev. They have taken into consideration the electric dipole ($^3S_1 + {}^3D_1 \xrightarrow{(E1)} {}^3P_{0,1,2} + {}^3F_2$), the electric quadrupole ($^3S_1 + {}^3D_1 \xrightarrow{(E2)} {}^3S_1 + {}^3D_{1,2,3} + {}^3G_3$), and the magnetic dipole spin-flip ($^3S_1 \rightarrow {}^1S_0$ and $^3D_1 \rightarrow {}^1D_2$) transitions. They took for the final state of the deuteron a Signell-Marshak potential (which is the Gartenhaus meson

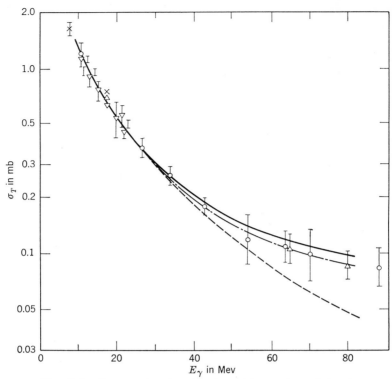

Fig. 12-3 Cross section for the photodisintegration of the deuteron.
———— Complete calculation, —·——·— only E1 transition, —————
Signell, Marshak, Gartenhaus theory (DeSwart and Marshak²).

theoretical potential with a spin-orbit term added to it). Their results are presented in Fig. 12-3 along with various experimental results. It shows remarkably good agreement in this range, but beyond 80 Mev, their method of calculation proves ineffective. Similar calculations by Rustgi, Zerink, Breit, and Andrews³ indicate good agreement in the medium-energy range.

12.9　The Internal Conversion Phenomenon

Once a nucleus is in an excited state, there are several ways for it to decay. In the case of low-energy excitation, the main competing processes are γ-emission, internal conversion, and, if the energy of excitation exceeds 1 Mev, internal pair production. Internal conversion occurs if the excited nucleus transfers its excess energy to one of the atomic electrons by direct electromagnetic interaction. The electron is ejected from the atom if the energy transferred exceeds the binding energy of the electron, which is usually the case except in very heavy atoms (in which the K and L shell electrons are extremely tightly bound). Semiclassically, the effect is due to a sudden perturbation of the electric (and magnetic) field in which the atomic electrons move because of an abrupt change in the distribution of electric charge (and magnetic moment) within the nucleus. This clearly has its greatest effect on electrons in the K-shell which are not shielded from the nucleus by any other electrons.

Study of the internal conversion phenomenon yields a great deal of information about the angular momentum and parity of the excited states and, to some extent, about the structure of the nucleus as a whole. Such information can be collected by studying the rate of ejection of the conversion electrons, but the most reliable information, however, comes from the study of internal conversion coefficients which relate internal conversion to γ-emission. Specifically, the conversion coefficient α is the ratio of the number of conversion electrons emitted to the number of γ-rays emitted in the same time interval.

At first it is not obvious that the number of electrons ejected should be proportional to the number of γ-rays, but the following discussion shows why it should. Quantum electrodynamics tells us that an electromagnetic interaction via the retarded potential can also be considered as being due to an exchange of a virtual or real photon. In this case the photon is real and is a γ-ray. Thus, for an electron which is at a distance of more than half the wavelength of the γ-ray from the nucleus, the rate of production of conversion electrons should be proportional to the rate of γ-ray production. That is, a certain fraction of the γ-rays emitted by the nucleus are absorbed by the atomic electrons and never leave the atom at all.

This simple situation must be modified somewhat when it is realized that electrons in s-states penetrate the nucleus to a small extent. This leads to interactions in which the γ-ray does not have to leave the nucleus. However, the γ-ray emission probabilities are calculated on the assumption that it does, thus resulting in a small error. In particular, conversion can occur when $J_f = J_i$, even though no photon can be emitted, since the electron can penetrate the nucleus and feel the radial redistribution of charge and magnetic moment. The major factors in the internal conversion coefficients can be calculated without knowing the nuclear eigenfunctions because they cancel out in the ratio.

An additional complication arises because the γ-rays may have any angular momentum between $|J_f - J_i|$ and $J_f + J_i$, each with its own emission probability. Each of these contributes to the production of conversion electrons, each with its own conversion coefficient, and in addition, the ejected electron may come from several different subshells: K, L_I, L_{II}, L_{III}, etc. There are several tables of conversion coefficients, calculated on different assumptions about the nucleus and the electron shells, which make the work of the experimentalist easier.

With this brief introduction to the phenomenon, we proceed with an outline of how the conversion coefficients are actually calculated. Instead of using the complete machinery of quantum electrodynamics, we will use the retarded-potential interaction Hamiltonian, break it up into multipoles, and use the "golden rule" to calculate transition probabilities. That is, the probability rate for emission of a conversion electron is found from

$$w_{fi} = \frac{2\pi}{\hbar} |\langle f| H'_{\text{int}} |i\rangle|^2 \rho_f \tag{107}$$

where H'_{int} is the electromagnetic interaction Hamiltonian between the nucleus and the atomic electrons, $|i\rangle$ and $\langle f|$ represent the initial and final states of the nucleus and the electron in question, and ρ_f is the density of final states (per unit energy) for the ejected electron.

Using the retarded potential, the interaction Hamiltonian H'_{int} can be written

$$\langle f| H'_{\text{int}} |i\rangle = -[4\pi] \int d^3 r_N \int d^3 r_e \left(\frac{\mathbf{j}_N \cdot \mathbf{j}_e}{c^2} - \rho_N \rho_e\right) \frac{e^{ik |\mathbf{r}_N - \mathbf{r}_e|}}{4\pi \epsilon_0 |\mathbf{r}_N - \mathbf{r}_e|} \tag{108}$$

where $k = (E_i - E_f)/\hbar c$ is the wave number of the "intermediate γ-ray" (E_i and E_f are the initial and final energies of the nucleus). The quantities $\mathbf{j}_N$, ρ_N, $\mathbf{j}_e$, and ρ_e are the Dirac current and charge densities for the nucleus and the atomic electrons. For instance:

$$\mathbf{j}_e = -ec\psi^*_{ef}(\mathbf{r}_e)\boldsymbol{\alpha}\psi_{ei}(\mathbf{r}_e) \tag{109a}$$

$$\rho_e = -e\psi^*_{ef}(\mathbf{r}_e)\psi_{ei}(\mathbf{r}_e) \tag{109b}$$

where $\boldsymbol{\alpha}$ are the Dirac matrices. Since, for heavy atoms, the innermost electrons are very tightly bound, the Dirac (relativistic) expressions must be used. However, for the nuclear particles, the Schrödinger expressions may be substituted since their velocities are much less than c. Thus

$$\rho_N(\mathbf{r}_N) = \sum_{j=1}^{A} e_j \psi^*_{jf}(\mathbf{r}_N)\psi_{ji}(\mathbf{r}_N) \tag{110a}$$

$$\mathbf{j}_N(\mathbf{r}_N) = \sum_j \frac{e_j}{M} \psi^*_{jf}(\mathbf{r}_N)\mathbf{p}\psi_{ji}(\mathbf{r}_N) \tag{110b}$$

There should be another term in $\mathbf{j}_N$ to reflect the tensor spin-spin inter-action† between the nucleus and the electron, but this is omitted here for simplicity.

To calculate the conversion coefficients for γ-rays of various (l, m), we must now break up the interaction into multipoles. To do this it is necessary to rewrite the $\mathbf{j}_N \cdot \mathbf{j}_e$ term with a unit dyadic in between $\mathbf{j}_N \cdot \mathbf{1} \cdot \mathbf{j}_e$, and then incorporate the potential as a scalar multiplying that dyadic. The potential has the following expansions:

$$\frac{e^{ik|\mathbf{r}_N - \mathbf{r}_e|}}{4\pi |\mathbf{r}_N - \mathbf{r}_e|} = ik \sum_{l,m} j_l(kr_N) Y_{lm}^*(\Omega_N) h_l^{(1)}(kr_e) Y_{lm}(\Omega_e) \qquad \text{for} \quad r_N \le r_e$$

(111a)

$$= ik \sum_{l,m} h_l^{(1)}(kr_N) Y_{lm}^*(\Omega_N) j_l(kr_e) Y_{lm}(\Omega_e) \qquad \text{for} \quad r_e \le r_N$$

(111b)

$$\frac{e^{ik|\mathbf{r}_N - \mathbf{r}_e|}}{4\pi |\mathbf{r}_N - \mathbf{r}_e|} \mathbf{1} = ik \sum_{l,m,j} (\mathbf{A}_{<lm}^j(kr_N))^* \mathbf{A}_{>lm}^j(kr_e); \quad r_N \le r_e$$

(111c)

$$= ik \sum_{l,m,j} (\mathbf{A}_{>lm}^j(kr_N))^* \mathbf{A}_{<lm}^j(kr_e); \quad r_e \le r_N$$

(111d)

where $j = M, E, L$ (for magnetic, electric, longitudinal). The vector fields $\mathbf{A}_<$ and $\mathbf{A}_>$ are dimensionless vectors proportional to the vector potentials associated with the various multipoles. The $\mathbf{A}_<$'s are the forms appropriate *inside* a charge distribution, whereas the $\mathbf{A}_>$'s are the exterior solutions, derived from the spherical Bessel and Hankel functions respectively. Explicitly:

$$\mathbf{A}_{<lm}^{\mathrm{M}}(kr) = j_l X_{lm}(\Omega) \qquad\qquad \mathbf{A}_{>lm}^{\mathrm{M}}(kr) = h_l^{(1)}(kr) X_{lm}(\Omega) \qquad (112a)$$

$$\mathbf{A}_{<lm}^{\mathrm{E}}(kr) = \frac{1}{k} \nabla \times (j_l X_{lm}(\Omega)) \quad \mathbf{A}_{>lm}^{\mathrm{E}}(kr) = \frac{1}{k} \nabla \times (h_l^{(1)}(kr) X_{lm}(\Omega)) \quad (112b)$$

$$\mathbf{A}_{<lm}^{\mathrm{L}}(kr) = \frac{1}{k} \nabla j_l(kr) Y_{lm}(\Omega) \qquad \mathbf{A}_{>lm}^{\mathrm{L}}(kr) = \frac{1}{k} \nabla h_l^{(1)}(kr) Y_{lm}(\Omega) \qquad (112c)$$

† This term would read

$$\mathbf{j}_N'(\mathbf{r}_N) = \sum_j \frac{e_j \hbar}{2M[c]} \mu_j [\psi_{jf}^*(\mathbf{r}_N) \boldsymbol{\sigma}_j \psi_{ji}(\mathbf{r}_N)] \cdot \text{curl}$$

where the "curl" operates on the potential, now regarded as being multiplied by a unit dyadic and dotted into $\mathbf{j}_e$ on the other side. This expression can be "simplified" to yield a term in H' as follows (for $r_e > r_N$)

$$-\frac{[4\pi]}{4\pi} \mu_0 \sum_j \frac{e_j \hbar}{2M[c]} \langle \psi_{jf} | \boldsymbol{\sigma}_j | \psi_{ji} \rangle \cdot \left(\frac{ik}{r^2} - \frac{1}{r^3} \right) e^{ikr} |\mathbf{r}_N - \mathbf{r}_e| \times \langle \psi_{ef} | \mathbf{j}_e | \psi_{ei} \rangle$$

For given l and m, the scalar, electric, and longitudinal parts have the same parity, whereas the magnetic part has the opposite parity. Therefore, we split up the interaction into several parts, grouped according to their parity-angular momentum behavior.

$$H'_{\text{int}} = \sum_{l=1}^{\infty} \sum_m H^{\text{mag}}_{lm} + \sum_{l=1}^{\infty} \sum_m (H^{\text{el}}_{lm} + H^{\text{long}}_{lm} + H^{\text{scalar}}_{lm}) + H(l=0) \quad (113)$$

where, for reference, we write the expressions obtained by putting the expansions Eq. (111) into Eq. (108)

$$\langle f | H^{\text{mag}}_{lm} | i \rangle = -ik\mu_0 \left[\frac{4\pi}{c^2}\right] \left\{ \int d^3 r_N \int_{r_e > r_N} d^3 r_e [\mathbf{j}_N \cdot \mathbf{A}^{M*}_{<lm}][\mathbf{j}_e \cdot \mathbf{A}^M_{>lm}] \right.$$

$$\left. + \int d^3 r_N \int_{r_e < r_N} d^3 r_e [\mathbf{j}_N \cdot \mathbf{A}^{M*}_{>lm}][\mathbf{j}_e \cdot \mathbf{A}^M_{<lm}] \right\} \quad (114a)$$

$$\langle f | H^{\text{elec}}_{lm} | i \rangle = \frac{-ik[4\pi]}{\epsilon_0 c^2} \left\{ \int d^3 r_N \int_{r_e > r_N} d^3 r_e [\mathbf{j}_N \cdot \mathbf{A}^{E*}_{<lm}][\mathbf{j}_e \cdot \mathbf{A}^E_{>lm}] \right.$$

$$\left. + \int d^3 r_N \int_{r_e r < _N} d^3 r_e [\mathbf{j}_N \cdot \mathbf{A}^{E*}_{>lm}][\mathbf{j}_e \cdot \mathbf{A}^E_{<lm}] \right\} \quad (114b)$$

$$\langle f | H^{\text{long}}_{lm} | i \rangle = \frac{-ik[4\pi]}{\epsilon_0 c^2} \left\{ \int d^3 r_N \int_{r_e > r_N} d^3 r_e [\mathbf{j}_N \cdot \mathbf{A}^{L*}_{<lm}][\mathbf{j}_e \cdot \mathbf{A}^L_{>lm}] \right.$$

$$\left. + \int d^3 r_N \int_{r_e < r_N} d^3 r_e [\mathbf{j}_N \cdot \mathbf{A}^{L*}_{>lm}][\mathbf{j}_e \cdot \mathbf{A}^L_{<lm}] \right\} \quad (114c)$$

$$\langle f | H^{\text{scalar}}_{lm} | i \rangle = \frac{-ik[4\pi]}{\epsilon_0} \left\{ \int d^3 r_N \int_{r_e > r_N} d^3 r_e [\rho_N j_l(kr_N) Y^*_{lm}(\Omega_N)] \right.$$

$$\times [\rho_e h^{(1)}_l(kr_e) Y_{lm}(\Omega_e)] + \int d^3 r_N \int_{r_e < r_N} d^3 r_e$$

$$\left. \times [\rho_N h^{(1)}_l(kr_N) Y^*_{lm}(\Omega_N)][\rho_e j_l(kr_e) Y_{lm}(\Omega_e)] \right\} \quad (114d)$$

$$\langle f | H(l=0) | i \rangle = \frac{-ik[4\pi]}{4\pi\epsilon_0} \left\{ \int d^3 r_N \int_{r_e > r_N} d^3 r_e [\rho_N j_0(kr_N)][\rho_e h^{(1)}_0(kr_e)] \right.$$

$$\left. + \int d^3 r_N \int_{r_e < r_N} d^3 r_e [\rho_N h^{(1)*}_0(kr_N)][\rho_e j_0(kr_e)] \right\} \quad (114e)$$

To show how these expressions imply approximate proportionality of the conversion probability to the γ-ray probability, it is necessary only to separate out the term proportional to the γ-ray probability. As shown in Section 12.7 the γ-ray probability is proportional to the square of the expectation value of the nucleus-gamma interaction Hamiltonian [Eqs. (59) to (61)]

$$\langle f | (H'_{N\gamma})_{lm} | i \rangle = \frac{-1}{[c]} \mathbf{j}_N \cdot \mathbf{A}$$

$$= - \sum_j \frac{e_j}{2M[c]} \langle \psi_{jf} | \mathbf{p}_j \cdot \mathbf{A}_{lm} + \mathbf{A}_{lm} \cdot \mathbf{p}_j | \psi_{ji} \rangle \quad (115)$$

We first discuss the magnetic part of the nucleus-electron interaction, which is simpler, and examine how the conversion coefficient is found. From Section 12.7, Eq. (62), the expectation value of $H'_{N\gamma}$ (neglecting the $\boldsymbol{\sigma}$ term) is

$$\langle f | (H'_{N\gamma})_{lm} | i \rangle = ik \sqrt{\frac{[4\pi]\mu_0 c \hbar}{kR}} \sum_{j=1}^{A} \frac{e_j}{M[c]} \langle \psi_{jf} | \mathbf{p}_j \cdot (j_l(kr_j) \mathbf{X}^*_{lm}(\Omega_j)) | \psi_{ji} \rangle$$

$$= \sum_j ik \sqrt{\left[\frac{4\pi}{c^2}\right] \frac{\mu_0 c \hbar}{Rk}} \sum_{j=1}^{A} \int d^3 r_j \mathbf{j}_j(\mathbf{r}_j) \cdot (j_l(kr_j) \mathbf{X}^*_{lm}(\Omega_j)) \quad (116)$$

After putting this in the "golden rule" [Eq. (107)], the γ-transition rate becomes, using Eq. (112a) for $\mathbf{A}^M_{<lm}$,

$$(w^M)_\gamma = \frac{2\pi}{\hbar} \left[\frac{4\pi}{c^2}\right] \frac{\mu_0 c \hbar k}{R} \left| \int d^3 r_N \mathbf{j}_N \cdot (\mathbf{A}^M_{<lm})^* \right|^2 \frac{R}{\pi c \hbar}$$

$$= \frac{2\pi}{\hbar} \left[\frac{4\pi}{c^2}\right] \frac{\mu_0 k}{\pi} \left| \int d^3 r_N \mathbf{j}_N \cdot (\mathbf{A}^M_{<lm})^* \right|^2 \quad (117)$$

Since the factor $2\pi/\hbar$ is common to both $(w^M)_\gamma$ and $(w^M)_{\text{electron}}$, and we want only the ratio, we see that the factor to be pulled out of $\langle f | H'_{lm} | i \rangle$ is

$$\sqrt{\left[\frac{4\pi}{c^2}\right]} \sqrt{\frac{\mu_0 k}{\pi}} \int d^3 r_N \mathbf{j}_N(\mathbf{r}_N) \cdot [\mathbf{A}^M_{<lm}(k\mathbf{r}_n)]^*$$

We therefore write H^{mag}_{lm}, Eq. (114a), in the following form:

$$\langle f | H^{\text{mag}}_{lm} | i \rangle = -i\mu_0 k \left[\frac{4\pi}{c^2}\right] \left\{ \int d^3 r_N \mathbf{j}_N \cdot (\mathbf{A}^M_{<lm})^* \int d^3 r_e \mathbf{j}_e \cdot \mathbf{A}^M_{>lm} \right.$$

$$- \int d^3 r_N \mathbf{j}_N \cdot (\mathbf{A}^M_{<lm})^* \int_{r_e < r_N} d^3 r_e \mathbf{j}_e \cdot \mathbf{A}^M_{>lm}$$

$$\left. + \int d^3 r_N \mathbf{j}_N \cdot (\mathbf{A}^M_{>lm})^* \int_{r_e < r_N} d^3 r_e \mathbf{j}_e \cdot \mathbf{A}^M_{<lm} \right\} \quad (118)$$

where the first double integral of Eq. (114a) has been split into an integral over *all* r_e minus one with $r_e < r_N$. Thus the first term is of the factored form required for calculation of the conversion coefficient, and the second and third are electron penetration terms (integrals over the subspace $r_e < r_N$). The last two terms in the braces can be put in a form analogous to the first by writing them as

$$\int d^3 r_N \mathbf{j}_N(\mathbf{r}_N) \cdot [\mathbf{A}^{\mathrm{M}}_{<lm}(\mathbf{r}_N)]^* \left\{ \int_{r_e < r_N} d^3 r_e \mathbf{j}_e \cdot \mathbf{A}^{\mathrm{M}}_{>lm} \right.$$
$$\left. - \frac{h_l^{(1)}(kr_N)}{j_l(kr_N)} \int_{r_e < r_N} d^3 r_e \mathbf{j}_e \cdot \mathbf{A}^{\mathrm{M}}_{<lm} \right\} \quad (119)$$

which explicitly shows the factor modifying the form of the γ-ray matrix element. The consequences of this term cannot be taken into account without referring to a specific nuclear model, since it depends on the details of the change in the current distribution within the nucleus during transition.

Three major tabulations of internal conversion coefficients now exist in the literature. The two earliest are those of Rose et al.[4,5] which are based on the point-nucleus approximation so that the penetration terms vanish. These internal conversion coefficients are thus given by [see Eqs. (117) and (118)]

$$\alpha^{\mathrm{M}}_{lm} = \frac{(w^{\mathrm{M}}_{lm})_{\mathrm{electron}}}{(w^{\mathrm{M}}_{lm})_{\gamma}} = \frac{\dfrac{2\pi}{\hbar} |\langle f| H^{\mathrm{mag}}_{lm} |i\rangle|^2 (\rho_f)_{\mathrm{electron}}}{\dfrac{2\pi}{\hbar} |\langle f| H'_{N\gamma} |i\rangle|^2 (\rho_f)_{\gamma\text{-ray}}}$$
$$= \pi \mu_0 k \left[\frac{4\pi}{c^2} \right] \left| \int d^3 r_e \mathbf{j}_e(\mathbf{r}_e) \cdot \mathbf{A}^{\mathrm{M}}_{>lm}(k\mathbf{r}_e) \right|^2 (\rho_f)_{\mathrm{electron}} \quad (120)$$

where $(\rho_f)_{\mathrm{electron}}$ is the density of free electron states per unit energy per unit solid angle, and its value is $mpV/(2\pi\hbar)^3$, where p is the final momentum of the electron and V is the normalization volume for the free-electron wave function. That is,

$$\psi_{ef} \sim \frac{1}{\sqrt{V}} \exp(i\mathbf{p} \cdot \mathbf{r}_e/\hbar)$$

The coefficients are calculated separately for each of the atomic subshells and then added, taking into account the number of electrons in each subshell. The partial shielding of the L-shell by the K-shell, however, is not taken into account in these calculations.

The finite size of the nucleus is considered in the calculations of Sliv.[6] The penetration terms are evaluated by assuming that the nuclear transition current lies only on the nuclear surface $|\mathbf{r}_N| = R$. Thus the penetration term from Eq. (119) becomes

$$\int_{|\mathbf{r}_N|=R} \mathbf{j}_N(\mathbf{r}_N) \cdot \mathbf{A}^{\mathrm{M}}_{<lm}(k\mathbf{r}_N) \left\{ \int_{r_e < R} \mathbf{j}_e(\mathbf{r}_e) \cdot \mathbf{A}^{\mathrm{M}}_{>lm}(k\mathbf{r}_e) \, d^3 r_e \right.$$
$$\left. - \frac{h_l^{(1)}(kR)}{j_l(kR)} \int \mathbf{j}_e(\mathbf{r}_e) \cdot \mathbf{A}^{\mathrm{M}}_{<lm}(k\mathbf{r}_e) \, d^3 r_e \right\} d^3 r_N \quad (121)$$

which is separable since the factor in the braces is independent of $\mathbf{r}_N$. Thus α^M_{lm} is given by

$$\alpha^M_{lm} = \pi\mu_0 k \left[\frac{4\pi}{c^2}\right]$$

$$\times \left| \int_{r_e > R} \mathbf{j}_e \cdot \mathbf{A}^M_{> lm}\, d^3 r_e - \frac{h^{(1)}_l(kR)}{j_l(kR)} \int_{r_e < R} \mathbf{j}_e \cdot \mathbf{A}^M_{< lm}\, d^3 r_e \right|^2 (\rho_f)_{\text{electron}} \quad (122)$$

The electric-like interaction consists of three terms [see Eqs. (113), (114b, c, d)] and appears much more complicated. However, Dancoff and Morrison[7] showed by means of a gauge transformation that the longitudinal and scalar parts cancel out, leaving only the electric multipole. This lengthy proof will not be presented here. However, it is useful to transform Eq. (114b) to a form similar to Eq. (114d), which exhibits explicitly the role of the corresponding electron transition charge ρ_e in the result. Using the identity [compare Eq. (41)]

$$\text{curl}\,(\mathbf{X}_{lm}) \equiv \frac{\text{curl}\,(\mathbf{1}Y_{lm})}{\sqrt{l(l+1)}}$$

$$= \frac{i}{\sqrt{l(l+1)}}\left\{\boldsymbol{\nabla}\frac{\partial}{\partial r} + k^2 \hat{r}\right\}(rY_{lm}) \quad (123)$$

we can write $\mathbf{A}^E_{< lm}$ and $\mathbf{A}^E_{> lm}$ in the form [see Eq. (112b)]

$$\mathbf{A}^E_{< lm}(k\mathbf{r}) = \frac{i}{k\sqrt{l(l+1)}}\left\{\boldsymbol{\nabla}\frac{\partial}{\partial r} + k^2 \hat{r}\right\}[rj_l(kr)Y_{lm}(\Omega)]$$

$$\mathbf{A}^E_{> lm}(k\mathbf{r}) = \frac{i}{k\sqrt{l(l+1)}}\left\{\boldsymbol{\nabla}\frac{\partial}{\partial r} + k^2 \hat{r}\right\}[rh^{(1)}_l(kr)Y_{lm}(\Omega)] \quad (124)$$

Substituting these into Eq. (114b) and using the anti-Hermitian property of $\boldsymbol{\nabla}$ to make it operate "backward" on $\mathbf{j}_e$, and, finally, using the continuity equation, $\boldsymbol{\nabla}\cdot\mathbf{j} + ick\rho = 0$, we obtain

$$\langle f| H^{\text{elec}}_{lm} |i\rangle = \frac{[4\pi]k}{\epsilon_0 c^2 \sqrt{l(l+1)}}\left[\int d^3 r_N \mathbf{j}_N \cdot (\mathbf{A}^E_{< lm}(k\mathbf{r}_N))^*\right.$$

$$\times \left\{\int d^3 r_e \left[k\mathbf{j}_e \cdot \hat{r}_e + ic\rho_e \frac{\partial}{\partial r_e}\right] r_e h^{(1)}_l(kr_e)Y_{lm}(\Omega_e)\right.$$

$$\left.- \int_{r_e < r_N} d^3 r_e \left[k\mathbf{j}_e \cdot \hat{r}_e + ic\rho_e \frac{\partial}{\partial r_e}\right] r_e h^{(1)}_l(kr_e)Y_{lm}(\Omega_e)\right\}$$

$$+ \int d^3 r_N \mathbf{j}_N \cdot (\mathbf{A}^E_{> lm}(k\mathbf{r}_N))^* \int_{r_e < r_N} d^3 r_e \left[k\mathbf{j}_e \cdot \hat{r}_e + ic\rho_e \frac{\partial}{\partial r_e}\right]$$

$$\left. \times r_e j_l(kr_e)Y_{lm}(\Omega_e)\right] \quad (125)$$

This expression is in a semifactored form entirely analogous to that of Eq. (114a), and can be similarly used for calculation of the conversion coefficients, using the point-nucleus or surface model. In particular, for the point-nucleus model, the result is

$$\alpha_{lm}^{E} = \frac{\pi k[4\pi]}{\epsilon_0 cl(l+1)} \left| \int d^3r \left[k\mathbf{j}_e \cdot \hat{r}_e + ic\rho_e \frac{\partial}{\partial r} \right] (rh_l^{(1)}(kr)Y_{lm}(\Omega)) \right|^2 \rho_f \quad (126a)$$

Since the term $\mathbf{j}_e \cdot \hat{r}_e$ usually makes a small contribution, it is usually neglected, which leads to

$$\alpha_{lm}^{E} \simeq \frac{\pi k[4\pi]}{\epsilon_0 l(l+1)} \left| \int d^3r \rho_e \frac{\partial}{\partial r} (rh_l^{(1)}(kr)Y_{lm}) \right|^2 \rho_f$$

$$= \frac{\pi k[4\pi]}{\epsilon_0 l(l+1)} \left| \int d^3r \rho_e \frac{\partial}{\partial r} [rh_l^{(1)}(kr)]Y_{lm} \right|^2 \rho_f \quad (126b)$$

A similarity of the integral above to the first term of Eq. (37a) exists. (In fact, one need only replace j_l by $h_l^{(1)}$, and conjugate.) Rose[8] carries through a finite size calculation, but without taking into account penetration terms.

It should be pointed out that the conversion coefficients, besides being dependent on l and m, also depend on the energy transfer $\hbar ck$, the atomic number Z of the nucleus (because this determines the size of the K- and L-shell orbitals), and on the subshell occupied by the electron in question. Also, it should be kept in mind that for $l = 0$ there is a finite probability for electron ejection, but none for γ-emission, so that $\alpha_{00}^E = \infty$. In this case, w_0, the transition rate per unit solid angle, is given by

$$w_0 = \frac{2\pi}{\hbar} \frac{k^2[4\pi]^2}{16\pi^2\epsilon_0^2} \left| \int d^3r_N \rho_N j_0(kr) \right|^2 \left| \int d^3r_e \rho_e h_0^{(1)}(kr_e) \right|^2 (\rho_f)_{\text{electron}} \quad (127)$$

Tables for the K-, L-, and M-shells and subshells have been calculated theoretically by Rose[8] as functions of atomic number, transition energy, and multipolarity for both electric and magnetic transitions and for multipoles $l = 1, 2, 3$.

One method of investigating nuclear decay properties is the experimental determination of conversion coefficients and a comparison of these with theoretical values. A second method is the determination of conversion coefficient ratios. In this method one measures the ratio of intensities of conversion electron lines as they would appear in an electron spectrum (taken, for example, in a magnetic spectrometer or with a semiconductor detector). If the difference between subshell binding energies is such that it is not possible to separate experimentally the conversion electrons from the various subshells, the shell coefficients must be

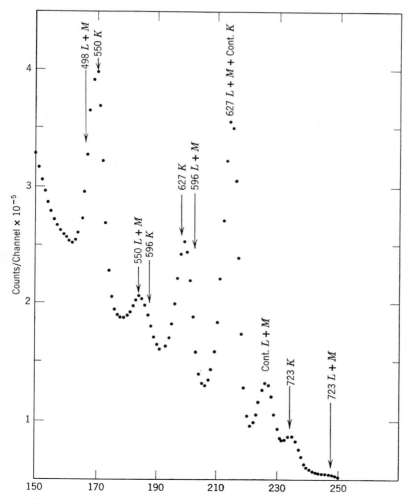

Fig. 12-4 Intermediate energy portion of beta-conversion electron spectrum of Sm[148] (Kurey and Roy[9]).

used instead when comparing experimental and theoretical values. That is, one compares the experimental K/L ratio with the theoretical value given by $[N_e(K)/\Sigma\, N_e(L)]$ which is equal to

$$\frac{\alpha(K)}{\alpha(L_{\rm I}) + \alpha(L_{\rm II}) + \alpha(L_{\rm III})}.$$

Consider the case of Sm[148] produced by the decay of Pm[148]. The K/L ratios of the 286, 550, and 627 Kev lines have been studied by Kurey and Roy[9] by the use of a solid-state detector. A typical spectrum is shown in Fig. 12-4, indicating the positions of the desired lines together with some feeble lines. Comparison with theoretical values indicated that both the 550 and 627 Kev lines are E2 transitions whereas the 286 Mev line is a mixture of M1 and E2 modes.

In the tables by Rose, the K-, L_I-, and L_{II}-shell calculations take into account the effect of electron screening and the finite size of the nucleus. The L_{III} coefficients include screening effects, but not the nuclear size effects (which are not expected to be appreciable). The M-shell coefficients are given for a point nucleus and unscreened electron, and screening may reduce these coefficients by 30 or 40% for heavy elements.[10] In addition, finite nuclear size reduces the coefficient about 10% in general and may reduce it as much as 50% for an M1 transition. For this reason, in calculating the ratio, the $[K/(L + M)]$ contribution may be estimated using the approximate rule[11] that $(K/L) \approx (L/M)$ for $(K/L) > 2$.

12.10 Gamma-Gamma Angular Correlation

Usually, in nuclear spectroscopy, the value of l, m, and the parity π for each nuclear level and transition has not been determined directly but, rather, has been inferred by cross-checking many different experiments until an assignment is found that gives reasonable agreement with all data on decay lifetimes and modes of decay. At first thought it seems reasonable that one could determine the l and m of a transition merely by observing the distribution of the emitted gamma rays and comparing this with the corresponding $|\mathbf{X}_{lm}|^2$ [Eqs. (49) and (50)]. However, at room temperature, the nuclei are randomly oriented, so that, whatever the l, m, and π values for the initial and final states of a particular nucleus, all values of m are equally represented in both the initial and final states of the system on the average. Thus, for any l_1, l_2, π_1, and π_2, the angular distribution of the radiation will be determined by a sum of $|\mathbf{X}_{lm}|^2$ terms, with different l's and all possible m's (the latter all being weighted equally). Since for any l, the sum $\sum_m |\mathbf{X}_{lm}|^2 = (1/4\pi)$, the total distribution will be spherically symmetric.

If, however, the initial state can be given a bias in favor of, say, positive m's, then the emitted radiation will also favor positive m's (even though the m-value of the final state can obviously not be controlled). This can be done by orienting the excited nuclei in a magnetic field. (Low temperatures are needed, since the splitting between nuclear levels of different m is small even in strong fields.) By measuring the number of γ-rays emitted at an angle θ to the magnetic field, and comparing this with the corresponding sum of $|\mathbf{X}_{lm}|^2$, properly weighted, the l, m, and π for the transition can be found directly.

In practice, the low temperature and high magnetic field may be objectionable, and thus another way must be found to obtain this information. The key to this is using sequential gamma radiations. The nucleus decays from state A to state C via an intermediate state B, emitting a γ-ray each time. The first γ-ray ($A \to B$) goes from the initial state, which may have any orientation, to a state having quantum numbers l_B, m_B. Since this ray is observed in a particular direction, not all values of m_B are equally likely. Then, the second γ-ray ($B \to C$) comes from a state whose m values are not all equally weighted, so that one can find a correlation between the direction of the second γ-ray and that of the first. In practice, one of the detectors is kept in a fixed position, waiting for the initial γ-ray. When a γ-ray actually registers, other detectors, arranged at various angles to the first, are gated to look for the second γ-ray which follows soon after. Thus, one experimentally obtains a function $W(\theta)\,d\Omega$, which expresses the probability of finding the second γ-ray within a solid angle $d\Omega$ at an angle θ from the first. The initial and final γ-rays are differentiated by measurement of their energies.

By comparing $W(\theta)$ with the theoretical values predicted for given $l_A\pi_A$, $l_B\pi_B$, and $l_C\pi_C$ the relative values of the l, π for the three levels can be determined. There are no perturbing fields which disturb the nucleus in its intermediate state. For this reason, gamma-gamma correlation is a very valuable tool in nuclear spectroscopy.

We shall describe the angular correlation problems in two parts, a simple approach to the theory to be followed by a somewhat more involved derivation of the angular correlation function.

A Simple Example of γ–γ Correlation

The best efforts to describe γ-ray transitions are based upon group theory, Racah algebra, and density matrix formalism. However, it is possible to understand the physics of γ-ray transition using a semi-classical treatment concerning multipole field expansions.

Electric and magnetic multipole fields of order l, m can be written in terms of products of radial wave functions of order l and vector spherical harmonics of order l, m. These electric and magnetic multipole fields form a complete set, so that an electric or magnetic field obeying free-space Maxwell equations can be expressed as linear combinations of these. In particular, the electromagnetic radiation associated with transitions between nuclear energy levels may be so described. The quantum numbers l and m refer to both the multipole order and the angular momentum carried by the photon from the initial state (total spin J_i, with z-component

M_i) to the final state (J_f, M_f) as in Fig. 12-5. From the conservation of angular momentum we have $\mathbf{J}_i = \mathbf{l} + \mathbf{J}_f$, and $M_i = m + M_f$. The quantum number l obeys the condition $|J_i - J_f| \leq l \leq J_i + J_f$. The order of a 2^l-multipole is given by l; $l = 0$ is a monopole, $l = 1$ a dipole, and $l = 2$ a quadrupole. Because no monopole radiation exists, transitions between states of angular momentum $J_i = J_f = 0$ do not occur; instead, the nucleus may transfer its energy of excitation to an orbital electron, which is then emitted.

Besides the angular-momentum selection rule, there are rules associated with conservation of parity The parity π of electric multipole radiation is given by $(-1)^l$, where, for example, $l = 1, 3, 5, \ldots$ has odd parity; $l = 2, 4, 6, \ldots$ has even parity. The parity $-(-1)^l$ of the magnetic multipole field is opposite to that of the electric. The matrix element between states ψ_i and ψ_f, and hence the transition probability T_{if}, vanishes unless parity is conserved: for even parity radiation $\pi_i = \pi_f$ whereas for odd parity radiation $\pi_i = -\pi_f$, where π_i and π_f are the parities of the initial and final nuclear states, ψ_i and ψ_f, respectively.

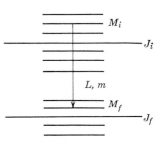

Fig. 12-5 Level scheme of transition between the initial and final state.

The transition probability diminishes rapidly with increasing order l. The decrease with increasing order arises from the large ratio of the wavelength to the nuclear dimensions. In fact, radiative transitions involving higher orders than $l = 3$ (magnetic octupole) have not been observed, and by far most of the contribution comes from $l = 1$ or 2. Because of the difference in parity of electric and magnetic radiation and in the selection rules, the lowest values of l for which a transition may occur can be stated for the two situations: (1) $J_i \neq J_f$, and (2) $J_i = J_f$ (but no $0 \rightarrow 0$ transitions). For case (1) when parity is favored, $\pi_i\pi_f = (-1)^{J_i-J_f}$. The corresponding electric and magnetic radiations respectively are given by $l = |J_i - J_f|$ and $l = |J_i - J_f| + 1$ (excepting $J_i = J_f = 0$). When the parity is not favored, $\pi_i\pi_f = (-1)^{J_i-J_f+1}$, the corresponding electric and magnetic radiations are $l = |J_i - J_f| + 1$ (except for $J_i = J_f = 0$) and $l = |J_i - J_f|$. For case (2) $J_i = J_f \neq 0$ and for $\pi_i = \pi_f$, the electric and magnetic radiations respectively are given by $l = 2$ (except for $J_i = J_f = \frac{1}{2}$) and $l = 1$. For $\pi_i = -\pi_f$, the electric radiation is $l = 1$ and the magnetic radiation is $l = 2$ (except for $J_i = J_f = \frac{1}{2}$).

When the transition probabilities are estimated, it is found that for the same value of l, electric multipole radiation is considerably more probable than magnetic. The magnetic radiation is suppressed because the velocities of the charges inside the nucleus are small compared to c. In the parity-favored case, the radiation is almost purely electric of order $l = |J_i - J_f|$. The magnetic radiation is less intense, because it is magnetic and because it is relegated to a higher order by parity conservation. In parity-unfavored cases, these effects partially nullify one another, so that the two radiations may be of roughly the same intensity, although the magnetic radiation is usually predominant.

The flow of energy associated with multipole radiation is given by the Poynting vector $\mathbf{S} = \left[\dfrac{c}{4\pi}\right] \mathbf{E} \times \mathbf{H}$, which, as shown in Section 12.4,

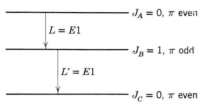

Fig. 12-6   Decay scheme of two γ-rays emitted in cascade.

results in the following expression for the power radiated within the solid angle $d\Omega$ for a pure electric and magnetic multipole (l, m):

$$P_{lm}^{(E)} \, d\Omega = \frac{c\epsilon_0}{2[4\pi]k^2} \, |C_{lm}^{(E)}|^2 \, |\mathbf{X}_{lm}(\theta, \phi)|^2 \, d\Omega \tag{128a}$$

$$P_{lm}^{(M)} \, d\Omega = \frac{c}{2[4\pi]k^2\mu_0} \, |C_{lm}^{(M)}|^2 \, |\mathbf{X}_{lm}(\theta, \phi)|^2 \, d\Omega \tag{128b}$$

where the angular distribution functions $\mathbf{X}_{lm}$ are defined by Eqs. (46) and (50).

It is clear from Eqs. (128) that a measurement of the angular distribution of the radiation emitted will determine the multipole order but not the parity. In order to determine the parity, the fields must actually be measured, making use of the $90°$ difference in polarizations of the electric and magnetic fields in the radiation zone.

Consider a nucleus decaying in cascade by the emission of γ-rays from the state $A \rightarrow B$ and then from $B \rightarrow C$ as in Fig. 12-6. We choose as a common example $J_A = J_C = 0$, $J_B = 1$ with a parity change in each case. The selection rules, besides stipulating mainly an E1 (electric dipole) transition, allow $m_A - m_B = \Delta m_{AB} = +1, 0$, or -1 with equal probability. Furthermore, $\Delta m_{BC} = -1, 0$, or $+1$, respectively. The directional distribution of each of these γ-rays is given by the angular distribution function and in a given direction (θ, ϕ) is

$$P_{10}^{(E,M)}(\theta, \phi)\, d\Omega = a^{(E,M)}C^{(E,M)}(1 - \cos^2\theta)\, d\Omega \qquad \Delta m = 0 \qquad (129a)$$

$$P_{1\pm1}^{(E,M)}(\theta, \phi)\, d\Omega = a^{(E,M)}C^{(E,M)}(1 + \cos^2\theta)\, d\Omega \qquad \Delta m = \pm 1 \quad (129b)$$

where

$$a^{E} = \frac{3c\epsilon_0}{16\pi[4\pi]k^2} \qquad a^{M} = \frac{3c}{16\pi[4\pi]k^2\mu_0}$$

and $C^{(E,M)}$ is a constant independent of the angles. By adding Eqs. (129a) and (129b), we see the radiation emitted is isotropic, with no preferred direction for the first photon

$$P^{(E,M)}(\theta, \phi) = 2a^{(E,M)}C^{(E,M)} = \text{constant} \qquad (129c)$$

If the polar axis of coordinates is chosen along the direction of emission of the first photon, emitted from $A \to B$, we see that $\Delta m = 0$ does not occur; by substituting $m = 0$ in the expression for $\mathbf{X}_{lm}(\theta, \phi)$, [Eq. (46)],

$$|\mathbf{X}_{10}(\theta, \phi)|^2\, Z_{10}(\theta, \phi) = \frac{3}{8\pi}\sin^2\theta$$

$$= 0 \qquad \text{for} \quad \theta = 0 \qquad (130)$$

Thus the transition $A \to B$ has $\Delta m = \pm 1$ only. Hence $\Delta m_{BC} = \mp 1$ and either of these gives Eq. (129b) for a directional distribution. Thus the directional distribution of the second quantum with respect to the first is given by

$$W_{0\to1\to0}^{11}(\theta)\, d\Omega = \frac{3}{16\pi}(1 + \cos^2\theta)\, d\Omega \qquad (131)$$

where $W_{J_A\to J_B\to J_C}^{LL'}(\theta)$ represents the angular γ-γ correlation function for transition from initial spin J_A to final spin J_C through the intermediate spin J_B by successive emission of two photons of angular momentum L and L'. It gives the probability that the direction of the second photon lies within the solid angle $d\Omega$ at angle θ with respect to the first quantum. Another symbol usually used is $W(J_A \to J_B \to J_C, LL', \theta)$.

As additional examples, we state below the results for angular γ-γ correlation functions $W(J_A \to J_B \to J_C, LL')$ for a few more cases.

$$W(1 \to 1 \to 0; 1\, 1) \sim (1 - \tfrac{1}{3}\cos^2\theta)$$

$$W(0 \to 2 \to 2; 2\, 2) \sim (1 - 3\cos^2\theta + 4\cos^4\theta)$$

We have chosen a simple example for illustration purposes. In general, the angular correlation depends upon the multipole orders of the two γ-rays and upon the total angular momentum J of the three states.

In the above discussion, we have not considered an important point. If the lifetime of the intermediate state B is long enough to permit outside influences to disturb it before the second photon is emitted, the angular correlation will be smoothed out. This is especially likely to happen for states emitting radiation of high l, since their multipole transition probabilities are smaller.

Derivation of the Angular Correlation Function

Here we show how one can calculate more generally the angular correlation function. The concept of directional correlation introduced previously is generalized to include polarization correlation as well. (If the detectors are polarization-insensitive, the end result must, of course, be summed over polarizations.) We shall follow closely the article by H. Frauenfelder and R. M. Steffen (*Alpha-, Beta-, and Gamma-Ray Spectroscopy*, Vol. 2, p. 997, K. Siegbahn, ed., North-Holland Publishing Co., Amsterdam, 1965).

Since the derivation makes use of the concept of the *density matrix,* we digress to give a brief review of its motivation. Since we are dealing with a group of objects (nuclei) in various states, the state of the system should be characterized by stating the probability of finding a particular nucleus in a particular state, which is the same as the fraction of the total number that are in that state at a given time. If all the states were nondegenerate, the preceding description would be completely satisfactory, since a given nucleus must be in one, and only one, of its eigenstates at a given time. However, for degenerate states, the situation is more complicated. In this case, there is nothing to prevent a given nucleus from being in a state which is not one of the set of orthogonal states we have chosen to span the degenerate subset of states. In other words, if states $|lm\rangle$ are degenerate for $-l \leq m \leq l$, the nucleus can be in a state described by $|\psi_l\rangle = \sum C_m |lm\rangle$. In this case, the probability of finding the nucleus in state $|lm\rangle$ is $|C_m|^2$. If we simply assign probabilities P_m to each state $|lm\rangle$, then it is impossible to distinguish between the following two cases: (1) The system consists of particles, where all are in the same state, given by $|\psi_l\rangle = \sum C_m |lm\rangle$; (2) The system consists of N particles, each in one of the "pure" states $|lm\rangle$, with the number in each state being given by $|C_m|^2 N = n_m$. However, the physics is completely different in these two cases since, in case (1), interference effects between different states $|lm\rangle$ are important, whereas, in case (2), there can be no interference.

The way to cope with this is to introduce a probability *matrix* (or density matrix), defined as follows. For a state $|\psi_l\rangle = \sum_m C_m |lm\rangle$, as in case (1), we have:

$$\langle l'm'| P |lm\rangle = \delta_{ll'}\langle l'm' \mid \psi_l\rangle\langle\psi_l \mid lm\rangle$$
$$\equiv \delta_{ll'}C_{m'}C_m^* \tag{132a}$$

For a mixture, the obvious generalization is

$$\langle l'm'| P |lm\rangle = \delta_{ll'}\frac{1}{N}\sum_k n_k\langle l'm' \mid \psi_k\rangle \langle\psi_k \mid lm\rangle \tag{132b}$$

where

$$n_k = \text{number of particles in state } |\psi_k\rangle.$$

In particular, if, as in case (2), each particle is in a "pure" state, $|lm''\rangle$, we have from Eq. (132b)

$$\langle l'm'| P |lm\rangle = \delta_{ll'}\sum_{m''} \frac{n_{m''}}{N} \langle l'm' \mid lm''\rangle \langle lm'' \mid lm\rangle$$
$$= \frac{n_m}{N} \delta_{ll'} \delta_{mm'} \tag{132c}$$

That is, for a system of particles each in one of the "pure" states $|lm\rangle$, the density matrix is diagonal, whereas for a homogeneous system it is factorable in the form (132a). It should be noted that the diagonal terms of $\langle l'm'| P |lm\rangle$ are just the probabilities of finding a nucleus in state $|lm\rangle$, so that $Tr[P] = 1$.

Now, using the concept of the density matrix, we can derive the formula for $W(\theta)$. Consider a two-gamma cascade, $A \to B \to C$, where state A is characterized by the quantum numbers J_A, m_A, π_A, and similarly for B and C. The population of state A is characterized by the density matrix $\langle m'_A| P_A |m_A\rangle$, and similarly for states B and C. Since the energy difference between the different m_A's is negligible, they are all populated equally, and it is easily proved that, in this case

$$\langle m'_A| P_A |m_A\rangle = \frac{\delta_{m'_A m_A}}{2J_A + 1} \tag{133}$$

Going back for a moment to the old probability notion and remembering that for the transition $A \to B + \gamma_1$, the transition rate depends on the final state of the nucleus m_B and on the direction Ω_1 assumed for the photon. The transition rate can be written

$$\rho_{fi} = \frac{2\pi}{h} |\langle m_B\Omega_1| H_I |m_A\rangle|^2 \rho_1(\Omega_1) d\Omega_1 \tag{134}$$

where ρ_1 is the density of final photon states per unit energy and solid angle. Thus, the final probability is $P_B(m_B) P(\Omega_1) d\Omega_1$ where $P(\Omega_1) d\Omega_1$ is the probability that the gamma ray is emitted at angle $\Omega_1 = [\theta, \phi]$ within the $d\Omega_1$. This can be written as

$$P_B(m_B)P_1(\Omega_1\sigma_1) \sim \sum_{m_A} |\langle m_B\Omega_1\sigma_1| H_I |m_A\rangle|^2 P_A(m_A)\rho_1(\Omega_1) \quad (135a)$$

where σ_1 denotes the polarization of the gamma ray.

In terms of the density matrix, this can be generalized as

$$\langle m_B'| P_B |m_B\rangle P_1(\Omega_1\sigma_1) \sim \sum_{m_A} \sum_{m_A'} \langle m_B'\Omega_1\sigma_1| H_I |m_A'\rangle \langle m_A'| P_A |m_A\rangle$$
$$\times \langle m_A| H_I |m_B\Omega_1\sigma_1\rangle \rho_1(\Omega_1) \quad (135b)$$

In matrix notation, this becomes

$$P_B P_1 \sim \rho_1 H_I P_A H_I \quad (135c)$$

Since ρ_1 is independent of angle, it becomes just a constant factor and may be dropped since we are only interested in the relative intensity of radiation in different directions.

Since the first radiation is detected by one detector at a fixed angle, which may be taken to coincide with the z-axis, the desired function $W(\theta)$ then is identical with the product of probabilities, $P_1(\theta = 0)P_2(\theta) \, d\Omega$, that the first γ is at $\theta = 0$ and the second is in the ring $[\theta, \theta + d\theta]$. We can find P_2 by the same procedure used for P_1 above, applied to the transition $B \to C + \gamma_2$. This result is

$$P_C P_2 \sim H_I P_B H_I \quad (136a)$$

or

$$\langle m_C'| P_C |m_C\rangle P_2(\Omega_2\sigma_2)$$
$$\sim \sum_{m_B m_B'} \langle m_C'\Omega_2\sigma_2| H_I |m_B'\rangle \langle m_B'| P |m_B\rangle \langle m_B| H_I |m_C\Omega_2\sigma_2\rangle \quad (136b)$$

Since we are only interested in $P_2(\Omega_2\sigma_2)$, we sum over m_C, that is, take the trace of this, because the state $|m_C\rangle$ is not observed.

$$\text{Tr}[P_C(m_C)]P_2(\Omega_2\sigma_2)$$
$$\sim \sum_{m_C} \sum_{m_B m_B'} \langle m_C\Omega_2\sigma_2| H_I |m_B'\rangle \langle m_B'| P_B |m_B\rangle \langle m_B| H_I |m_C\Omega_2\sigma_2\rangle \quad (137)$$

Since the trace is unity, it can be dropped. Combining this with Eqs. (135) gives, with Eq. (133),

$$W(\theta) = P_2(\Omega_2\sigma_2)P_1(\Omega_1\sigma_1)$$
$$\simeq \sum_{m_C} \sum_{m_B m_B'} \sum_{m_A m_A'} \langle m_C\Omega_2\sigma_2| H_I |m_B'\rangle \langle m_B'\Omega_1\sigma_1| H_I |m_A'\rangle$$
$$\times \langle m_A'| P_A |m_A\rangle \langle m_A| H_I |m_B\Omega_1\sigma_1\rangle \langle m_B| H_I |m_C\Omega_2\sigma_2\rangle$$
$$= \frac{1}{2J_A + 1} \sum_{m_C} \sum_{m_B m_B'} \sum_{m_A} \langle m_C\Omega_2\sigma_2| H_I |m_B'\rangle$$
$$\times \langle m_B'\Omega_1\sigma_1| H_I |m_A\rangle \langle m_A| H_I |m_B\Omega_1\sigma_1\rangle \langle m_B| H_I |m_C\Omega_2\sigma_2\rangle$$

or

$$W(\theta) \sim \sum_{m_C} \sum_{m'_B m_B} \sum_{m_A} \langle m_C | H_2 | m'_B \rangle \langle m'_B | H_1 | m_A \rangle$$
$$\times \langle m_A | H_1 | m_B \rangle \langle m_B | H_2 | m_C \rangle$$
$$= \text{Tr}[H_2 H_1 H_1 H_2] \tag{138}$$

where $H_{1,2}$ means the interaction evaluated for a photon having direction $\Omega_{1,2}$ and polarization $\sigma_{1,2}$.

The correlation function $W(\theta)$ can be written in another form:

$$W(\theta) = \text{Tr}\,[H_2 H_2 H_1 H_1]$$
$$= \text{Tr}\,[B \cdot A] \tag{139}$$

where, in matrix form, $B = H_2^2$, $A = H_1^2$, or, algebraically,

$$\langle m_B | A | m'_B \rangle = \sum_{m_A} \langle m_B | H_1 | m_A \rangle \langle m_A | H_1 | m'_B \rangle \tag{140a}$$

$$\langle m_B | B | m'_B \rangle = \sum_{m_C} \langle m_B | H_2 | m_C \rangle \langle m_C | H_2 | m'_B \rangle \tag{140b}$$

This division obviously allows one to carry out transformations for each photon separately. Thus, we investigate a typical term in the expansion of A or B, for instance $\langle m_B | H_1 | m_A \rangle$, which is defined as $\langle m_B \Omega_1 \sigma_1 | H_I | m_A \rangle$. The energy difference $E_B - E_A$ defines the magnitude of the momentum of the photon, whereas $\Omega_1 \sigma_1$ gives us its direction and polarization. In order to correlate this matrix element with that of the multipole expansion, which gives the properties of the photon in terms of angular momentum and parity, a transformation matrix is needed. Denoting the latter quantum numbers by L_1, M_1, π_1, we need the matrix $\langle L_1 M_1 \pi_1 | \Omega_1 \sigma_1 \rangle$. Thus, each term in Eq. (140a) splits up into a sum over various L_1 (such that $|J_B - J_A| \le L_1 \le J_B + J_A$) and M_1. (There is no sum over π_1 since parity is conserved and $\pi_1 = \pi_A \pi_B$.) Denoting the z axis by $\Omega_1 = 0$, we want, particularly, the special case $\langle L_1 M_1 \pi_1 | 0 \sigma_1 \rangle$.

The eigenfunctions belonging to an angular momentum L transform according to the matrices D^L, so that

$$\langle LM\pi | \Omega\sigma \rangle = \sum_m D^L_{Mm}(R^{-1}) \langle Lm\pi | 0\sigma \rangle \tag{141}$$

where R represents the rotation from the z axis to the direction of radiation. The first term of Eq. (140a) transforms in the following manner:

$$\langle m_B \Omega_1 \sigma_1 | H_I | m_A \rangle = \sum_{L_1 M_1} \langle \Omega_1 \sigma_1 | L_1 M_1 \pi_1 \rangle \langle m_B L_1 M_1 \pi_1 | H_I | m_A \rangle \tag{142}$$

Using Clebsch-Gordan coefficients, the last term can be expressed (remembering that the J's have been understood all along) as

$$\langle J_B m_B L_1 M_1 \pi_1 | H_I | J_A m_A \rangle = \sum_{J_A' m_A'} \langle J_B L_1 m_B M_1 | J_A' m_A' \rangle$$
$$\times \langle J_A' m_A' J_B L_1 \pi_1 | H_I | J_A m_A \rangle \tag{143a}$$

Since H_I is basically invariant under rotations, the last matrix element is nonzero only when $J'_A = J_A$, $m'_A = m_A$, and is independent of m_A. The resulting "reduced" matrix element is denoted by $(J_B \| L_1 \pi_1 \| J_A)$, which can be chosen to be real, so Eq. (143a) becomes

$$\langle J_B m_B L_1 M_1 \pi_1 | H_I | J_A m_A \rangle = \langle J_B L_1 m_B M_1 | J_A m_A \rangle (J_B \| L_1 \pi_1 \| J_A) \quad \text{(143b)}$$

Combining this with Eqs. (142) and (141), we get:

$$\begin{aligned}
\langle m_B | H_I | m_A \rangle &\equiv \langle m_B \Omega_1 \sigma_1 | H_I | m_A \rangle \\
&= \sum_{L_1 M_1 m} \langle 0\sigma_1 | L_1 m \pi_1 \rangle D^L_{Mm} \langle J_B L_1 m_B M_1 | J_A m_A \rangle \\
&\quad \times (J_B \| L_1 \pi_1 \| J_A)
\end{aligned} \quad \text{(144)}$$

When this expression is used in Eq. (140), the result is quite unwieldy, but it can be further reduced by using the relations:

$$(D^L_{Mm})^* = (-1)^{M-m} D^L_{-M,-m} \quad \text{(145a)}$$

$$\begin{aligned}
D^L_{Mm} D^{L'}_{M'm'} &= \sum_l \langle LL'mm' | l, m+m' \rangle \\
&\quad \times \langle LL'MM' | l, M+M' \rangle D^l_{M+M',m+m'} \quad \text{(145b)}
\end{aligned}$$

These formulas are combined with the use of Racah's technique, that is, we use the following formula for the product of three Clebsch-Gordan coefficients:

$$\begin{aligned}
\sum \langle l_1 l_2 m_1 m_2 | l_3 m_3 \rangle \langle l_3 l_4 m_3 m_4 | l_5 m_5 \rangle \langle l_2 l_4 m_2 m_4 | l_6 m_6 \rangle \\
= \sqrt{(2l_3+1)(2l_6+1)} \langle l_1 l_6 m_1 m_6 | l_5 m_5 \rangle W(l_1 l_2 l_4 l_5; l_3 l_6) \quad \text{(146)}
\end{aligned}$$

where W is the so called Racah coefficient. Before writing the final expression for the A and B matrices, we introduce, with Racah, the following "radiation parameters."

$$C_{lm}(LL') = \sum_{\mu\mu'} (-1)^{L'-\mu'} \langle LL'\mu, -\mu' | lm \rangle \langle 0\sigma | L\mu\pi \rangle^* \langle 0\sigma' | L'\mu'\pi' \rangle \quad \text{(147)}$$

These parameters are characteristic of the emitted radiation through the transformation matrices $\langle 0\sigma | L\mu\pi \rangle$. It happens that they are also eigenfunctions of the total angular momentum operator with eigenvalues l, m.

Thus we find for the A and B matrices:

$$\begin{aligned}
\langle m'_B | A | m_B \rangle &= \sum_{L_1 L_1'} \sum_{l_1 m_1 m_1'} (-)^{J_B - m_B - l_1} (2J_A + 1)(J_B \| L_1 \pi_1 \| J_A) \\
&\quad \times (J_B \| L_1' \pi_1' \| J_A) \langle J_B J_B m_B, -m'_B | l_1 m_1' \rangle \\
&\quad \times W(J_B J_A l_1 L_1'; L_1 J_B) C_{l_1 m_1}(L_1' L_1) D^{l_1}_{m_1' m_1}(R_1^{-1}) \quad \text{(148a)}
\end{aligned}$$

$$\begin{aligned}
\langle m'_B | B | m_B \rangle &= \sum_{L_2 L_2'} \sum_{l_2 m_2 m_2'} (-)^{J_B - m_B - l_2} (2J_B + 1)(J_C \| L_2 \pi_2 \| J_B) \\
&\quad \times (J_C \| L_2' \pi_2' \| J_B) \langle J_B J_B m_B, -m'_B | l_2 m_2' \rangle \\
&\quad \times W(J_B J_C l_2 L_2'; L_2 J_B) C_{l_2 m_2}(L_2' L_2) D^{l_2}_{m_2' m_2}(R_2^{-1}) \quad \text{(148b)}
\end{aligned}$$

These are now inserted into Eq. (140a) for $W(\theta)$, using the orthogonality of the Clebsch-Gordan coefficients. Specifically,

$$\sum_{m_B m_B} \langle J_B J_B m_B, -m_B' \mid l_1 m_1' \rangle \langle J_B J_B m_B, -m_B' \mid l_2 m_2' \rangle = \delta_{l_1 l_2} \delta_{m_1' m_2'} \quad (149)$$

Also, with l_1 now equal to l_2, and $m_1' = m_2'$, it is possible to combine the two representations of the D's

$$\sum_{m'} D^l_{m' m_2}(R_2^{-1}) D^l_{m' m_1}(R_1^{-1}) = D^l_{m_1 m_2}(R_2^{-1} R_1) \quad (150)$$

so that these final D's refer to the rotation $R_2^{-1} R_1$, which rotates the second rotation into the first (i.e., through the angle θ). Thus we call it $D^l_{m_1 m_2}(\theta)$. This gives

$$
\begin{aligned}
W(\theta) \sim \sum (-1)^l (J_B \| L_1 \pi_1 \| J_A)(J_B \| L_1' \pi_1' \| J_A)(J_C \| L_2 \pi_2 \| J_B) \\
\times (J_C \| L_2' \pi_2' \| J_B) W(J_B J_A l L_1'; L_1 J_B) \\
\times W(J_B J_C l L_2'; L_2 J_B) C_{l m_1}(L_1' L_1) C_{l m_2}(L_2' L_2) D^l_{m_1 m_2}(\theta) \quad (151)
\end{aligned}
$$

where the sum is over L_1, L_1', L_2, L_2', l, m_1, m_2. This looks quite complicated, but it simplifies considerably if the gammas are essentially pure multipole radiations. Then $L_1 = L_1'$ and $L_2 = L_2'$, and the reduced matrix elements are constants which can be factored out. Thus, in this case

$$
\begin{aligned}
W(\theta) = \sum_{l m_1 m_2} (-1)^l W(J_B J_A l L_1; L_1 J_B) W(J_B J_C l L_2; L_2 J_B) \\
\times C_{l m_1}(L_1 L_1) C_{l m_2}(L_2 L_2) D^l_{m_1 m_2}(\theta) \quad (152)
\end{aligned}
$$

It is also interesting to note that the correlation functions, as given by Eq. (151), are the same for the two cascades $J_A(L_1) J_B(L_2) J_C$ and $J_C(L_2) J_B(L_1) L_A$. This can also be seen directly from Eq. (138). In addition, we note that the Racah coefficients, $W(l_1 l_2 l_3 l_4; l_5 l_6)$, vanish unless each of the triplets $(l_1 l_2 l_5)$, $(l_3 l_4 l_5)$, $(l_1 l_3 l_6)$, and, $(l_2 l_4 l_6)$ forms a triangle. Applying these restrictions to Eq. (151) yields selection rules for l

$$0 \leq l \leq \text{Min} (2J_B, 2L_1, 2L_2) \quad (153)$$

In addition, l is always even for linearly polarized gammas.

γ-γ Directional Correlation for Pure Multipoles

If only *directional correlation* is observed, then the functions C_{lm} involve only $m = 0$, since the detectors sum over all linear polarizations and thus are independent of m's (m_1 and m_2 are measured with respect to the direction *to the detector* as the z-axis). In this case, the D^l become Legendre polynomials, and W can be expressed as

$$W(\theta) = \sum_{l=\text{even}} A_l P_l(\cos \theta) \tag{154}$$

with l restricted by Eq. (153).

Calculation of the A_l of Eq. (154) is facilitated by the fact that they can be broken up into two factors (corresponding to the A and B matrices).

$$A_l = F_l(L_1 J_A J_B) F_l(L_2 J_C J_B) \tag{155}$$

From Eqs. (152) and (153),

$$A_l = W(J_B J_A l L, L J_B) C_{l0}(LL) \tag{156}$$

The radiation parameters $C_{l0}(LL)$ follow from Eq. (147)

$$C_{l0}(LL) = \sum_{\mu} (-1)^{L-\mu} \langle LL\mu, -\mu \mid l0 \rangle \sum_{\sigma} \langle 0\sigma \mid L\mu\pi \rangle^* \langle 0\sigma \mid L\mu\pi \rangle$$

where $\mu = \pm 1$. The sum over σ can be calculated easily and is proportional to $2L + 1$. Thus

$$C_{l0}(LL) \propto (-)^{L-1}(2L + 1) \langle L, L, 1, -1 \mid l0 \rangle$$

so that

$$F_l(LJ_A J_B) \sim (-)^{L-1}(2L + 1)\langle LL1, -1 \mid l0 \rangle W(J_B J_A l L, L J_B) \tag{157}$$

Thus, the coefficients F_l can be calculated numerically from Clebsch-Gordan and Racah coefficients. In particular, for the cascade 4(2)2(2)0 we have

$$
\begin{array}{ll}
F_0 = 1 & F_0 = 1 \\
F_2(2, 4, 2) = -0.1707 & F_2(2, 0, 2) = -0.5976 \\
F_4(2, 4, 2) = -0.0085 & F_4(2, 0, 2) = -1.069
\end{array}
$$

$$A_0 = 1$$
$$A_2 = 0.1020$$
$$A_4 = 0.0091$$

so that

$$W(4 \to 2 \to 0, 2, 2, \theta) = 1 + 0.1020 P_2(\theta) + 0.0091 P_4(\theta) \tag{158}$$

For given values of A_l, $W(\theta)$ is determined theoretically. Following this, a least-square fit of Eq. (154) to the experimental values of $W(\theta)$ is obtained for comparison.

It should be pointed out that for multipoles with $L > 2$, an experimental difficulty arises which makes directional correlation experiments difficult. For large L, the half-life becomes longer, and thus the source intensity must be reduced to avoid confusing the L_2 photons from two different L_1 transitions which might occur within the lifetime of state B. Consequently, it is more difficult to obtain adequate counting rates. In addition, if the lifetime of state B exceeds about 10^{-5} sec, exchange of thermal energy tends to destroy correlation. As a result, in practice, only the first three terms of Eq. (22) are experimentally useful.

Examples

1. The angular correlations of 1.17 Mev and 1.33 Mev γ-rays emitted from Ni^{60} in cascade were first studied by Brady and Deutsch.[12] The anisotropic angular correlations can be fitted, by least squares, with the following expression.

$$W(\theta) = 1 + 0.1020P_2(\cos \theta) + 0.0091P_4(\cos \theta)$$

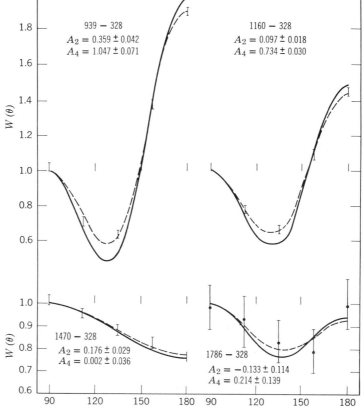

Fig. 12-7 Directional correlation patterns of the four cascades studied in this work. The dashed lines indicate the least-squares fit to the experimental points, while the solid lines result when the correlation for the finite size of the detectors is applied (MacArthur and Johns[13]).

This expression agrees very well with $W(4 \rightarrow 2 \rightarrow 0; 2, 2)$, given above. The spins of the states between which the two γ-rays are emitted are thus 4, 2, and 0, and both the transitions are E2 type.

2. Recently, MacArthur and Johns[13] have published a decay scheme of Ir[194]. The directional correlations of some of the γ-rays emitted in cascade are given in Fig. 12-7. All the correlations show anisotropic distribution. The coefficients A_2 and A_4 were determined by the method of least squares fit of the experimental data which are shown in the figure. This analysis of the angular correlation data agrees with the assumption that the spins of the levels 1.267, 1.480, 1.512, 1.798, and 2.114 Mev in Pt[194] (formed by the beta decay of Ir[194]) are, respectively, 0, 0, 1, 1, and 2.

3. The directional correlation of the 485 to 475 Kev cascade in Rh[105] has been studied by Arya.[14] The A_2 and A_4 coefficients measured in this case are $A_2 = +0.171 \pm 0.016$ and $A_4 = +0.137 \pm 0.004$. The angular

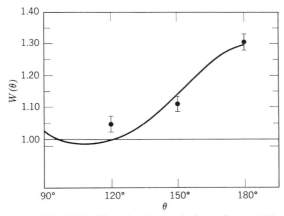

Fig. 12-8 Directional correlation of the 485–475-Kev cascade. Solid line is the least-square fit of the experimental points. Flags indicate the probable error (Arya[14]).

correlations obtained are given in Fig. 12-8 and can be fitted by $W(\theta) = 1 + (0.171 \pm 0.016)P_2(\cos \theta) + (0.137 \pm 0.004)P_4(\cos \theta)$, which agrees with a spin assignment of $\frac{7}{2}, \frac{7}{2}, \frac{7}{2}$ to the ground state, 475, and 960 Kev levels of Rh[105].

References

1. Bishop, G. R., and R. Wilson, in *Handbuch der Physik*, **42**, p. 324, S. Flügge, ed., Springer-Verlag, Berlin, 1957.

2. Wilkinson, D. H., *Ann. Rev. Nucl. Sc.* **9**, 1, 1959; de Swart, J. J., and R. E. Marshak, *Physica*, **25**, 1001, 1959.

3. Rustgi, M. L., W. Zerink, G. Breit, and D. J. Andrews, *Phys. Rev.* **120**, 1881, 1960.

4. Rose, M. E., G. H. Goertzel, B. I. Spinard, J. Harr, and P. Strong, *Phys. Rev.* **83**, 79, 1951.

5. Rose, M. E., in *Theory of Internal Conversion. Beta and Gamma Ray Spectroscopy*, p. 396. K. Siegbahn, ed., North-Holland Publishing Co., Amsterdam, 1956.

6. Sliv, L. A., *Zh. Eksperim. i Teor. Fiz.*, **21**, 770, 1951; Sliv, L. A., and M. A. Listengarten, *Zh. Eksperim. i Teor. Fiz.*, **22**, 29, 1952; Sliv, L. A., *J. Phys. Radium* **16**, 523, 1955; Sliv, L. A., and I. M. Band, *Coefficients of Internal Conversion of Gamma Radiation*, Part 1—K shell, Physico-Technical Institute, Academy of Science, Leningrad, 1956; issued in U.S. as Rept. 571CC Kl, Physics Dept., University of Illinois, Urbana, Ill; Sliv, L. A., and I. M. Band, *Tables of Gamma-ray conversion coefficients*, Part II—L shell, Physico-Technical Institute, Academy of Science, Leningrad, 1958; issued in U.S., as Rept. 581CC LI, Physics Dept., University of Illinois, Urbana, Ill.

7. Dancoff, S., and P. Morrison, *Phys. Rev.*, **55**, 122, 1939.

8. Rose, M. E., *Internal Conversion Coefficients*. North-Holland Publishing Co., Amsterdam, 1958.

9. Kurey, T. J., and R. R. Roy, *Nucl. Phys.* **44**, 670, 1963.

10. Rose, M. E., Analysis of Internal Conversion Data, in *Nuclear Spectroscopy*, Part B, p. 834, F. Ajzenberg-Selove, ed., Academic Press, New York, 1960.

11. Alburger, D. E., Gamma Decay of Bound Nuclear States, in *Nuclear Spectroscopy*, Part A. p. 246, F. Ajzenberg-Selove, ed., Academic Press, New York, 1960.

12. Brady, E. L., and M. Deutsch, *Phys. Rev.* **72**, 870, 1947; **74**, 1541, 1948; **78**, 558, 1950.

13. MacArthur, J. D., and M. W. Johns, *Nucl. Phys.* **61**, 394, 1965.

14. Arya, A. P., *Nucl. Phys.* **40**, 387, 1963.

Problems

1. Expand a plane wave as a sum of multipoles. (Hint: Decompose the plane wave into circularly polarized components.)

2. Show that the angular distribution of the intensity in dipole transitions is

$$I(\theta) \sim 1 + \cos^2 \theta \qquad \text{for} \quad M_i = J_i \quad J_f = J_i - 1$$

$$I(\theta) \sim 1 - \frac{2J_i - 1}{2J_i + 1} \cos^2 \theta \qquad \text{for} \quad M_i = J_i \quad J_f = J_i$$

$$I(\theta) \sim 1 + \frac{J_i(2J_i - 1)}{2J_i^2 + 7J_i + 4} \cos^2 \theta \qquad \text{for} \quad M_i = J_i \quad J_f = J_i + 1$$

3. Obtain the angular correlation function between two successive gamma emissions of multipolarities J_1 and J_2 in the following cases:

J_i	$\frac{1}{2}$	2	0	2
J_1	1	1	2	2
J_{in}	$\frac{3}{2}$	1	2	1
J_2	1	1	2	1
J_f	$\frac{1}{2}$	0	0	0

Where J_i, J_f and J_{in} are the spins of the initial, final, and intermediate states.

4. Calculate the theoretical values (ref. 8) of the K/L ratios of the conversion electrons corresponding to 550 and 627 Kev states of Fig. 12-4. Compare these values with that of the experimental results of Ref. 9 to draw conclusions concerning the nature of these transitions.

5. Derive Eq. (22b).

6. Show that $\mathbf{l}f(r) = 0$ for any function of the radius r only.

7. Prove the statement that l_x and l_y operating on Y_{lm} give linear combinations of $Y_{l,m+1}$ and $Y_{l,m-1}$ (Hint: Use Equation (17b) and $l_{\pm} = l_x \pm il_y$).

8. Derive Eq. (64) from Eq. (62) using Eq. (63).

13

BETA DECAY

13.1 Introduction

Following the discovery of nonconservation of parity by Lee and Yang[1] and its experimental verification,[2] the study of β-decay has undergone a radical change. In spite of this great shift in ideas, Fermi's original theory[3] of beta decay still remains the basis of calculations.

The analysis of a beta spectrum shows that the energy-distribution curve starts from a very low energy, passes through a rather broad maximum, then intersects the energy axis at a definite point, which gives the end point of the transition energy. The Q-value in the β-decay process is, for e^--emission,

$$\frac{Q}{c^2} = M_1(_ZX^A) - M_2(_{Z+1}Y^A)$$

where M_1 and M_2 are the atomic masses of the parent nucleus and the daughter product and Q is the disintegration energy. The condition for emission of an electron is that the mass of the parent nucleus must be greater than the mass of the daughter product, that is, $M_1(_ZX^A) > M_2(_{Z+1}Y^A)$. For positron emission the condition is

$$M_1(_ZX^A) > M_2(_{Z-1}Y^A) + 2m$$

where m is the electron mass. Similarly for electron capture to be energetically possible, the condition is that

$$M_1(_ZX^A) > M_2(_{Z-1}Y^A)$$

These formulas take properly into account the electron rest mass but neglect the binding energy of the electrons to the atom.

The energy available for beta decay can be computed from the difference of masses of the parent and daughter nuclei. This energy corresponds to

496

the point where the beta-decay curve intersects the energy axis, the end-point energy. If the beta particle is the only particle emitted during beta decay, then from energy-momentum conservation we should expect the emitted beta particle to be monoenergetic. However, in any other part of the spectrum other than the end point, it is observed that the energy of the β-particle is less than that computed from the mass difference. The problem is to account for this missing energy. Pauli, in 1927, suggested that the missing energy is carried off by another particle called a neutrino. Fermi gave his famous beta-decay theory on the basis of the neutrino hypothesis. Since there are now three particles involved in the beta-decay process, continuous energy distribution can easily be obtained from the consideration of kinematics. Without going into details we shall conjecture some properties of the neutrino.

The mass of the neutrino must be very small compared to that of the beta particle and may possibly be zero. This is evident from the fact that the maximum energy of the emitted electron completely accounts for the available energy due to the difference of masses between parent and daughter nuclei. From the conservation of charge, we can conclude that the neutrino must be a neutral particle. Considering the decay $n \rightarrow p + e + \bar{\nu}$, the conservation of angular momentum requires that the neutrino ν must have a spin which is an odd integral multiple of $\frac{1}{2}$. The study of the shape of beta spectra[4] indicates that the neutrino spin is $\frac{1}{2}$. The neutrino, like the beta particle, is a fermion. The distinction between a neutrino and an antineutrino will be made later.

13.2   Experimental Verification of the Existence of the Neutrino

The fact that the neutrino has at best a vanishingly small mass, zero charge, and, most likely, a zero magnetic moment posed a formidable problem for its experimental detection. Many ingenious procedures and ideas were developed but, more often than not, the experimental results proved inconclusive. However, in recent years with the introduction of more modern techniques, it has been conclusively demonstrated that the neutrino does indeed exist. We shall briefly describe some of these experiments.

Mass of the Neutrino

Fermi's theory of beta decay suggests that the shape of the beta spectrum depends upon the rest mass of the neutrino.[5] This is more sensitive near the end-point energy. Taking into account a relativistic mass correction term[6] for the neutrino, the momentum distribution for the β-particle can be written as

$$N(p_e)\, dp_e = \text{const.} \times F(Z, E_e)p_e^2(E_{max} - E_e + m_v)$$
$$\times\; [(E_{max} - E_e + m_v)^2 - m_v^2]^{1/2}$$
$$\times\; \left\{1 \mp \frac{m_v}{E_e(E_{max} - E_e + m_v)}\right\} dp_e$$

where E_{max} is the maximum energy of the β-particle including the rest mass energy, and m_v is the mass of the neutrino. The function $F(Z, E_e)$ describes the effect of the Coulomb field of the nucleus on the outgoing β-particles. It changes very slowly for light elements, but its effect is greater for medium and heavy elements. The momentum p_e and the energies E_e and E_{max} are expressed in units of mc and mc^2, respectively. The experimental spectrum is compared with the above theoretical expression with the help of the so-called Kurie plot or Fermi plot. This plot gives a straight line which intersects the energy axis at a definite point, giving the maximum energy E_{max}. Near the high-energy end of the spectrum, the Fermi plot of the previous equation can be written (noting $E_{max} - E_e + m_v \gg m_v$)

$$\left[\frac{N(p)}{F(Z, E_e)p_e^2}\right]^{1/2} = \text{const.} \times \left[(E_{max} - E_e) + m_v\left(1 \mp \frac{1}{2E_e}\right)\right]$$

We have introduced a correction term

$$1 \mp \frac{m_v}{2E_e(E_{max} - E_e + m_v)}$$

which depends upon the mass of the neutrino. Without this correction term if

$$\left[\frac{N(p_e)}{F(Z, E_e)p_e^2}\right]^{1/2}$$

is plotted against E_e, then a straight line is obtained, and by noting its extrapolated intersection on the energy axis, E_{max} is determined. Because of this correction, for a nonvanishing neutrino mass, the Fermi plot near the end-point energy is not a straight line but turns sharply to intersect the energy axis at a point smaller than the value for zero mass neutrino. We observe that the study of the beta spectrum near the end-point energy can provide information concerning the mass of the neutrino. A great many experiments have been carried out[7] on the beta spectrum of H^3, using either proportional counters or the beta spectrograph. In Fig. 13-1, we reproduce the results obtained by Langer and Moffat,[7] which set a possible upper limit of 250 ev for the rest mass of neutrino. Similar conclusions that the rest mass of the neutrino is very close to zero have also been reached by other workers.

Some experiments have been performed to ascertain that a single neutrino is emitted during the electron-capture process.[8] The underlying principle is that in an allowed transition the capture process is typified by the fact that an electron from the K- or L-shell is captured by the nucleus, giving

$$_{z+1}Y^A + e^-_{K,L} \rightarrow {}_z X^A + v$$

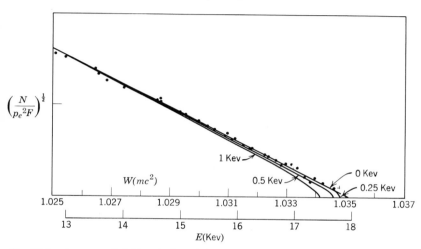

Fig. 13-1 An expanded Fermi plot of the end of the H³ spectrum obtained with a high-resolution magnetic spectrometer. The data are consistent with a neutrino rest mass of zero, and set an upper limit of 250 ev for a possible finite mass, assuming that an antineutrino is emitted in the decay process (Langer and Moffat[7]).

The total energy of the neutrino W_v (including rest mass) is

$$W_v = M(_{z+1}Y^A) - M(_z X^A) - E_r - B_{K,L}$$

where $M(_{z+1}Y^A)$ is the atomic mass of $_{z+1}Y^A$ (initial) and $M(_z X^A)$ is the atomic mass of $_z X^A$ (final). E_r is the energy of the recoiling atom following the capture and $B_{K,L}$ is the binding energy of the electron in the shell from which it is captured. If the total energy of the neutrino is very much greater than the combined energies of recoil E_r and binding $B_{K,L}$, we may write $W_v = M(_{z+1}Y^A) - M(_z X^A)$. The energy of the recoiling atom E_r should be a line spectrum if a single neutrino is emitted during the process or should be a continuous spectrum if more than one are emitted. These experiments have been performed using radioactive sources such as Be⁷, A³⁷, and Cd¹⁰⁷.

In the following we describe the experiment of Smith and Allen,[8] who used Be[7] to study the recoil of Li[7] through an electron-capture process according to the following reaction

$$Be^7 + e^-_{K,L} \rightarrow Li^7 + \nu$$

Be[7] decays with a half-life of 53.6 days. In about 10% of the cases Li[7] is also formed in an excited state which then decays by the emission of a γ-ray, and the recoil-energy spectrum of Li[7] due to the neutrino and the γ-ray will be continuous. Where Li[7] is formed in the ground state, for a single-neutrino emission one should expect a line spectrum of energy 57.3 ± 0.5 ev computed from the Be[7] $-$ Li[7] mass difference. The recoiling ion was first allowed to pass through two grids and then was accelerated by a known voltage into an electron multiplier tube for detection. From knowing the retarding potential needed in order to stop the recoil atom, we can compute the recoil energy. Figure 13-2 gives the relative counting rate as a function of the retarding potential for three different sources.[8] The curve D corresponds to the emission of a single neutrino. Although the shape of the curves A, B, and C do not agree with the single-neutrino hypothesis, however, the point of intersection of these curves is at 56.6 ± 1.0 ev which is in excellent agreement with the expected value of 57.3 ± 0.5 ev for the single-neutrino hypothesis deduced from the relationship discussed above.

The most direct verification of the existence of the neutrino has been demonstrated by Cowan, Reines, Harrison, Kruse, and McGuire.[9] In this experiment these authors studied the interaction of a free neutrino with the target material. The reaction detected was

$$\bar{\nu} + p \rightarrow \bar{e} + n$$

where $\bar{\nu}$, p, $\bar{e}$, and n are respectively antineutrino, proton, positron, and neutron. The cross section for the above reaction according to the two-component neutrino theory (see Section 13.12) is

$$\sigma(E_{\bar{\nu}}) = \frac{G^2}{\pi}\left(\frac{h}{mc}\right)^2\left[E_{\bar{\nu}} - \left(\frac{M_n - M_p}{m}\right)\right]\left[\left(E_{\bar{\nu}} - \frac{M_n - M_p}{m}\right)^2 - 1\right]^{1/2}$$

where G^2 is the coupling constant, $E_{\bar{\nu}}$ the energy of the antineutrino in units of mc^2 and the neutron-proton mass difference is $M_n - M_p$. An abundant supply of antineutrinos can be obtained from the nuclear reactor in which a large number of β-active sources are produced every instant as a result of fission. If N is the number of antineutrinos per fission ($N = 6.1$), then from the two-component neutrino theory, $N\sigma = (6.1 \pm 1) \times 10^{-43}$ cm²/fission.[10] In the experiment of Cowan et al.[9] the antineutrinos produced in the reactor were allowed to bombard a water

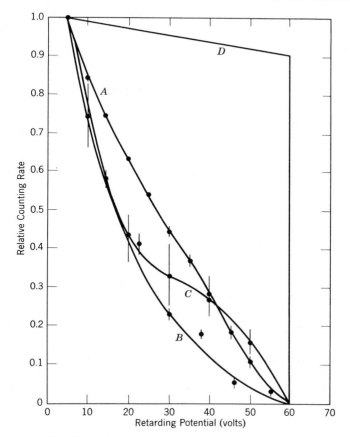

Fig. 13-2 *A*, *B*, and *C* are retarding potential curves
for the neutrino recoils from Be[7] surfaces of decreasing
thickness. *D* is the curve expected if single neutrinos are
emitted during the decay of Be[7] (Smith and Allen[8]).

target containing dissolved CdCl$_2$. Because of the interaction of the $\bar{\nu}$
with a p (the hydrogen nucleus), a positron and a neutron are produced.

The two annihilation γ-rays of 0.5 Mev each, produced by the slowed-
down positrons, were detected by two scintillation counters in coincidence.
The neutron was slowed down in water and finally captured by Cd, giving
γ-rays which were observed in coincidence. The presence of the antineutrino was indicated by the delayed coincidence between the prompt-
positron annihilation pulses and the microsecond delayed pulses produced
by the γ-ray due to capture of the neutron in Cd. The average antineutrino
cross section[9] from fission fragments as measured in the experiment was

$\sigma = (1.10 \pm 0.25) \times 10^{-43}$ cm², in agreement with the predicted value from the two-component neutrino theory.

In the original theory of Fermi, the decay rate and the decay energy determine the coupling strength or interaction constant. The generalized Fermi theory contains five different covariant interactions. The strengths of these interactions appear as free parameters in the theory. These interactions are known as scalar (S), vector (V), tensor (T), axial vector (A), and pseudoscalar (P). The scalar and vector interactions are involved in the allowed Fermi transitions, whereas the tensor and axial vector interactions appear in the allowed Gamow-Teller transitions. Experiments have been performed to determine their relative strengths. Nonconservation of parity in the beta-decay process implies that the emitted β-particles are polarized—a fact which has been confirmed experimentally.[2] Both the two-component neutrino theory[11] and $V - A$ theory suggest that the polarization of $\beta^{\pm}$ particles is exactly $\pm v/c$ and that of neutrinos is exactly $+100\%$ or -100%. The $V - A$ theory[12] predicts that the polarization of the neutrino is opposite in sign to that of the emitted β-particle. In the subsequent sections, we shall discuss various aspects of the beta-decay theory together with some experimental results to examine to what extent the theoretical predictions are supported by experimental measurements.

Lee and Yang[1] pointed out that if β-particles are emitted from oriented nuclei, then the nonconservation of parity can be demonstrated if the intensity of the emitted β-particles with respect to the nuclear polarization direction is asymmetric. The asymmetry in the emitted β-particles was successfully demonstrated by the famous experiment of Wu et al.[2] They used Co^{60} which decays by beta emission mainly to the second excited state of Ni^{60}, which then emits two γ-rays in cascade leaving Ni^{60} in the ground state. Wu et al. actually demonstrated that the angular distribution of β-particles emitted from the oriented Co^{60} was indeed asymmetric as was postulated by Lee and Yang, and thereby verified the nonconservation of parity in a beta-decay process.

Finally, we mention another consequence of the nonconservation of parity; it is the lack of symmetry between neutrino and antineutrino. Consider the beta-decay processes:

β^{-}-decay	$n \rightarrow p + e + \bar{\nu}$
β^{+}-decay	$p \rightarrow n + \bar{e} + \nu$
electron capture	$e + p \rightarrow n + \nu$

where $\bar{\nu}$ (antineutrino) and $\bar{e}$ (positron) are the antiparticles of ν (neutrino) and e (electron). It has been confirmed (see Section 13.13) that the direction of the spin of the antineutrino is along that of its linear momentum. The antineutrino is right-handed and has positive helicity (the rotation of the spin is clockwise when seen from behind). On the other hand the neutrino is left-handed and has negative helicity because its spin and linear momentum are in opposite directions. The sense of rotation of the neutrino's spin is counterclockwise when seen from behind. We therefore note that there are two kinds of neutrino: one kind is only left-handed (neutrino), the other kind is only right-handed (antineutrino).

Another additional fact about neutrinos is worth noting. Danby, Gaillard, Goulianos, Lederman, Mistry, Schwartz, and Steinberger[13] have demonstrated experimentally that there are two different types of neutrinos, ν_e and ν_μ. The neutrino ν_e is involved in the beta-decay process $n \rightarrow p + e + \bar{\nu}_e$ with which we are concerned in this chapter, whereas the neutrino ν_μ is coupled to the μ-particle which appears in the decay of the π-meson according to the reaction $\pi^- \rightarrow \mu^- + \bar{\nu}_\mu$. In the experiment of Danby et al.[13] the interaction of high-energy neutrinos with matter was observed.

The neutrinos were produced by the decay of the pion beam in the Brookhaven Alternate Gradient Synchrotron. It was demonstrated that these neutrinos on interaction with matter produce μ-mesons but do not produce electrons through the inverse beta-decay process. Thus the basic reactions observed from the neutrinos formed from pion decay are $\nu_\mu + n \rightarrow p + \mu^-$ and $\bar{\nu}_\mu + p \rightarrow n + \mu^+$ and the reactions not observed are $\nu_\mu + n \rightarrow p + e^-$ and $\bar{\nu}_\mu + p \rightarrow n + e^+$. From the work of Cowan et al.,[9] there is, however, no doubt that the reactions $\nu_e + n \rightarrow p + e^-$ and $\bar{\nu}_e + p \rightarrow n + e^+$ take place; the neutrinos, however, used in their reaction were produced in the reactor and therefore are the beta-decay neutrinos. The conclusion is therefore that the neutrinos of beta decay (ν_e) are different from the neutrinos of pion decay (ν_μ).

13.3   Interaction Operators

In the theory of beta decay, we deal with the interaction between fermions. It is therefore necessary to classify the forms of all the possible operators by which two fermions can interact. The basic relativistic interaction operators for fermions can be obtained by forming all possible linearly independent products of the Dirac matrices γ_μ which satisfy the following commutation rules

$$\gamma_\mu \gamma_\nu + \gamma_\nu \gamma_\mu = 2\delta_{\mu\nu} \tag{1a}$$

where μ and ν take the values 1, 2, 3, 4. When $\mu \neq \nu$, γ_μ and γ_ν anticommute. For $\mu = \nu$, we have $\gamma_1^2 = \gamma_2^2 = \gamma_3^2 = \gamma_4^2 = 1$. It is well known[14] that the products of the Dirac matrices give sixteen linearly independent elements which can be classified into five groups as follows

$$\Gamma_1 = \Gamma_S = I \tag{1b}$$

$$\Gamma_2 = \Gamma_V = \gamma_\mu (\gamma_k = \boldsymbol{\gamma} = \beta\boldsymbol{\alpha}, \ \gamma_4 = \beta) \tag{1c}$$

$$\Gamma_3 = \Gamma_T = \sigma_{\mu\nu} = -\sigma_{\nu\mu} = \frac{1}{2i}(\gamma_\mu\gamma_\nu - \gamma_\nu\gamma_\mu) \qquad \mu \neq \nu \tag{1d}$$

$$\Gamma_4 = \Gamma_A = \gamma_\mu\gamma_\nu\gamma_\rho = i\gamma\delta\gamma_5 \qquad \mu \neq \nu \neq \rho \tag{1e}$$

$$\Gamma_5 = \Gamma_P = \gamma_5 = \gamma_1\gamma_2\gamma_3\gamma_4 \tag{1f}$$

where the Greek indices μ, ν, and ρ take the value 1, 2, 3, and 4 and the Latin indices take the values 1, 2, and 3. The number of components of

Table 13-1 Large and Small Components of the Interaction Matrices Γ_λ

Γ_λ	Large Components $\Gamma_{\lambda l}$	Small Components $\Gamma_{\lambda s}$
$\Gamma_S = I$	I	
$\Gamma_V = \gamma_\mu$	β	$\beta\boldsymbol{\alpha}$
$\Gamma_T = \sigma_{\mu\nu}$	$\boldsymbol{\sigma} = \sigma_k = \sigma_{ij}$	$\boldsymbol{\alpha}$
$\Gamma_A = i\gamma_\mu\gamma_5$	$-\beta\boldsymbol{\sigma}$	$-\beta\gamma_5$
$\Gamma_P = \gamma_5$		γ_5

Γ_S, Γ_V, Γ_T, Γ_A, and Γ_P are 1, 4, 6, 4, and 1 respectively. These matrices are so defined that under a Lorentz transformation, bilinear quantities formed with the help of the Dirac spinors $\bar{\psi}(\mathbf{x}) = \psi^*(\mathbf{x})\gamma_4$ and $\psi(\mathbf{x})$ [where $\psi^*(\mathbf{x})$ is the Hermitian conjugate of $\psi(\mathbf{x})$], have definite transformation properties. Thus the bilinear quantities

$$\bar{\psi}(\mathbf{x})\Gamma_\lambda\psi(\mathbf{x}), \ \lambda = 1, 2, 3, 4, \text{ and } 5 \text{ for } S, V, T, A, \text{ and } P, \text{ respectively}, \tag{2}$$

transform like a scalar, a four-vector, an antisymmetric tensor of the second rank, a tensor of the third rank—antisymmetric in all three indices (pseudovector or axial vector), and a pseudoscalar, for $\lambda = S, V, T, A$, and P, respectively.

It is of interest to remark that each of the matrices can be separated into "large" and "small" components with respect to the velocity of the Dirac particles involved. This distinction is, of course, possible only when the particles are nonrelativistic ($v/c \ll 1$). The large and small components $\Gamma_{\lambda l}$ and $\Gamma_{\lambda s}$ are given in Table 13-1.

13.4 Interaction Hamiltonian for Beta Decay

The interaction Hamiltonian used to describe beta decay was first proposed by Fermi.[3] It is a four-fermion interaction, the spinors for the four fermions being evaluated at the same space point. It is clear that the basic process of beta decay, namely the decay of the neutron $n \rightarrow p + e^- + \bar{\nu}$, involves four spinor fields corresponding to neutron, proton, electron, and the (anti) neutrino. The Hamiltonian density $\mathscr{H}_F(\mathbf{x})$ proposed by Fermi was

$$\mathscr{H}_F(\mathbf{x}) = g_F \bar{\psi}_p(\mathbf{x}) \psi_n(\mathbf{x}) \bar{\psi}_e(\mathbf{x}) \psi_\nu(\mathbf{x}) + \text{hc} \tag{3a}$$

which can be interpreted as the creation of a proton and an electron with the annihilation of the neutron and neutrino. g_F is the coupling constant and hc stands for the Hermitian conjugate term. The total Hamiltonian H_F is given by

$$H_F = \int d^3x \mathscr{H}_F(\mathbf{x}) \tag{3b}$$

The general forms of the four-fermion interaction can be written using the bilinear quantities $\bar{\psi}\Gamma_\lambda\psi$ introduced in Eq. (2) and the requirements of invariance under Lorentz transformation. The interaction Hamiltonian densities permitted under the requirement of invariance under proper Lorentz transformations (the Lorentz transformations without space and time reflections; improper Lorentz transformations involve space and time reflections which are designated by operators P and T), and which do not contain derivatives of the fields, are given by

$$\mathscr{H}_\lambda(\mathbf{x}) = \frac{1}{\sqrt{2}}(\bar{\psi}_p\Gamma_\lambda\psi_n)[g_\lambda(\bar{\psi}_e\Gamma_\lambda\psi_\nu) + g'_\lambda(\bar{\psi}_e\Gamma_\lambda\gamma_5\psi_\nu)] + \text{hc} \tag{4a}$$

where $\lambda = S, V, T, A$, and P, and g_λ and g'_λ are arbitrary coupling constants. The factor $1/\sqrt{2}$ is inserted in order to conform to usual conventions. Also the argument $\mathbf{x}$ of the spinors is not explicitly shown. The most general form of the interaction for beta decay is therefore a linear combination of the five interactions in Eq. (4a).

$$\mathscr{H}_\beta(\mathbf{x}) = \sum_\lambda \mathscr{H}_\lambda(\mathbf{x}) \qquad \lambda = S, V, T, A, P \tag{4b}$$

The interaction Hamiltonian $\mathscr{H}_\beta(\mathbf{x})$ contains ten complex constants g_λ and g'_λ and therefore twenty real arbitrary parameters. If, however, one imposes invariance with respect to space reflection (P), time reversal (T), or charge conjugation (C), restrictions on the constants g_λ and g'_λ result. From definitions of the operators P, C, and T, it can be shown that invariance of the beta-interaction Hamiltonian under

space reflection P requires	$g'_\lambda = 0$	(5a)
charge conjugation C requires	$g_\lambda = g^*_\lambda$ and $g'_\lambda = -g'^*_\lambda$	(5b)
time reversal T requires	$g_\lambda = g^*_\lambda$ and $g'_\lambda = g'^*_\lambda$	(5c)

Until the discovery of parity nonconservation by Lee and Yang,[1] the beta-decay Hamiltonian was assumed to be invariant under space reflection and time reversal so that it was customary to take $g'_\lambda = 0$ and $g_\lambda = g^*_\lambda$ in Eq. (4b). In the present theory of beta decay, since time reversal is assumed to be a valid invariance (but not space reflection and charge conjugation separately), the only restriction imposed on the coupling constants is $g_\lambda = g^*_\lambda$. It is, of course, a remarkable fact that all existing data on beta decay are in very good agreement with a combination of the vector and axial vector interactions—the V−A theory.

13.5   Transition Probability for Beta Decay

The transition probability for beta decay is given by using the formula derived in the first-order time-dependent perturbation theory

$$w_{fi} = \frac{2\pi}{\hbar} |\langle f| H_\beta |i\rangle|^2 \rho_f \tag{6a}$$

where the matrix element of the beta-interaction H_β between the initial state Φ_i and the final state Φ_f of the complete system (nucleus and other relevant light particles) is

$$\langle f| H_\beta |i\rangle = \int d^3x \Phi^*_f(\mathbf{x}) \mathcal{H}_\beta(\mathbf{x}) \Phi_i(\mathbf{x}) \tag{6b}$$

and ρ_f is the density of states in the final system. The final state of the system is specified by the electron and neutrino momenta and energies, (p_e, E_e) and (p_v, E_v), with $cp_v = E_v$ (rest mass of neutrino = 0). If E_f denotes the energy of the final system, we have

$$\rho_f \, dE_f = V^2 \frac{p_e^2 \, dp_e \, d\Omega_e}{(2\pi\hbar)^3} \frac{p_v^2 \, dp_v \, d\Omega_v}{(2\pi\hbar)^3} \tag{7a}$$

where

$$E_f = \sqrt{M_f^2 c^4 + c^2(\mathbf{p}_e + \mathbf{p}_v)^2} + \sqrt{m^2 c^4 + c^2 p_e^2} + cp_v \tag{7b}$$

$$= E_i = M_i c^2$$

and M_i and M_f are the masses of the initial and final nuclei. From Eq. (7b) we obtain, after neglecting terms of order $(p_v/M_f c)$,

$$\rho_f \simeq V^2 \frac{p_e^2 \, dp_e \, d\Omega_e p_v^2 \, d\Omega_v}{c(2\pi\hbar)^6} \tag{7c}$$

$$= V^2 \frac{p_e E_e \, dE_e \, d\Omega_e p_v^2 \, d\Omega_v}{c^3(2\pi\hbar)^6} \tag{7d}$$

where we have used $E_e^2 = m^2 c^4 + c^2 p_e^2$.

We will first treat the case of a parity-conserving beta interaction; i.e. take $g'_\lambda = 0$ in Eqs. (4a) and (4b). The beta-decay interaction is given by

$$\mathscr{H}_\beta(\mathbf{x}) = \sum_\lambda \mathscr{H}_\lambda(\mathbf{x}) \qquad \lambda = S, V, T, A, P \tag{8a}$$

where

$$\mathscr{H}_\lambda(\mathbf{x}) = g_\lambda(\bar{\psi}_p \Gamma_\lambda \psi_n)(\bar{\psi}_e \Gamma_\lambda \psi_\nu) \tag{8b}$$

In order to write down the matrix element $\langle f \mid H_\beta \mid i \rangle$, Eq. (6b), between the initial and final states of the system, we make the following observations.

1. The energies involved in beta decay are of the order of a few Mev so that the nucleus (and nucleons) can be treated in the nonrelativistic approximation. This implies that the operators Γ_λ between the states of the nucleus can be replaced by their large components $\Gamma_{\lambda l}$ shown in Table 14-1 with $\beta \approx 1$.

2. The nucleus consists of A nucleons and it is possible for each nucleon to undergo a beta transition. Introducing the isotopic spin operator $\tau_n^{(+)} = \frac{1}{2}(\tau_x + i\tau_y)_n$ which carries out the transformation of the nth neutron into a proton, we should make the following replacement for the matrix element between the initial and final states $\Psi_i(\mathbf{x})$ and $\Psi_f(\mathbf{x})$ of the nucleus

$$\overline{\Psi}_f(\mathbf{x})\Gamma_{\lambda l}\Psi_i(\mathbf{x}) \to \sum_{n=1}^{A} \overline{\Psi}_f(\mathbf{x})\Gamma_{\lambda l}\tau_n^{(+)}\Psi_i(\mathbf{x})$$

3. The electron and the antineutrino are emitted with momenta $\mathbf{p}_e$ and $\mathbf{p}_\nu$. We write the wave functions of the electron and antineutrino in the momentum space representation, calculating the matrix elements between plane-wave states. Also we neglect the Coulomb interaction of the electron with the nucleus.

In view of statements 1 to 3, Eq. (6b) for the matrix element $\langle f \mid H_\beta \mid i \rangle$ can be written as follows:

$$\langle f \mid H_\beta \mid i \rangle = \frac{1}{V} \sum_{n=1}^{A} \sum_{\lambda=1}^{5} g_\lambda \int d^3x (\overline{\Psi}_f(\mathbf{x})\Gamma_{\lambda l}\tau_n^{(+)}\Psi_i(\mathbf{x}))$$
$$\times (\bar{u}_e^{(+)}(\mathbf{p}_e)\Gamma_\lambda u_\nu^{(-)}(-\mathbf{p}_\nu))e^{[-i\mathbf{x}\cdot(\mathbf{p}_e+\mathbf{p}_\nu)/\hbar]} \tag{8c}$$

where $\int d^3x$ represents integration (and summation) over the nuclear variables.

The exponential factor $\exp[-i(\mathbf{x}, \mathbf{p}_e + \mathbf{p}_\nu)/\hbar] \simeq 1$ if $|\mathbf{x}| < (\hbar/p_e)$ and $(\hbar/p_\nu)$; that is, as long as $|\mathbf{x}|$ is less than the Compton wavelength of the light particles. Since the energies of the light particles involved in beta decay are of the order of a few Mev, the Compton wavelengths of the electron and neutrino λ_e and $\lambda_\nu \simeq 10^{-11}$ cm are about one hundred times larger than the nuclear sizes over which integration occurs. It is therefore justifiable to approximate the exponential factor inside the integral by unity. Thus we have

$$\langle f | H_\beta | i \rangle \simeq \frac{1}{V} \sum_{\lambda=1}^{5} g_\lambda \langle \Psi'_f | \; \Gamma_{\lambda l} | \Psi'_i \rangle (\bar{u}_e^{(+)}(\mathbf{p}_e) \Gamma_\lambda u_\nu^{(-)}(-\mathbf{p}_\nu)) \qquad (8d)$$

where the nuclear matrix element is

$$\langle \Psi'_f | \; \Gamma_{\lambda l} | \Psi'_i \rangle = \sum_{n=1}^{A} \int d^3 x (\overline{\Psi}_f(\mathbf{x}) \Gamma_{\lambda l} \tau_n^{(+)} \Psi_i(\mathbf{x})) \qquad (8e)$$

Substituting Eqs. (7d) and (8d) in Eq. (6a) we obtain for the transition probability per unit time

$$w_{fi} = \frac{1}{(2\pi)^5 c^5 \hbar^7} \, p_e E_e (E_{max} - E_e)^2 \left| \sum_{\lambda=1}^{5} g_\lambda \langle \Psi'_f | \; \Gamma_{\lambda l} | \Psi'_i \rangle \right.$$
$$\left. \times (\bar{u}_e^{(+)}(\mathbf{p}_e) \Gamma_\lambda u_\nu^{(-)}(-\mathbf{p}_\nu)) \right|^2 dE_e \, d\Omega_e \, d\Omega_\nu \qquad (9)$$

where we have replaced $cp_\nu = E_{max} - E_e$, E_{max} being the maximum energy of the electron in the beta decay.

13.6 Nuclear Matrix Elements for Unpolarized Initial and Final Nucleus

If the initial nucleus is unpolarized (that is, it has no preferential orientation in space), we must average over the different orientations of the initial nucleus. This involves the operation $\dfrac{1}{2j_i + 1} \sum\limits_{m_i}$ which sums over the various magnetic quantum numbers m_i of the initial nucleus of spin j_i and takes the average. Similarly, if we are not interested in observing the polarization of the final nucleus, we must sum over the magnetic quantum numbers of the final nucleus by the operation $\sum\limits_{m_f}$. We therefore replace the matrix elements squared as follows

$$|\langle f | H_\beta | i \rangle|^2 = \frac{1}{V^2} \left| \sum_{\lambda=1}^{5} g_\lambda \langle \Psi'_f | \; \Gamma_{\lambda l} | \Psi'_i \rangle (\bar{u}_e^{(+)}(\mathbf{p}_e) \Gamma_\lambda u_\nu^{(-)}(-\mathbf{p}_\nu)) \right|^2$$

$$\rightarrow \frac{1}{V^2} \frac{1}{2J_i + 1} \sum_{m_i, m_f} \left| \sum_{\lambda=1}^{5} g_\lambda \langle \Psi'_f | \; \Gamma_{\lambda l} | \Psi'_i \rangle [\bar{u}_e^{(+)}(\mathbf{p}_e) \Gamma_\lambda u_\nu^{(-)}(-\mathbf{p}_\nu)] \right|^2$$

$$= \frac{1}{V^2} \frac{1}{2J_i + 1} \sum_{m_i, m_f} \sum_{\lambda, \lambda'=1}^{5} g_\lambda g_{\lambda'}^* \langle \Psi'_f | \; \Gamma_{\lambda l} | \Psi'_i \rangle \langle \Psi'_f | \; \Gamma_{\lambda' l} | \Psi'_i \rangle^*$$
$$\times [\bar{u}_e^{(+)}(\mathbf{p}_e) \Gamma_\lambda u_\nu^{(-)}(-\mathbf{p}_\nu)][\bar{u}_e^{(+)}(\mathbf{p}_e) \Gamma_{\lambda'} u_\nu^{(-)}(-\mathbf{p}_\nu)]^* \qquad (10)$$

where the nuclear matrix elements $\langle \Psi_f | \Gamma_{\lambda l} | \Psi_i \rangle$ are defined by Eq. (8e) and $\Gamma_{\lambda l}$ are given in Table 13-1. Since the nuclei are unpolarized, it is easy to calculate the products of the nuclear matrix elements in Eq. (10).

We have from Eq. (8e)

$$\frac{1}{2j_i + 1} \sum_{m_i, m_f} \langle \Psi_f | \Gamma_{\lambda l} | \Psi_i \rangle \langle \Psi_f | \Gamma_{\lambda' l} | \Psi_i \rangle^* \equiv (\langle \Psi_f | \Gamma_{\lambda l} | \Psi_i \rangle \langle \Psi_f | \Gamma_{\lambda' l} | \Psi_i \rangle^*)_{\text{av}}$$

$$= \left[\left(\sum_{n=1}^{A} \int d^3 x \Psi_f(\mathbf{x}) \Gamma_{\lambda l} \tau_n^{(+)} \Psi_i(\mathbf{x}) \right) \left(\sum_{n'=1}^{A} \int d^3 x' \Psi_f(\mathbf{x'}) \Gamma_{\lambda' l} \tau_{n'}^{(+)} \Psi_i(\mathbf{x'}) \right)^* \right]_{\text{av}}$$

(11a)

where the symbol av denotes the operation $[1/(2j_i + 1)] \sum_{m_i, m_f}$. The following cases arise:

1. $\Gamma_{\lambda l} = \Gamma_{\lambda' l} = 1$ for $\lambda, \lambda' = S$ or V

$$(\langle \Psi_f | 1 | \Psi_i \rangle \langle \Psi_f | 1 | \Psi_i \rangle^*)_{\text{av}} = \left| \sum_{n=1}^{A} \int d^3 x \Psi_f^*(\mathbf{x}) \tau_n^{(+)} \Psi_i(\mathbf{x}) \right|^2 = |M_F|^2 \quad (11b)$$

where

$$M_F = \sum_{n=1}^{A} \int d^3 x \Psi_f^*(\mathbf{x}) \tau_n^{(+)} \Psi_i(\mathbf{x}) \quad (11c)$$

and in arriving at the right-hand side of Eq. (11b), we have used the fact that, since each magnetic quantum number state m_i is equally probable, $\sum_{m_i}$ cancels the factor $2j_i + 1$ in the denominator.

2. $\Gamma_{\lambda l} = 1$ (and $\pm \boldsymbol{\sigma}$) $\qquad \Gamma_{\lambda' l} = \pm \boldsymbol{\sigma}$ (and 1)

$$\text{for} \quad \lambda = S \text{ or } V \quad (\text{and } T, A)$$
$$\lambda' = T, A \quad (\text{and } S \text{ or } V)$$

$$(\langle \Psi_f | 1 | \Psi_i \rangle \langle \Psi_f | \boldsymbol{\sigma} | \Psi_i \rangle^*)_{\text{av}} = 0 \quad (11d)$$

since the average of a single $\boldsymbol{\sigma}$-operator for an unpolarized nucleus is zero.

3. $\Gamma_{\lambda l} = \pm \boldsymbol{\sigma}, \Gamma_{\lambda' l} = \pm \boldsymbol{\sigma}$ for $\lambda, \lambda' = T$ and A (lower sign for A)

We consider the two possibilities: (a) $\lambda = \lambda'$, and (b) $\lambda \neq \lambda'$,

(a) $\lambda = \lambda'$

$$(\langle \Psi_f | \pm \sigma_k | \Psi_i \rangle \langle \Psi_f | \pm \sigma_{k'} | \Psi_i \rangle^*)_{\text{av}} = (\langle \Psi_f | \sigma_k | \Psi_i \rangle \langle \Psi_i | \sigma_{k'}^* | \Psi_f \rangle)_{\text{av}}$$

$$= \delta_{kk'} (\langle \Psi_f | \sigma_k | \Psi_i \rangle \langle \Psi_i | \sigma_{k'}^* | \Psi_f \rangle)_{\text{av}}$$

where the $\delta_{kk'}$ appears since the operators σ_x and σ_y change the magnetic quantum number of the state on which they operate; thus, in order to obtain a nonzero result, k and k' must be the same. Also, since

$$\sigma_x^2 = \sigma_y^2 = \sigma_z^2 = \tfrac{1}{3} \sum_{k=1}^{3} \sigma_k^2 = \tfrac{1}{3} (\boldsymbol{\sigma} \cdot \boldsymbol{\sigma}),$$

we can rewrite the above equation as follows:

$$((\langle\Psi_f| \pm\sigma_k |\Psi_i\rangle\langle\Psi_f| \pm\sigma_{k'} |\Psi_i\rangle^*)_{\text{av}} = \tfrac{1}{3}\delta_{kk'}(|\langle\Psi_f| \boldsymbol{\sigma} |\Psi_i\rangle|^2)_{\text{av}}$$

$$= \tfrac{1}{3}\delta_{kk'} |M_{GT}|^2 \tag{11e}$$

where

$$|M_{GT}|^2 = \left(\sum_{k=1}^{3} \left| \sum_{n=1}^{A} \int d^3x\Psi_f^*(\mathbf{x})\sigma_k\tau_n^{(+)}\Psi_i(\mathbf{x}) \right|^2\right)_{\text{av}} \tag{11f}$$

(b) $\lambda \neq \lambda'$

$$((\langle\Psi_f| \pm\sigma_k |\Psi_i\rangle\langle\Psi_f| \mp\sigma_{k'} |\Psi_i\rangle^*)_{\text{av}} = -\tfrac{1}{3}\delta_{kk'} |M_{GT}|^2 \tag{11g}$$

The nuclear matrix elements M_F and M_{GT} defined by Eqs. (11c) and (11f) are referred to as the Fermi and Gamow-Teller matrix elements.

13.7 Nuclear Matrix Elements for Beta Decay of Polarized Nuclei

We now consider the case of the initial nucleus polarized in a specific direction. We denote by $w(m_i)$ the weight factors which specify the relative population of the orientation m_i in the initial nucleus. Thus $\sum_{m_i} w(m_i) = 1$, and $w(m_i) = (1/2j_i + 1)$ for an unpolarized nucleus. The nuclear matrix elements involved for beta decay of polarized nuclei corresponding to cases (1) to (3) are given as follows:

1. $\lambda,\lambda' = S$ or V

$$((\langle\Psi_f| \Gamma_{\lambda l} |\Psi_i\rangle\langle\Psi_f| \Gamma_{\lambda'l} |\Psi_i\rangle^*)_{\text{avp}} = |M_F|^2 \tag{12a}$$

2. $\lambda = S$ or V (and T, A); $\lambda' = T, A$ (and S or V)

$$((\langle\Psi_f| \Gamma_{\lambda l} |\Psi_i\rangle \langle\Psi_f| \Gamma_{\lambda'l} |\Psi_i\rangle^*)_{\text{avp}} = \sum_{m_i,m_f} w(m_i)\langle\Psi_f| 1 |\Psi_i\rangle \langle\Psi_f| \pm\sigma_k |\Psi_i\rangle^*$$

$$= \sum_{m_i,m_f} w(m_i)\left(\sum_{n=1}^{A} \int d^3x\Psi_f^*(\mathbf{x})\tau_n^{(+)}\Psi_i(\mathbf{x})\right)\left(\sum_{n=1}^{A} \int d^3x\Psi_f^*(\mathbf{x})(\pm\sigma_k)\tau_n^{(+)}\Psi_i(\mathbf{x})\right)^* \tag{12b}$$

3. $\lambda,\lambda' = T, A$

$$((\langle\Psi_f| \Gamma_{\lambda l} |\Psi_i\rangle \langle\Psi_f| \Gamma_{\lambda'l} |\Psi_i\rangle^*)_{\text{avp}}$$

$$= \pm \sum_{m_i,m_f} w(m_i)\langle\Psi_f| \pm\sigma_k |\Psi_i\rangle \langle\Psi_f| \pm\sigma_{k'} |\Psi_i\rangle^*$$

$$= \pm \sum_{m_i,m_f} w(m_i)\left(\sum_{n=1}^{A} \int d^3x\Psi_f^*(\mathbf{x})\sigma_k\tau_n^{(+)}\Psi_i(\mathbf{x})\right)$$

$$\times \left(\sum_{n=1}^{A} \int d^3x\Psi_f^*(\mathbf{x})\sigma_{k'}\tau_n^{(+)}\Psi_i(\mathbf{x})\right)^* \tag{12c}$$

where the plus sign is for $\lambda = \lambda'$ and the minus sign for $\lambda \neq \lambda'$. We will evaluate these fully, together with the calculation of the matrix elements of the leptons.

13.8 Fermi and Gamow-Teller Selection Rules for Allowed Beta Decay

Equations (11c) and (11f) for the Fermi and Gamow-Teller nuclear matrix elements lead to selection rules for the change in spin and parity of the nuclear states. In the Fermi matrix element M_F, the operator connecting the initial and final nuclear states is the unit operator, which is a scalar. Therefore no change in spin and parity is involved. In the Gamow-Teller nuclear matrix element M_{GT}, however, we calculate the matrix elements of the spin operator σ between the initial and final nuclear states. Since σ is a pseudovector, which has three components, but is not changed under space reflection, the initial and final spins of the nucleus are coupled vectorially by a unit vector and the two states have the same parity. Thus we can summarize the selection rules for allowed beta decay as follows:

$$\Delta j = 0 \qquad \Delta P = 0 \qquad \text{Fermi selection rule} \qquad (13a)$$

$$\begin{cases} \Delta j = \pm 1, 0; \ j_i = 0 \to j_f = 0 & \text{is forbidden} \quad \text{Gamow-Teller} \\ \Delta P = 0 & \text{selection rule} \end{cases} \qquad (13b)$$

In the beta-decay process, two leptons of spin $\tfrac{1}{2}$ each are emitted. The spin orientations of these leptons may be parallel or antiparallel. We can therefore think of electrons and neutrinos as being emitted in a singlet state (spins antiparallel) or in a triplet state (spins parallel). In the Fermi selection rule which requires $\Delta j = 0$ (that is, $j_i = j_f$), the electrons and neutrinos are emitted in the singlet state. If the leptons are emitted in the triplet state, we have $\mathbf{j}_f = \mathbf{j}_i + \mathbf{1}$; consequently, $j_f = j_i$ or $j_i \pm 1$, which gives the selection rules

$$\Delta j = j_f - j_i = 0, \pm 1$$

for the Gamow-Teller transitions. Both Fermi and Gamow-Teller (G-T) selection rules offer $\Delta j = 0$, but from the consideration of the spin orientation the $0^+ \to 0^+$ transition according to the G-T selection rule is forbidden, although $\Delta j = 0$. Hence the $0^+ \to 0^+$ transition is a pure allowed Fermi transition. One excellent example of an allowed Fermi transition is O^{14} which decays by the emission of a positron from the state 0^+ of O^{14} to the state 0^+ of N^{14}. On the other hand, a pure Gamow-Teller transition is characterized by $\Delta j = \pm 1$ and a typical example is the case of He^6 which decays by $0^+ \to 1^+$ transition.

The allowed and forbidden nature of the transitions is often determined from the estimation of a quantity which is known as the ft-value. The ft-value is the product of a dimensionless function f multiplied by the half-life of beta decay. The product ft depends upon the atomic number, the end-point energy, and mean life τ (note: half-life/mean life $= 0.693$). The mean life τ of an allowed beta emitter can be expressed in terms of (1) the square of the matrix element $|M|^2$ as given in Eqs. (11b) and (11f), (2) $F(Z, E_e)$ which gives the effect of the Coulomb field upon the emitted beta particles, and (3) a statistical factor which indicates how the energy is distributed among the beta particles

$$\frac{1}{\tau} = G^2 |M|^2 \int_1^{E_{\max}} F(Z, E_e) E_e p_e (E_{\max} - E_e)^2 \, dE_e$$

where G^2 is a constant and represents the Fermi coupling constant and $E_{\max}$ is the maximum energy of the beta particles. For $Z = 0$, the value of F is unity; it varies very slowly at small values of Z but more rapidly after $Z = 20$. Classically, we may visualize the effect of the nuclear Coulomb field upon the emitted β-particles in the following way: If the emitted β-particle is an electron, it will be decelerated by the positively charged nucleus, so that the electron spectrum should contain more small-energy electrons than are given by the statistical factor alone. Similarly, for positron emission, because of the repulsion due to the Coulomb field, the positron spectrum should contain a smaller number of very-low-energy positrons. The effect of the nuclear Coulomb field can be estimated as a perturbation on the electron wave function.

The value of the integral can be computed and can be represented by a function $f(Z, E_{\max})$. The preceding equation can be rewritten as

$$\frac{1}{\tau} = G^2 |M|^2 f(Z, E_{\max})$$

or

$$f\tau = \frac{1}{G^2|M|^2}$$

In practice, ft is usually written, rather than $f\tau$, keeping in mind the relationship between the half-life and mean life. The allowed transitions which show small spin change in the transition have small ft-value while higher ft-values are usually obtained for large spin change in the transition. Some typical examples are: for $n(\frac{1}{2}^+) \rightarrow p(\frac{1}{2}^+)$, the $\log_{10} ft = 3.075$; for $H^3(\frac{1}{2}^+) \rightarrow He^3(\frac{1}{2}^+)$, the $\log_{10} ft$-value is 3.06; for $He^6(0^+) \rightarrow Li^6(1^+)$, $\log_{10} ft = 2.91$; and for $O^{14}(0^+) \rightarrow N^{14}(0^+)$, the value is 3.49.

13.9   Matrix Elements between Lepton States for Unpolarized Electron and Neutrino

The matrix elements between lepton states appearing in the expression for the transition probability, Eqs. (9) and (10), are

$$|\mathcal{M}_{ev}^{\lambda\lambda'*}|^2 = (\bar{u}_e^{(r)(+)}(\mathbf{p}_e)g_\lambda\Gamma_\lambda u_v^{(s)(-)}(-\mathbf{p}_v))(\bar{u}_e^{(r)(+)}(\mathbf{p}_e)g_{\lambda'}\Gamma_{\lambda'}u_v^{(s)(-)}(-\mathbf{p}_v))^*$$

with

$$\lambda, \lambda' = S, V, T, \text{ and } A \tag{14a}$$

where the superscripts r and s indicate the spin states of the electron and neutrino respectively, and λ, λ' do not take the value P since, in the non-relativistic approximation for the nucleus, the contribution from the pseudoscalar interaction can be neglected. If we are not interested in the polarization directions of the electron and neutrino, we must sum over their spin states. Thus, Eq. (14a) should be replaced by

$$|\mathcal{M}_{ev}^{\lambda,\lambda'*}|^2 = \sum_{r,s=1}^{2} (\bar{u}_e^{(r)(+)}(\mathbf{p}_e)g_\lambda\Gamma_\lambda u_v^{(s)(-)}(-\mathbf{p}_v))$$
$$\times (\bar{u}_v^{(s)(-)}(-\mathbf{p}_v)\gamma_4 g_{\lambda'}^*\Gamma_{\lambda'}^*\gamma_4 u_e^{(r)(+)}(\mathbf{p}_e)) \tag{14b}$$

The sum over the spins is most readily accomplished by inserting the projection operators

$$\Lambda^{(\pm)}(\pm\mathbf{p}_e) = \frac{\pm mc^2 - i\gamma p_e c}{2E_e}$$

for the electron and the neutrino and then making use of the completeness property of the spinors [Appendix, Section 21]. We then obtain from Eq. (14b)

$$|\mathcal{M}_{ev}^{\lambda,\lambda'*}|^2 = \frac{c^2}{4E_e E_v} \operatorname{Sp} [(i\gamma p_e - mc)g_\lambda\Gamma_{\lambda}(i\gamma p_v)\gamma_4 g_{\lambda'}^*\Gamma_{\lambda'}^*\gamma_4] \tag{14c}$$

We next discuss the case of unpolarized nuclei. From Eqs. (10), (11d), (11e), and (11g) we can write the relevant matrix element squared $|\langle f| H_\beta |i\rangle|^2$ for beta decay. If we include the parity-nonconserving terms in the interaction, as in Eq. (4a), we should make the following replacement in Eq. (10):

$$g_\lambda\Gamma_\lambda \to \Gamma_\lambda(g_\lambda + g_\lambda'\gamma_5)$$
$$g_{\lambda'}^*\Gamma_{\lambda'}^* \to (g_{\lambda'}^* + g_{\lambda'}'^*\gamma_5)\Gamma_{\lambda'}^* \tag{14d}$$

so that Eq. (14c) is replaced by

$$|M_{ev}^{\lambda\lambda'*}|^2 = \frac{c^2}{4E_e E_v} \operatorname{Sp} [(i\gamma p_e - mc)\Gamma_{\lambda}(g_\lambda + g_\lambda'\gamma_5)(i\gamma p_v)\gamma_4$$
$$\times (g_{\lambda'}^* + g_{\lambda'}'^*\gamma_5)\Gamma_{\lambda'}^*\gamma_4)] \tag{14e}$$

We therefore obtain the following result for the beta decay matrix element squared

$$|\langle f| H_\beta |i\rangle|^2_{\text{unpolarized}} = \frac{1}{2V^2} [|M_{ev}^{SS*}|^2 + |M_{ev}^{VV*}|^2 + 2 \operatorname{Re} |M_{ev}^{SV*}|^2] |M_F|^2$$

$$+ \frac{1}{6V^2} [|M_{ev}^{TT*}|^2 + |M_{ev}^{AA*}|^2 - 2 \operatorname{Re} |M_{ev}^{TA*}|^2] |M_{GT}|^2 \quad (15)$$

where the $|M_{ev}|$'s are given by

$$|M_{ev}^{SS*}|^2 = \frac{c^2}{4E_e E_v} \operatorname{Sp} [(i\gamma p_e - mc)(g_S + g_S'\gamma_5)(i\gamma p_v)\gamma_4(g_S^* + g_S'^*\gamma_5)\gamma_4]$$
$$(15a)$$

$$|M_{ev}^{VV*}|^2 = \frac{c^2}{4E_e E_v} \operatorname{Sp} [(i\gamma p_e - mc)\gamma_4(g_V + g_V'\gamma_5)(i\gamma p_v)\gamma_4$$
$$\times (g_V^* + g_V'^*\gamma_5)\gamma_4^*\gamma_4] \quad (15b)$$

$$|M_{ev}^{TT*}|^2 = \frac{c^2}{4E_e E_v} \operatorname{Sp} [(i\gamma p_e - mc)\sigma_k(g_T + g_T'\gamma_5)(i\gamma p_v)\gamma_4$$
$$\times (g_T^* + \gamma_5 g_T'^*)\sigma_k^*\gamma_4] \quad (15c)$$

$$|M_{ev}^{AA*}|^2 = \frac{c^2}{4E_e E_v} \operatorname{Sp} [(i\gamma p_e - mc)i\gamma_k\gamma_5(g_A + g_A'\gamma_5)(i\gamma p_v)\gamma_4$$
$$\times (g_A^* + g_A'^*\gamma_5)(i\gamma_k\gamma_5)^*\gamma_4] \quad (15d)$$

$$|M_{ev}^{SV*}|^2 = \frac{c^2}{4E_e E_v} \operatorname{Sp} [i\gamma p_e - mc)(g_S + g_S'\gamma_5)(i\gamma p_v)\gamma_4$$
$$\times (g_V^* + g_V'^*\gamma_5)\gamma_4^*\gamma_4] \quad (15e)$$

$$|M_{ev}^{TA*}|^2 = \frac{c^2}{4E_e E_v} \operatorname{Sp} [(i\gamma p_e - mc)\sigma_k(g_T + g_T'\gamma_5)(i\gamma p_v)\gamma_4$$
$$\times (g_A^* + g_A'^*\gamma_5)(i\gamma_k\gamma_5)^*\gamma_4] \quad (15f)$$

The γ_4 appearing at the extreme right can be eliminated by moving the one in the center, using the relations, $\gamma_4^2 = 1$, $[\gamma_\mu, \gamma_5]_+ = 0$, $[\gamma_\mu, \gamma_v]_+ = 2\delta_{\mu v}$, and $[\gamma_4, \sigma_k]_- = 0$. Also using the relation $\gamma_5^2 = 1$, we can rewrite the above equations as follows:

$$|M_{ev}^{SS*}|^2 = \frac{c^2}{4E_e E_v} \{(|g_S|^2 + |g_S'|^2) \operatorname{Sp} [(i\gamma p_e - mc)i\gamma p_v]$$
$$+ (g_S g_S'^* + g_S' g_S^*) \operatorname{Sp} [(i\gamma p_e - mc)\gamma_5 i\gamma p_v]\} \quad (16a)$$

$$|M_{ev}^{VV*}|^2 = \frac{c^2}{4E_e E_v} \{(|g_V|^2 + |g_V'|^2) \operatorname{Sp} [(i\gamma p_e - mc)\gamma_4 i\gamma p_v\gamma_4]$$
$$+ (g_V g_V'^* + g_V' g_V^*) \operatorname{Sp} [(i\gamma p_e - mc)\gamma_4 i\gamma p_v\gamma_4\gamma_5]\} \quad (16b)$$

$$|M_{ev}^{TT*}|^2 = \frac{c^2}{4E_eE_v} \{(|g_T|^2 + |g_T'|^2) \; \text{Sp} \; [(i\gamma p_e - mc)\sigma_k i\gamma p_v \sigma_k]$$

$$- (g_T g_T'^* + g_T' g_T^*) \; \text{Sp} \; [(i\gamma p_e - mc)\sigma_k i\gamma p_v \gamma_5 \sigma_k]\} \quad (16c)$$

$$|M_{ev}^{AA*}|^2 = \frac{c^2}{4E_eE_v} \{-(|g_A|^2 + |g_A'|^2) \; \text{Sp} \; [(i\gamma p_e - mc)\gamma_k i\gamma p_v \gamma_k]$$

$$- (g_A g_A'^* + g_A' g_A^*) \; \text{Sp} \; [(i\gamma p_e - mc)\gamma_k i\gamma p_v \gamma_k \gamma_5]\} \quad (16d)$$

$$|M_{ev}^{SV*}|^2 = \frac{c^2}{4E_eE_v} \{(g_S g_V^* + g_S' g_V'^*) \; \text{Sp} \; [(i\gamma p_e - mc)i\gamma p_v \gamma_4]$$

$$+ (g_S g_V'^* + g_S' g_V^*) \; \text{Sp} \; [(i\gamma p_e - mc)\gamma_5 i\gamma p_v \gamma_4]\} \quad (16e)$$

$$|M_{ev}^{TA*}|^2 = \frac{c^2}{4E_eE_v} \{(g_T g_A^* + g_T' g_A'^*) \; \text{Sp} \; [(i\gamma p_e - mc)\sigma_k i\gamma p_v i\gamma_k \gamma_5]$$

$$+ (g_T g_A'^* + g_T' g_A^*) \; \text{Sp} \; [(i\gamma p_e - mc)\sigma_k i\gamma p_v i\gamma_k]\} \quad (16f)$$

The calculations of the spurs can be carried out by using the following relations:

$$\text{Sp (odd number of } \gamma_\mu) = 0 \quad (17a)$$

$$\text{Sp (1)} = 4 \quad (17b)$$

$$\text{Sp} \; (\gamma_\mu \gamma_v) = 4\delta_{\mu v} \quad (17c)$$

$$\text{Sp} \; (\gamma_\mu \gamma_v \gamma_\rho \gamma_\delta) = 4(\delta_{\mu v}\delta_{\rho\delta} - \delta_{\mu\rho}\delta_{v\delta} + \delta_{\mu\delta}\delta_{v\rho}) \quad (17d)$$

$$\text{Sp} \; (\gamma_5) = \text{Sp} \; (\gamma_5\gamma_\mu) = \text{Sp} \; (\gamma_5\gamma_\mu\gamma_v) = \text{Sp} \; (\gamma_5\gamma_\mu\gamma_v\gamma_\rho) = 0 \quad (17e)$$

$$\text{Sp} \; (\gamma_5\gamma_\mu\gamma_v\gamma_\rho\gamma_\delta) = 4\epsilon_{\mu v\rho\delta} \quad (17f)$$

where $\epsilon_{\mu v\rho\delta} = \pm 1$ if an even (odd) number of permutations is required to obtain the order 1, 2, 3, 4. $\epsilon_{\mu v\rho\delta} = 0$ for any two or more equal indices. We consider the evaluation of a few of the above spurs.

$$\text{Sp} \; [(i\gamma p_e - mc)i\gamma p_v] = -4p_e p_v = -4\left(\mathbf{p}_e \cdot \mathbf{p}_v - \frac{E_e E_v}{c^2}\right) \quad (18)$$

$$\text{Sp} \; [(i\gamma p_e - mc)\gamma_4 i\gamma p_v \gamma_4] = \text{Sp} \; [(i\gamma p_e - mc)\gamma_4 i(-\gamma_4\gamma_\mu + 2\,\delta_{4\mu})(p_v)_\mu]$$

$$= \text{Sp} \; [(i\gamma p_e - mc)(-i\gamma p_v + 2i\gamma_4 p_{v4})]$$

$$= 4[p_{e\mu}p_{v\mu} - 2p_{e\mu}p_{v4}\,\delta_{\mu 4}]$$

$$= 4\left[\mathbf{p}_e \cdot \mathbf{p}_v + \frac{E_e E_v}{c^2}\right] \quad (19)$$

The matrix representation for γ_k, γ_4, and σ_k is

$$\gamma_k = \begin{pmatrix} 0 & -i\sigma_k \\ i\sigma_k & 0 \end{pmatrix} \qquad \gamma_4 = \begin{pmatrix} 1 & 0 \\ 0 & -1 \end{pmatrix} \qquad \sigma_k = \begin{pmatrix} \sigma_k & 0 \\ 0 & \sigma_k \end{pmatrix} \qquad (20a)$$

where σ_k are the Pauli matrices. We have, therefore,

$$\mathrm{Sp}\,[(i\gamma p_e - mc)\sigma_k i\gamma p_\nu \sigma_k]$$

$$= \mathrm{Sp} \begin{pmatrix} -\dfrac{E_e}{c} - mc & \boldsymbol{\sigma}\cdot\mathbf{p}_e \\ -\boldsymbol{\sigma}\cdot\mathbf{p}_e & \dfrac{E_e}{c} - mc \end{pmatrix} \begin{pmatrix} \sigma_k & 0 \\ 0 & \sigma_k \end{pmatrix} \begin{pmatrix} -\dfrac{E_\nu}{c} & \boldsymbol{\sigma}\cdot\mathbf{p}_\nu \\ -\boldsymbol{\sigma}\cdot\mathbf{p}_\nu & \dfrac{E_\nu}{c} \end{pmatrix} \begin{pmatrix} \sigma_k & 0 \\ 0 & \sigma_k \end{pmatrix}$$

$$= \mathrm{Sp} \begin{pmatrix} -\left(\dfrac{E_e}{c} + mc\right)\sigma_k & (\boldsymbol{\sigma}\cdot\mathbf{p}_e)\sigma_k \\ -(\boldsymbol{\sigma}\cdot\mathbf{p}_e)\sigma_k & \left(\dfrac{E_e}{c} - mc\right)\sigma_k \end{pmatrix} \begin{pmatrix} -\dfrac{E_\nu}{c}\sigma_k & (\boldsymbol{\sigma}\cdot\mathbf{p}_\nu)\sigma_k \\ -(\boldsymbol{\sigma}\cdot\mathbf{p}_\nu)\sigma_k & \dfrac{E_\nu}{c}\sigma_k \end{pmatrix}$$

$$= \mathrm{Sp}\,2\left[\frac{E_e E_\nu}{c^2}\sigma_k^2 - (\boldsymbol{\sigma}\cdot\mathbf{p}_e)\sigma_k(\boldsymbol{\sigma}\cdot\mathbf{p}_\nu)\sigma_k\right] \qquad (20b)$$

We make use of the following relations

$$\sum_k \sigma_k^2 = 3 \qquad [\sigma_i, \sigma_j]_- = 2i\epsilon_{ijk}\sigma_k \qquad \epsilon_{ijk}\sigma_i\sigma_j = 2i\sigma_k$$

$$(\boldsymbol{\sigma}\cdot\mathbf{p}_1)(\boldsymbol{\sigma}\cdot\mathbf{p}_2) = (\mathbf{p}_1\cdot\mathbf{p}_2) + i\boldsymbol{\sigma}\cdot(\mathbf{p}_1\times\mathbf{p}_2) \qquad (20c)$$

We have then

$$(\boldsymbol{\sigma}\cdot\mathbf{p}_e)\sigma_k(\boldsymbol{\sigma}\cdot\mathbf{p}_\nu)\sigma_k = (\boldsymbol{\sigma}\cdot\mathbf{p}_e)\{(\boldsymbol{\sigma}\cdot\mathbf{p}_\nu)\sigma_k + 2i\epsilon_{klm}\sigma_m p_{\nu l}\}\sigma_k$$

$$= 3(\boldsymbol{\sigma}\cdot\mathbf{p}_e)(\boldsymbol{\sigma}\cdot\mathbf{p}_\nu) + (2i)^2(\boldsymbol{\sigma}\cdot\mathbf{p}_e)\sigma_l p_{\nu l}$$

$$= -[(\mathbf{p}_e\cdot\mathbf{p}_\nu) + i\boldsymbol{\sigma}\cdot(\mathbf{p}_e\times\mathbf{p}_\nu)] \qquad (20d)$$

From Eqs. (20b) and (20d) we have

$$\mathrm{Sp}\,[(i\gamma p_e - mc)\sigma_k i\gamma p_\nu \sigma_k] = 4\left(3\frac{E_e E_\nu}{c^2} + \mathbf{p}_e\cdot\mathbf{p}_\nu\right) \qquad (20e)$$

Similarly,

$$\mathrm{Sp}\,[(i\gamma p_e - mc)\gamma_k i\gamma p_\nu \gamma_k] = 4\left(3\frac{E_e E_\nu}{c^2} - \mathbf{p}_e\cdot\mathbf{p}_\nu\right) \qquad (21)$$

$$\mathrm{Sp}\,[(i\gamma p_e - mc)i\gamma p_\nu \gamma_4] = 4mE_\nu \qquad (22)$$

$$\mathrm{Sp}\,[(i\gamma p_e - mc)\sigma_k i\gamma p_e i\gamma_k \gamma_5] = -12mE_\nu \qquad (23)$$

Substituting the values of spurs, we obtain from Eqs. (15) and (16)

$$
\begin{aligned}
|\langle f | H_\beta | i \rangle|^2_{\text{unpolarized}} = \frac{1}{2V^2} \Bigg[& \{|g_S|^2 + |g_S'|^2\} \left(1 - \frac{\mathbf{p}_e \cdot \mathbf{p}_\nu}{E_e E_\nu} c^2 \right) \\
& + \{|g_V|^2 + |g_V'|^2\} \left(1 + \frac{\mathbf{p}_e \cdot \mathbf{p}_\nu}{E_e E_\nu} c^2 \right) \\
& + \frac{2mc^2}{E_e} \operatorname{Re} \{g_S g_V^* + g_S' g_V'^*\} \Bigg] |M_F|^2 \\
& + \frac{1}{2V^2} \Bigg[\{|g_T|^2 + |g_T'|^2\} \left(1 + \frac{1}{3} \frac{\mathbf{p}_e \cdot \mathbf{p}_\nu}{E_e E_\nu} c^2 \right) \\
& + \{|g_A|^2 + |g_A'|^2\} \left(1 - \frac{1}{3} \frac{\mathbf{p}_e \cdot \mathbf{p}_\nu}{E_e E_\nu} c^2 \right) \\
& + \frac{2mc^2}{E_e} \operatorname{Re} \{g_T g_A^* + g_T' g_A'^*\} \Bigg] |M_{\text{GT}}|^2 \quad (24)
\end{aligned}
$$

The transition probability per unit time w_{fi} is given by Eqs. (9) and (24). The integration over the solid angle $d\Omega_\nu$ can be carried out quite readily. Denoting by θ the angle between the electron momentum and the neutrino momentum and by $v_e = c^2 p_e / E_e$ the velocity of the electron, we write the transition probability w_{fi} in the conventional form

$$
w_{fi} = \frac{\xi}{4\pi^3} \frac{p_e E_e}{c^5 \hbar^7} (E_{\max} - E_e)^2 \left(1 + a \frac{v_e}{c} \cos \theta + b \frac{2mc^2}{E_e} \right) \sin \theta \, d\theta \quad (25a)
$$

where

$$
\xi = \tfrac{1}{2}\{|g_S|^2 + |g_S'|^2 + |g_V|^2 + |g_V'|^2\} |M_F|^2
$$
$$
+ \tfrac{1}{2}\{|g_T|^2 + |g_T'|^2 + |g_A|^2 + |g_A'|^2\} |M_{\text{GT}}|^2 \quad (25b)
$$
$$
a\xi = \tfrac{1}{2}\{|g_V|^2 + |g_V'|^2 - |g_S|^2 - |g_S'|^2\} |M_F|^2 + \tfrac{1}{6}\{|g_T|^2 + |g_T'|^2
$$
$$
- |g_A|^2 - |g_A'|^2\} |M_{\text{GT}}|^2 \quad (25c)
$$
$$
b\xi = \tfrac{1}{2} \operatorname{Re} \{g_S g_V^* + g_S' g_V'^*\} |M_F|^2 + \tfrac{1}{2} \operatorname{Re} \{g_T g_A^* + g_T' g_A'^*\} |M_{\text{GT}}|^2
$$
$$
(25d)
$$

Various combinations of the coupling constants are included in Eqs. (25b) to (25d). The unprimed and primed constants respectively represent the relative strengths of the parity-conserving and the parity-nonconserving interactions. The values of the coupling constants can be determined from various experiments which are usually not easy to perform. These experiments, however, can determine the relative magnitudes of the various coupling constants in the beta decay transitions.

We first discuss the vector coupling constant g_V. For this we select O^{14} which has been observed to undergo a pure Fermi transition and for which many precise experimental results are available. Since, in a pure Fermi transition, the combinations which involve the Gamow-Teller matrix elements are absent, we may write from Eqs. (25b) and (25d) for pure $0 \to 0$, Fermi transitions

$$\xi = \tfrac{1}{2}\{|g_S|^2 + |g'_S|^2 + |g_V|^2 + |g'_V|^2\} |M_F|^2 \qquad (25e)$$

and

$$b\xi = \tfrac{1}{2} \operatorname{Re} (g_S g_V^* + g'_S g'^*_V) |M_F|^2 \qquad (25f)$$

For allowed beta decay, the beta-energy spectrum, after integrating Eq. (25a) over θ, is

$$N(E_e)\, dE_e = (2\pi^3 c^5 \hbar^7)^{-1} p_e E_e (E_{\max} - E_e)^2 F(Z, E_e)\xi \left(1 + \frac{2mc^2 b}{E_e}\right) dE_e \qquad (26a)$$

where the function $F(Z, E_e)$ has been introduced to take account of the Coulomb effects. The integration of Eq. (26a) over the range of beta decay energy gives

$$2\pi^3 c^5 \hbar^7 (ft)^{-1} \ln 2 = \xi + b2mc^2\xi \langle E_e^{-1} \rangle \qquad (26b)$$

where

$$f = \int_{mc^2}^{E_{\max}} F(Z, E_e) p_e E_e (E_{\max} - E_e)^2 \, dE_e \qquad (26c)$$

and

$$\langle E_e^{-1} \rangle = f^{-1} \int_{mc^2}^{E_{\max}} F(Z, E_e) p_e (E_{\max} - E_e)^2 \, dE_e \qquad (26d)$$

The Fermi plot of Eq. (26a) is a straight line; therefore the Fierz constant $b = 0$ for the allowed beta-ray spectrum. Equation (26b) can then be written in the form

$$2\pi^3 c^5 \hbar^7 (ft)^{-1} \ln 2 = \xi = \tfrac{1}{2}\{|g_S|^2 + |g'_S|^2 + |g_V|^2 + |g'_V|^2\} |M_F|^2 \quad (26e)$$

Since the Fermi plot for an allowed transition gives $b = 0$, we conclude that there are several different possibilities which will yield $\operatorname{Re} (g_S g_V^* + g'_S g'^*_V) = 0$, namely: (1) $g_S = g'_S = 0$, (2) $g_V = g'_V = 0$, (3) $g_S = g'_S = g_V = -g'_V$, etc. To eliminate some of the possibilities, we refer to the electron-neutrino angular correlation expression given in Eq. (25a). The angular correlation coefficient a is obtained by dividing Eq. (25c) by Eq. (25b). We can thus write for a pure Fermi transition

$$a = \frac{|g_V|^2 + |g'_V|^2 - |g_S|^2 - |g'_S|^2}{|g_V|^2 + |g'_V|^2 + |g_S|^2 + |g'_S|^2}$$

The experimentally observed value[15] of the coefficient is $a = 0.97 \pm 0.14$, which can be taken as unity. Consequently, we need $|g_S|^2 + |g'_S|^2 = 0$, so that $a = 1$. If $|g_S|^2 + |g'_S|^2 = 0$, then $|g_S| = |g'_S| = 0$. Therefore Eq. (26e) reduces to the form

$$2\pi^3 c^5 \hbar^7 (ft)^{-1} \ln 2 = \tfrac{1}{2}\{|g_V|^2 + |g'_V|^2\} |M_{\mathrm{F}}|^2 \tag{26f}$$

In Section 13.10, we shall see that the experimentally observed polarization is consistent with the choice $g_V = g'_V$ for a pure Fermi transition (and also $g_T = g'_T$ for a pure G-T transition). Hence we may write from Eq. (26f)

$$2\pi^3 c^5 \hbar^7 (ft)^{-1} \ln 2 = |g_V|^2 |M_{\mathrm{F}}|^2 \tag{26g}$$

Knowing the experimentally determined ft-value and the matrix element $|M_{\mathrm{F}}|^2$, we can compute the vector coupling constant g_V in the allowed Fermi transition. From the theory of angular momentum, it can be shown that $|M_{\mathrm{F}}|^2 = 2$. The ft-value for the $0^+ \to 0^+$ transition of $\mathrm{O}^{14} \xrightarrow{\beta^+} \mathrm{N}^{14}$ is accurately known[16]. The value thus obtained is modified if we take into account the screening effect due to the Coulomb field.[17] The ft-value of 3075 ± 10 sec for O^{14} was obtained by Bardin et al.[16] Using this value, Bardin et al. find

$$g_V = (1.4025 \pm 0.0022) \times 10^{-49} \text{ erg-cm}^3$$

Recently a number of $0^+ \xrightarrow{\beta^+} 0^+$ transitions such as $\mathrm{Al}^{26*} \to \mathrm{Mg}^{26}$ (Wu[18]); $\mathrm{Cl}^{34} \to \mathrm{S}^{34}$ (Freeman et al.[19]); $\mathrm{V}^{46} \to \mathrm{Ti}^{46}$ (Jänecke,[20] Freeman et al.[21]) have been analyzed. After introducing the screening correction,[17] Wu finds an average value of $ft = 3125 \pm 10$ sec and the value of

$$g_V = (1.4029 \pm 0.0022) \times 10^{-49} \text{ erg-cm}^3$$

in close agreement with the value given by Bardin et al.

We now estimate the value of the axial vector coupling constant g_A. This can be obtained from those beta decays which are pure G-T transitions such as He^6. He^6 decays by β^- to Li^6 from a state 0^+ to a state 1^+. We shall study the beta-neutrino angular correlation to obtain information concerning $(|g_T|^2 + |g'_T|^2) - (|g_A|^2 + |g'_A|^2)$.

The electron-neutrino angular correlation is given by Eq. (25a). The angular correlation coefficient a for pure G-T transition is obtained by dividing Eq. (25c) by Eq. (25b).

$$a = \frac{1}{3} \frac{\{|g_T|^2 + |g'_T|^2 - |g_A|^2 - |g'_A|^2\}}{\{|g_T|^2 + |g'_T|^2 + |g_A|^2 + |g'_A|^2\}} \tag{26h}$$

From experimental results[15] it is possible to conclude that in allowed G-T transitions, the tensor contribution is practically zero within the experimental error.

We note from Eq. (26h) that

$$a = \begin{cases} \frac{1}{3} & \text{for} \quad g_A = g'_A = 0 \\ -\frac{1}{3} & \text{for} \quad g_T = g'_T = 0 \end{cases} \qquad (26i)$$

It is possible to conclude that in allowed Fermi or G-T transitions, the tensor contribution is practically zero within the experimental error. The experimental value as obtained by Ridley[22] gives

$$a = -0.35 \begin{cases} +0.033 \\ -0.053 \end{cases}$$

This value is in excellent agreement with the theoretically predicted value for $g_T = g'_T = 0$. This result also indicates that the Fermi angular correlation coefficient is greater than the G-T angular correlation coefficient.

Additional support of the axial vector interaction in a G-T transition has been obtained by the results of another precise experiment,[23] also with He[6]. The value of the angular correlation coefficient was found to be $a = -0.3343 \pm 0.0030$ in excellent agreement with the theory, with the limit of the tensor interaction given by

$$\frac{|g_T|^2 + |g'_T|^2}{|g_A|^2 + |g'_A|^2} \le 0.4\%.$$

13.10 Polarization of Electrons in Beta Emission

In this section, the case considered is that in which the initial nucleus is unpolarized but the polarization direction of the emitted electron is observed. The neutrino direction is unobserved, which is the same as not observing the direction of the recoil of the final nucleus; thus we should integrate over the solid angle $d\Omega_\nu$ of the neutrino. In addition, the sum over the spin directions of the electron should not be carried out. Thus the results for the polarization of beta particles can be obtained from Eq. (15) by replacing $|M_{e\nu}^{\lambda\lambda'}{}^*|^2$ by $|M_{e(p)\nu}^{\lambda\lambda'}{}^*|^2$, where

$$|M_{e(p)\nu}^{\lambda\lambda'}{}^*|^2 = \frac{1}{2E_\nu} [\bar{u}_e^{(r)(+)}(\mathbf{p}_e)\Gamma_{\lambda i}(g_\lambda + g'_\lambda\gamma_5)(i\gamma p_\nu)\gamma_4(g^*_{\lambda'} + g'^*_{\lambda'}\gamma_5)$$
$$\times \Gamma^*_{\lambda' i}\gamma_4 u_e^{(r)(+)}(\mathbf{p}_e)] \qquad (27a)$$

and

$$|\langle f| H_\beta |i\rangle|^2_{\substack{\text{electron} \\ \text{polarization}}} = \frac{1}{2V^2} [|M^{SS*}_{e(p)\nu}|^2 + |M^{VV*}_{e(p)\nu}|^2 + 2 \, \text{Re} \, |M^{SV*}_{e(p)\nu}|^2] |M_F|^2$$

$$+ \frac{1}{6V^2} [|M^{TT*}_{e(p)\nu}|^2 + |M^{AA*}_{e(p)\nu}|^2 - 2 \, \text{Re} \, |M^{TA*}_{e(p)\nu}|^2] |M_{GT}|^2 \qquad (27b)$$

In Eq. (27a) the superscript r on the electron spinors u_e denotes the polarization direction of the electron. The equations corresponding to Eqs. (15) and (16) can be obtained by replacing

$$\frac{1}{2E_e} \text{Sp} \, (i\gamma p_e - mc) \, [\cdots] \qquad \text{by} \quad \{\bar{u}_e^{(r)(+)}(\mathbf{p}_e)[\cdots]u_e^{(r)(+)}(\mathbf{p}_e)\} \qquad (27c)$$

We take into account the results regarding the coupling constants as obtained from experiments with unpolarized particles, namely that very good agreement is obtained by taking (the V − A theory for beta decay) $g_S = g'_S = 0$, and $g_T = g'_T = 0$. Integrating over the solid angle of the neutrino, we obtain

$$V^2 \int d\Omega_\nu \, |\langle f| H_\beta |i\rangle|^2_{\substack{\text{electron} \\ \text{polarization}}} = \int d\Omega_\nu [\tfrac{1}{2} |M^{VV*}_{e(p)\nu}|^2 |M_F|^2 + \tfrac{1}{6} |M^{AA*}_{e(p)\nu}|^2 |M_{GT}|^2]$$

$$= \pi \, [u_e^{*(+)(r)}(\mathbf{p}_e)\{(|g_V|^2 + |g'_V|^2) + \gamma_5 2 \, \text{Re} \, (g_V^* g'_V)\} u_e^{(+)(r)}(\mathbf{p}_e) \, |M_F|^2$$

$$+ u_e^{*(+)(r)}(\mathbf{p}_e)\{(|g_A|^2 + |g'_A|^2) + \gamma_5 2 \, \text{Re} \, (g_A^* g'_A)\} u_e^{(+)(r)}(\mathbf{p}_e) \, |M_{GT}|^2]$$

$$= \pi [\{(|g_V|^2 + |g'_V|^2) |M_F|^2 + (|g_A|^2 + |g'_A|^2) |M_{GT}|^2$$

$$+ 2\{\text{Re} \, (g_V^* g'_V) |M_F|^2 + \text{Re} \, (g_A^* g'_A) |M_{GT}|^2\} \, u_e^{*(+)(r)}(\mathbf{p}_e)\gamma_5 u_e^{(+)(r)}(\mathbf{p}_e)$$

$$\qquad (27d)$$

where in the last step we have made use of the normalization of the spinors The matrix element of γ_5 between the spinor states can be obtained by writing the Dirac spinor in terms of the two-component spinors $\phi^{(1)} = \begin{pmatrix} 1 \\ 0 \end{pmatrix}$ and $\phi^{(2)} = \begin{pmatrix} 0 \\ 1 \end{pmatrix}$, corresponding to spin direction along the positive and negative z-axis. We have ($c \equiv 1$, here):

$$u_e^{(+)(r)}(\mathbf{p}_e) = \sqrt{\frac{m + E_e}{2E_e}} \begin{pmatrix} \phi^{(r)} \\ \dfrac{\boldsymbol{\sigma} \cdot \mathbf{p}_e}{m + E_e} \phi^{(r)} \end{pmatrix} \qquad r = 1, 2 \qquad (27e)$$

where $\boldsymbol{\sigma}$ are the Pauli matrices.

Using the matrix representation $\gamma_5 = \begin{pmatrix} 0 & 1 \\ 1 & 0 \end{pmatrix}$, we find

$$V^2 \int d\Omega_e \, |\langle f| H_\beta |i\rangle|^2 = \pi \Big[\{(|g_V|^2 + |g'_V|^2) |M_F|^2 + (|g_A|^2 + |g'_A|^2) |M_{GT}|^2\}$$

$$- 2\{\text{Re} \, (g_V^* g'_V) |M_F|^2 + \text{Re} \, (g_A^* g'_A) |M_{GT}|^2\} \Big\langle \phi^{(r)} \Big| \frac{(\boldsymbol{\sigma} \cdot \mathbf{p}_e)}{E_e} \Big| \phi^{(r)} \Big\rangle \Big] \qquad (27f)$$

The operator $h = (\boldsymbol{\sigma} \cdot \mathbf{p}_e / |\mathbf{p}_e|)$ is the helicity operator, whose expectation value is $+1$ for electron spin parallel (to the direction of motion) and -1 for spin direction antiparallel to $\mathbf{p}_e$. If we choose the z-axis parallel to the momentum $\mathbf{p}_e$,

$$\left\langle \phi^{(r)} \left| \frac{\boldsymbol{\sigma} \cdot \mathbf{p}_e}{E_e} \right| \phi^{(r)} \right\rangle = \begin{cases} + & \text{for} \quad r = 1 \\ - & \text{for} \quad r = 2 \end{cases} \tag{27g}$$

Defining the polarization P as the ratio of the number of electrons with spin along the positive z-axis ($h = 1$) minus the number of electrons with spin along the negative z-axis to the total number of electrons, we have from Eq. (27f)

$$P = - \frac{2 \operatorname{Re}(g_V^* g_V') |M_F|^2 + 2 \operatorname{Re}(g_A^* g_A') |M_{GT}|^2}{(|g_V|^2 + |g_V'|^2) |M_F|^2 + (|g_A|^2 + |g_A'|^2) |M_{GT}|^2} v_e \tag{28a}$$

$$= \begin{cases} - \text{ for electrons} \\ + \text{ for positrons} \end{cases} \quad \begin{array}{l} \text{for pure Fermi } (M_{GT} = 0, g_V = g_V') \\ \text{or pure Gamow-Teller } (M_F = 0, g_A = g_A') \\ \text{transitions} \end{array} \tag{28b}$$

Lee and Yang[1] suggested that parity may not be conserved in weak interaction processes such as beta decay. To test this hypothesis it was proposed to study the directional asymmetry of electrons emitted from polarized Co^{60} nuclei. The classic experiment of Wu et al.[2] verified the contention of Lee and Yang by observing a fore-and-aft asymmetry, relative to polarized Co^{60} nuclei, in the angular distribution of emitted beta-particles. It was also pointed out[11] that the electrons are emitted with longitudinal polarization [see Eq. (28)] in beta-decay processes. The experiments on longitudinal polarization of the electrons have been performed by many workers.[24]

The case of P^{32} has been studied extensively. It falls within the category of allowed G-T transitions with spin change $1^+ \rightarrow 0^+$. An accurate experiment has been performed on the longitudinal polarization of 616 Kev electrons emitted from the decay of P^{32}. In this experiment Brosi et al.[25] used the Mott scattering method to determine the polarization. The spin was rotated from longitudinal to transverse by a spherical electrostatic analyzer. It is this transverse component which was analyzed by the Mott scattering method. The result obtained was that the polarization $P = (-0.990 \pm 0.009)\beta$, where $\beta = 0.891$. This is consistent both with the $V - A$ theory and the expression given in Eq. (28b). Other equally good results have been reported by Ullman et al.[26] $[P = (-1.00 \pm 0.02)\beta$ for electron energies lying between 660 and 990 Kev] and by Spivak et al.[24] $[P = (-1.02 \pm 0.033)\beta$ for electron energy of 340 Kev from P^{32}].

13.11 Beta Decay from Oriented (Polarized) Nuclei

The nuclear matrix elements involved for oriented nuclei are given in Eqs. (12). We shall restrict our derivations to vector and axial vector interactions. From Eqs. (12), (11a), (8d), (14d), and (15) we have

$$|\langle f| H_\beta |i\rangle|^2_{\substack{\text{polarized} \\ \text{nuclei}}} = \frac{1}{2V^2}[|M_\text{F}|^2 |M_{ev}^{VV}*|^2 + (\langle \Psi'_f| \sigma_k |\Psi'_i\rangle\langle\Psi'_f| \sigma_{k'} |\Psi'_i\rangle^*)_\text{avp}$$

$$\times |M_{ev}^{AA}*|^2 - (\langle \Psi'_f| 1 |\Psi'_i\rangle \langle\Psi'_f| \sigma_k |\Psi'_i\rangle^*)_\text{avp} 2\, \text{Re}\, |M_{ev}^{AV}*|^2] \quad (29a)$$

where $|M_{ev}^{VV}*|^2$ is given by Eq. (15b) and where

$$|M_{ev}^{AA}*|^2 = \frac{c^2}{4E_e E_\nu} \text{Sp}\, [(i\gamma p_e - mc)i\gamma_k\gamma_5(g_A + g'_A\gamma_5)$$

$$\times (i\gamma p_\nu)\gamma_4(g_A^* + g_A'^*\gamma_5)(i\gamma_{k'}\gamma_5)^*\gamma_4] \quad (29b)$$

$$|M_{ev}^{AV}*|^2 = \frac{c^2}{4E_e E_\nu} \text{Sp}\, [(i\gamma p_e - mc)\gamma_4(g_V + g'_V\gamma_5)$$

$$\times (i\gamma p_\nu)\gamma_4(g_A^* + g_A'^*\gamma_5)(i\gamma_k\gamma_5)^*\gamma_4] \quad (29c)$$

$$(\langle \Psi'_f| \sigma_k |\Psi'_i\rangle \langle\Psi'_f| \sigma_{k'} |\Psi'_i\rangle^*)_\text{avp} = \sum_{m_i,m_f} w(m_i)\left(\sum_{n=1}^A \int d^3x\Psi_f^*(\mathbf{x})\sigma_k\tau_n^{(+)}\Psi_i(\mathbf{x})\right)$$

$$\times \left(\sum_{n=1}^A \int d^3x\Psi_f^*(\mathbf{x})\sigma_{k'}\tau_n^{(+)}\Psi_i(\mathbf{x})\right)^* \quad (29d)$$

$$(\langle \Psi'_f| 1 |\Psi'_i\rangle\langle\Psi'_f| \sigma_k |\Psi'_i\rangle^*)_\text{avp} = \sum_{m_i,m_f} w(m_i)\left(\sum_{n=1}^A \int d^3x\Psi_f^*(\mathbf{x})\tau_n^{(+)}\Psi_i(\mathbf{x})\right)$$

$$\times \left(\sum_{n=1}^A \int d^3x\Psi_f^*(\mathbf{x})\sigma_k\tau_n^{(+)}\Psi_i(\mathbf{x})\right)^* \quad (29e)$$

In Eqs. (29d) and (29e), $w(m_i)$ is the weight function specifying the spin orientations of the initial nucleus. The calculations of the spurs in Eqs. (29b) and (29c) can be carried out quite easily. In the following we shall take $g_V = g'_V$ and $g_A = g'_A$. Evaluating the spurs and integrating over the solid angle $d\Omega_\nu$ of the neutrino, we obtain

$$\int |\langle f| H_\beta |i\rangle|^2_{\substack{\text{polarized} \\ \text{nuclei}}} d\Omega_\nu$$

$$= \frac{4\pi}{V^2}\left\{|g_V|^2 |M_\text{F}|^2 + |g_A|^2 [\langle \Psi'_f| \sigma_k |\Psi'_i\rangle\langle\Psi'_f| \sigma_{k'} |\Psi'_i\rangle^*]_\text{avp}\left[\delta_{kk'} + i\epsilon_{kk'l}\frac{(p_e)_l}{E_e}\right]\right.$$

$$\left. - 2\, \text{Re}\, g_V g_A^*[\langle \Psi'_f| 1 |\Psi'_i\rangle\langle\Psi'_f| \sigma_k |\Psi'_i\rangle^*]_\text{avp}\frac{(p_e)_k}{E_e}\right\} \quad (30)$$

where $\epsilon_{kk'l} = +1$ or -1 for k, k', l cyclic or noncyclic. We have for the second term in Eq. (30)

$$\sum_k [\langle \Psi_f | \sigma_k | \Psi_i \rangle \langle \Psi_f | \sigma_k | \Psi_i \rangle^*]_{\text{avp}} = \sum_k |\langle \Psi_f | \sigma_k | \Psi_i \rangle|^2_{\text{avp}}$$

$$= \sum_{k,m_i,m_f} w(m_i) |\langle \Psi_f | \sigma_k | \Psi_i \rangle|^2 = \sum_{k,m_i,m_f} w(m_i)$$

$$\times \left[\sum_{n=1}^A \int d^3x \Psi_f^*(\mathbf{x}) \sigma_k \tau_n^{(+)} \Psi_i(\mathbf{x}) \right] \left[\sum_{n=1}^A \int d^3x \Psi_f^*(\mathbf{x}) \sigma_k \tau_n^{(+)} \Psi_i(\mathbf{x}) \right]^* \quad (31a)$$

In order to evaluate the right-hand side of Eq. (31a), we make use of the Wigner-Eckart theorem, which enables us to write the matrix elements of an operator between two states a and b of spins j_a and j_b with z-components equal to m_a and m_b, respectively, in the form

$$\langle b | O_j^m | a \rangle = \langle j_a j m_a m | j_b m_b \rangle \frac{\langle b \| O_j \| a \rangle}{\sqrt{2j_b + 1}} \quad (31b)$$

where the reduced matrix element $\langle b \| O_j \| a \rangle$ depends only on spins j_a, j_b, and j. Applying Eq. (31b) to Eq. (31a) and noting that the operator σ_k can equivalently be expressed in terms of the circular components σ^m where $m = \pm 1, 0$, we have

$$\sum_k |\langle \Psi_f | \sigma_k | \Psi_i \rangle|^2_{\text{avp}} = \frac{|\langle \Psi_f \| \boldsymbol{\sigma} \| \Psi_i \rangle|^2}{2j_f + 1} \sum_{m,m_i,m_f} w(m_i) |\langle j_i 1 \; m_i m | j_f m_f \rangle|^2$$

$$= \frac{|\langle \Psi_f \| \boldsymbol{\sigma} \| \Psi_i \rangle|^2}{2j_f + 1} \frac{2j_f + 1}{2j_i + 1} \sum_{m_i} w(m_i) \sum_{m,m_f} |\langle j_f 1 \; -m_f m | j_i - m_i \rangle|^2$$

$$= \frac{|\langle \Psi_f \| \boldsymbol{\sigma} \| \Psi_i \rangle|^2}{2j_i + 1} \sum_{m_i} w(m_i) = \frac{|\langle \Psi_f \| \boldsymbol{\sigma} \| \Psi_i \rangle|^2}{2j_i + 1} \quad (31c)$$

where in the second step, using the properties of the Clebsch-Gordan coefficients, the expression is rewritten so that summation over m and m_f can be carried out before summation over m_i. We can relate the expression in Eq. (31c) to the Gamow-Teller nuclear matrix element. From Eqs. (11f) and (31b), we have

$$|M_{\text{GT}}|^2 = \left(\sum_k |\langle \Psi_f | \sigma_k | \Psi_i \rangle|^2 \right)_{\text{av}}$$

$$= \frac{1}{(2j_i + 1)} \frac{|\langle \Psi_f \| \boldsymbol{\sigma} \| \Psi_i \rangle|^2}{(2j_f + 1)} \sum_{m,m_i,m_f} |\langle j_i 1 \; m_i m | j_f m_f \rangle|^2$$

$$= \frac{|\langle \Psi_f \| \boldsymbol{\sigma} \| \Psi_i \rangle|^2}{2j_i + 1} \quad (31d)$$

where the factor $1/(2j_i + 1)$ comes from average over the initial polarizations. From Eqs. (31c) and (31d), we obtain

$$\sum_k |\langle \Psi_f| \sigma_k |\Psi_i\rangle|^2_{\text{avp}} = |M_{\text{GT}}|^2 \tag{31e}$$

which is the same as for unpolarized nuclei.

In the following we consider the evaluation of the fourth term in Eq. (30).

$$(\langle \Psi_f'| 1 |\Psi_i'\rangle\langle \Psi_f'| \sigma_k |\Psi_i'\rangle^*)_{\text{avp}}$$

$$= \sum_{m_i, m_f} w(m_i)\langle \Psi_f'| 1 |\Psi_i'\rangle\langle \Psi_f'| \sigma_k |\Psi_i'\rangle^*$$

$$= \sum_{m_i, m_f, m} w(m_i)\delta_{j_f j_i}\delta_{m_f m_i} M_{\text{F}}\langle j_i 1\, m_i m \,| j_f m_f\rangle^* \frac{\langle \Psi_f'\| \sigma \|\Psi_i'\rangle^*}{\sqrt{2j_f + 1}}$$

$$= \sum_{m_i} w(m_i)\delta_{j_f j_i} M_{\text{F}}\langle j_i 1\, m_i 0 \,| j_i m_i\rangle^* \hat{z} M_{\text{GT}}^*$$

$$= \delta_{j_f j_i} M_{\text{F}} M_{\text{GT}}^* \hat{z} \frac{1}{\sqrt{j_i(j_i + 1)}} \sum_{m_i} m_i w(m_i) \tag{32a}$$

where we have made use of Eqs. (11c) and (31b) in the second step, and Eq. (31d) in the following step. Since $m_i = m_f$, we have $m = 0$, so that only the matrix elements of σ_z are nonzero, thus accounting for the appearance of the unit vector along the z-direction. We observe that

$$\begin{aligned}\sum_{m_i} m_i w(m_i) &= 0 \quad &&\text{for unpolarized nucleus} \\ &= j_i \quad &&\text{for nucleus completely polarized} \end{aligned}$$

along the z-axis, whence $m_i = j_i$, $w(j_i) = 1$, and $w(m_i \neq j_i) = 0$ (32b)

We now evaluate the term

$$i\epsilon_{kk'l}(\langle \Psi_f'| \sigma_k |\Psi_i'\rangle\langle \Psi_f'| \sigma_{k'} |\Psi_i'\rangle^*)_{\text{avp}}$$

$$= i(\langle \Psi_f'| \sigma |\Psi_i'\rangle \times \langle \Psi_f'| \sigma |\Psi_i'\rangle^*)_{l\,\text{avp}} \tag{33a}$$

Since $k \neq k' \neq l$, it follows that k or $k' \neq z$ for the above term to be nonzero. Since $\langle \Psi_f'| \sigma_z |\Psi_i'\rangle \propto \delta_{m_i m_f}$, it follows that for k (or k') $= z$, it is necessary that k' (or k) $= z$ for a nonzero result. Therefore Eq. (33a) reduces to

$$i(\langle \Psi_f'| \sigma |\Psi_i'\rangle \times \langle \Psi_f'| \sigma |\Psi_i'\rangle^*)_{z\,\text{avp}}$$

$$= i[\langle \Psi_f'| \sigma_x |\Psi_i'\rangle\langle \Psi_f'| \sigma_y |\Psi_i'\rangle^* - \langle \Psi_i'| \sigma_y |\Psi_f'\rangle\langle \Psi_f'| \sigma_x |\Psi_i'\rangle^*]_{\text{avp}}$$

$$= [|\langle \Psi_f'| \sigma_+ |\Psi_i'\rangle|^2 - |\langle \Psi_f'| \sigma_- |\Psi_i'\rangle|^2]_{\text{avp}} \tag{33b}$$

where

$$\sigma_{\pm} = \mp \frac{1}{\sqrt{2}} (\sigma_x \pm i\sigma_y) \tag{33c}$$

Using Eqs. (31b), (31d), and (29d), we obtain from Eq. (33b)

$$i\epsilon_{kk'l}(\langle \Psi'_f | \, \sigma \, | \Psi'_i \rangle \langle \Psi'_f | \, \sigma \, | \Psi'_i \rangle^*)_{\text{avp}}$$

$$= |M_{\mathrm{GT}}|^2 \frac{2j_i + 1}{2j_f + 1} \sum_{m_i, m_f} w(m_i)\{|\langle j_i 1 \ m_i 1 \ | j_f m_f \rangle|^2 - \langle j_i 1 \ m_i \ {-1} \ | j_f m_f \rangle|^2\}$$

$$= \sqrt{6}(2j_i + 1) \sum_{m_i} w(m_i) \sum_{m_f, m} \begin{pmatrix} j_i & 1 & j_f \\ m_i & m & -m_f \end{pmatrix} \begin{pmatrix} 1 & 1 & 1 \\ m & -m & 0 \end{pmatrix}$$

$$= \sqrt{6}(-1)^{j_f+1}(2j_i + 1) \begin{pmatrix} j_i & j_i & 1 \\ 1 & 1 & j_f \end{pmatrix} \sum_{m_i} (-1)^{m_i} w(m_i) \begin{pmatrix} j_i & j_i & 1 \\ m_i & -m_i & 0 \end{pmatrix}$$

$$= -\frac{2 + j_i(j_i + 1) - j_f(j_f + 1)}{2(j_i + 1)} \frac{1}{j_i} \sum_{m_i} m_i w(m_i) \tag{33d}$$

Combining Eqs. (31e), (32a), and (33d), we obtain from Eq. (30)

$$\int |\langle f | \, H_\beta \, |i\rangle|^2_{\substack{\text{polarized} \\ \text{nucleus}}} d\Omega_\nu = \frac{4\pi\xi}{V^2} \left\{ 1 + A \frac{\hat{z} \cdot \mathbf{p}_e}{E_e} \frac{1}{j_i} \sum_{m_i} m_i w(m_i) \right\} \tag{34a}$$

where ξ is given by Eq. (25b) with $g_S = g'_S = 0$, $g_T = g'_T = 0$, $g_V = g'_V$, $g_A = g'_A$,

$$\xi A = -|g_A|^2 |M_{\mathrm{GT}}|^2 \frac{2 + j_i(j_i + 1) - j_f(j_f + 1)}{2(j_i + 1)}$$

$$-2 \, \mathrm{Re} \, (g_V g_A^* M_{\mathrm{F}} M_{\mathrm{GT}}^*) \sqrt{\frac{j_i}{j_i + 1}} \, \delta_{j_i j_f} \tag{34b}$$

and $\hat{z} \dfrac{1}{j_i} \sum_{m_i} w(m_i)$ is the polarization vector of the nucleus.

Equations (34a) and (34b) can be used to determine the relative phase between the coupling constants g_V (Fermi coupling constant) and g_A (Gamow-Teller coupling constant). The correlation between the direction of the outgoing electron and the direction of polarization of the neutron is noted. The results for the beta decay of the polarized (free) neutron are obtained by substituting in Eqs. (34a) and (34b) the following:

$$j_i = j_f = \tfrac{1}{2} \tag{35a}$$

$$M_{\mathrm{F}} = 1 \quad \text{and} \quad M_{\mathrm{GT}} = \sqrt{3} \tag{35b}$$

so that
$$\xi = |g_V|^2 + 3|g_A|^2 \tag{36a}$$

$$\xi A = -2|g_A|^2 - 2\,\mathrm{Re}\,(g_V g_A^*)$$
$$= -2|g_A|^2 - 2|g_V||g_A|\cos\phi \tag{36b}$$

where ϕ is the (complex) phase difference between the couplings g_V and g_A. From Eqs. (36a) and (36b), we have

$$A = -\frac{2|g_A|^2 + 2|g_V||g_A|\cos\phi}{|g_V|^2 + 3|g_A|^2} \tag{37a}$$

$$= -\tfrac{1}{2}(1 + \cos\phi) \qquad \text{for} \quad |g_A| = |g_V|$$

$$= \begin{cases} -1 & \text{for} \quad \phi = 0 \\ 0 & \text{for} \quad \phi = \pi \end{cases} \tag{37b}$$

The experimental measurements of the parameter A have been carried out by Burgy et al.,[27] by Robson et al.,[28] and by several Russian groups.[28] The experimental value is given by $A_{\mathrm{obs}} = -0.11 \pm 0.02$, which favors a relative phase difference of π between the g_V and g_A couplings (with $g_A/g_V = -1.24$).

13.12   General Expressions

Equation (34a) and several of the equations derived previously are special cases of the general result due to Jackson, Treiman, and Wyld,[29] who obtained the general distribution functions including recoil, nuclear orientation, and the electron polarization effects for allowed beta decay. No assumptions in regard to the invariance with respect to space inversion, time reversal, or charge conjugation were introduced in this calculation. They later also took account of the Coulomb correction. For completeness, in the following, we give the results of their calculations, ignoring, however, Coulomb corrections.

The distribution in electron and neutrino direction and electron polarization for allowed beta decay from *nonoriented* nuclei is ($c \equiv 1$)

$$w(\boldsymbol{\sigma}\,|\,E_e, \Omega_e, \Omega_\nu)\,dE_e\,d\Omega_e\,d\Omega_\nu$$
$$= (2\pi)^{-5} p_e E_e (E_{\max} - E_e)^2\,dE_e\,d\Omega_e\,d\Omega_\nu$$
$$\times \tfrac{1}{2}\xi\Bigg\{ 1 + a\,\frac{\mathbf{p}_e\cdot\mathbf{p}_\nu}{E_e E_\nu} + b\,\frac{m}{E_e}$$
$$+ \boldsymbol{\sigma}\cdot\left[G\,\frac{\mathbf{p}_e}{E_e} + H\,\frac{\mathbf{p}_\nu}{E_\nu} + K\,\frac{\mathbf{p}_e}{E_e + m}\frac{\mathbf{p}_e\cdot\mathbf{p}_\nu}{E_e E_\nu} + L\,\frac{\mathbf{p}_e\times\mathbf{p}_\nu}{E_e E_\nu} \right] \Bigg\} \tag{38a}$$

The distribution function in electron and neutrino directions and electron energy for an allowed transition from *oriented* nuclei is given by

$$
w(\langle \mathbf{J} \rangle \mid E_e, \Omega_e, \Omega_\nu) \, dE_e \, d\Omega_e \, d\Omega_\nu
$$
$$
= (2\pi)^{-5} p_e E_e (E_{\max} - E_e)^2 \, dE_e \, d\Omega_e \, d\Omega_\nu
$$
$$
\times \xi \left\{ 1 + a \frac{\mathbf{p}_e \cdot \mathbf{p}_\nu}{E_e E_\nu} + b \frac{m}{E_e} \right.
$$
$$
+ c \left[\frac{\mathbf{p}_e \cdot \mathbf{p}_\nu}{3 E_e E_\nu} - \frac{(\mathbf{p}_e \cdot \hat{\jmath})(\mathbf{p}_\nu \cdot \hat{\jmath})}{E_e E_\nu} \right] \left[\frac{J(J+1) - 3 \langle (\mathbf{J} \cdot \hat{\jmath})^2 \rangle}{J(2J-1)} \right]
$$
$$
\left. + \frac{\mathbf{J}}{J} \left[A \frac{\mathbf{p}_e}{E_e} + B \frac{\mathbf{p}_\nu}{E_\nu} + D \frac{\mathbf{p}_e \times \mathbf{p}_\nu}{E_e E_\nu} \right] \right\} \tag{38b}
$$

where $\mathbf{J}$ is the angular momentum of the initial nucleus and $\hat{\jmath}$ is a unit vector in the direction of $\mathbf{J}$.

The distribution in electron energy and angle and electron polarization for allowed beta decay from *oriented* nuclei is

$$
w(\langle \mathbf{J} \rangle, \boldsymbol{\sigma} \mid E_e, \Omega_e) \, dE_e \, d\Omega_e
$$
$$
= (2\pi)^{-4} p_e E_e (E_{\max} - E_e)^2 \, dE_e \, d\Omega_e
$$
$$
\times \xi \left\{ 1 + b \frac{m}{E_e} + \frac{\mathbf{p}_e}{E_e} \cdot \left(A \frac{\langle \mathbf{J} \rangle}{J} + G \boldsymbol{\sigma} \right) \right.
$$
$$
\left. + \boldsymbol{\sigma} \cdot \left[N \frac{\langle \mathbf{J} \rangle}{J} + Q \frac{\mathbf{p}_e}{E_e + m} \left(\frac{\langle \mathbf{J} \rangle}{J} \cdot \frac{\mathbf{p}_e}{E_e} \right) + R \frac{\langle \mathbf{J} \rangle}{J} \times \frac{\mathbf{p}_e}{E_e} \right] \right\} \tag{38c}
$$

The values of the coefficients appearing in the above formulas are

$$
\xi = (|g_S|^2 + |g_S'|^2 + |g_V|^2 + |g_V'|^2) |M_{\mathrm{F}}|^2
$$
$$
+ (|g_T|^2 + |g_T'|^2 + |g_A|^2 + |g_A'|^2) |M_{\mathrm{GT}}|^2 \tag{38d}
$$
$$
a\xi = (-|g_S|^2 - |g_S'|^2 + |g_V|^2 + |g_V'|^2) |M_{\mathrm{F}}|^2
$$
$$
+ \tfrac{1}{3}(|g_T|^2 + |g_T'|^2 - |g_A|^2 - |g_A'|^2) |M_{\mathrm{GT}}|^2 \tag{38e}
$$
$$
b\xi = 2 \,\mathrm{Re}\, \{ (g_S g_V^* + g_S' g_V'^*) |M_{\mathrm{F}}|^2 + (g_T g_A^* + g_T' g_A'^*) |M_{\mathrm{GT}}|^2 \tag{38f}
$$
$$
c\xi = \Lambda_{J'J}(|g_T|^2 + |g_T'|^2 - |g_A|^2 - |g_A'|^2) |M_{\mathrm{GT}}|^2 \tag{38g}
$$

where

$$
\Lambda_{J'J} = \begin{cases} 1 & J \to J' = J - 1 \\ -(2J-1)/(J+1) & J \to J' = J \\ J(2J-1)/[(J+1)(2J+3)] & J \to J' = J + 1 \end{cases} \tag{38h}
$$

$$
A\xi = 2\lambda_{J'J} \,\mathrm{Re}\, (g_T g_T'^* - g_A g_A'^*) |M_{\mathrm{GT}}|^2
$$
$$
+ \delta_{J'J} \sqrt{\frac{J}{J+1}} \, 2 \,\mathrm{Re}\, (g_S g_T'^* + g_S' g_T^* - g_V g_A'^* - g_V' g_A^*) M_{\mathrm{F}} M_{\mathrm{GT}}^* \tag{39a}
$$

where

$$\lambda_{J'J} = \frac{1}{2}\frac{1}{J+1}\,[2 + J(J+1) - J'(J'+1)] \qquad (39b)$$

$$B\xi = 2\,\text{Re}\left\{\lambda_{J'J}\left[\frac{m}{E_e}(g_T g_A'^* + g_T' g_A^*) + (g_T g_T'^* + g_A g_A'^*)\right]|M_{\text{GT}}|^2\right.$$

$$- \delta_{J'J}\sqrt{\frac{J}{J+1}}\left[(g_S g_T'^* + g_S' g_T^* + g_V g_A'^* + g_V' g_A^*)\right.$$

$$\left.+ \frac{m}{E_e}(g_S g_A'^* + g_S' g_A^* + g_V g_T'^* + g_V' g_T^*)\right]M_{\text{F}}M_{\text{GT}}^*\right\} \qquad (39c)$$

$$D\xi = \delta_{J'J}\sqrt{\frac{J}{J+1}}\,[2\,\text{Im}\,(g_S g_T^* - g_V g_A^* + g_S' g_T'^* - g_V' g_A'^*)]M_{\text{F}}M_{\text{GT}}^*$$

$$\qquad (39d)$$

$$G\xi = 2\,\text{Re}\,(g_S g_S'^* - g_V g_V'^*)\,|M_{\text{F}}|^2 + 2\,\text{Re}\,(g_T g_T'^* - g_A g_A'^*)\,|M_{\text{GT}}|^2$$

$$\qquad (39e)$$

$$H\xi = 2\,\text{Re}\left\{\left[-(g_S g_V'^* + g_S' g_V^*) - \frac{m}{E_e}(g_S g_S'^* + g_V g_V'^*)\right]|M_{\text{F}}|^2\right.$$

$$\left.+ \frac{1}{3}\left[(g_T g_A'^* + g_T' g_A^*) + \frac{m}{E_e}(g_T g_T'^* + g_A g_A'^*)\right]|M_{\text{GT}}|^2\right\} \qquad (39f)$$

$$K\xi = 2\,\text{Re}\,\{(-g_S g_S'^* - g_V g_V'^* + g_S g_V'^* + g_S' g_V^*)\,|M_{\text{F}}|^2$$

$$+ \tfrac{1}{3}(g_T g_T'^* + g_A g_A'^* - g_T g_A'^* - g_T' g_A^*)\,|M_{\text{GT}}|^2\} \qquad (39g)$$

$$L\xi = 2\,\text{Im}\,(g_S g_V^* + g_S' g_V'^*)\,|M_{\text{F}}|^2 - \tfrac{2}{3}\,\text{Im}\,(g_T\,g_A^* + g_T'\,g_A'^*)\,|M_{\text{GT}}|^2$$

$$\qquad (40a)$$

$$N\xi = 2\,\text{Re}\left\{\lambda_{J'J}\left[\frac{1}{2}\frac{m}{E_e}(|g_T|^2 + |g_T'|^2 + |g_A|^2 + |g_A'|^2)\right.\right.$$

$$\left.+ (g_T g_A^* + g_T' g_A'^*)\right]|M_{\text{GT}}|^2$$

$$+ \delta_{J'J}\sqrt{\frac{J}{J+1}}\left[(g_S g_A^* + g_V g_T^* + g_S' g_A'^* + g_V' g_T'^*)\right.$$

$$\left.\left.+ \frac{m}{E_e}(g_S g_T^* + g_V g_A^* + g_S' g_T'^* + g_V' g_A'^*)\right]M_{\text{F}}M_{\text{GT}}^*\right\} \qquad (40b)$$

$$R\xi = \lambda_{J'J}2\,\text{Im}\,(g_T g_A'^* + g_T' g_A^*)\,|M_{\text{GT}}|^2$$

$$+ \delta_{J'J}\sqrt{\frac{J}{J+1}}\,2\,\text{Im}\,(g_S g_A'^* + g_S' g_A^* - g_V g_T'^* - g_V' g_T^*)M_{\text{F}}M_{\text{GT}}^*$$

$$\qquad (40c)$$

$$Q\xi = 2 \operatorname{Re} \left\{ \lambda_{J'J} [\tfrac{1}{2}(|g_T|^2 + |g_A|^2 + |g_T'|^2 \right.$$

$$+ |g_A'|^2 - (g_T g_A^* + g_T' g_A'^*)] |M_{GT}|^2$$

$$- \delta_{J'J} \sqrt{\frac{J}{J+1}} \left[(g_S g_A^* + g_V g_T^* + g_S' g_A'^* + g_V' g_T'^*) \right.$$

$$\left. \left. - (g_S g_T^* + g_V g_A^* + g_S' g_T'^* + g_V' g_A'^*)] M_F M_{GT}^* \right\} \tag{40d}$$

At this stage, it is worth summarizing the results of the previous sections. In the following we list the various conclusions and their basis.

1. $$\operatorname{Re}(g_S g_V^* + g_S' g_V'^*) = \operatorname{Re}(g_T g_A^* + g_T' g_A'^*) = 0 \tag{41a}$$

This result follows from Eq. (25) which gives for the probability for emission of an electron with energy between E_e and $E_e + dE_e$,

$$w(E_e)\, dE_e = \frac{\xi}{2\pi^3} \frac{p_e E_e}{c^5 \hbar^7} (E_{max} - E_e)^2 \left(1 + b\, \frac{2mc^2}{E_e}\right) dE_e \tag{41b}$$

It is found experimentally that for both allowed pure Fermi and allowed pure Gamow-Teller transitions, the Fermi plot $-[w(E_e)/p_e E_e]^{1/2}$ against E_e is a straight line, thus suggesting very strongly that the nonlinear term is not present; that is, $b = 0$.

2. $$g_S = g_S' = g_T = g_T' = 0$$

The electron-neutrino angular coefficient is

$$a = \frac{\{\tfrac{1}{2}[|g_V|^2 + |g_V'|^2 - |g_S|^2 - |g_S'|^2]\, |M_F|^2 + \tfrac{1}{6}[|g_T|^2 + |g_T'|^2 - |g_A|^2 - |g_A'|^2]\, |M_{GT}|^2\}}{\{\tfrac{1}{2}[|g_S|^2 + |g_S'|^2 + |g_V|^2 + |g_V'|^2]\, |M_F|^2 + \tfrac{1}{2}[|g_T|^2 + |g_T'|^2 + |g_A| + |g_A'|^2]\, |M_{GT}|^2\}} \tag{42a}$$

The experimental values of a are consistent with

$$\left. \begin{aligned} a &= 1 \quad \text{for} \quad \text{pure Fermi transition} \\ &= -\tfrac{1}{3} \quad \text{for} \quad \text{pure G-T transition} \end{aligned} \right\} \tag{42b}$$

which in view of (1) gives

$$g_S = g_S' = 0, \qquad g_T = g_T' = 0 \tag{42c}$$

3. $$g_V = g_V', \qquad g_A = g_A'$$

The longitudinal polarization of electrons emitted in beta decay is obtained from Eqs. (38a) and (38c) and found to be

$$P = \frac{G v_e / c}{(1 + bm/E_e)} = G v_e / c \qquad \text{for} \quad b = 0$$

$$= - \frac{\text{Re} \, (g_V g_V'^*) \, |M_F|^2 + \text{Re} \, (g_A g_A'^*) \, |M_{GT}|^2}{|g_V|^2 \, |M_F|^2 + |g_A|^2 \, |M_{GT}|^2} \frac{v_e}{c} \qquad (43)$$

where c has been explicitly inserted.

The observed longitudinal polarization of the electron is consistent with the value $-v_e/c$ in pure Fermi and pure G-T transitions, which gives $g_V = g_V'$ and $g_A = g_A'$.

4. Relative phase difference between the couplings g_V and g_A is π.

The beta decay of a polarized neutron allows a determination of the angular correlation coefficient A between the direction of the outgoing electron and the direction of polarization of the neutron.

$$A = - \frac{2 \, |g_A|^2 + 2 \, |g_A| \, |g_V| \cos \phi}{|g_V|^2 + 3 \, |g_A|^2} \qquad (44)$$

The observed value $A_{\text{obs}} = -0.11$ is consistent with $\phi = \pi$ and $g_A/g_V = -1.24$.

13.13 Two-Component Theory of the Neutrino

The two-component theory of the neutrino with zero mass and spin $\frac{1}{2}$ was first proposed by Weyl,[30] but was rejected since it does not lead to invariance of the theory under space reflections. With the discovery of nonconservation of parity in beta decay by Lee and Yang,[1,11] the two-component theory of the neutrino was revived by Landau[11] and by Salam.[11]

The two-component theory of Weyl is equivalent to the four-component Dirac theory, provided some constraints are imposed on the Dirac amplitudes ψ. The Dirac equation for zero mass is

$$\gamma_\mu \frac{\partial}{\partial x_\mu} \psi(x) = 0 \qquad (45a)$$

which can be rewritten in the Hamiltonian form

$$\gamma_4 \gamma_k \frac{\partial}{\partial x_k} \psi = i \frac{\partial \psi}{\partial t} \qquad (45b)$$

or in momentum representation in the form

$$(E_v - i\gamma_4 \gamma_k p_{vk}) u = 0 \qquad (45c)$$

Using the representations

$$\gamma_k = \begin{pmatrix} 0 & -i\sigma_k \\ i\sigma_k & 0 \end{pmatrix} \qquad \gamma_4 = \begin{pmatrix} 1 & 0 \\ 0 & -1 \end{pmatrix} \qquad \gamma_5 = \begin{pmatrix} 0 & 1 \\ 1 & 0 \end{pmatrix} \tag{46a}$$

$$u = \begin{pmatrix} \chi \\ \phi \end{pmatrix} \tag{46b}$$

where σ_k are the 2×2 Pauli matrices and χ and ϕ are two-component spinors, we have from Eqs. (46) and (45c)

$$E_\nu \phi + \boldsymbol{\sigma} \cdot \mathbf{p}_\nu \chi = 0 \tag{47a}$$

$$E_\nu \chi + \boldsymbol{\sigma} \cdot \mathbf{p}_\nu \phi = 0 \tag{47b}$$

Introducing

$$\psi_+ = \frac{1}{2}\begin{pmatrix} \phi + \chi \\ \phi + \chi \end{pmatrix} \tag{48a}$$

$$\psi_- = \frac{1}{2}\begin{pmatrix} -(\phi - \chi) \\ (\phi - \chi) \end{pmatrix} \tag{48b}$$

Equations (48a) and (48b) are equivalent to

$$\psi_\pm = \tfrac{1}{2}(1 \pm \gamma_5)\psi \tag{48c}$$

Multiplying Eq. (48c) by γ_5, we obtain

$$\gamma_5 \psi_\pm = \tfrac{1}{2}(\gamma_5 \pm 1)\psi = \pm\psi_\pm; \tag{48d}$$

that is,

$$(1 \mp \gamma_5)\psi_\pm = 0 \tag{48e}$$

Thus ψ_+ and ψ_- are eigenfunctions of γ_5 with eigenvalues $+1$ and -1.

From Eqs. (47), we have

$$\phi = -\frac{(\boldsymbol{\sigma} \cdot \mathbf{p}_\nu)}{p_\nu}\chi \qquad \chi = -\frac{(\boldsymbol{\sigma} \cdot \mathbf{p}_\nu)}{p_\nu}\phi \qquad E_\nu = p_\nu \tag{49a}$$

so that

$$\psi_+ = \frac{1}{2}\begin{pmatrix} (1 - h)\phi \\ (1 - h)\phi \end{pmatrix} \qquad \psi_- = \frac{1}{2}\begin{pmatrix} -(1 + h)\phi \\ (1 + h)\phi \end{pmatrix} \tag{49b}$$

where the helicity

$$h = \frac{\boldsymbol{\sigma} \cdot \mathbf{p}_\nu}{p_\nu} \tag{49c}$$

Equations (47) or the equivalent Eq. (49a) can be written as

$$\psi_+ = \phi + \chi = (1 - h)\chi = (1 - h)\phi = \tfrac{1}{2}(1 - h)(\phi + \chi)$$
$$= \tfrac{1}{2}(1 - h)\psi_+;$$

that is,

$$\psi_+ = -h\psi_+ \tag{50a}$$

Similarly

$$\psi_- = h\psi_- \tag{50b}$$

It follows from Eqs. (50a) and (50b) that ψ_+ and ψ_- are fields with only two independent components; ψ_+ corresponds to a particle with negative helicity (spin antiparallel to the momentum) and ψ_- corresponds to a particle with positive helicity (spin parallel to the momentum).

The fields ψ_+ and ψ_- are invariant under a proper Lorentz transformation. Under space reflection, the helicity (chirality) is changed. Since the operator for space reversal for a Dirac field is γ_4, we have the space-reversed field

$$(\psi_+)^P = P\psi_+ = \gamma_4\psi_+ = \tfrac{1}{2}\gamma_4(1 + \gamma_5)\psi = \tfrac{1}{2}(1 - \gamma_5)\psi^P \tag{51a}$$

Similarly,

$$(\psi_-)^P = P\psi_- = \gamma_4\psi_- = \tfrac{1}{2}(1 + \gamma_5)\psi^P \tag{51b}$$

Thus the eigenvalue of the operator γ_5, called the chirality, changes sign under space reflection (ψ_+ have ± 1 chirality).

We know now that the Hamiltonian for beta decay which fits the experimental results can be written as:

$$H_\beta = \frac{g_V}{\sqrt{2}} \int d^3x (\bar\psi_p(\mathbf{x})\gamma_\mu\psi_n(\mathbf{x}))[\bar\psi_e(\mathbf{x})\gamma_\mu(1 + \gamma_5)\psi_\nu(\mathbf{x})]$$
$$- \frac{g_A}{\sqrt{2}} \int d^3x (\bar\psi_p(\mathbf{x})\gamma_\mu\gamma_5\psi_n(\mathbf{x}))[\bar\psi_e(\mathbf{x})\gamma_\mu(1 + \gamma_5)\psi_\nu(\mathbf{x})] + \text{hc} \tag{52a}$$

where

$$\frac{g_A}{g_V} = \lambda = 1.18 \pm 0.05 \tag{52b}$$

The appearance of the factor $(1 + \gamma_5)$ before $\psi_\nu(x)$ is very suggestive of the use of the two-component theory of the neutrino. It has been pointed out by several authors[12,31] that if it is possible to accept the value $\lambda = g_A/g_V = 1$, the beta interaction Hamiltonian Eq. (52a) can be derived by a simple prescription from the following general Hamiltonian density:

$$\mathscr{H} = \frac{1}{\sqrt{2}} \sum_\lambda (\psi_p\Gamma_\lambda\psi_n)[\bar\psi_e\Gamma_\lambda(g_\lambda + g'_\lambda\gamma_5)\psi_\nu] + \text{hc} \tag{53a}$$

We make the following replacement for each ψ and $\bar\psi$ occurring in Eq. (53a)

$$\psi \rightarrow \tfrac{1}{2}(1 + \gamma_5)\psi \tag{53b}$$
$$\bar\psi \rightarrow \bar\psi\tfrac{1}{2}(1 - \gamma_5) \tag{53c}$$

Making use of the commutation relations, we have

$$[\tfrac{1}{2}(1 + \gamma_5)]^2 = \tfrac{1}{2}(1 + \gamma_5) \tag{54a}$$

$$|\tfrac{1}{2}(1 + \gamma_5)|^2 = \tfrac{1}{4}(1 - \gamma_5)(1 + \gamma_5) = 0 \tag{54b}$$

Thus under the replacements in Eqs. (53b) and (53c), we find

$$\bar{\psi}\Gamma_\lambda\psi \to \bar{\psi}\tfrac{1}{2}(1 - \gamma_5)\Gamma_\lambda\tfrac{1}{2}(1 + \gamma_5)\psi \tag{54c}$$

with

$$\tfrac{1}{2}(1 - \gamma_5)\Gamma_\lambda\tfrac{1}{2}(1 + \gamma_5)$$
$$= \begin{cases} \tfrac{1}{4}\Gamma_\lambda(1 - \gamma_5)(1 + \gamma_5) = 0 & \text{for} \quad \lambda = S, T, P \\ \tfrac{1}{4}\Gamma_\lambda(1 + \gamma_5)^2 = \tfrac{1}{2}\Gamma_\lambda(1 + \gamma_5) & \text{for} \quad \lambda = V, A \end{cases} \tag{54d}$$

Therefore if we require the theory to be invariant under the substitutions of Eqs. (53b) and (53c), only the V and A terms exist in Eq. (53a), giving the following interaction Hamiltonian density for the $V - A$ theory

$$\mathscr{H}_\beta = \frac{g_\beta}{\sqrt{2}}[\bar{\psi}_p\gamma_\mu(1 + \gamma_5)\psi_n][\bar{\psi}_e\gamma_\mu(1 + \gamma_5)\psi_\nu] \tag{55}$$

The two-component neutrino theory arose because of the nonconservation of parity. According to this theory the mass of neutrino or antineutrino is zero whereas the conventional Fermi theory of beta decay does not make any postulate regarding the mass of the neutrino. The neutrino and antineutrino are distinguishable when we consider their helicity. For a given momentum, a neutrino has only one spin state and the spin is antiparallel to its momentum whereas the spin of antineutrino is parallel to its momentum. The spin and momentum define the helicity. A neutrino can be defined to have a left-handed screw motion and helicity of -1 whereas an antineutrino will have a right-handed screw motion and helicity of $+1$. The helicity of the neutrino and antineutrino has been demonstrated experimentally[44] and is consistent with the above discussion. We can therefore state that there are two kinds of neutrinos—a left-handed neutrino (ν_L) and a right-handed antineutrino ($\bar{\nu}_R$)—in conformity with the two-component neutrino theory.

13.14 Conservation of Leptons

Neutrinos, electrons, and muons are known as leptons. Each of the particles, neutrino, electron, and muon, has been given a lepton number of $+1$, whereas its antiparticle has a lepton number of -1.

The law of lepton conservation which was first formulated by Konopinski and Mahmoud[32] states that in a given reaction the total number of leptons is conserved. For example

$$e^+ + e^- \rightarrow \gamma + \gamma$$
$$-1 + 1 \rightarrow 0 + 0$$

In the case of muon decay we have

$$\mu^{\pm} \rightarrow e^{\pm} + \nu + \bar{\nu}$$

where $\bar{\nu}$ is the antineutrino.

The law of lepton conservation has some physical significance. By its application it is possible to see whether a particular process is allowed. Reactions such as $\nu + p \rightarrow n + e^+$ or $\mu^- \rightarrow e^- + 2\nu$ are not allowed, whereas reactions $\mu \rightarrow e + \gamma$ or $\mu + p \rightarrow e + p$ are. The reaction $\bar{\nu}(p, \bar{e})n$ is of particular interest since it provides a check on the two-component neutrino theory. Such experiments have been performed by Cowan et al.,[9] and the details are given in Section 13.1. We have also indicated that the experimentally observed antineutrino cross section is in accord[10,33] with the cross section computed from the two-component neutrino theory.

13.15   Conservation of Vector Current (CVC) Theory

Experimentally it has been observed that the vector-coupling constants $g_{V\beta}$ in beta decay and $g_{V\mu}$ in muon decay are practically the same, which supports the postulate of the universal $V - A$ Fermi interaction.[12] In the case of muon decay no nucleons are present; consequently, there is no need for renormalization of the muon-decay coupling strengths since there is no strong pion-nucleon interaction. On the other hand, if such renormalization is needed for beta decay due to pion-nucleon interaction, then the coupling constants in the above two processes cannot be identical. Feynman and Gell-Mann[34] have proposed the CVC (conservation of vector current) theory in order to explain the lack of renormalization in the beta-decay process. A similar explanation has also been suggested by Gershtein and Zel'dovich.[35] Apparently the pions when they are virtually emitted from the nucleons carry with them the beta-interaction strength, and the vector part of nuclear interaction is such that it does not have any renormalization effect. Thus the coupling constant $g_{V\beta}$ remains unaffected.

The theory of Feynman and Gell-Mann is based on analogies with electromagnetism and gives the $V - A$ form for the weak interaction. We shall not go into the details of the CVC theory, but limit our discussion to experimental results.

Many experiments have been performed to verify the CVC theory. One of these experiments originated from the suggestions made by Gell-Mann[36] and by Gell-Mann and Berman[37] and was successfully carried out in many laboratories.[38]

Consider the nuclei B^{12}, C^{12}, and N^{12}. Both B^{12} and N^{12} decay to C^{12} by the emission of electrons and positrons, respectively. The CVC theory predicts a shape-correction factor for the form of the beta spectra obtained from B^{12} and N^{12}. The shape-correction factor is given by $(1 + aE)$ where a is a coefficient and E is the beta energy. The most precise experimental values[38] of the coefficient are $a^-(B^{12}) = +0.55 \pm 0.10\%$ and $a^+(N^{12}) = -0.52 \pm 0.06\%$, which give excellent agreement with the CVC theory predicted values $a^-(B^{12}) = +0.55 \pm 0.12\%$, and $a^+(N^{12}) = -0.55 \pm 0.12\%$. The change of sign of the coefficient a is due to $(V - A)$ interference which changes sign from electron to positron transition.

The beta-alpha angular correlations in the Li^8 and B^8 beta decays have also been used[39] to study the validity of the CVC theory. Both Li^8 and B^8 decay respectively by the electron from the $J = 2^+$ state and by the positron from the $J = 2^+$ state by an allowed Gamow-Teller transition to the 2.90 Mev excited state $J = 2^+$ of Be^8. Be^8 then decays by the emission of two α-particles. The angular correlation between the directions of emission of the electron and α-particle is given by the form

$$W(\theta_{\beta\alpha}) = 1 + B \cos^2 \theta_{\beta\alpha} \tag{56}$$

where the coefficient B depends on the details of the matrix elements involved in the transition. The value[18] of the anisotropy coefficient B, according to the CVC theory, lies between $0.0025E_\beta$ and $0.0045E_\beta$, where E_β is the total energy of the electron. This small value of B has been very carefully determined by Nordberg et al.[40] For Li^8, it is

$$B = (0.00316 \pm 0.00060)E_\beta,$$

and for B^8 it is $B = (-0.00386 \pm 0.00100)E_\beta$. The value for Li^8 is in agreement with another precise value[41] $B = (0.0037 \pm 0.0010)E_\beta$. From these data it appears that within the experimental error the CVC theory gains additional support.

The universal Fermi interaction has gained support from the fact that the coupling constants $g_{V\beta}$ in beta decay and $g_{V\mu}$ in muon decay are the same. The CVC theory arises as a consequence of this equivalence. The value of $g_{V\mu}$ is obtained from the relationship

$$\frac{1}{T_\mu} = \frac{g_{V\mu}^2 m_\mu^5 e^4}{192\pi^3 \hbar^7} \tag{57}$$

where $T_\mu = 2.198 \pm 0.001$ microsecond is the muon lifetime and the muon mass[42] is $m_\mu = (206.768 \pm 0.003)m_e$. Taking into account the radiative corrections,[43] Wu[18] finds $g_{V_\mu} = (1.4350 \pm 0.0011) \times 10^{-49}$ erg-cm³, which is in excellent agreement with the value[18] of

$$g_{V_\beta} = (1.4029 \pm 0.0022) \times 10^{-49} \text{ erg-cm}^3.$$

The small difference noted may be due to the uncertain nature of the corrections.

References

1. Lee, T. D., and C. N. Yang, *Phys. Rev.* **104**, 254, 1956.
2. Wu, C. S., E. Ambler, R. W. Hayward, D. D. Hoppes, and R. P. Hudson, *Phys. Rev.* **105**, 1413, 1957.
3. Fermi, E., *Z. Physik*, **88**, 161, 1934.
4. Kusaka, S., *Phys. Rev.* **60**, 61, 1941.
5. Kofoed-Hansen, O., *Phys. Rev.* **71**, 451, 1947.
6. Pruett, J. R., *Phys. Rev.* **73**, 1219, 1948.
7. Hanna, G. C., and B. Pontecorvo, *Phys. Rev.* **75**, 984, 1949; Curran, S. C., J. Angus, and A. L. Cockroft, *Phil. Mag.* **40**, 53, 1949; *Phys. Rev.* **76**, 853, 1949; Langer, L. M., and R. J. D. Moffat, *Phys. Rev.* **88**, 689, 1952; Hamilton, D. R., W. P. Alford, and L. Gross, *Phys. Rev.* **92**, 1521, 1953.
8. Smith, P. B., and J. S. Allen, *Phys. Rev.* **81**, 381, 1951; Davis, R., *Phys. Rev.* **86**, 976, 1952; Rodeback, G. W., and J. S. Allen, *Phys. Rev.* **86**, 446, 1952; Kofoed-Hansen, O., *Phys. Rev.* **96**, 1045, 1954.
9. Cowan, C. L., F. Reines, F. B. Harrison, H. W. Kruse, and A. D. McGuire, *Science*, **124**, 103, 1956.
10. Reines, F., *Ann. Rev. Nucl. Soc.* **10**, 1, 1960.
11. Lee, T. D., and C. N. Yang, *Phys. Rev.* **105**, 1671, 1957; L. Landau, *Nucl. Phys.* **3**, 127, 1957; Salam, A., *Nuovo Cimento* **5**, 299, 1957.
12. Feynman, R. P., and M. Gell-Mann, *Phys. Rev.* **109**, 193, 1958; Sudarshan, E. C. G., and R. E. Marshak, *Phys. Rev.* **109**, 1860, 1958; Sakurai, J. J., *Nuovo Cimento* **7**, 649, 1958.
13. Danby, G., J. M. Gaillard, K. Goulianos, L. M. Lederman, N. Mistry, M. Schwartz, and J. Steinberger, *Phys. Rev. Letters* **9**, 36, 1962.
14. Pauli, W., *Zeeman Verhandelingen*, p. 31, Martinus Nijhoff, The Hague, 1935; *ibid, Ann. Inst. Henri Poincaré* **6**, 137, 1936; see also Schweber, S. S., *An Introduction to Relativistic Quantum Field Theory*, p. 70. Harper and Row, New York, 1961.
15. Allen, J. S., R. L. Burman, W. B. Hermannsfeldt, and T. Stähelin, T. H. Braid, *Phys. Rev.* **116**, 134, 1959.
16. Bardin, R. K., C. A. Barnes, W. A. Fowler, and P. A. Seeger, *Phys. Rev.* **127**, 583, 1962; Butler, J. W., and R. O. Bondelid, *Phys. Rev.* **121**, 1770, 1961.
17. Rose, M. E., *Phys. Rev.* **49**, 727, 1936.
18. Wu, C. S., *Rev. Mod. Phys.* **36**, 618, 1964.
19. Freeman, J. M., J. H. Montague, D. West, and R. E. White, *Phys. Letters*, **3**, 136, 1962.
20. Jänecke, J., *Phys. Letters* **6**, 69, 1963.
21. Freeman, J. M., R. E. White, J. H. Montague, G. Murray, and W. E. Burcham. *Phys. Letters* **8**, 115, 1964.
22. Ridley, B. W., *Nucl. Phys.* **25**, 483, 1961.
23. Johnson, C. H., F. Pleasonton, and T. A. Carlson, *Phys. Rev.* **132**, 1149, 1963.

24. Frauenfelder, H., R. Bobone, E. Von Goeler, N. Levine, H. R. Lewis, R. N. Peacock, A. Rossi, and G. De Pasquali, *Phys. Rev.* **106**, 386, 1957; Spivak, P, E., and L. A. Mikaelyan, *Nucl. Phys.* **20**, 475, 1960; Spivak, P. E., L. A. Mikaelyan. I. E. Kutikov, and V. F. Apalin, *Soviet Phys. JETP* **12**, 1027, 1961.
25. Brosi, A. R., A. I. Galonsky, B. H. Ketelle, and H. B. Willard, *Nucl. Phys.* **33**, 353. 1962.
26. Ullman, J. D., H. Frauenfelder, H. J. Lipkin, and A. Rossi, *Phys. Rev.* **122**, 536, 1961.
27. Burgy, M. T., V. E. Krohn, T. B. Novey, G. R. Ringo, and V. L. Telegdi, *Phys. Rev.* **120**, 1829, 1960.
28. Robson, J. M., *Phys. Rev.* **100**, 933, 1955; Clark, M. A., J. M. Robson, and R. Nathans, *Phys. Rev. Letters* **1**, 100, 1958; Sosnovskiĭ, A. N., P. E. Spivak, Yu. A. Prokof'ev, I. E. Kutikov, and Yu. P. Dobrynin, *JETP* **36**, 717, 1959; Trebukhovskiĭ, Yu. V., V. V. Vladimirskiĭ, V. K. Grigor'ev, and V. A. Ergakov, *JETP* **36**, 931, 1959.
29. Jackson, J. D., S. B. Treiman and H. W. Wyld, *Nucl. Phys.* **4**, 206, 1957; *ibid.*, *Phys. Rev.* **106**, 517, 1957.
30. Weyl, H., *Z. Physik* **56**, 330, 1929.
31. Lee, T. D., and C. N. Yang, *Phys. Rev.* **119**, 1410, 1960.
32. Konopinski, E., and H. M. Mahmoud, *Phys. Rev.* **92**, 1045, 1953.
33. Carter, R. E., F. Reines, J. J. Wagner, and M. E. Wyman, *Phys. Rev.* **113**, 280, 1959.
34. Feynman, R. P., and M. Gell-Mann, *Phys. Rev.* **109**, 193, 1958.
35. Gershtein, S. S., and I. B. Zel'dovich, *Soviet Phys. JETP*, **2**, 576, 1956.
36. Gell-Mann, M., *Phys. Rev.* **111**, 362, 1958.
37. Gell-Mann, M., and S. M. Berman, *Phys. Rev. Letters* **3**, 99, 1959.
38. Mayer-Kuckuk, T., and F. C. Michel, *Phys. Rev.* **127**, 545, 1962; Glass, N. W., and R. W. Peterson, *Phys. Rev.* **130**, 299, 1963. Lee, Y. K., L. W. Mo, and C. S. Wu, *Phys. Rev. Letters* **10**, 253, 1963.
39. Bernstein, J., and R. R. Lewis, *Phys. Rev.* **112**, 232, 1958; Morita, M., *Phys. Rev.* **113**, 1584, 1959.
40. Nordberg, M. E., F. B. Morinigo, and C. A. Barnes, *Phys. Rev.* **125**, 321, 1962.
41. Gruhle, W., K. H. Lauterjung, and B. Schimmer, *Nucl. Phys.* **42**, 321, 1963.
42. Charpak, G., F. J. M. Farley, R. L. Garwin, T. Muller, J. C. Sens, and A. Zichichi, *Phys. Letters* **1**, 16, 1962.
43. Kinoshita, T., and A. Sirlin, *Phys. Rev.* **113**, 1652, 1959. Berman, S. M., and A. Sirlin, *Ann. Phys. N.Y.* **20**, 20, 1962.
44. Goldhaber, M., L. Grodzins, and A. W. Sunyar, *Phys. Rev.* **109**, 1015, 1958.

Problems

1. Some early experiments on the detection of the neutrino were performed with the aid of a low-pressure cloud chamber. In these experiments, the total number of ions produced (estimated from the number of droplets) by the recoiled daughter nucleus gave a measure of its energy. Discuss the reasons for which such experiments did not give definite evidence on the existence of the neutrino.

2. From the Fermi plot, taking into account the neutrino mass correction term, Langer and Moffat (See Ref. 7) concluded that the possible upper limit for the rest mass of the neutrino is 250 ev. From the data published in Ref. 7, draw the necessary Fermi plot to justify the above conclusion.

3. From the consideration of spin orientations, show that in the Gamow-Teller selection rule the $0^+ \rightarrow 0^+$ transition is forbidden.

4. Obtain an expression for the momentum distribution for the beta particle when the rest mass of the neutrino is m_ν.

5. Obtain an expression for the energy distribution for the beta particle assuming that two neutrinos (rest mass zero) are emitted in the process of beta decay.

6. Derive the result in Eq. (15) from the previous equations.

7. Show that for the decay of O^{14}, the value of the Fermi transition matrix squared

$$|M_\mathrm{F}|^2 = \left| \sum_{n=1}^{A} \int d^3x \Psi_f^*(\mathbf{x}) \tau_n^{(+)} \Psi_i(\mathbf{x}) \right|^2$$

is 2.

8. Using the extreme single-particle model for odd-A nuclei, show that for the Gamow-Teller transition

$$|M_\mathrm{GT}|^2 = \left(\sum_{k=1}^{3} \left| \sum_{n=1}^{A} \int d^3x \Psi_f^*(\mathbf{x}) \sigma_k \tau_n^{(+)} \Psi_i(\mathbf{x}) \right|^2 \right)_{\mathrm{av}}$$

$$= K \delta_{l_i l_f} \int dr r^2 R_i R_f$$

where R_i and R_f are the initial and final radial wave functions and the constant K is given as follows

$$K = \begin{cases} \dfrac{j}{j+1} & \text{for } \Delta j = 0 \quad \text{and} \quad j = l - \tfrac{1}{2} \\[2ex] \dfrac{j+1}{j} & \text{for } \Delta j = 0 \quad \text{and} \quad j = l + \tfrac{1}{2} \\[2ex] \dfrac{2(2j_f + 1)}{2l + 1} & \text{for } \Delta j = 1 \quad \text{and} \quad j_i + j_f = 2l \end{cases}$$

APPENDIX

MATHEMATICAL PRELIMINARIES

The main purpose of this appendix is to summarize the mathematical results which are frequently used in nuclear physics. Several are only stated, but a great number of them are derived. Whenever possible, concepts have been introduced which are necessary for the development of topics in nuclear physics. Some sections may present difficulties to the uninitiated student but their applicability will be clearer after reading the relevant chapters. Their inclusion in the appendix has been motivated with an aim to avoid lengthy mathematical discussions which seem to somewhat digress from development of the main topics throughout the book.

A.1   Expressions for ∇, ∇^2, and $\mathbf{l} = \mathbf{r} \times \mathbf{p}$ in Different Coordinate Systems

The Gradient Operator

$$\nabla = \hat{x}\frac{\partial}{\partial x} + \hat{y}\frac{\partial}{\partial y} + \hat{z}\frac{\partial}{\partial z} \qquad \text{Cartesian coordinates}$$

$$= \hat{r}\frac{\partial}{\partial r} + \hat{\theta}\frac{1}{r}\frac{\partial}{\partial \theta} + \hat{\phi}\frac{1}{r \sin \theta}\frac{\partial}{\partial \phi} \qquad \text{Polar coordinates}$$

$$= \hat{r}\frac{\partial}{\partial r} + \hat{\theta}\frac{1}{r}\frac{\partial}{\partial \theta} + \hat{z}\frac{\partial}{\partial z} \qquad \text{Cylindrical coordinates} \quad (1)$$

where for polar coordinates (Morse and Feshbach, p. 116)

$$\hat{r} = \hat{x} \sin \theta \cos \phi + \hat{y} \sin \theta \sin \phi + \hat{z} \cos \theta$$
$$\hat{\phi} = -\hat{x} \sin \phi + \hat{y} \cos \phi$$
$$\hat{\theta} = \hat{x} \cos \theta \cos \phi + \hat{y} \cos \theta \sin \phi - \hat{z} \sin \theta \qquad (2)$$

541

and for cylindrical coordinates

$$\hat{r} = \hat{x} \cos \theta + \hat{y} \sin \theta$$

$$\hat{\theta} = -\hat{x} \sin \theta + \hat{y} \cos \theta$$

$$\hat{z} = \hat{z} \tag{3}$$

The Del-Square Operator

$$\nabla^2 = \frac{\partial^2}{\partial x^2} + \frac{\partial^2}{\partial y^2} + \frac{\partial^2}{\partial z^2} \qquad \text{Cartesian coordinates}$$

$$= \frac{1}{r^2} \frac{\partial}{\partial r}\left(r^2 \frac{\partial}{\partial r}\right) + \frac{1}{r^2 \sin \theta} \frac{\partial}{\partial \theta}\left(\sin \theta \frac{\partial}{\partial \theta}\right) + \frac{1}{r^2 \sin^2 \theta} \frac{\partial^2}{\partial \phi^2}$$

Polar coordinates

$$= \frac{1}{r} \frac{\partial}{\partial r}\left(r \frac{\partial}{\partial r}\right) + \frac{1}{r^2} \frac{\partial^2}{\partial \theta^2} + \frac{\partial^2}{\partial z^2} \qquad \text{Cylindrical coordinates} \tag{4}$$

where x, y, z are related to the polar (r, θ, ϕ) and cylindrical (r, θ, z) coordinates as follows:

$$x = r \sin \theta \cos \phi \qquad x = r \cos \theta$$

$$y = r \sin \theta \sin \phi \qquad y = r \sin \theta$$

$$z = r \cos \theta \qquad z = z \tag{5}$$

The components of the angular momentum operator are

$$l_x = y p_z - z p_y = -i\hbar\left(y \frac{\partial}{\partial z} - z \frac{\partial}{\partial y}\right)$$

$$= i\hbar\left(\sin \phi \frac{\partial}{\partial \theta} + \cot \theta \cos \phi \frac{\partial}{\partial \phi}\right) \tag{6a}$$

$$l_y = z p_x - x p_z = -i\hbar\left(z \frac{\partial}{\partial x} - x \frac{\partial}{\partial z}\right)$$

$$= i\hbar\left(-\cos \phi \frac{\partial}{\partial \theta} + \cot \theta \sin \phi \frac{\partial}{\partial \phi}\right) \tag{6b}$$

$$l_z = x p_y - y p_x = -i\hbar\left(x \frac{\partial}{\partial y} - y \frac{\partial}{\partial x}\right)$$

$$= -i\hbar \frac{\partial}{\partial \phi} \tag{6c}$$

and

$$\mathbf{l}^2 = l_x^2 + l_y^2 + l_z^2$$

$$= -\hbar^2 \left[\frac{1}{\sin \theta} \frac{\partial}{\partial \theta} \left(\sin \theta \frac{\partial}{\partial \theta} \right) + \frac{1}{\sin^2 \theta} \frac{\partial^2}{\partial \phi^2} \right] \tag{7a}$$

The commutation relations satisfied by the angular momentum operator are

$$\mathbf{l} \times \mathbf{l} = i\hbar \mathbf{l}, \qquad \text{that is,} \quad [l_x, l_y]_- = i\hbar l_z, \text{ etc.} \tag{7b}$$

A.2   Spherical Harmonics

The eigenfunctions of the operator $\mathbf{l}^2$ are the spherical harmonics $Y_{lm}(\theta, \phi)$ with the eigenvalue $l(l + 1)\hbar^2$. Also $Y_{lm}(\theta, \phi)$ is an eigenfunction of l_z with the eigenvalue $m\hbar$.

$$\mathbf{l}^2 Y_{lm}(\theta, \phi) = l(l + 1)\hbar^2 Y_{lm}(\theta, \phi) \tag{8a}$$

$$l_z Y_{lm}(\theta, \phi) = m\hbar Y_{lm}(\theta, \phi). \tag{8b}$$

The spherical harmonics $Y_{lm}(\theta, \phi)$ are defined in terms of the associated Legendre polynomial as (Condon and Shortley[1]):

$$Y_{lm}(\theta, \phi) = \sqrt{\frac{2l + 1}{4\pi} \frac{(l - m)!}{(l + m)!}} (-1)^m e^{im\phi} P_{lm}(\cos \theta) \tag{9a}$$

where

$$P_{lm}(\cos \theta) = \frac{(-1)^{l+m}}{2^l l!} \frac{(l + m)!}{(l - m)!} \sin^{-m} \theta \frac{d^{l-m}}{d(\cos \theta)^{l-m}} \sin^{2l} \theta \tag{9b}$$

with $-l \leq m \leq l$. The complex conjugate spherical harmonic $Y_{lm}^*(\theta, \phi)$ is given in terms of that of negative m by the relation

$$Y_{lm}^*(\theta, \phi) = (-1)^m Y_{l,-m}(\theta, \phi) \tag{10}$$

Under space reversal $\mathbf{r} \to -\mathbf{r}$, we have $\theta \to \pi - \theta$ and $\phi \to \pi + \phi$, so that $e^{im\phi} \to (-1)^m e^{im\phi}$, $P_{lm}(\cos \theta) \to (-1)^{l+m} P_{lm}(\cos \theta)$, and therefore

$$Y_{lm}(\theta, \phi) \to (-1)^l Y_{lm}(\theta, \phi) \text{ under } \mathbf{r} \to -\mathbf{r} \tag{11}$$

The spherical harmonics have been so defined that they form an orthonormal set

$$\int_0^{2\pi} \int_0^{\pi} Y_{lm}^*(\theta, \phi) Y_{l'm'}(\theta, \phi) \, d\Omega = \delta_{ll'} \delta_{mm'} \tag{12}$$

where the solid angle $d\Omega = d\hat{r} = \sin \theta \, d\theta \, d\phi$.

In the following we list some of the spherical harmonics:

$$Y_{00} = \frac{1}{\sqrt{4\pi}}$$

$$Y_{10} = \sqrt{\frac{3}{4\pi}} \cos\theta = \sqrt{\frac{3}{4\pi}} \frac{z}{r} = \sqrt{\frac{3}{4\pi}} P_1(\cos\theta)$$

$$Y_{1,\pm 1} = \mp\sqrt{\frac{3}{8\pi}} e^{\pm i\phi} \sin\theta = \mp\sqrt{\frac{3}{8\pi}} \frac{x \pm iy}{r}$$

$$Y_{20} = \sqrt{\frac{5}{16\pi}} (3\cos^2\theta - 1) = \sqrt{\frac{5}{16\pi}} \frac{2z^2 - x^2 - y^2}{r^2} = \sqrt{\frac{5}{16\pi}} P_2(\cos\theta)$$

$$Y_{2,\pm 1} = \mp\sqrt{\frac{15}{8\pi}} e^{\pm i\phi} \cos\theta \sin\theta = \mp\sqrt{\frac{15}{8\pi}} \frac{(x \pm iy)z}{r^2}$$

$$Y_{2,\pm 2} = \sqrt{\frac{15}{32\pi}} e^{\pm 2i\phi} \sin^2\theta = \sqrt{\frac{15}{32\pi}} \frac{(x \pm iy)^2}{r^2} \tag{13}$$

We note that

$$Y_{l0}(\theta, \phi) = \sqrt{\frac{2l + 1}{4\pi}} P_l(\cos\theta) \tag{14a}$$

$$Y_{lm}(0, \phi) = \sqrt{\frac{2l + 1}{4\pi}} \delta_{m0} \tag{14b}$$

Addition Theorem

$$P_l(\hat{r} \cdot \hat{r}') = \frac{4\pi}{2l + 1} \sum_{m=-l}^{l} Y_{lm}^*(\hat{r}) Y_{lm}(\hat{r}') \tag{15}$$

where $\hat{r}$ and $\hat{r}'$ are unit vectors specifying the directions $\Omega = (\theta, \phi)$ and $\Omega' = (\theta', \phi')$, respectively, with respect to an arbitrary axis and $\hat{r} \cdot \hat{r}' = \cos\theta\cos\theta' + \sin\theta\sin\theta'\cos(\phi - \phi')$.

The following are some useful properties of the spherical harmonics.

$$\cos\theta Y_{lm}(\hat{r}) = \left[\frac{(l + m + 1)(l - m + 1)}{(2l + 1)(2l + 3)}\right]^{1/2} Y_{l+1,m}$$
$$+ \left[\frac{(l + m)(l - m)}{(2l + 1)(2l - 1)}\right]^{1/2} Y_{l-1,m} \tag{16a}$$

$$\sin\theta e^{\pm i\phi} Y_{lm}(\hat{r}) = \mp\left[\frac{(l \pm m + 1)(l \pm m + 2)}{(2l + 1)(2l + 3)}\right]^{1/2} Y_{l+1,m\pm 1}$$
$$\pm \left[\frac{(l \mp m)(l \mp m - 1)}{(2l + 1)(2l - 1)}\right]^{1/2} Y_{l-1,m\pm 1} \tag{16b}$$

These relations can be simplified by introducing the raising and lowering operators l_+ and l_-.

$$l_\pm = l_x \pm il_y$$
$$= \pm\hbar e^{\pm i\phi}\left(\frac{\partial}{\partial\theta} \pm i\cot\theta\frac{\partial}{\partial\phi}\right) \tag{17a}$$

Then

$$l_\pm Y_{lm}(\hat{r}) = \hbar\sqrt{(l \mp m)(l \pm m + 1)}\, Y_{l,m\pm1}(\hat{r}) \tag{17b}$$
$$= \hbar\sqrt{l(l + 1) - m(m \pm 1)}\, Y_{l,m\pm1}(\hat{r})$$

A.3 Three-Dimensional Square-Well Potential

The Schrödinger equation for a three-dimensional square-well potential is given by

$$\left[\frac{-\hbar^2}{2m}\nabla^2 + V(\mathbf{r})\right]\psi(\mathbf{r}) = E\psi(\mathbf{r}) \tag{18a}$$

where

$$V(\mathbf{r}) = -V_0 \quad \text{for} \quad r < a \quad \text{interior region} \tag{18b}$$
$$= 0 \quad \text{for} \quad r > a \quad \text{exterior region}$$

Introducing

$$\psi(\mathbf{r}) = \sum_{l,m} \frac{u_l(r)}{r} Y_{lm}(\theta, \phi) \tag{19a}$$

Eq. (18a) becomes

$$-\frac{\hbar^2}{2m}\frac{d^2 u_l}{dr^2} + \left[V(r) + \frac{l(l + 1)\hbar^2}{2mr^2}\right]u_l = Eu_l \tag{19b}$$

where we have made use of

$$\left[\frac{1}{\sin\theta}\frac{\partial}{\partial\theta}\left(\sin\theta\frac{\partial}{\partial\theta}\right) + \frac{1}{\sin^2\theta}\frac{\partial^2}{\partial\phi^2}\right]Y_{lm}(\theta,\phi) = -l(l+1)Y_{lm}(\theta,\phi) \tag{19c}$$

Interior solutions $(r < a)$.

The solutions of Eqs. (18a) and (19b) in the interior region, $r < a$, are the spherical Bessel function[2] j_l which is regular at the origin $r = 0$. This function j_l is related to the ordinary Bessel function $J_{l+\frac{1}{2}}$ of half-odd-integral order. Thus the radial solution of Eqs. (18a) and (19b) which is finite at the origin $r = 0$ is

$$\psi_l(r) = \frac{1}{r}u_l(r) = A_l j_l(\alpha r)$$
$$= A_l \sqrt{\frac{\pi}{2\alpha r}} J_{l+\frac{1}{2}}(\alpha r) \quad \text{for} \quad r < a \tag{20a}$$

where

$$\alpha = \sqrt{\frac{2m(V_0 - |E|)}{\hbar^2}} \tag{20b}$$

and A_l are constants to be determined by the boundary conditions.

Exterior solutions $(r > a)$.

The other solution of Eqs. (18a) and (19b) is the spherical Neumann function n_l which is singular at the origin. This function n_l is related to the ordinary Neumann function $N_{l+\frac{1}{2}}$ and the ordinary Bessel function $J_{-l-\frac{1}{2}}$ by the formula

$$n_l(x) = \sqrt{\frac{\pi}{2x}} N_{l+\frac{1}{2}}(x) = -\sqrt{\frac{\pi}{2x}} J_{-l-\frac{1}{2}}(x) \qquad (20c)$$

In the exterior region, $r > a$, the solution of Eqs. (18a) and (19b) is a linear combination of the spherical Bessel and Neumann functions, with argument $x = i\beta r$ where $\beta = \sqrt{\dfrac{2mE}{\hbar^2}}$. Thus the solution can be written as

$$\psi_l(r) = \frac{1}{r} u_l(r) = B_l j_l(i\beta r) + C_l n_l(i\beta r) \qquad \text{for } r > a \qquad (21a)$$

where B_l and C_l are constants. Since, for a bound state, the asymptotic form of the wave function should fall off exponentially for large r, the linear combination in Eq. (21a) should be so chosen that this requirement is satisfied. The spherical Hankel functions, $h_l^{(1)}$ and $h_l^{(2)}$, of the first and second kinds have an exponential behavior for large r.

$$h_l^{(1)}(x) = j_l(x) + in_l(x) \xrightarrow[x \to \infty]{} \frac{1}{x} e^{i[x-(\pi/2)(l+1)]} \qquad (21b)$$

$$h_l^{(2)}(x) = j_l(x) - in_l(x) \xrightarrow[x \to \infty]{} \frac{1}{x} e^{-i[x-(\pi/2)(l+1)]} \qquad (21c)$$

From Eqs. (21a) to (21c), it follows that the wave function which decays exponentially at large r is given by

$$\psi_l(r) = \frac{1}{r} u_l(r) = B_l h_l^{(1)}(i\beta r)$$

$$= B_l[j_l(i\beta r) + in_l(i\beta r)] \qquad \text{for } r > a \qquad (22)$$

Explicit Expressions For the First Three j, n, and $h^{(1)}$

$$j_0(x) = \frac{\sin x}{x} \qquad j_1(x) = \frac{\sin x}{x^2} - \frac{\cos x}{x}$$

$$j_2(x) = \left(\frac{3}{x^3} - \frac{1}{x}\right)\sin x - \frac{3}{x^2}(\cos x)$$

$$n_0(x) = -\frac{\cos x}{x}, \quad n_1(x) = -\frac{\cos x}{x^2} - \frac{\sin x}{x}$$

$$n_2(x) = -\left(\frac{3}{x^2} - \frac{1}{x}\right)\cos x - \frac{3}{x^2}\sin x$$

$$h_0^{(1)}(ix) = -\frac{1}{x} e^{-x} \qquad h_1^{(1)}(ix) = i\left(\frac{1}{x} + \frac{1}{x^2}\right)e^{-x}$$

$$h_2^{(1)}(ix) = \left(\frac{1}{x} + \frac{3}{x^2} + \frac{3}{x^3}\right)e^{-x} \qquad (23)$$

Some Useful Properties

Asymptotic Expressions

$$j_l(x) \xrightarrow[x \to 0]{} \frac{x^l}{(2l+1)!!} \qquad j_l(x) \xrightarrow[x \to \infty]{} \frac{1}{x} \cos\left[x - \frac{\pi}{2}(l+1)\right]$$

$$n_l(x) \xrightarrow[x \to 0]{} -\frac{1 \cdot [(2l-1)!!]}{x^{l+1}} \qquad n_l(x) \xrightarrow[x \to \infty]{} \frac{1}{x} \sin\left[x - \frac{\pi}{2}(l+1)\right]$$

where

$$(2l+1)!! = 1 . 3 . 5 \ldots (2l+1) \quad \text{and} \quad (2l-1)!! = 1 . 3 . 5 \ldots (2l-1) \tag{24}$$

Recursion Relations

$$n_{l-1}(x) j_l(x) - n_l(x) j_{l-1}(x) = \frac{1}{x^2} \qquad \text{for} \quad l > 0$$

$$j_l(x) \frac{d}{dx} n_l(x) - n_l(x) \frac{d}{dx} j_l(x) = \frac{1}{x^2}$$

The following equations are valid for both j and n.

$$j_{l-1}(x) + j_{l+1}(x) = \frac{2l+1}{x} j_l(x) \qquad \text{for} \quad l > 0$$

$$\frac{d}{dx} j_l(x) = \frac{1}{2l+1} [l j_{l-1}(x) - (l+1) j_{l+1}(x)]$$

$$\frac{d}{dx} [x^{l+1} j_l(x)] = x^{l+1} j_{l-1}(x) \qquad \text{for} \quad l > 0$$

$$\frac{d}{dx} [x^{-l} j_l(x)] = -x^{-l} j_{l+1}(x) \tag{25}$$

Integrals

$$\int dx \, x^2 j_0^2(x) = \tfrac{1}{2} x^3 [j_0^2(x) + n_0(x) j_1(x)]$$

$$\int dx \, x^2 n_0^2(x) = \tfrac{1}{2} x^3 [n_0^2(x) - n_0(x) n_1(x)]$$

The following integrals are valid for both j and n.

$$\int dx \, j_1(x) = -j_0(x)$$

$$\int dx \, x^2 j_0(x) = x^2 j_1(x)$$

$$\int dx \, x^2 j_l(x) = \tfrac{1}{2} x^3 [j_l^2(x) - j_{l-1}(x) j_{l+1}(x)] \qquad \text{for} \quad l > 0. \tag{26}$$

A.4 Plane-Wave Expansion in Spherical Harmonics

Consider a plane wave $\exp(i\mathbf{k} \cdot \mathbf{r})$ with wave vector $\mathbf{k}$. If we choose the z-axis along the direction of propagation of the plane wave, we have

$$\exp(i\mathbf{k} \cdot \mathbf{r}) = \exp(ikr\cos\theta) = \exp(ikz) \tag{27a}$$

where θ is the polar angle between the vectors $\mathbf{k}$ and $\mathbf{r}$. We can expand the plane-wave function $\exp(i\mathbf{k} \cdot \mathbf{r})$ in terms of spherical harmonics. Because of our choice of axes, there is no dependence on the azimuthal angle ϕ, and therefore only the spherical harmonics $Y_{l0}(\theta)$ with $m = 0$ will appear in the expansion

$$e^{ikz} = e^{ikr\cos\theta} = \sum_{l=0}^{\infty} C_l(r)Y_{l0}(\theta) \tag{27b}$$

where

$$
\begin{aligned}
C_l(r) &= \int d\Omega\, Y_{l0}^*(\theta)e^{ikr\cos\theta} \\
&= i^l\sqrt{4\pi(2l+1)}\, j_l(kr)
\end{aligned} \tag{27c}
$$

and where the $j_l(kr)$ are the spherical Bessel functions.[2] The result, Eqs. (27b) and (27c), can easily be made general to correspond to an arbitrary choice of coordinate axes by using the addition theorem, Eq. (15), of spherical harmonics.

$$e^{i\mathbf{k}\cdot\mathbf{r}} = 4\pi \sum_{l=0}^{\infty} \sum_{m=-l}^{l} i^l j_l(kr)Y_{lm}^*(\hat{k}\cdot\hat{r}')Y_{lm}(\hat{r}\cdot\hat{r}') \tag{28}$$

where the carets denote unit vectors.

A.5 Spherical Harmonics: Transformation Properties under Rotation

The spherical harmonics $Y_{lm}(\theta\phi)$ are eigenfunctions of the operators $\mathbf{l}^2$ and l_z, Eqs. (8). Under the rotation of the reference frame, the coordinates of a point P change from x_i to x_i' ($i = 1, 2, 3$). We denote the rotation operator by R. Thus

$$Rx_i = x_i' = \sum_j a_{ij}x_j \tag{29a}$$

where a_{ij} are the elements of the transformation matrix describing rotation and satisfy the relations

$$\sum_i a_{ij}a_{ik} = \sum_i a_{ji}a_{ki} = \delta_{jk} \tag{29b}$$

In polar coordinates, the rotation operator R changes the polar angles $\hat{r} = (\theta, \phi)$ of the point P to $\hat{r}' = (\theta', \phi')$

$$R\hat{r} = \hat{r}' \tag{29c}$$

However the operator l^2 remains invariant under rotation.

$$R l^2 = l'^2 = \frac{1}{\hbar^2} [(\mathbf{r}' \times \mathbf{p}')]^2 = -\left[\frac{1}{\sin \theta'} \frac{\partial}{\partial \theta'} \left(\sin \theta' \frac{\partial}{\partial \theta'} \right) + \frac{1}{\sin^2 \theta'} \frac{\partial^2}{\partial \phi'^2} \right]$$

$$= \frac{1}{\hbar^2} [(\mathbf{r} \times \mathbf{p})]^2 = -\left[\frac{1}{\sin \theta} \frac{\partial}{\partial \theta} \left(\sin \theta \frac{\partial}{\partial \theta} \right) + \frac{1}{\sin^2 \theta} \frac{\partial^2}{\partial \phi^2} \right]$$

$$= l^2 \tag{30a}$$

But

$$R l_z = l_z' \neq l_z \tag{30b}$$

Because the spherical harmonics Y_{lm} are eigenfunctions of the operators l^2 and l_z and since l^2 is invariant under rotation, whereas l_z is not, we arrive at the following equations for the tranformation properties of the spherical harmonics.

$$l'^2 R Y_{lm}(\theta \phi) = l(l + 1)\hbar^2 R Y_{lm}(\theta \phi) \tag{31a}$$

$$l_z' R Y_{lm}(\theta \phi) \neq m\hbar R Y_{lm}(\theta \phi) \tag{31b}$$

with

$$l^2 Y_{lm}(\theta \phi) = l(l + 1)\hbar^2 Y_{lm}(\theta \phi) \tag{32a}$$

$$l_z Y_{lm}(\theta \phi) = m\hbar Y_{lm}(\theta \phi) \tag{32b}$$

It follows from Eqs. (31a) and (31b) that $R Y_{lm}(\theta \phi)$ is a superposition of spherical harmonics (of arguments $\theta' \phi'$) with same l but different m. We may express this by saying that $Y_{lm'}(\theta' \phi')$ can be expanded in terms of a linear combination of $Y_{lm}(\theta \phi)$ with several different values of m.

$$Y_{lm'}(\theta' \phi') = \sum_m D_{mm'}^{(l)}(R) Y_{lm}(\theta \phi) \tag{33a}$$

where the expansion coefficients $D_{mm'}^{(l)}(R)$ depend on the rotation R. Since for a given value of l, m as well as m' take $2l + 1$ values, $D_{mm'}(R)$ can be represented by a $(2l + 1) \times (2l + 1)$ matrix $D^{(l)}(R)$, called the Wigner D-matrix. In matrix notation, Eq. (33a) becomes

$$Y_l(\theta' \phi') = D^{(l)}(R) Y_l(\theta \phi) \tag{33b}$$

Rotation around the z-Axis

As an example, we consider a rotation R_z by an angle ϕ_z around the z-axis.

$$R_z(\theta \phi) = (\theta' = \theta, \phi' = \phi - \phi_z) \tag{34a}$$

Therefore, from Eq. (33a),

$$Y_{lm'}(\theta'\phi') = Y_{lm'}(R_z(\theta\phi)) = e^{-im'\phi_z}Y_{lm'}(\theta\phi)$$
$$= \sum_m D_{mm'}^{(l)}(R_z)Y_{lm}(\theta\phi) \tag{34b}$$

Hence we have

$$D_{mm'}^{(l)}(R_z) = e^{-im'\phi_z}\delta_{mm'} \tag{34c}$$

that is, rotation about the z-axis does not change the z-component of the angular momentum.

Euler Angles (Θ, Φ, Ψ)

It is usual to describe the rotation in terms of Euler angles (Θ, Φ, Ψ) which involves a rotation by Θ about the initial z-axis (resulting in the new axes x_1, y_1, z), followed by a rotation Φ about the new y_1-axis (resulting in the new axes x_2, y_1, z_1), followed by a rotation Ψ about the new z_1-axis (resulting in the new axes x_3, y_2, z_1 in which the polar coordinates of the point P are r, θ', ϕ'; the polar coordinates of P with respect to the initial axes x, y, z being r, θ, ϕ). Thus the rotation R, Eq. (29c), can be described in terms of the Euler angles (Θ, Φ, Ψ). The integration over all rotations can be defined by

$$\int dR\, f = \int_0^{2\pi} d\Theta \int_0^\pi d\Phi \sin\Phi \int_0^{2\pi} d\Psi f \tag{35}$$

A.6   Properties of the D-Matrices

Group Property

Let us consider two rotations R_1 and R_2 performed successively. The product of the two rotations can be represented by a single rotation R_3.

$$R_3(\theta''\phi'') = R_2(\theta'\phi')R_1(\theta\phi) \tag{36}$$

Applying these rotations to the spherical harmonics, we obtain

$$Y_{lm''}(\theta''\phi'') = \sum_m D_{mm''}^{(l)}(R_3)Y_{lm}(\theta\phi)$$
$$= \sum_{m'} D_{m'm''}^{(l)}(R_2)Y_{lm'}(\theta'\phi')$$
$$= \sum_{mm'} D_{m'm''}^{(l)}(R_2)D_{mm'}^{(l)}(R_1)Y_{lm}(\theta, \phi) \tag{37a}$$

Hence

$$D_{mm''}^{(l)}(R_3) = \sum_{m'} D_{m'm''}^{(l)}(R_2)D_{mm'}^{(l)}(R_1) \tag{37b}$$

which in matrix notation can be written as

$$D^{(l)}(R_3) = D^{(l)}(R_2)D^{(l)}(R_1) \tag{37c}$$

It follows from Eqs. (36) and (37c) that the *D*-matrices form a representation* of the rotation group since the matrix representing the product of two rotations is the product of the matrices representing each of the rotations.

Other Properties

From Eq. (33a) we have the orthogonality relations

$$\sum_m D_{mm'}^{(l)*}(R) D_{mm''}^{(l)}(R) = [D^{(l)}(R)^+ D^{(l)}(R)]_{m'm''} = \delta_{m'm''} \qquad (38a)$$

Also, it can be shown that

$$\int dR \; D_{m_1 m_2}^{(l)*}(R) D_{m_1' m_2'}^{(l')}(R) = \frac{8\pi^2}{(2l+1)} \delta_{ll'} \delta_{m_1 m_1'} \delta_{m_2 m_2'} \qquad (38b)$$

Consider a rotation $R = (\Theta, \Phi, \Psi)$ in Euler angles. If the polar coordinates of the point P in the initial coordinate system xyz are $P\,(\theta = \Phi, \phi = \Theta)$, then in the new coordinate system $x'y'z' = R(\Theta = \phi, \Phi = \theta)\,xyz$, the polar coordinates of P are $(\theta' = 0, \phi' = \text{undetermined})$. Using Eq. (33a), we have

$$Y_{lm'}(0\phi') = \sum_m D_{mm'}^{(l)}(\Theta\Phi\Psi) Y_{lm}(\Phi\Theta) \qquad (38c)$$

Multiplying by $D_{mm'}^{(l)*}(\Theta\Phi\Psi)$, summing over m', and using Eq. (38a), we obtain

$$\sum_{m'} D_{mm'}^{(l)*}(\Theta\Phi\Psi) Y_{lm'}(0\phi') = Y_{lm}(\Phi\Theta) \qquad (39a)$$

But

$$Y_{lm'}(0\phi') = \sqrt{\frac{2l+1}{4\pi}} \, \delta_{m'0} \qquad (40a)$$

Therefore

$$D_{m0}^{(l)*}(\Theta\Phi\Psi) = \sqrt{\frac{4\pi}{2l+1}} \, Y_{lm}(\Phi\Theta)$$

$$= \text{independent of } \Psi \qquad (40b)$$

Since rotation about z-axis $R_z \equiv (\Phi = \Psi = 0)$, we have from Eq. (40b)

$$D_{m0}^{(l)*}(R_z) = \delta_{m0} \qquad (40c)$$

Similarly, we can show that

$$D_{0m}^{(l)*}(\Theta\Phi\Psi) = (-1)^m \sqrt{\frac{4\pi}{2l+1}} \, Y_{lm}(\Phi\Psi) \qquad (40d)$$

---

* A representation of a group G is a set of square nonsingular matrices D ($n \times n$ matrices for an *n*-dimensional representation), one matrix $D(g_i)$ for each group element g_i, such that the multiplication of group elements $g_i g_j = g_k$ corresponds to multiplication of the matrices $D(g_i) D(g_j) = D(g_i g_j) = D(g_k)$. This set of matrices thus satisfies the same properties as the group elements, and therefore the set constitutes a group.

Explicit Formula

$$D_{mm'}^{(l)}(\Theta\Phi\Psi') = e^{-im\Theta}e^{-im'\Psi'} d_{mm'}^{(l)}(\Phi) \tag{41a}$$

where

$$d_{mm'}^{(l)}(\Phi) = \sum_k (-1)^k \frac{\sqrt{(l+m)!\,(l-m)!\,(l+m')!\,(l-m')!}}{(l-m-k)!\,(l+m'-k)!\,k!\,(m-m'+k)!}$$

$$\times \left(\cos\frac{\Phi}{2}\right)^{2l+m'-m-2k} \left(-\sin\frac{\Phi}{2}\right)^{2k+m-m'} \tag{41b}$$

Symmetry and Other Relations

$$d_{mm'}^{(l)}(\Phi) = d_{m'm}^{(l)}(-\Phi) \tag{42a}$$

$$d_{mm'}^{(l)}(\Phi) = (-1)^{m-m'} d_{m'm}^{(l)}(\Phi) \tag{42b}$$

$$d_{mm'}^{(l)}(\Phi) = (-1)^{m-m'} d_{-m,-m'}^{(l)}(\Phi) = d_{-m',-m}^{(l)}(\Phi) \tag{42c}$$

$$d_{mm'}^{(l)}(\pi - \Phi) = (-1)^{l-m} d_{m,-m'}^{(l)}(\Phi) = (-1)^{l+m'} d_{-m,m'}^{(l)}(\Phi) \tag{42d}$$

$$d_{mm'}^{(l)}(0) = \delta_{mm'}, \quad d_{mm'}^{(l)}(\pi) = (-1)^{l-m}\delta_{m,-m'} \tag{42e}$$

Also

$$D_{mm'}^{(l)*}(\Theta, \Phi, \Psi') = (-1)^{m-m'} D_{-m,-m'}^{(l)}(\Theta, \Phi, \Psi') \tag{43a}$$

$$= D_{m'm}^{(l)}(-\Psi', -\Phi, -\Theta) \tag{43b}$$

A.7   Addition of Two Angular Momenta

In nuclear spectroscopy, it is frequently necessary to form a composite angular momentum state $\mathbf{J} = \mathbf{j}_1 + \mathbf{j}_2$ of two noninteracting particles in the angular momentum states $\mathbf{j}_1$ and $\mathbf{j}_2$ with z-components m_1 and m_2 (or to form the total angular momentum state of the particle with orbital angular momentum $\mathbf{l}$, m_l and spin $\mathbf{s}$, m_s). We denote the angular momentum states by $|j, m\rangle$, which, for the orbital angular momentum $\mathbf{l}$, m, are simply the spherical harmonics $Y_{lm}(\theta\phi)$. We define the product wave function

$$|j_1 j_2 m_1 m_2\rangle = |j_1 m_1\rangle |j_2 m_2\rangle \tag{44}$$

The product wave function $|j_1 j_2 m_1 m_2\rangle$ is an eigenfunction of the operator $J_z = j_{1z} + j_{2z}$ with the eigenvalue $M = m_1 + m_2$. However, it is not, in general, a simultaneous eigenfunction of the operator $\mathbf{J}^2 = (\mathbf{j}_1 + \mathbf{j}_2)^2$, because l_{1z} and l_{2z} do not commute with $\mathbf{J}^2$. Writing

$$\mathbf{J}^2 = (\mathbf{j}_1 + \mathbf{j}_2)^2 = \mathbf{j}_1^2 + \mathbf{j}_2^2 + 2\mathbf{j}_1 \cdot \mathbf{j}_2$$

$$= \mathbf{j}_1^2 + \mathbf{j}_2^2 + [(j_{1x} + ij_{1y})(j_{2x} - ij_{2y}) + (j_{1x} - ij_{1y})(j_{2x} + ij_{2y}) + 2j_{1z}j_{2z}] \tag{45}$$

and using Eqs. (44) and (45), it is easy to show that

$$J^2 |j_1 j_2 m_1 m_2\rangle = [j_1(j_1 + 1) + j_2(j_2 + 1) + 2m_1 m_2] |j_1 j_2 m_1 m_2\rangle$$
$$+ [\{j_1(j_1 + 1) - m_1(m_1 + 1)\}\{j_2(j_2 + 1) - m_2(m_2 - 1)\}]^{1/2}$$
$$\times |j_1 j_2 m_1 + 1, m_2 - 1\rangle$$
$$+ [\{j_1(j_1 + 1) - m_1(m_1 - 1)\}\{j_2(j_2 + 1) - m_2(m_2 + 1)\}]^{1/2}$$
$$\times |j_1 j_2 m_1 - 1, m_2 + 1\rangle \qquad (46)$$

It is evident from Eq. (46) that unless $m_1 = j_1$ and $m_2 = j_2$ (or $m_1 = -j_1$, $m_2 = -j_2$), $|j_1 j_2 m_1 m_2\rangle$ is not an eigenfunction of the operator $\mathbf{J}^2$. However, it is possible to form linear combinations of the products $|j_1 m_1\rangle |j_2 m_2\rangle$ with allowed values of m_1 and m_2 ($m_1 + m_2 = M$) such that the resulting combination $|j_1 j_2 JM\rangle$ is an eigenfunction of $\mathbf{J}^2$ and $J_z = j_{1z} + j_{2z}$ with eigenvalues $J(J + 1)$ and M. Thus

$$|j_1 j_2 JM\rangle = \sum_{m_1, m_2} \langle j_1 j_2 m_1 m_2 | JM\rangle | j_1 m_1\rangle | j_2 m_2\rangle \qquad (47a)$$

where

$$\mathbf{J} = \mathbf{j}_1 + \mathbf{j}_2 \qquad M = m_1 + m_2 \qquad (47b)$$

and J can take the values

$$J = |j_1 - j_2| \quad \text{to} \quad j_1 + j_2 \quad \text{with} \quad -J \le M \le J \qquad (47c)$$

The expansion coefficients $\langle j_1 j_2 m_1 m_2 | JM\rangle$ are called the Clebsch-Gordan coefficients. The phase convention[1] used for these coefficients is such that they are real. Since the wave functions $|j_1 j_2 JM\rangle$, $|j_1 m_1\rangle$, and $|j_2 m_2\rangle$ are orthonormal, when we multiply the expansion (47a) for $|j_1 j_2 J'M\rangle$ with Eq. (47a), we obtain

$$\langle j_1 j_2 J'M | j_1 j_2 JM\rangle = \sum_{\substack{m_1, m_2 \\ m_1', m_2'}} \langle j_1 j_2 m_1 m_2 | JM\rangle$$
$$\times \langle j_1 j_2 m_1' m_2' | J'M\rangle \langle j_1 m_1' | j_1 m_1\rangle \langle j_2 m_2' | j_2 m_2\rangle$$

giving the orthogonality relation

$$\sum_{m_1, m_2} \langle j_1 j_2 m_1 m_2 | JM\rangle \langle j_1 j_2 m_1 m_2 | J'M\rangle = \delta_{JJ'} \qquad (48)$$

Similar to Eq. (48) another orthogonality condition for the Clebsch-Gordan coefficients (C-coefficients) follows, namely,

$$\sum_{\substack{J=|j_1-j_2| \\ m_1+m_2=m_1'+m_2'=M}}^{j_1+j_2} \langle j_1 j_2 m_1 m_2 | JM\rangle \langle j_1 j_2 m_1' m_2' | JM\rangle = \delta_{m_1 m_1'} \delta_{m_2 m_2'} \qquad (49)$$

By using Eq. (48), it is easy to obtain from Eq. (47a) the inverse expansion

$$|j_1 m_1\rangle | j_2 m_2\rangle = \sum_{\substack{J=|j_1-j_2| \\ \text{with } M=m_1+m_2}}^{j_1+j_2} \langle j_1 j_2 m_1 m_2 | JM\rangle | j_1 j_2 JM\rangle \qquad (50)$$

Because of Eqs. (47b) and (47c), the Clebsch-Gordan coefficients vanish unless the three angular momenta j_1, j_2, and J form a triangle. Thus

$$\langle j_1 j_2 m_1 m_2 | JM \rangle \neq 0 \quad \text{only when} \quad \Delta(j_1 j_2 J) \tag{51a}$$

and

$$m_1 + m_2 = M \quad |m_1| \leq j_1, \quad |m_2| \leq j_2 \quad |M| \leq J \tag{51b}$$

To summarize, the Clebsch-Gordan coefficients $\langle j_1 j_2 m_1 m_2 | JM \rangle$ are the elements of the unitary transformation which takes us from the representation in which j_1^2, j_{1z} and $j_2^2 \cdot j_{2z}$ are diagonal to the representation in which J^2, J_z and j_1^2, j_2^2 are diagonal.

A.8 Explicit Expressions for the Clebsch-Gordan Coefficients

Wigner[3] has given the following expression for the C-coefficients.

$$\langle j_1 j_2 m_1 m_2 | j_3 m_3 \rangle$$

$$= \delta_{m_3, m_1 + m_2} \left[(2j_3 + 1) \frac{\begin{array}{c}(j_3 + j_1 - j_2)!(j_3 - j_1 + j_2)!(j_1 + j_2 - j_3)! \\ \times (j_3 + m_3)!(j_3 - m_3)!\end{array}}{\begin{array}{c}(j_1 + j_2 + j_3 + 1)!(j_1 - m_1)!(j_1 + m_1)! \\ \times (j_2 - m_2)!(j_2 + m_2)!\end{array}} \right]^{1/2}$$

$$\times \sum_{k = \text{integer}} \frac{(-1)^{k + j_2 + m_2}}{k!}$$

$$\times \frac{(j_2 + j_3 + m_1 - k)!(j_1 - m_1 + k)!}{(j_3 - j_1 + j_2 - k)!(j_3 + m_3 - k)!(k + j_1 - j_2 - m_3)!} \tag{52}$$

where k takes all integral values such that none of the arguments under the factorial sign is negative. Racah[4] has derived an alternative result which is in a more usable form.

$$\langle j_1 j_2 m_1 m_2 | j_3 m_3 \rangle$$

$$= \delta_{m_3, m_1 + m_2} \left[\frac{(2j_3 + 1)(j_1 + j_2 - j_3)!(j_3 + j_1 - j_2)!(j_3 + j_2 - j_1)!}{(j_1 + j_2 + j_3 + 1)!} \right.$$

$$\left. \times (j_1 + m_1)!(j_1 - m_1)!(j_2 + m_2)!(j_2 - m_2)!(j_3 + m_3)!(j_3 - m_3)! \right]^{1/2}$$

$$\times \sum_{k = \text{integer}} \frac{(-1)^k}{k!} [(j_1 + j_2 - j_3 - k)!(j_1 - m_1 - k)!(j_2 + m_2 - k)!$$

$$\times (j_3 - j_2 + m_1 + k)!(j_3 - j_1 - m_2 + k)!]^{-1} \tag{53}$$

In Tables A-1 and A-2 we list the explicit values of the C-coefficients for $j_2 = \frac{1}{2}$ and 1 which are frequently used.

Table A.1   Values of $\langle j_1 \tfrac{1}{2} m - m_2, m_2 \mid j\, m\rangle$

j	$m_2 = \tfrac{1}{2}$	$m_2 = -\tfrac{1}{2}$
$j_1 + \tfrac{1}{2}$	$\left[\dfrac{j_1 + m + \tfrac{1}{2}}{2j_1 + 1}\right]^{\!\frac{1}{2}}$	$\left[\dfrac{j_1 - m + \tfrac{1}{2}}{2j_1 + 1}\right]^{\!\frac{1}{2}}$
$j_1 - \tfrac{1}{2}$	$-\left[\dfrac{j_1 - m + \tfrac{1}{2}}{2j_1 + 1}\right]^{\!\frac{1}{2}}$	$\left[\dfrac{j_1 + m + \tfrac{1}{2}}{2j_1 + 1}\right]^{\!\frac{1}{2}}$

Symmetry Relations

The following independent symmetry relations can be proved from the explicit expressions, (52) and (53):

$$\langle j_1 j_2 m_1 m_2 \mid j_3 m_3 \rangle = (-1)^{j_1 + j_2 - j_3} \langle j_1 j_2 - m_1 - m_2 \mid j_3 - m_3 \rangle \tag{54a}$$

$$= (-1)^{j_1 + j_2 - j_3} \langle j_2 j_1 m_2 m_1 \mid j_3 m_3 \rangle \tag{54b}$$

$$= (-1)^{j_1 - m_1} \sqrt{\frac{2j_3 + 1}{2j_2 + 1}} \, \langle j_1 j_3 m_1 - m_3 \mid j_2 - m_2 \rangle \tag{54c}$$

Other symmetry relations which can be derived from the above relations are

$$\langle j_1 j_2 m_1 m_2 \mid j_3 m_3 \rangle = (-1)^{j_2 + m_2} \sqrt{\frac{2j_3 + 1}{2j_1 + 1}} \, \langle j_3 j_2 - m_3 m_2 \mid j_1 - m_1 \rangle$$
$$\text{[from (54b) and (54c)]} \tag{55a}$$

$$\langle j_1 j_2 m_1 m_2 \mid j_3 m_3 \rangle = (-1)^{j_1 - m_1} \sqrt{\frac{2j_3 + 1}{2j_2 + 1}} \, \langle j_3 j_1 m_3 - m_1 \mid j_2 m_2 \rangle$$
$$\text{[from (54c), (54b), and (54a)]} \tag{55b}$$

$$\langle j_1 j_2 m_1 m_2 \mid j_3 m_3 \rangle = (-1)^{j_2 + m_2} \sqrt{\frac{2j_3 + 1}{2j_1 + 1}} \, \langle j_2 j_3 - m_2 m_3 \mid j_1 m_1 \rangle$$
$$\text{[from (55a), (54b), and (54a)]} \tag{55c}$$

The Clebsch-Gordan coefficients are related to the Racah V-coefficients and to the Wigner $3j$-symbols as follows:

$$\langle j_1 j_2 m_1 m_2 \mid j_3 m_3 \rangle = (-1)^{j_3 + m_3} \sqrt{2j_3 + 1} \, V(j_1 j_2 j_3, m_1, m_2, -m_3) \tag{56a}$$

$$\begin{pmatrix} j_1 & j_2 & j_3 \\ m_1 & m_2 & m_3 \end{pmatrix} = \frac{(-1)^{j_1 - j_2 - m_3}}{(2j_3 + 1)^{\frac{1}{2}}} \langle j_1 j_2 m_1 m_2 \mid j_3 - m_3 \rangle \tag{56b}$$

A.9   Coupling of Three Angular Momenta

We now consider three angular momenta $\mathbf{j}_1$, $\mathbf{j}_2$, and $\mathbf{j}_3$ which are coupled to form the total angular momentum $\mathbf{J} = \mathbf{j}_1 + \mathbf{j}_2 + \mathbf{j}_3$. In the uncoupled

Table A-2 Values of $\langle j_1\, 1\, m-m_2, m_2 \mid j\, m\rangle$

j	$m_2 = 1$	$m_2 = 0$	$m_2 = -1$
$j_1 + 1$	$\left[\dfrac{(j_1+m)(j_1+m+1)}{(2j_1+1)(2j_1+2)}\right]^{1/2}$	$\left[\dfrac{(j_1-m+1)(j_1+m+1)}{(2j_1+1)(j_1+1)}\right]^{1/2}$	$\left[\dfrac{(j_1-m)(j_1-m+1)}{(2j_1+1)(2j_1+2)}\right]^{1/2}$
j_1	$-\left[\dfrac{(j_1+m)(j_1-m+1)}{2j_1(j_1+1)}\right]^{1/2}$	$\dfrac{m}{[j_1(j_1+1)]^{1/2}}$	$\left[\dfrac{(j_1-m)(j_1+m+1)}{2j_1(j_1+1)}\right]^{1/2}$
$j_1 - 1$	$\left[\dfrac{(j_1-m)(j_1-m+1)}{2j_1(2j_1+1)}\right]^{1/2}$	$-\left[\dfrac{(j_1-m)(j_1+m)}{j_1(2j_1+1)}\right]^{1/2}$	$\left[\dfrac{(j_1+m+1)(j_1+m)}{2j_1(2j_1+1)}\right]^{1/2}$

556

representation, the six operators $\mathbf{j}_1^2, \mathbf{j}_2^2, \mathbf{j}_3^2, j_{1z}, j_{2z},$ and j_{3z} are diagonal. The resultant $\mathbf{J}$ of the three vectors $\mathbf{j}_1, \mathbf{j}_2,$ and $\mathbf{j}_3$ can be reached in three different ways: by first coupling any two vectors and then the third vector. The coupled representation will be diagonal in the six operators $\mathbf{j}_1^2, \mathbf{j}_2^2, \mathbf{j}_3^2, \mathbf{j}_{kl}^2, \mathbf{J}^2,$ $\mathbf{J}_z$, where $\mathbf{j}_{kl} = \mathbf{j}_k + \mathbf{j}_l$ with (kl) equal to (12) or (23) or (13). Any two eigenstates $|(j_k j_l) j_{kl} j_n; \ JM\rangle$ and $|(j_{k'} j_{l'}) j_{k'l'} j_{n'}; \ JM\rangle$ of the coupled representation are related by unitary transformation whose elements are $R(j_{k'l'}, j_{kl})$ (j_n and $j_{n'}$ denote the third uncoupled vector). Thus

$$|(j_k j_l) j_{kl} j_n; \ JM\rangle = \sum_{j_{k'l'}} R(j_{k'l'}, j_{kl}) \, |(j_{k'} j_{l'}) j_{k'l'} j_{n'}; \ JM\rangle \qquad (57)$$

The Racah coefficients W are defined as follows:

$$R(j_{k'l'}, j_{kl}) = [(2j_{k'l'} + 1)(2j_{kl} + 1)]^{1/2} W(j_1 j_2 J j_3; j_{kl} j_{k'l'}) \qquad (58)$$

By repeatedly coupling two angular momenta by using the Clebsch-Gordan coefficients and their properties, it is easy to show from Eq. (57) that

$$R(j_{k'l'}, j_{kl}) = \sum_{\substack{m_k, m_l \\ m_{k'}, m_{l'}}} \langle j_k j_l m_k m_l \,|\, j_{kl} m_{kl} \rangle \langle j_{kl} j_n m_{kl} m_n |\ JM \rangle$$

$$\times \langle j_{k'} j_{l'} m_{k'} m_{l'} \,|\, j_{k'l'} m_{k'l'} \rangle \langle j_{n'} j_{k'l'} m_{n'} m_{k'l'} | JM \rangle \qquad (59a)$$

where

$$m_{kl} = m_k + m_l \qquad m_{k'l'} = m_{k'} + m_{l'}$$

$$M = m_{kl} + m_n = m_{k'l'} + m_{n'} = m_1 + m_2 + m_3 \qquad (59b)$$

In view of Eq. (59b), the summations in Eq. (59a) reduce to a double summation.

Following Racah's notation, we denote the angular momenta $j_k j_l J j_n$; $j_{kl} j_{k'l'}$ by the lower-case letters $abcd; ef$. Using the closed expressions for the C-coefficients, the double summation in Eq. (59a) can be extended to obtain the following result for the Racah coefficients.

$$W(abcd; ef) = \Delta_R(abe) \, \Delta_R(cde) \, \Delta_R(acf) \, \Delta_R(bdf)$$
$$\times \sum_k (-1)^{k+a+b+c+d}(k + 1)!$$
$$\times [(k - a - b - e)! \, (k - c - d - e)! \, (k - a - c - f)!$$
$$\times (k - b - d - f)! \, (a + b + c + d - k)!$$
$$\times (a + d + e + f - k)! \, (b + c + e + f - k)!]^{-1} \quad (60)$$

where the triangle coefficient Δ_R, which is symmetric in its arguments, is given by

$$\Delta_R(abc) = \left[\frac{(a + b - c)! \, (a - b + c)! \, (-a + b + c)!}{(a + b + c + 1)!} \right]^{1/2} \qquad (61)$$

$$= 0 \qquad \text{if } a, b, c \text{ do not satisfy the triangular condition}$$

The Racah coefficients satisfy the following symmetry relations:

$$W(abcd; ef) = W(badc; ef) = W(cdab; ef) = W(acbd; fe)$$
$$= (-1)^{e+f-b-c}W(aefd; bc) = (-1)^{e+f-a-d}W(ebcf; ad) \quad (62)$$

The matrix R satisfies the relations

$$\sum_e R_{fe}R_{ge} = \sum_e R_{ef}R_{eg} = \delta_{fg} \quad (63a)$$

so that the Racah coefficients obey the orthonormality condition

$$\sum_e (2e + 1)(2f + 1)W(abcd; ef)W(abcd; eg) = \delta_{fg} \quad (63b)$$

The Racah coefficients W satisfy the sum rule

$$\sum_e (2e + 1)(-1)^{a+b-e}W(abcd; ef)W(bacd; eg) = W(afgb; cd) \quad (64)$$

The W-coefficients are related to the Wigner $6j$-symbol

$$\begin{Bmatrix} j_1 & j_2 & j_{12} \\ j & j_3 & j_{13} \end{Bmatrix} = (-1)^{j_1+j_2+j_3+j}W(j_1 j_2 j_3 j; j_{12} j_{13}) \quad (65)$$

A.10 Further Discussion of the Rotation Matrix D

Two angular momentum states $|j_1 m_1\rangle$ and $|j_2 m_2\rangle$ can be coupled to form a resultant state $|JM(=m_1 + m_2)\rangle$. According to Eq. (49)

$$|j_1 m_1\rangle |j_2 m_2\rangle = \sum_J \langle j_1 j_2 m_1 m_2 | JM\rangle |j_1 j_2 JM\rangle \quad (66)$$

We consider the effect of rotation of the coordinate system through the Euler angles $(\Theta\Phi\Psi)$. Under the rotation operator $R(\Theta\Phi\Psi)$ we have for each state

$$R |jm\rangle = \sum_{m'} D^j_{m'm}(\Theta\Phi\Psi) |jm'\rangle \quad (67)$$

Combining Eqs. (66) and (67), we obtain

$$\sum_{m'_1 m'_2} D^{j_1}_{m'_1 m_1} D^{j_2}_{m'_2 m_2} |j_1 m'_1\rangle |j_2 m'_2\rangle$$
$$= \sum_{J,M'} \langle j_1 j_2 m_1 m_2 | JM\rangle D^J_{M'M} |j_1 j_2 JM'\rangle$$
$$= \sum_{J,M',m''_1,m''_2} \langle j_1 j_2 m_1 m_2 | JM\rangle\langle j_1 j_2 m''_1 m''_2 | JM'\rangle D^J_{M'M} |j_1 m''_1\rangle |j_2 m''_2\rangle \quad (68)$$

where we have used Eq. (47a) to express $|j_1 j_2 JM\rangle$ in terms of $|j_1 m''_1\rangle$ and $|j_2 m''_2\rangle$ and the Euler angles in D have not been indicated explicitly. On the right-hand side we can replace m''_1, m''_2 by m'_1, m'_2 since they are indices of summation. Comparing the coefficients of $|j_1m_1'\rangle|j_2m_2'\rangle$ on both sides, we obtain

$$D^{j_1}_{m'_1m_1}D^{j_2}_{m'_2m_2} = \sum_{\substack{J \\ M=m_1+m_2, M'=m'_1+m'_2}} \langle j_1j_2m_1m_2 | JM\rangle\langle j_1j_2m'_1m'_2 | JM'\rangle D^J_{M'M}$$

$$(69)$$

This is the coupling scheme of the D-matrices, and the relation is known as the Clebsch-Gordan series.

The inverse relation to Eq. (69) can be easily obtained by starting with the expansion of $|JM\rangle$ in terms of $|j_1m_1\rangle|j_2m_2\rangle$ [Eq. (47a)]. The inverse of the Clebsch-Gordan series is

$$D^J_{M'M} = \sum_{\substack{m_1,m_2,m'_1,m'_2 \\ M=m_1+m_2, \quad M'=m'_1+m'_2}} \langle j_1j_2m_1m_2 | JM\rangle$$

$$\times \langle j_1j_2m'_1m'_2 | JM'\rangle D^{j_1}_{m'_1m_1}D^{j_2}_{m'_2m_2} \quad (70)$$

Rotation Matrices for Integral j

We consider a point P with polar coordinates $(\theta\phi)$ with respect to the initial axes S. If we perform a rotation on the initial axes by Euler angles $\Theta\Phi\Psi'$, the polar coordinates of P with respect to the new axes S' are $(\theta_1\phi_1)$. Then

$$Y_{lm'}(\theta_1\phi_1) = \sum_m D^l_{mm'}(\Theta\Phi\Psi')Y_{lm}(\theta\phi) \quad (71)$$

If we choose the rotation such that $\Psi' = 0$, then the polar coordinates of a point on the new z'-axis with respect to S are $(\theta' = \Phi, \phi' = \Theta)$. Moreover, if the Euler angles are such that P is on the x'-axis, then $\phi_1 = 0$ and we can set $m' = 0$. Under these conditions, Eq. (71) becomes

$$Y_{l0}(\theta_1 0) = \sum_m D^l_{m0}(\phi'\theta'0)Y_{lm}(\theta\phi)$$

$$= \left[\frac{4\pi}{2l+1}\right]^{1/2} \sum_m Y^*_{lm}(\theta'\phi')Y_{lm}(\theta\phi) \quad (72a)$$

where in the last step we have made use of the addition theorem of spherical harmonics, Eq. (15). We have therefore from Eq. (72a)

$$D^l_{m0}(\Theta\Phi 0) = \left[\frac{4\pi}{2l+1}\right]^{1/2} Y^*_{lm}(\Phi\Theta) \quad (72b)$$

Substituting Eq. (72b) in the Clebsch-Gordan series, Eq. (70), we obtain

$$Y_{l_1m_1}(\theta\phi)Y_{l_2m_2}(\theta\phi) = \sum_l \left[\frac{(2l_1+1)(2l_2+1)}{4\pi(2l+1)}\right]^{1/2}$$

$$\times \langle l_1l_2m_1m_2 | lm\rangle\langle l_1l_200 | l0\rangle Y_{lm}(\theta\phi) \quad (73)$$

This coupling rule for the spherical harmonics involves the same arguments of every Y_{lm} and differs from the coupling formula of eigenstates of spherical harmonics, namely

$$Y_{l_1 m_1}(\theta_1 \phi_1) Y_{l_2 m_2}(\theta_2 \phi_2) = \sum_l \langle l_1 l_2 m_1 m_2 \mid lm \rangle \mathscr{Y}_{l_1 l_2 lm}(\theta_1 \phi_1 \theta_2 \phi_2) \qquad (74)$$

where $\mathscr{Y}_{l_1 l_2 lm}(\theta_1 \phi_1 \theta_2 \phi_2)$ is a wave function in the joint space $\theta_1 \phi_1 \theta_2 \phi_2$; previously we have denoted Y_{lm} and $\mathscr{Y}_{l_1 l_2 lm}$ by $|lm\rangle$ and $|l_1 l_2 lm\rangle$, respectively.

Multiplying Eq. (73) by $Y^*_{l_3 m_3}(\theta \phi)$, integrating over the solid angle, and using the orthonormality of the spherical harmonics, we obtain

$$\int d\Omega\, Y^*_{l_3 m_3}(\theta \phi) Y_{l_2 m_2}(\theta \phi) Y_{l_1 m_1}(\theta \phi)$$
$$= \left[\frac{(2l_1 + 1)(2l_2 + 1)}{4\pi(2l_3 + 1)} \right]^{1/2} \langle l_1 l_2 m_1 m_2 \mid l_3 m_3 \rangle \langle l_1 l_2 0\, 0 \mid l_3 0 \rangle \qquad (75a)$$

The following is a more general result which corresponds to Eq. (75a):

$$\int d\Omega\, D^{j_3 *}_{m'_3 m_3} D^{j_2}_{m'_2 m_2} D^{j_1}_{m'_1 m_1} = \frac{8\pi^2}{(2j_3 + 1)} \delta_{m'_1 + m'_2, m'_3} \delta_{m_1 + m_2, m_3}$$
$$\times \langle j_1 j_2 m_1 m_2 \mid j_3 m_3 \rangle \langle j_1 j_2 m'_1 m'_2 \mid j_3 m'_3 \rangle \qquad (75b)$$

from which Eq. (75a) follows. The orthogonality integral satisfied by the D-matrices is

$$\int d\Omega\, D^{j_1 *}_{m'_1 m_1}(\Theta \Phi \Psi) D^{j_2}_{m'_2 m_2}(\Theta \Phi \Psi) = \frac{8\pi^2}{2j_1 + 1} \delta_{m_1 m_2} \delta_{m'_1 m'_2} \delta_{j_1 j_2} \qquad (76)$$

A.11 The Wigner-Eckart Theorem

It is common to take the matrix elements of an irreducible tensor operator T_{LM} of rank L between the initial and final angular momentum states $|jm\rangle$ and $|j'm'\rangle$. The Wigner-Eckart theorem enables us to separate the magnetic quantum number dependence of the matrix element in the form of the Clebsch-Gordan coefficient. Thus we have

$$\langle j'm' \mid T_{LM} \mid jm \rangle = \langle jLm\, M \mid j'm' \rangle \langle j' \| T_L \| j \rangle \qquad (77)$$

where $\langle j' \| T_L \| j \rangle$ is independent of m, m', and M and is called the reduced matrix element. From the properties of the Clebsch-Gordan coefficient it is obvious that conservation of angular momentum $\mathbf{j} + \mathbf{L} = \mathbf{j}'$ and $m' = M + m$ follows. In the following we shall derive Eq. (77).

An irreducible tensor T_{LM} of rank L is defined as a set of $2L + 1$ functions $(M = -L, -L + 1, \ldots, L)$ which, under the $(2L + 1)$-dimensional representation of the rotation group, transforms as follows:

$$RT_{LM}R^{-1} = \sum_{M'} D^L_{M'M}(\Theta \Phi \Psi) T_{LM'} \qquad (78)$$

where the rotation operator $R = \exp(-i\theta \mathbf{n} \cdot \mathbf{J})$ rotates the coordinate system through an angle θ about the direction $\mathbf{n}$, $\mathbf{J}$ being the total angular momentum. An equivalent definition of an irreducible tensor is that the set T_{LM} satisfy the commutation relation

$$[J_{\pm}, T_{LM}]_- = [J_x \pm iJ_y, T_{LM}]_- = [(L \mp M)(L \pm M + 1)]^{1/2} T_{LM \pm 1} \tag{79a}$$

$$[J_z, T_{LM}]_- = MT_{LM} \tag{79b}$$

In considering the matrix elements of Eqs. (79b) and (79a), from Eq. (79b) we have

$$\langle j'm'| [J_z, T_{LM}] | jm \rangle = M\langle j'm'| T_{LM} | jm \rangle$$
$$= \langle j'm'| J_z T_{LM} | jm \rangle - \langle j'm'| T_{LM} J_z | jm \rangle$$
$$= m'\langle j'm'| T_{LM} | jm \rangle - m\langle j'm'| T_{LM} | jm \rangle,$$

which gives

$$(m' - m - M)\langle j'm'| T_{LM} | jm \rangle = 0 \tag{80a}$$

Therefore for $\langle j'm'| T_{LM} | jm \rangle \neq 0$, we require that $m' = m + M$.

From Eq. (79a), we have

$$\langle j'm'| J_{\pm} T_{LM} | jm \rangle - \langle j'm'| T_{LM} J_{\pm} | jm \rangle$$
$$= [(L \mp M)(L \pm M + 1)]^{1/2} \langle j'm'| T_{L,M \pm 1} | jm \rangle$$
$$= [(j' \pm m')(j' \mp m' + 1)]^{1/2} \langle j' \, m' \mp 1| T_{LM} | jm \rangle$$
$$- [(j \mp m)(j \pm m + 1)]^{1/2} \langle j' \, m'| T_{LM} | j \, m \pm 1 \rangle \tag{80b}$$

where in the last expression we have made use of the properties of $J_{\pm}$. From Eq. (80a) it follows that each matrix element in Eq. (80b) vanishes unless $m' = m + M \pm 1$.

We next consider the coupling of angular momentum states $|jm\rangle$ and $|LM\rangle$ to form the composite state $|j'm'\rangle$, as implied by Eq. (77).

$$|j'm'\rangle = \sum_{\substack{m, M \\ m' = m + M}} \langle jL \, mM \mid j'm' \rangle |jm\rangle |LM\rangle \tag{81}$$

Operating with the operator $J'_{\mp} = J_{\mp} + L_{\mp}$ on both sides of Eq. (81), we obtain

$$[(j' \pm m')(j' \mp m' + 1)]^{1/2} |j'm' \mp 1\rangle$$
$$= \sum_{m, M} [(j \pm m)(j \mp m + 1)]^{1/2} \langle jL \, m \, M \mid j'm' \rangle |j \, m \mp 1\rangle |LM\rangle$$
$$+ \sum_{m, M} [(L \pm M)(L \mp M + 1)]^{1/2} \langle jL \, m \, M \mid j'm' \rangle |jm\rangle |LM \mp 1\rangle$$
$$= \sum_{\substack{m'', M' \\ m'' + M' = m' \mp 1}} [(j' \pm m')(j' \mp m' + 1)]^{1/2} \langle jL \, m''M' \mid j' \, m' \mp 1\rangle |jm''\rangle |LM'\rangle \tag{82a}$$

where in the last line we have used Eq. (81) to express the first line. Multiplying Eq. (82a) through by $\langle jm''|\langle LM''|$, using the orthonormality conditions of the states, and relabeling the z-components, we obtain

$$[(j \mp m)(j \pm m + 1)]^{\frac{1}{2}}\langle jL\, m \pm 1\, M\,|\,j'm'\rangle$$
$$+ [(L \mp M)(L \pm M + 1)]^{\frac{1}{2}}\langle jLm\, M \pm 1\,|\,j'm'\rangle$$
$$= [(j' \pm m')(j' \mp m' + 1)]^{\frac{1}{2}}\langle jL\, m\, M\,|\,j'm' \mp 1\rangle \quad (82b)$$

By comparing Eqs. (80b) and (82b), it is clear that the matrix elements $\langle j'm'|\,T_{LM}\,|jm\rangle$ are proportional to the Clebsch-Gordan coefficient $\langle jL\, m\, M\,|\,j'm'\rangle$ which completely takes into account the m, m', M dependence of the matrix element. Hence the result Eq. (77) follows. The factor $\langle jL\, m\, M\,|\,j'm'\rangle$ depends only on the rank of the tensor T_{LM}, and the physical nature of the tensor is contained in the reduced matrix element $\langle j'\|\,T_L\,\|j\rangle$.

Reduced Matrix Elements for the Spherical Harmonics

From Eq. (75a) we have

$$\int d\Omega\, Y^*_{l_3 m_3}(\theta\phi) Y_{l_2 m_2}(\theta\phi) Y_{l_1 m_1}(\theta\phi)$$
$$= \langle l_3 m_3\,|\,Y_{l_2 m_2}\,|\,l_1 m_1\rangle$$
$$= \left[\frac{(2l_1 + 1)(2l_2 + 1)}{4\pi(2l_3 + 1)}\right]^{\frac{1}{2}} \langle l_1 l_2 m_1 m_2\,|\,l_3 m_3\rangle\langle l_1 l_2\, 0\, 0\,|\,l_3 0\rangle$$
$$= \langle l_1 l_2 m_1 m_2\,|\,l_3 m_3\rangle\langle l_3\|\,Y_{l_2}\,\|l_1\rangle \quad (83a)$$

Therefore, we have

$$\langle l_3\|\,Y_{l_2}\,\|l_1\rangle = \left[\frac{(2l_1 + 1)(2l_2 + 1)}{4\pi(2l_3 + 1)}\right]^{\frac{1}{2}} \langle l_1 l_2\, 0\, 0\,|\,l_3 0\rangle \quad (83b)$$

Reduced Matrix Elements of the Angular Momentum Operator

It is useful, for this purpose, to introduce the spherical components J_λ ($\lambda = \pm 1, 0$) of the angular momentum $\mathbf{J}(J_x, J_y, J_z)$ as follows:

$$J_{\pm 1} = \mp \frac{1}{\sqrt{2}}(J_x \pm iJ_y) = \mp \frac{1}{\sqrt{2}} J_\pm, \qquad J_0 = J_z \quad (84a)$$

$$\mathbf{J}^2 = J_x^2 + J_y^2 + J_z^2 = \sum_\lambda (-1)^\lambda J_\lambda J_{-\lambda} \quad \text{with} \quad \lambda = \pm 1, 0 \quad (84b)$$

The commutation relations satisfied by the angular momentum operator are ($\hbar = 1$)

$$\mathbf{J} \times \mathbf{J} = i\mathbf{J} \quad (85a)$$

$$[\mathbf{J}^2, J_k] = 0 \quad \text{with} \quad k = x, y, z \quad (85b)$$

Equivalently,

$$[J_z, J_\pm] = \pm J_\pm \qquad [J_+, J_-] = 2J_z \tag{85c}$$

$$[\mathbf{J}^2, J_\lambda] = 0 \qquad \text{with} \quad \lambda = \pm 1, 0 \tag{85d}$$

It is easy to obtain commutation relations for $J_{\pm 1}$, J_0 corresponding to Eqs. (79a) and (79b). It follows that $J_{\pm 1}$, J_0 form the components of a tensor $T_{1M} = J_\lambda$ ($\lambda = \pm 1, 0$) of the first rank. In general, if the commutation relations, Eqs. (79a) and (79b), are rewritten in terms of spherical components, we obtain

$$[J_{\pm 1}, T_{LM}] = \mp [\tfrac{1}{2}(L \mp M)(L \pm M + 1)]^{1/2} T_{L, M\pm 1} \tag{86a}$$

$$[J_0, T_{LM}] = M T_{LM} \tag{86b}$$

Equations (86a) and (86b) can be obtained by using the Clebsch-Gordan coefficient $\langle L1\ M + \mu, -\mu \mid L\ M \rangle$.

$$[J_\lambda, T_{LM}] = (-1)^\lambda \langle L1\ M + \lambda, -\lambda \mid LM \rangle \sqrt{L(L+1)}\, T_{L, M+\lambda} \tag{86c}$$

with $\lambda = \pm 1, 0$.

The matrix elements of $\mathbf{J}$ are given by

$$\langle j'm' \mid J_\pm \mid jm \rangle = [(j \mp m)(j \pm m + 1)]^{1/2} \delta_{jj'} \delta_{m', m\pm 1} \tag{87a}$$

$$\langle j'm' \mid J_z \mid jm \rangle = m \delta_{jj'} \delta_{mm'} \tag{87b}$$

which in terms of the spherical components can be written in the form

$$\begin{aligned}
\langle j'm' \mid J_\lambda \mid jm \rangle &= \delta_{jj'} \delta_{m', m+\lambda} (-1)^\lambda \sqrt{j(j+1)}\, \langle j\ 1\ m + \lambda, -\lambda \mid jm \rangle \\
&= \delta_{jj'} (-1)^\lambda \sqrt{j(j+1)}\, \langle j'\ 1\ m' - \lambda \mid jm \rangle \\
&= \delta_{jj'} (-1)^\lambda \sqrt{j(j+1)}\, (-1)^{1-\lambda} (-1)^{j+1-j'} \langle j\ 1\ m\ \lambda \mid j'm' \rangle
\end{aligned} \tag{87c}$$

where in the last step the symmetry relations of the C-coefficients have been used. Hence the reduced matrix elements of J are given by

$$\langle j' \| J \| j \rangle = \sqrt{j(j+1)}\, \delta_{jj'}$$

A.12 Scattering of a Particle by a Central Potential

The scattering of mass m, energy E, and momentum $\mathbf{p} = \hbar \mathbf{k}$ by a central potential $V(r)$ is now discussed by using the stationary-state method. The Schrödinger equation is given by

$$[\nabla^2 + k^2 - U(r)]\psi(\mathbf{r}) = 0 \tag{88a}$$

where

$$k^2 = \frac{2mE}{\hbar^2} \qquad U(r) = \frac{2m}{\hbar^2} V(r) \tag{88b}$$

The solutions of Eq. (88a), which satisfy the boundary condition that in the asymptotic region ($r \to \infty$) they consist of an incident plane wave $\exp(ikz)$ along the z-axis and a spherical outgoing (scattered) wave e^{ikr}/r, are

$$\psi(\mathbf{r}) \sim e^{ikz} + f(\theta, \phi) \frac{e^{ikr}}{r} \qquad r \to \infty \tag{89}$$

where $f(\theta, \phi)$ is the amplitude of the scattered wave and θ is the angle between the scattered wave vector $\mathbf{k}'$ and the incident wave vector $\mathbf{k}(|\mathbf{k}'| = |\mathbf{k}|)$. Since, for a spherically symmetric potential, $f(\theta, \phi)$ should be independent of the azimuthal angle ϕ, we shall write it simply as $f(\theta)$.

The differential cross section $d\sigma$ is defined as the flux $N_{sc}\, d\Omega$ of the particles scattered through a large sphere of radius R within the solid angle $d\Omega = \sin\theta\, d\theta\, d\phi$ divided by the flux of the incident particles per unit area. The latter is simply the velocity $v = p/m$ of the incident particles. The number $N_{sc}\, d\Omega$ of particles scattered per unit time (flux) in the solid angle $d\Omega$ is given by

$$N_{sc}\, d\Omega = \frac{\hbar}{2im}\left(\frac{\partial \psi_{sc}}{\partial r} \psi_{sc}^* - \frac{\partial \psi_{sc}^*}{\partial r} \psi_{sc}\right) R^2\, d\Omega \tag{90a}$$

From Eq. (89), we have

$$\psi_{sc}(r) \sim f(\theta) \frac{e^{ikr}}{r} \qquad \text{for} \quad r \to \infty \tag{90b}$$

Substituting Eq. (90b) in (90a), we obtain

$$N_{sc}\, d\Omega = \frac{\hbar k}{m} |f(\theta)|^2\, d\Omega \tag{90c}$$

Thus the differential cross section $d\sigma(\theta)$ is given by

$$d\sigma(\theta) = N_{sc}\frac{d\Omega}{v} = |f(\theta)|^2\, d\Omega$$
$$= \sigma(\theta)\, d\Omega \tag{91a}$$

The total cross section

$$\sigma = \int d\sigma(\theta) = \int |f(\theta)|^2\, d\Omega$$
$$= 2\pi \int_0^\pi d\theta\, \sin\theta\, |f(\theta)|^2 \tag{91b}$$

Partial Wave (Phase Shift) Analysis

The scattering amplitude $f(\theta)$ can be expanded in terms of the Legendre polynomials $P_l(\cos\theta)$,

$$f(\theta) = \frac{i}{2k} \sum_{l=0}^\infty f_l(2l + 1)P_l(\cos\theta) \tag{92a}$$

where the coefficients f_l are to be determined. The well-known expansion of the plane wave in terms of Legendre polynomials is

$$e^{ikz} = \exp\,(ikr\cos\theta)$$

$$= \sum_{l=0}^{\infty} i^l(2l + 1)j_l(kr)P_l(\cos\theta) \qquad (92b)$$

where $j_l(kr)$ are the spherical Bessel functions. Since Eq. (89) gives $\psi(\mathbf{r})$ in the asymptotic region, we use the asymptotic form of the Bessel function

$$j_l(kr) \sim \frac{\sin\left(kr - l\dfrac{\pi}{2}\right)}{kr} \qquad (93)$$

Substituting Eqs. (92a) to (93) in Eq. (89), we obtain

$$\psi(\mathbf{r}) \sim \frac{1}{2ikr} \sum_{l=0}^{\infty} i^l(2l + 1)[(1 - f_l)e^{i[kr-l\pi/2]} - e^{-i[kr-l\pi/2]}]P_l(\cos\theta)$$

$$= \frac{1}{2ikr} \sum_{l} (2l + 1)[(1 - f_l)e^{ikr} - (-1)^l e^{-ikr}]P_l(\cos\theta) \qquad (94)$$

In analogy with the expansion, Eq. (92b), of the plane wave, we can write the solution of Eq. (88a) as follows:

$$\psi(\mathbf{r}) = \sum_{l} i^l(2l + 1)\psi_l(r)P_l(\cos\theta) \qquad (95a)$$

where $\psi_l(r)$ satisfies the differential equation

$$\left[\frac{1}{r^2}\frac{\partial}{\partial r}\left(r^2\frac{\partial}{\partial r}\right) - \frac{l(l + 1)}{r^2} + k^2 - U(r)\right]\psi_l = 0 \qquad (95b)$$

Introducing

$$\psi_l(r) = \frac{1}{kr} u_l(r) \qquad (96a)$$

Eq. (95b) becomes

$$\left[\frac{d^2}{dr^2} + k^2 - U(r) - \frac{l(l + 1)}{r^2}\right]u_l(r) = 0 \qquad (96b)$$

The two independent solutions of Eq. (95b) in the asymptotic region $r \to \infty$ are the spherical Bessel and Neumann functions, $j_l(kr)$ and $n_l(kr)$. Therefore the general scattering solution is

$$\psi_l(r) \sim A_l j_l(kr) + B_l n_l(kr)$$

$$= \frac{1}{kr} C_l \sin\left(kr - \frac{l\pi}{2} + \delta_l\right) \qquad (97)$$

where C_l and δ_l are related to A_l and B_l. The parameter δ_l is called the phase shift since it determines the difference in phase of the scattered solution, Eq. (97), from the asymptotic solution which is regular at the origin (in the interior region), namely, the solution $j_l(kr) \sim (1/kr) \times \sin [kr - (l\pi/2)]$ for large r.

Substituting the asymptotic expression, Eq. (97), for $\psi_l(r)$ in Eq. (95a) and comparing the result with Eq. (94), we obtain

$$f_l = [1 - e^{2i\delta_l}] \tag{98a}$$

$$C_l = e^{i\delta_l} \tag{98b}$$

From Eqs. (98a) and (92a), the scattering amplitude $f(\theta)$ is given by

$$f(\theta) = \frac{1}{2ik} \sum_l (2l + 1)[\exp (2i\delta_l) - 1]P_l(\cos \theta)$$

$$= \frac{1}{k} \sum_l (2l + 1)e^{i\delta_l} \sin \delta_l P_l(\cos \theta) \tag{99}$$

From Eqs. (99), (91a), and (91b), the differential and total cross sections are given by

$$d\sigma(\theta) = |f(\theta)|^2 \, d\Omega = \left| \frac{1}{k} \sum_l (2l + 1)e^{i\delta_l} \sin \delta_l P_l(\cos \theta) \right|^2 d\Omega \tag{100a}$$

$$\sigma = \int d\sigma(\theta) = \frac{4\pi}{k^2} \sum_l (2l + 1) \sin^2 \delta_l \tag{100b}$$

A.13   The Scattering Matrix: S-Matrix

In the formal theory of scattering, it is convenient to introduce the S-matrix (scattering matrix) which was first used by Wheeler[5] and later investigated by Heisenberg.[6] The matrix elements of the S-matrix between initial and final plane wave (noninteracting) states in the infinite past and the infinite future, respectively, correspond to the probability amplitudes for a transition of the system from the initial state to the final state. In the following we shall obtain the form of the S-matrix in terms of the phase shifts for a central potential.

We look at the incoming incident plane wave and the outgoing wave in the asymptotic region $r \to \infty$. From Eqs. (92b), (94), and (98a) we have

$$e^{ikz} \sim \sum_{l=0}^{\infty} \frac{1}{2kr} i^{l+1}(2l + 1)[e^{-i[kr-l\pi/2]} - e^{i[kr-l\pi/2]}]P_l(\cos \theta) \tag{101a}$$

$$\psi(\mathbf{r}) \sim \sum_{l=0}^{\infty} \frac{1}{2kr} i^{l+1}(2l + 1)[e^{-i[kr-l\pi/2]} - S_l(k)e^{i[kr-l\pi/2]}]P_l(\cos \theta) \tag{101b}$$

where $S_l(k)$ is given by

$$S_l(k) = \exp [2i\,\delta_l(k)] \tag{102}$$

In Eq. (101a), the incident plane wave is written as a superposition of an incoming and an outgoing spherical wave of equal amplitudes. Equation (101b) indicates that after interaction with the potential $V(r)$, the outgoing wave $\psi(\mathbf{r})$ has its outgoing spherical wave amplitude modified by a factor $S_l(k)$ for the lth partial wave. As is clear from Eq. (102), the S-matrix is unitary, that is, $S^\dagger = S^{-1}$, where $S^\dagger$ is the Hermitian conjugate of S. The unitarity of the S-matrix is an important property. In terms of $S_l(k)$, the scattering amplitude $f(\theta)$, the differential and total cross sections $d\sigma(\theta)$ and σ are given by

$$f(\theta) = \frac{1}{2ik} \sum (2l + 1)(S_l - 1)P_l(\cos\theta) \tag{103a}$$

$$d\sigma(\theta) = \left| \frac{1}{2ik} \sum (2l + 1)(S_l - 1)P_l(\cos\theta) \right|^2 d\Omega \tag{103b}$$

$$\sigma = \frac{1}{k^2} \sum (2l + 1)\,|1 - S_l|^2 \tag{103c}$$

Other Matrices

It is convenient to define other matrices[7] in terms of the S-matrix. The reaction matrix, or the R-matrix, is defined by the relation

$$S_{ba} = \delta(a - b) - 2\pi i\,\delta(E_a - E_b)R_{ba} \tag{104a}$$

where a and b are the initial and the final states of the system, and $S_{ba} = \langle b|\,S\,|a\rangle$ and $R_{ba} = \langle b|\,R\,|a\rangle$ are the ba matrix elements of the S- and R-matrices. In matrix notation, Eq. (104a) can be written as

$$S = 1 - \mathbf{R} \tag{104b}$$

where the operator $\mathbf{R}$ is defined on the energy shell, that is, for such initial and final states which have the same energy

$$\mathbf{R}_{ba} = 2\pi i\,\delta(E_a - E_b)R_{ba} \tag{104c}$$

The reactance matrix K is usually defined by the equations

$$\mathbf{K}_{ba} = 2\pi\,\delta(E_b - E_a)K_{ba} \tag{105a}$$

$$\mathbf{R} = i(\mathbf{K} - \tfrac{1}{2}\mathbf{KR}) \tag{105b}$$

Equation (105b) is often known as the Heitler equation. Using the fact that the S-matrix is unitary, $S^\dagger S = SS^\dagger = 1$, where the dagger denotes Hermitian conjugate, we have from Eq. (104b)

$$SS^\dagger = 1 = S(1 - \mathbf{R}^\dagger) \tag{106a}$$

which defines the S-matrix by the relation

$$\mathbf{R} = -S\mathbf{R}^\dagger \tag{106b}$$

Also, since unitarity of the S-matrix implies

$$S^\dagger = S^{-1},$$

that is,

$$(1 - \mathbf{R}^\dagger) = S^{-1}, \tag{107a}$$

we have from Eqs. (104b) and (107a)

$$S = 1 - \mathbf{R} = (1 - \mathbf{R}^\dagger)^{-1} \tag{107b}$$

Another representation of the S-matrix follows from Eqs. (104b) and (105b). Eliminating $\mathbf{R}$ from Eqs. (107b) and (105b), we obtain

$$S = \frac{1 - (i/2)\mathbf{K}}{1 + (i/2\mathbf{K})} = (S^{-1})^\dagger$$

$$= \frac{1 - (i/2)\mathbf{K}^\dagger}{1 + (i/2)\mathbf{K}^\dagger} \tag{108a}$$

which implies that the $\mathbf{K}$-matrix is Hermitian, that is,

$$\mathbf{K}^\dagger = \mathbf{K} \tag{108b}$$

A.14 Scattering by a Coulomb Field

The Schrödinger equation which describes the relative motion of two particles in a Coulomb potential is given by

$$\left[\nabla^2 + k^2 - \frac{2\varepsilon k}{r}\right]\psi_c(\mathbf{r}) = 0 \tag{109a}$$

where

$$k = \left(2\frac{\mu E}{\hbar^2}\right)^{1/2} \qquad \varepsilon = \mu\,\frac{ZZ'e^2}{\hbar^2 k} = ZZ'\,\frac{e^2}{\hbar v} \tag{109b}$$

and μ is the reduced mass, v the relative velocity, $\mathbf{r}$ the relative coordinate, and E the energy associated with the relative motion. In spherical coordinates, we have

$$\nabla^2 = \frac{1}{r^2}\frac{\partial}{\partial r}\left(r^2\frac{\partial}{\partial r}\right) + \frac{1}{r^2\sin\theta}\frac{\partial}{\partial\theta}\left(\sin\theta\frac{\partial}{\partial\theta}\right) + \frac{1}{r^2\sin^2\theta}\frac{\partial^2}{\partial\phi^2} \tag{110}$$

The solution of Eq. (109a) can be written in the form

$$\psi_c(\mathbf{r}) = \sum_{lm} R_l(r)Y_{lm}(\theta, \phi) \tag{111a}$$

where the angular functions $Y_{lm}(\theta, \phi)$ are the usual spherical harmonics satisfying the differential equation

$$\frac{1}{\sin \theta} \frac{\partial}{\partial \theta}\left(\sin \theta \frac{\partial Y_{lm}}{\partial \theta}\right) + \frac{1}{\sin^2 \theta} \frac{\partial^2 Y_{lm}}{\partial \phi^2} + l(l + 1)Y_{lm} = 0 \qquad (111b)$$

and the radial function $R(r)$ satisfies the equation

$$\frac{1}{r^2} \frac{d}{dr}\left(r^2 \frac{dR_l}{dr}\right) + \left[k^2 - 2\frac{\varepsilon k}{r} - \frac{l(l + 1)}{r^2}\right]R_l = 0 \qquad (111c)$$

The solution of the Coulomb scattering problem can be obtained in terms of the phase shifts δ_l from the Schrödinger equation (109a) in spherical coordinates. However, this procedure is not as straightforward as when the Coulomb field is not present, since the Coulomb field has an infinite range of interaction and the radial solutions never approach the sinusoidal free-particle solutions. The phase shifts contain a logarithmic term which cannot be neglected for large distances.

Before considering the solutions in spherical coordinates, we treat the problem in parabolic coordinates in which the problem of scattering by a Coulomb field is exactly solvable. The parabolic coordinates are defined as follows:

$$\xi = r - z = r(1 - \cos \theta)$$
$$\eta = r + z = r(1 + \cos \theta)$$
$$\phi = \phi \qquad (112a)$$

and

$$\nabla^2 = \frac{4}{\xi + \eta}\left[\frac{\partial}{\partial \xi}\left(\xi \frac{\partial}{\partial \xi}\right) + \frac{\partial}{\partial \eta}\left(\eta \frac{\partial}{\partial \eta}\right)\right] + \frac{1}{\xi \eta} \frac{\partial^2}{\partial \phi^2} \qquad (112b)$$

Because of axial symmetry, the solution ψ_c has no dependence on ϕ. We write

$$\psi_c = e^{ikz}(C_1 X_1(\xi) + C_2 X_2(\eta)) \qquad (113)$$

where the incident plane wave e^{ikz} has been factored out. For large r, the asymptotic form of $\psi \sim e^{ikr}/r$, and therefore only the first term in Eq. (113) should be retained so that it can yield the required asymptotic form. The differential equation for $X_1(\xi) = X_1(r - z)$ is given by

$$\xi \frac{d^2 X_1}{d\xi^2} + (1 - ik\xi)\frac{dX_1}{d\xi} - \varepsilon k X_1 = 0 \qquad (114)$$

which is the differential equation satisfied by the confluent hypergeometric[8] function $F(a, b, \xi)$. The solution which is regular at $z = 0$ is

$$X_1(\xi) = CF(-i\varepsilon, 1, ik\xi) \qquad (115a)$$

where C is a constant, and

$$F(a, b, \xi) = \sum_{p=0}^{\infty} \frac{\Gamma(a + p)\Gamma(b)\xi^p}{\Gamma(a)\Gamma(b + p)\Gamma(1 + p)}$$

$$= 1 + a\frac{\xi}{1!} + \frac{a(a + 1)}{b(b + 1)}\frac{\xi^2}{2!} + \cdots \qquad (115b)$$

It is usual to write

$$F(a, b, \xi) = W_1(a, b, \xi) + W_2(a, b, \xi) \qquad (116)$$

where W_1 and W_2 are independently solutions of Eq. (114). They are given by

$$W_1(a, b, \xi) = \frac{\Gamma(b)}{\Gamma(b - a)} (-\xi)^{-a} g(a, a - b + 1, -\xi) \qquad (117a)$$

$$W_2(a, b, \xi) = \frac{\Gamma(b)}{\Gamma(a)} e^{\xi}\xi^{a-b} g(1 - a, b - a, \xi) \qquad (117b)$$

$$g(c, d, \xi) \sim 1 + cd\frac{\xi^{-1}}{1!} + c(c + 1) d(d + 1)\frac{\xi^{-2}}{2!} + \cdots ,$$

$$\text{for large } \xi \quad (117c)$$

The solution of Eq. (114) which is irregular at $z = 0$ is

$$X_1(\xi) = C'G(-i\varepsilon, 1, 2k\xi) \qquad (118a)$$

where

$$G(a, b, \xi) = i[W_1(a, b, \xi) - W_2(a, b, \xi)] \qquad (118b)$$

Gordon[9] has shown that the complete solution for the Coulomb wave function is given by

$$\psi_c(r, \theta) = e^{-\frac{1}{4}\pi\varepsilon}\Gamma(1 + i\varepsilon)e^{ikr\cos\theta}F[-i\varepsilon, 1, ikr(1 - \cos\theta)]$$

$$\xrightarrow[r \to \infty]{} I(r, \theta) + f_c(\theta)S(r) \quad (119)$$

where I and S are the modified (Coulomb distorted) incident and scattered waves given by [using Eqs. (116) and (117)]

$$I(r, z) = \left[1 - \frac{\varepsilon^2}{ik(r - z)}\right] \exp\left[ikz + i\varepsilon \ln k(r - z)\right] \qquad (120a)$$

$$S(r) = \frac{1}{r}\exp\left[ikr - i\varepsilon \ln kr\right] \qquad (120b)$$

with

$$f_c(\theta) = \frac{\Gamma(1 + i\varepsilon)}{i\Gamma(-i\varepsilon)}\frac{e^{-i\varepsilon \ln [\sin^2(\theta/2)]}}{2k\sin^2(\theta/2)}$$

$$= \frac{\varepsilon}{2k\sin^2(\theta/2)}\exp\left[-i\varepsilon \ln\left(\sin^2\frac{\theta}{2}\right) + i\pi + 2i\eta_0\right] \qquad (121a)$$

$$\eta_0 = \arg \Gamma(1 + i\varepsilon) \qquad (121b)$$

and

$$|f_c(\theta)|^2 = \sigma_c(\theta) = \left(\frac{ZZ'e^2}{2\mu v^2}\right)^2 \mathrm{cosec}^4 \frac{\theta}{2} \tag{121c}$$

In Eq. (120a) the term $-\varepsilon^2/[ik(r - z)]$ can be neglected in the asymptotic region of large r. Equation (121c) is the Rutherford scattering cross section formula.

We now return to the solution in spherical coordinates, Eqs. (110) to (111c). Substituting

$$R_l(r) = r^l e^{ikr} X_l(r) \tag{122}$$

in the radial equation (111c), we obtain

$$r\frac{d^2 X_l}{dr^2} + [2(l + 1) + 2ikr]\frac{dX_l}{dr} + [2ik(l + 1) - 2\varepsilon k]X_l = 0 \tag{123a}$$

whose solution is a confluent hypergeometric function. The bounded solution which is regular at the origin $r = 0$ is

$$X_l(r) = C_l F(l + 1 + i\varepsilon, 2l + 2, -2ikr) \tag{123b}$$

The complete Coulomb wave function can be shown to be

$$\psi_c(r, \theta) = \sum_{l=0}^{\infty} (2l + 1)i^l \psi_{lc}^R(k, r) P_l(\cos \theta) \tag{124a}$$

where the solution ψ_{lc}^R which is regular at the origin is given by

$$\psi_{lc}^R(k, r) = e^{-(\pi/2)\varepsilon} \frac{\Gamma(l + 1 + i\varepsilon)}{(2l + 1)!}(2kr)^l e^{ikr}$$

$$\times F(l + 1 + i\varepsilon, 2l + 2, -2ikr) \tag{124b}$$

In writing Eqs. (124) we have dropped the ϕ dependence because of axial symmetry, and the constant C_l is inserted by matching the solution with Eq. (119) near the origin $r = 0$.

According to Eqs. (116) to (118), the asymptotic behavior of $\psi_{lc}^R(k, r)$ is

$$\psi_{lc}^R(k, r) \xrightarrow[r \to \infty]{} \frac{1}{kr} \sin\left(kr - \tfrac{1}{2}l\pi + \eta_l - \varepsilon \ln 2kr\right) \tag{125a}$$

with

$$\eta_l = \arg \Gamma(l + 1 + i\varepsilon) \tag{125b}$$

$$= \eta_0 + \sum_{s=1}^{l} \tan^{-1}\frac{\varepsilon}{s}$$

A.15   Scattering by Combined Nuclear and Coulomb Potentials

In the case of proton-proton scattering, we have not only the Coulomb interaction which has an infinite range but also the nuclear interaction which is of finite range. Outside the range of the nuclear potential, the solution is a linear combination of the solution F, which is regular at the origin, and the irregular solution G. From Eq. (118b), the irregular solution is given by

$$\psi_{lc}^I(k, r) = ie^{-(1/2)\pi\varepsilon}\frac{\Gamma(l + 1 + i\varepsilon)}{(2l + 1)!}(2kr)^l e^{ikr}G(l + 1 + i\varepsilon, 2l + 2, -2ikr)$$

$$\xrightarrow[r\to\infty]{} \frac{1}{kr}\cos(kr - \tfrac{1}{2}l\pi + \eta_l - \varepsilon \ln 2kr) \quad (126)$$

Therefore, outside the nuclear potential the complete solution is

$$\psi(r, \theta) = \sum_{l=0}^{\infty} C_l(2l + 1)i^l\psi_l(k, r)P_l(\cos\theta) \quad (127a)$$

where

$$\psi_l(k, r) = \psi_{lc}^R\cos\delta_l + \psi_{lc}^I\sin\delta_l$$

$$\to \frac{1}{kr}\sin(kr - \tfrac{1}{2}l\pi - \varepsilon \ln 2kr + \delta_l + \eta_l) \quad (127b)$$

and δ_l is the nuclear phase shift.

According to Eq. (119), the Coulomb distorted incident wave is

$$\exp[ikz + i\varepsilon \ln k(r - z)] \xrightarrow[r\to\infty]{} \sum_{l=0}^{\infty}\frac{1}{kr}(2l + 1)i^l$$

$$\times \sin(kr - \tfrac{1}{2}l\pi - \varepsilon \ln 2kr)P_l(\cos\theta) \quad (128)$$

Therefore if we choose $C_l = \exp i(\delta_l + \eta_l)$, Eq. (127a) yields the following for the complete solution:

$$\psi(r, \theta) = I(r, \theta) + f(\theta)S(r) \quad (129)$$

where

$$I(r, \theta) = e^{i[kz+\varepsilon \ln k(r-z)]} \quad (130a)$$

$$S(r) = \frac{1}{r}e^{i[kr-\varepsilon \ln kr]} \quad (130b)$$

$$f(\theta) = -\frac{1}{2ik}\sum_{l=0}^{\infty}(2l + 1)[e^{2i(\delta_l+\eta_l)} - 1]P_l(\cos\theta) \quad (130c)$$

For a pure Coulomb field ($\delta_l = 0$), Eqs. (129) and (130) reduce to Eqs. (119) and (120). The combined scattering amplitude $f(\theta)$ can be written in the following form:

$$f(\theta) = f_c(\theta) + f_N(\theta) \tag{131}$$

where

$$f_c(\theta) = -\frac{1}{2ik} \sum_{l=0}^{\infty} (2l + 1)[e^{2i\eta_l} - 1]P_l(\cos \theta) \tag{132a}$$

$$f_N(\theta) = -\frac{1}{2ik} \sum_{l=0}^{\infty} (2l + 1)e^{2i\eta_l}[e^{2i\delta_l} - 1]P_l(\cos \theta) \tag{132b}$$

A.16 Tensor Operator

It is well known (see Chapter 3) that the two-body nuclear force is spin-dependent. The electric quadrupole moment and the magnetic moment of the deuteron and the difference in scattering of a proton (neutron) by parahydrogen (spin antiparallel) and by orthohydrogen (spin parallel) were among the earlier experimental facts which led to the suggestion that the interaction between the two nucleons depends on their spin states. The nature of this interaction was determined by requiring it to be:

1. Symmetric between particles 1 and 2.
2. Invariant under the transformations of parity (space reversal).

In the following, we shall construct the tensor operator which satisfies these restrictions.

We shall denote by $\mathbf{r} = \mathbf{x}_1 - \mathbf{x}_2$ the relative coordinates of particles 1 and 2 and their spins by $\boldsymbol{\sigma}_1$ and $\boldsymbol{\sigma}_2$ where the $\boldsymbol{\sigma}$'s satisfy the Pauli matrix algebra,

$$\sigma_i \sigma_j + \sigma_j \sigma_i = 2\delta_{ij} \qquad i, j = x, y, z \tag{133a}$$

$$\boldsymbol{\sigma} \times \boldsymbol{\sigma} = 2i\boldsymbol{\sigma} \tag{133b}$$

$$\sigma_x^2 = \sigma_y^2 = \sigma_z^2 = 1 \tag{134a}$$

$$(\boldsymbol{\sigma} \cdot \mathbf{A})(\boldsymbol{\sigma} \cdot \mathbf{B}) = (\mathbf{A} \cdot \mathbf{B}) + i\boldsymbol{\sigma} \cdot (\mathbf{A} \times \mathbf{B}) \tag{134b}$$

Explicit matrix representations for the σ matrices are

$$\sigma_x = \begin{pmatrix} 0 & 1 \\ 1 & 0 \end{pmatrix} \qquad \sigma_y = \begin{pmatrix} 0 & -i \\ i & 0 \end{pmatrix} \qquad \sigma_z = \begin{pmatrix} 1 & 0 \\ 0 & -1 \end{pmatrix} \tag{135}$$

Under space reversal operator P, the operators $\mathbf{r}$ and $\boldsymbol{\sigma}$ transform as follows:

$$P\mathbf{r} \rightarrow -\mathbf{r}, \qquad P\boldsymbol{\sigma} \rightarrow \boldsymbol{\sigma}$$

It follows from the requirement (2) that the vector $\mathbf{r}$ should appear an even number of times. Furthermore, from (1) we have that $\boldsymbol{\sigma}_1$ and $\boldsymbol{\sigma}_2$ should appear in a bilinear combination. From Eqs. (133) and (134), the only linearly independent quantities which can be constructed from $\mathbf{r}$, $\boldsymbol{\sigma}_1$, and $\boldsymbol{\sigma}_2$ are

$$(\boldsymbol{\sigma}_1 \cdot \boldsymbol{\sigma}_2) \quad \text{and} \quad (\boldsymbol{\sigma}_1 \cdot \mathbf{r})(\boldsymbol{\sigma}_2 \cdot \mathbf{r}) \tag{136}$$

The tensor operator S_{12} is conventionally defined by the relation

$$S_{12} = 3(\boldsymbol{\sigma}_1 \cdot \hat{r})(\boldsymbol{\sigma}_2 \cdot \hat{r}) - (\boldsymbol{\sigma}_1 \cdot \boldsymbol{\sigma}_2) \tag{137a}$$

where the unit vector $\hat{r}$ is defined by

$$\hat{r} = \frac{\mathbf{r}}{|\mathbf{r}|} \tag{137b}$$

Properties of S_{12}

1. The average value of S_{12} over all directions vanishes

$$\langle S_{12} \rangle = 0 \tag{138}$$

Proof: The average value

$$\langle (\boldsymbol{\sigma}_1 \cdot \hat{r})(\boldsymbol{\sigma}_2 \cdot \hat{r}) \rangle = \frac{1}{4\pi} \int d\hat{r} (\boldsymbol{\sigma}_1 \cdot \hat{r})(\boldsymbol{\sigma}_2 \cdot \hat{r}) \tag{139a}$$

where

$$d\hat{r} = d\Omega_r = \sin\theta \, d\theta \, d\phi \tag{139b}$$

By taking $\boldsymbol{\sigma}_1$ along the z-axis, $\boldsymbol{\sigma}_2$ in the x-z plane making an angle α with the z-axis, and the vector $\mathbf{r}$ with polar angles (θ, ϕ), we can represent these vectors as follows:

$$\boldsymbol{\sigma}_1 = \sigma_1 \hat{z} \tag{140a}$$
$$\boldsymbol{\sigma}_2 = \sigma_2 (\sin\alpha \, \hat{x} + \cos\alpha \, \hat{z}) \tag{140b}$$
$$\hat{r} = \sin\theta \cos\phi \, \hat{x} + \sin\theta \sin\phi \, \hat{y} + \cos\theta \, \hat{z} \tag{140c}$$

Substituting Eqs. (140) in Eq. (139b) and integrating over θ and ϕ, we obtain

$$\langle (\boldsymbol{\sigma}_1 \cdot \hat{r})(\boldsymbol{\sigma}_2 \cdot \hat{r}) \rangle = \tfrac{1}{3}\sigma_1\sigma_2 \cos\alpha = \tfrac{1}{3}(\boldsymbol{\sigma}_1 \cdot \boldsymbol{\sigma}_2) \tag{141}$$

From Eqs. (141) and (137a), the result $\langle S_{12} \rangle = 0$ follows immediately.

2. S_{12} satisfies the following commutation relations:

$$[\mathbf{S}^2, S_{12}] = [\mathbf{J}^2, S_{12}] = [J_z, S_{12}] = 0 \tag{142a}$$
$$[S_z, S_{12}] \neq 0 \tag{142b}$$
$$[\mathbf{L}^2, S_{12}] \neq 0 \tag{142c}$$
$$[L_z, S_{12}] \neq 0 \tag{142d}$$

where **S**, **J**, and **L** are the total spin, total angular momentum, and relative orbital angular momentum operators defined by

$$\mathbf{S} = \mathbf{S}_1 + \mathbf{S}_2 = \tfrac{1}{2}(\boldsymbol{\sigma}_1 + \boldsymbol{\sigma}_2) \tag{143a}$$

$$\mathbf{J} = \mathbf{L} + \mathbf{S} \tag{143b}$$

We note that

$$\mathbf{S}^2 = \tfrac{1}{2}(3 + \boldsymbol{\sigma}_1 \cdot \boldsymbol{\sigma}_2) \tag{144}$$

Equations (142a) to (142d) imply that in the presence of tensor interaction only the total angular momentum **J**, its z-component J_z, and the total spin **S** are constants of motion and therefore conserved.

3. Effect of S_{12} operating on spin singlet and triplet states χ_0^0 and $\chi_1^{m_s}(m_s = \pm 1, 0)$:

The singlet and triplet spin state functions are given by

$$\chi_0^0 = \frac{1}{\sqrt{2}} [\alpha(1)\beta(2) - \beta(1)\alpha(2)] \tag{145}$$

$$\chi_1^1 = \alpha(1)\alpha(2) \tag{146a}$$

$$\chi_1^0 = \frac{1}{\sqrt{2}} [\alpha(1)\beta(2) + \beta(1)\alpha(2)] \tag{146b}$$

$$\chi_1^{-1} = \beta(1)\beta(2) \tag{146c}$$

where

$$\alpha = \begin{pmatrix} 1 \\ 0 \end{pmatrix} \qquad \beta = \begin{pmatrix} 0 \\ 1 \end{pmatrix} \tag{147}$$

and 1 and 2 refer to the particles. α and β are to be interpreted as the spin wave functions for the individual particle with spin up $(s_z = \tfrac{1}{2})$ and down $(s_z = -\tfrac{1}{2})$ respectively. Noting that

$$\sigma_x \alpha = \beta \qquad \sigma_x \beta = \alpha \tag{148a}$$

$$\sigma_y \alpha = i\beta \qquad \sigma_y \beta = -i\alpha \tag{148b}$$

$$\sigma_z \alpha = \alpha \qquad \sigma_z \beta = -\beta \tag{148c}$$

it is easy to show that

$$S_{12}\chi_0^0 = 0 \tag{149a}$$

$$(\boldsymbol{\sigma}_1 \cdot \boldsymbol{\sigma}_2)\chi_1^{m_s} = \chi_1^{m_s} \tag{149b}$$

$$S_{12}^2 = 6 + 2\boldsymbol{\sigma}_1 \cdot \boldsymbol{\sigma}_2 - 2S_{12} \tag{150}$$

Choose the vector **r** along the z-axis. Then

$$S_{12} = 2\sigma_{1z}\sigma_{2z} - \sigma_{1x}\sigma_{2x} - \sigma_{1y}\sigma_{2y} \tag{151a}$$

Using Eqs. (133a) to (134b), we find that

$$S_{12}^2 = 6 - 2\sigma_{1z}\sigma_{2z} + 4\sigma_{1y}\sigma_{2y} + 4\sigma_{1x}\sigma_{2x}$$

$$= 6 + 2\boldsymbol{\sigma}_1 \cdot \boldsymbol{\sigma}_2 - 2S_{12} \qquad \text{[from Eq. (151a)]} \tag{151b}$$

A.17 Scattering Phase-Shift Analysis with Tensor Forces

The theory of phase-shift analysis when the interaction potential includes tensor forces was given by Blatt and Biedenharn.[10] In the following we describe their procedure along the lines discussed by Hulthen and Sugawara.[11] The Schrödinger equation in the center-of-mass system is given by

$$\left[-\frac{\hbar^2}{M} \nabla^2 + V(\mathbf{r}) \right] \psi(\mathbf{r}) = E\psi(\mathbf{r}) \tag{152}$$

where $V(\mathbf{r})$ includes a central potential $V_c(r)$ and a tensor potential $V_T(r)$,

$$V(\mathbf{r}) = V_c(r) + S_{12}V_T(r) \tag{153a}$$

S_{12} is the tensor operator given by

$$S_{12} = \frac{3(\boldsymbol{\sigma}_1 \cdot \mathbf{r})(\boldsymbol{\sigma}_2 \cdot \mathbf{r})}{r^2} - (\boldsymbol{\sigma}_1 \cdot \boldsymbol{\sigma}_2) \tag{153b}$$

The asymptotic scattering solution of Eq. (152) has the form

$$\psi(\mathbf{r}) \xrightarrow[r \to \infty]{} \left[e^{ikz} + f(\theta, \phi) \frac{e^{ikr}}{r} \right] \tag{154a}$$

$$k^2 = \frac{EM}{\hbar^2} \tag{154b}$$

In a pure central potential the scattering amplitude $f(\theta, \phi)$ was found to be independent of the azimuthal angle ϕ. When tensor force is included, this is no longer true. Also the expansion of the wave function $\psi(\mathbf{r})$ in terms of Legendre polynomials alone is not possible. It is necessary to expand the wave function in terms of angular functions which are labeled by parameters which are constants of motion. For the interaction potential $V(\mathbf{r})$, Eq. (153a), the constants of motion are the total angular momentum J, its z-component $J_z = M$, and the spin S of the two-particle system. We will therefore need to expand $\psi(\mathbf{r})$ in terms of states which are eigenstates of J, J_z, and S.

It should be observed that the two-nucleon system has two values of the spin, $S = 1$ and 0. In the latter case $J = L$ and the tensor operator $S_{12} = 0$. Therefore the singlet state ($S = 0$) scattering phase-shift analysis follows precisely the lines of Section A.12. It is then necessary to discuss the scattering analysis only for the triplet state ($S = 1$). In this case, for a given value of J, the orbital angular momentum L takes the values $L = J - 1, J$, and $J + 1$.

The incident plane wave e^{ikz} traveling along the z-axis can be expanded as follows:

$$e^{ikz}\chi_1^{m_s} = \sum_{L=0}^{\infty} \sqrt{4\pi(2L+1)}\, i^L j_L(kr) Y_{L0}(\theta, \phi)\chi_1^{m_s} \tag{155a}$$

where $\chi_1^{m_s}$ is the spin function in the triplet state. In the spherical harmonic, $m_L = 0$ because of the choice of the z-axis along the direction of the incident plane wave. Combining Y_{L0} and $\chi_1^{m_s}$ into a composite angular function $\mathscr{Y}_{L1J}$ by using the Clebsch-Gordan coefficients, we can rewrite Eq. (155a) as follows:

$$e^{ikz}\chi_1^{m_s} = \sum_{J=0}^{\infty} \sum_{L=J-1}^{J+1} \sqrt{4\pi(2L+1)}\ i^L j_L(kr)\langle L10m_s \,|\, Jm_s\rangle \mathscr{Y}_{L1J}^{m_s}(\theta,\phi) \tag{155b}$$

where the summation over L is over the three values $J \pm 1$ and J (in the case of $J = 0$, the allowed value of $L = 1$). In analogy with Eq. (155b), the solution $\psi(\mathbf{r})$ of the Schrödinger equation can be expanded as follows.

$$\psi(\mathbf{r}) = \sum_{J=0}^{\infty} \sum_{L=J-1}^{J+1} \frac{1}{r}\, u_{LJ}(r) \mathscr{Y}_{L1J}^{J_z(=m_s)}(\theta,\phi) \tag{156}$$

where $u_{LJ}(r)$ are the radial wave functions which, from Eqs. (152) to (153b) and (156), satisfy the following coupled differential equations:

$$\left[\frac{d^2}{dr^2} - \frac{L(L+1)}{r^2} + \frac{M}{\hbar^2}(E - V_c(r))\right] u_{LJ}(r)$$

$$- \frac{M}{\hbar^2} V_T(r) \sum_{L'} \langle L1JJ_z|\, S_{12}\, |L'1JJ_z\rangle u_{L'J}(r) = 0 \tag{157a}$$

The matrix elements of the tensor operator S_{12} appearing in Eq. (157a) are defined by

$$\langle L1JJ_z|\, S_{12}\, |L'1JJ_z\rangle = \int d\Omega\, \mathscr{Y}_{L1J}^{J_z\,*} S_{12} \mathscr{Y}_{L'1J}^{J_z} \tag{157b}$$

which is independent of J_z because of the symmetry. $\int d\Omega$ stands for integration over the solid angle as well as summation over the spins. The matrix elements in Eq. (157b) can be calculated easily and are given in Table A-3.

Table A-3   Values of $\langle L1J|\, S_{12}\, |L'1J\rangle$

L' \ L	$J+1$	J	$J-1$
$J+1$	$-\dfrac{2(J+2)}{2J+1}$	0	$+\dfrac{6\sqrt{J(J+1)}}{2J+1}$
J	0	$+2$	0
$J-1$	$+\dfrac{6\sqrt{J(J+1)}}{2J+1}$	0	$-\dfrac{2(J-1)}{2J+1}$

In order to establish connection with phase shifts, we should examine Eqs. (155b) and (156) in the asymptotic region $r \to \infty$. Asymptotically Eq. (155b) becomes

$$e^{ikz}\chi_1^{m_s} \to \sum_{J=0}^{\infty} \sum_{L=J-1}^{J+1} \sqrt{4\pi(2L+1)}\, i^L \frac{\sin\left(kr - L\frac{\pi}{2}\right)}{kr} \langle L10m_s \mid Jm_s\rangle \mathscr{Y}_{LJ}^{m_s}$$

$$= \sum_{J=0}^{\infty} \sum_{L=J-1}^{J+1} \sqrt{4\pi(2L+1)}\, \frac{i^{L+1}}{2kr} [e^{-i[kr-L\pi/2]} - e^{i[kr-L\pi/2]}]$$

$$\langle L10m_s \mid Jm_s\rangle \mathscr{Y}_{LJ}^{m_s} \quad (158)$$

which expresses the incident plane wave in terms of spherical outgoing and incoming waves with equal amplitudes. The radial wave functions $u_{LJ}(L = J, J \pm 1)$ will have similar asymptotic behavior but with unequal amplitudes B and A for the outgoing and incoming waves. We therefore have

$$u_{JJ}(r) \to A_0 e^{-i(kr-J\pi/2)} - B_0 e^{i(kr-J\pi/2)} \quad (159a)$$

$$u_{J-1,J}(r) \to A_1 e^{-i[kr-(J-1)\pi/2]} - B_1 e^{i[kr-(J-1)\pi/2]} \quad (159b)$$

$$u_{J+1,J}(r) \to A_2 e^{-i[kr-(J+1)\pi/2]} - B_2 e^{i[kr-(J+1)\pi/2]} \quad (159c)$$

The connection between B and A is established by the S-matrix.

$$B = SA \quad (160)$$

It is important to realize now, from Eqs. (157a), (157b), and Table A-3, that the radial function u_{JJ} for $L = J$ state is uncoupled and corresponds to a pure elastic scattering so that the incident flux and outgoing flux are equal, $|B_0|^2 = |A_0|^2$. In this case the S in Eq. (159a) can be parametrized in terms of the real phase-shift δ_{JJ} by the relation

$$S = \exp(2i\delta_{JJ}) \quad (161a)$$

with

$$u_{JJ}(r) \to -2iA_0 e^{i\delta_{JJ}} \sin\left(kr - \frac{J\pi}{2} + \delta_{JJ}\right). \quad (161b)$$

The situation is similar to the simple scattering theory of Section A.12.

The radial functions $u_{J-1,J}$ and $u_{J+1,J}$ are coupled, because the tensor interaction S_{12} mixes up the $L = J - 1$ and $J + 1$ states, and they satisfy coupled differential equations (157a). The scattering matrix S is therefore a 2×2 matrix, and it follows from Eqs. (159b) and (159c) that

$$B = \begin{pmatrix} B_1 \\ B_2 \end{pmatrix} \quad A = \begin{pmatrix} A_1 \\ A_2 \end{pmatrix} \quad (162a)$$

$$S = \begin{pmatrix} S_{11} & S_{12} \\ S_{21} & S_{22} \end{pmatrix} \quad (162b)$$

In the scattering problem, since the outgoing flux is equal to the incident flux (conservation of flux), we have

$$A^\dagger A = B^\dagger B \qquad (163a)$$

and

$$S^\dagger S = SS^\dagger = 1 \qquad (163b)$$

where the dagger sign denotes Hermitian conjugation. A representation for the S-matrix, Eq. (162b), can be written in the following form:

$$S = U^{-1} e^{2i\Delta} U \qquad (164a)$$

where U is a unitary matrix containing only one real parameter and Δ is a diagonal matrix whose elements are real. These are conventionally written in the form

$$U = \begin{pmatrix} \cos \varepsilon_J & \sin \varepsilon_J \\ -\sin \varepsilon_J & \cos \varepsilon_J \end{pmatrix} \quad \text{and} \quad \Delta = \begin{pmatrix} \delta_{J\alpha} & 0 \\ 0 & \delta_{J\gamma} \end{pmatrix} \qquad (164b)$$

where ε_J is called the mixing parameter, since, in the limit of $\varepsilon_J \to 0$, the S-matrix becomes diagonal and the coupling between the $L = J - 1$ and $J + 1$ states disappears. It is easy to see from Eqs. (159b), (162a), and (162b) that in this limit $\delta_{J\alpha}(\varepsilon_J = 0) \to \delta_{J-1,J}$ and $\delta_{J\gamma}(\varepsilon_J = 0) \to \delta_{J+1,J}$. Also, since the tensor operator S_{12} is responsible for the coupling of the differential equations for $u_{J-1,J}$ and $u_{J+1,J}$, the vanishing of the tensor force implies $\varepsilon_J \to 0$ (or $\pi/2$), and then $\mathscr{Y}_{L1L-1}^{m_s}$ and $\mathscr{Y}_{L1L+1}^{m_s}$ are eigenstates.

We consider the general case when $\varepsilon_J \neq 0$. It is clear from Eq. (164a) that the U-matrix diagonalizes the S-matrix, that is,

$$S' = USU^{-1} = \begin{pmatrix} \exp(2i\delta_{J\alpha}) & 0 \\ 0 & \exp(2i\delta_{J\gamma}) \end{pmatrix} \qquad (165a)$$

Also, from Eq. (159c) and (165a), we have

$$UB = USU^{-1}UA = \begin{pmatrix} \exp(2i\delta_{J\alpha}) & 0 \\ 0 & \exp(2i\delta_{J\gamma}) \end{pmatrix} UA \qquad (165b)$$

If we choose the two eigenvectors UA as follows:

$$A'_\alpha = UA_\alpha = \begin{pmatrix} 1 \\ 0 \end{pmatrix} \quad \text{and} \quad A'_\gamma = UA_\gamma = \begin{pmatrix} 0 \\ 1 \end{pmatrix}, \qquad (166a)$$

then the vectors A'_α and A'_γ are eigenstates of the diagonal matrix S' with eigenvalues $\exp(2i\delta_{J\alpha})$ and $\exp(2i\delta_{J\gamma})$, respectively, with the corresponding outgoing amplitudes given by

$$B'_\alpha = UB_\alpha = S'A'_\alpha = \exp(2i\delta_{J\alpha}) \begin{pmatrix} 1 \\ 0 \end{pmatrix} \qquad (166b)$$

$$B'_\gamma = UB_\gamma = S'A'_\gamma = \exp(2i\delta_{J\gamma}) \begin{pmatrix} 0 \\ 1 \end{pmatrix} \qquad (166c)$$

From Eqs. (164b) and (165a)–(166c), we therefore have

$$A_\alpha = \begin{pmatrix} A_{1\alpha} \\ A_{2\alpha} \end{pmatrix} = U^{-1} \begin{pmatrix} 1 \\ 0 \end{pmatrix} = \begin{pmatrix} \cos \varepsilon_J \\ \sin \varepsilon_J \end{pmatrix} \tag{167a}$$

$$A_\gamma = \begin{pmatrix} A_{1\gamma} \\ A_{2\gamma} \end{pmatrix} = U^{-1} \begin{pmatrix} 0 \\ 1 \end{pmatrix} = \begin{pmatrix} -\sin \varepsilon_J \\ \cos \varepsilon_J \end{pmatrix} \tag{167b}$$

$$B_\alpha = \begin{pmatrix} B_{1\alpha} \\ B_{2\alpha} \end{pmatrix} = U^{-1} \begin{pmatrix} \exp(2i\delta_{J\alpha}) \\ 0 \end{pmatrix} = \begin{pmatrix} \exp(2i\delta_{J\alpha}) \cos \varepsilon_J \\ \exp(2i\delta_{J\alpha}) \sin \varepsilon_J \end{pmatrix} \tag{168a}$$

$$B_\gamma = \begin{pmatrix} B_{1\gamma} \\ B_{2\gamma} \end{pmatrix} = U^{-1} \begin{pmatrix} 0 \\ \exp(2i\delta_{J\gamma}) \end{pmatrix} = \begin{pmatrix} -\exp(2i\delta_{J\gamma}) \sin \varepsilon_J \\ \exp(2i\delta_{J\gamma}) \cos \varepsilon_J \end{pmatrix} \tag{168b}$$

The states A_α, A_γ and B_α, B_γ which are mixtures of the two states with $L = J - 1$ and $L = J + 1$ are eigenstates of the scattering problem in the presence of tensor force. Substituting Eqs. (167a) and (168a) in Eq. (159b), and Eqs. (167b) and (168b) in Eq. (159c), we obtain the following two sets of asymptotic solutions for the states α and γ.

$$u_{J-1J\alpha}(r) \to -2iA_\alpha e^{2i\delta_{J\alpha}} \sin \left[kr - (J - 1)\frac{\pi}{2} + \delta_{J\alpha} \right] \tag{169a}$$

$$u_{J+1J\alpha}(r) \to -2iA_\alpha \tan \varepsilon_J e^{2i\delta_{J\gamma}} \sin \left[kr - (J + 1)\frac{\pi}{2} + \delta_{J\alpha} \right] \tag{169b}$$

$$u_{J-1J\gamma}(r) \to 2iA_\gamma \tan \varepsilon_J e^{2i\delta_{J\gamma}} \sin \left[kr - (J - 1)\frac{\pi}{2} + \delta_{J\gamma} \right] \tag{170a}$$

$$u_{J+1J\gamma}(r) \to -2iA_\gamma e^{2i\delta_{J\gamma}} \sin \left[kr - (J + 1)\frac{\pi}{2} + \delta_{J\gamma} \right] \tag{170b}$$

The wave functions for the specific states $JS\,m_s$ can be written as follows:

$$\psi_{\alpha SJ}{}^{m_s}(\mathbf{r}) = \frac{1}{r} u_{J-1J\alpha}(r)\mathcal{Y}_{J-1SJ}{}^{m_s} + \frac{1}{r} u_{J+1J\alpha}(r)\mathcal{Y}_{J+1SJ}{}^{m_s} \tag{171a}$$

$$\psi_{\beta SJ}{}^{m_s}(\mathbf{r}) = \frac{1}{r} u_{JJ}(r)\mathcal{Y}_{JSJ}{}^{m_s} \tag{171b}$$

$$\psi_{\gamma SJ}{}^{m_s}(\mathbf{r}) = \frac{1}{r} u_{J-1J\gamma}(r)\mathcal{Y}_{J-1SJ}{}^{m_s} + \frac{1}{r} u_{J+1J\gamma}(r)\mathcal{Y}_{J+1SJ}{}^{m_s} \tag{171c}$$

where β has been used to denote the unmixed state $L = J$, and $S = 1$ all through; $m_L = 0$, $J_z = m_s$ (because of the choice of the z-axis along the incident wave). The asymptotic behavior is given by

$$\psi_{\alpha S J}{}^{m_s} \rightarrow -\frac{2i}{r} A_{\alpha J}{}^{m_s} e^{i\delta_{J\alpha}} \sin\left[kr - (J-1)\frac{\pi}{2} + \delta_{J\alpha}\right]$$
$$\times (\mathscr{Y}_{J-1SJ}{}^{m_s} - \tan \varepsilon_J \mathscr{Y}_{J+1SJ}{}^{m_s}) \quad (172a)$$

$$\psi_{\beta S J}{}^{m_s} \rightarrow -\frac{2i}{r} A_{\beta J}{}^{m_s} e^{i\delta_{J\beta}} \sin\left(kr - \frac{J\pi}{2} + \delta_{J\beta}\right) \mathscr{Y}_{JSJ}{}^{m_s} \quad (172b)$$

$$\psi_{\gamma S J}{}^{m_s} \rightarrow -\frac{2i}{r} A_{\gamma J}{}^{m_s} e^{i\delta_{J\gamma}} \sin\left[kr - (J+1)\frac{\pi}{2} + \delta_{J\gamma}\right]$$
$$\times (\tan \varepsilon_J \mathscr{Y}_{J-1SJ}{}^{m_s} + \mathscr{Y}_{J+1SJ}{}^{m_s}) \quad (172c)$$

We note in the above that the $L = J - 1$ and $J + 1$ states are mixed. We have denoted by α the state which goes over to $L = J - 1$ in the absence of tensor force, by γ the state which goes to $L = J + 1$. In Eq. (156) the sum over L should be replaced by sum over α, β, and γ. Thus

$$\psi(\mathbf{r}) = \sum_{J=0}^{\infty} \sum_{i=\alpha,\beta,\gamma} \psi_{iSJ}{}^{m_s} \quad (173)$$

where $\psi_{iSJ}{}^{m_s}$ are given by Eqs. (171) and (172).

The expression for the scattering amplitude $f^{m_s}(\theta, \phi)$ can be obtained by examining Eq. (173) in the asymptotic region $r \rightarrow \infty$ and comparing it with Eq. (154b). The differential cross section in the triplet state scattering of an unpolarized beam is obtained by summing over spin coordinates and averaging over m_s.

$$\sigma_t(\theta, \phi) = \frac{1}{3} \sum_{m_s=-1}^{1} \sum_{\substack{\text{spin} \\ \text{coordinates}}} |f^{m_s}(\theta, \phi)|^2 \quad (174)$$

The expression for the differential cross section $\sigma(\theta, \phi)$ is given by Rohrlich and Eisenstein[12] and Matsumoto[13], whose papers give the details. At low energies, retaining only the S-phase shift $\delta_{1\alpha}$ and the mixing parameter ε_1, the differential scattering cross section in the triplet state is given by

$$\sigma_t(\theta) = \frac{1}{k^2} \sin^2 \delta_{1\alpha}\left[1 + \sin^2 \varepsilon_1 \left(2 \cos \varepsilon_1 + \frac{1}{\sqrt{2}} \sin \varepsilon_1\right)^2 P_2(\cos \theta)\right] \quad (175a)$$

The expression for the triplet total cross section is quite simple because of the orthonormality of the $\mathscr{Y}_{LSJ}$ functions. The result is

$$\sigma_t = \frac{4\pi}{k^2} \sum_{J=0}^{\infty} \frac{2J+1}{3} \sum_{i=\alpha,\beta,\gamma} \sin^2 \delta_{Ji} \quad (175b)$$

which is independent of the mixing parameter ε_J.

A.18   Isotopic Spin of the Nucleon

The charge symmetry and charge independence of nuclear forces and the almost equality of the masses of the neutron and the proton are strongly suggestive that the neutron and the proton are the same particle in two different charge states. Mathematically, it should therefore be possible to treat them on an equal footing. This is conveniently done by introducing a mathematical three-dimensional "charge space," which is called the isotopic spin or isospin space (or isospace). The neutron and proton are described by an isotopic spinor (isospinor) field in the isospace, the two isospinor components corresponding to the two charge states of the particle. Since ordinary spin also has two states, the formal development of the isospinor algebra is exactly the same as for the spin $\mathbf{s} = (\hbar/2)\boldsymbol{\sigma}$ whose z-components are $s_z = \pm\hbar/2$.

The common name given to neutron and proton is the nucleon which is a particle with isospin

$$\mathbf{t} = \tfrac{1}{2}\boldsymbol{\tau} \tag{176a}$$

whose z-components in the isospin space

$$t_3 = \tfrac{1}{2}\tau_3 = +\tfrac{1}{2} \text{ and } -\tfrac{1}{2} \tag{176b}$$

correspond respectively to the proton ($t_3 = +\tfrac{1}{2}$) and neutron ($t_3 = -\tfrac{1}{2}$). (Sometimes the opposite convention is used.) The three components of the matrix $\boldsymbol{\tau}$ are given by

$$\tau_1 = \begin{pmatrix} 0 & 1 \\ 1 & 0 \end{pmatrix} \qquad \tau_2 = \begin{pmatrix} 0 & -i \\ i & 0 \end{pmatrix} \qquad \tau_3 = \begin{pmatrix} 1 & 0 \\ 0 & -1 \end{pmatrix} \tag{177}$$

The wave functions for the proton and neutron in the isospace can be represented by

$$\eta(p) = \eta(t_3 = +\tfrac{1}{2}) = \begin{pmatrix} 1 \\ 0 \end{pmatrix} \tag{178a}$$

and

$$\eta(n) = \eta(t_3 = -\tfrac{1}{2}) = \begin{pmatrix} 0 \\ 1 \end{pmatrix} \tag{178b}$$

so that

$$t_3\eta(p) = \tfrac{1}{2}\eta(p) \qquad t_3\eta(n) = -\tfrac{1}{2}\eta(n) \tag{178c}$$

that is, the eigenvalues of the operator t_3 are $+\tfrac{1}{2}$ and $-\tfrac{1}{2}$ for proton and neutron respectively. The charge operator Q whose eigenvalues are $+1$

for the proton state and 0 for the neutron state is

$$Q = \tfrac{1}{2}(1 + \tau_3)$$

$$= \begin{pmatrix} 1 & 0 \\ 0 & 0 \end{pmatrix} \tag{179a}$$

with

$$Q\eta(p) = \eta(p) \qquad Q\eta(n) = 0 \tag{179b}$$

The operators τ_+ and τ_- which, respectively, increase and decrease charge of the nucleon by one unit are

$$\tau_+ = \tfrac{1}{2}(\tau_1 + i\tau_2) \qquad \tau_- = \tfrac{1}{2}(\tau_1 - i\tau_2) \tag{180a}$$

so that

$$\tau_+\eta(p) = 0 \qquad \tau_-\eta(p) = \eta(n) \tag{180b}$$

$$\tau_+\eta(n) = \eta(p) \qquad \tau_-\eta(n) = 0 \tag{180c}$$

A.19   Two-Nucleon Wave Function in Isospin Space

The total isospin $\mathbf{T}$ of two nucleons 1 and 2 is defined by

$$\mathbf{T} = \mathbf{t}^{(1)} + \mathbf{t}^{(2)} = \tfrac{1}{2}(\boldsymbol{\tau}^{(1)} + \boldsymbol{\tau}^{(2)}) \tag{181a}$$

with

$$T = 1 \text{ or } 0 \tag{181b}$$

The two-nucleon wave function $\eta(\tfrac{1}{2}\tfrac{1}{2} Tm_T)$ which is an eigenfunction of $\mathbf{T}$ and T_3 is easily obtained by using the Clebsch-Gordan coefficients. Thus

$$\eta(\tfrac{1}{2}\tfrac{1}{2} Tm_T) = \sum_{\substack{m_t, m_t' \\ m_T = m_t + m_t'}} \langle \tfrac{1}{2}\tfrac{1}{2} m_t m_t' \mid Tm_T \rangle \eta^{(1)}(m_t) \eta^{(2)}(m_t') \tag{182}$$

where m_t and m_t' take the values $\pm\tfrac{1}{2}$. From Eq. (182) we find the following

Isospin Singlet State

$$\eta_0^0 = \eta(\tfrac{1}{2}\tfrac{1}{2} 0\, 0) = \frac{1}{\sqrt{2}}\, [\eta^{(1)}(p)\eta^{(2)}(n) - \eta^{(1)}(n)\eta^{(2)}(p)] \tag{183}$$

Isospin Triplet States

$$\eta_1^1 = \eta(\tfrac{1}{2}\tfrac{1}{2} 1\, 1) = \eta^{(1)}(p)\eta^{(2)}(p) \tag{184a}$$

$$\eta_1^0 = \eta(\tfrac{1}{2}\tfrac{1}{2} 1\, 0) = \frac{1}{\sqrt{2}}\, [\eta^{(1)}(p)\eta^{(2)}(n) + \eta^{(1)}(n)\eta^{(2)}(p)] \tag{184b}$$

$$\eta_1^{-1} = \eta(\tfrac{1}{2}\tfrac{1}{2} 1\, {-1}) = \eta^{(1)}(n)\eta^{(2)}(n) \tag{184c}$$

The isospin singlet state Eq. (183) is antisymmetric in nucleons 1 and 2, and the isospin triplet states Eqs. (184a) to (184c) are symmetric in nucleons 1 and 2.

A.20   Complete Wave Function for the Two-Nucleon System: Pauli Principle

We first consider two identical particles in the states $\phi_1(l_1 s_1 j_1)$ and $\phi_2(l_2 s_2 j_2)$. The unsymmetrized two-particle state is given by

$$\phi_{\text{unsym}}(l_1 s_1 j_1, l_2 s_2 j_2; JM) = \sum_{m_1, m_2} \langle j_1 m_1 j_2 m_2 \mid JM \rangle$$
$$\times \; \phi_1(l_1 s_1 j_1 m_1)\phi_2(l_2 s_2 j_2 m_2) \quad (185a)$$

where for particles 1 and 2

$$\phi(l \, s \, j \, m) = \sum_{m_l, m_s} \langle l m_l \, s m_s \mid j m \rangle \, |l m_l\rangle \, |s m_s\rangle \quad (185b)$$

In Eq. (185a), we shall drop s_1 and s_2 since each one of them is $\frac{1}{2}$. However, Eq. (185a) is not an admissible wave function, since according to the Pauli principle, it should be antisymmetric. Denoting the quantum states by the numbers $l_a j_a m_a$ and $l_b j_b m_b$, the antisymmetric wave function is given by

$$\phi_A(l_a j_a l_b j_b; JM) = \frac{1}{\sqrt{2}} \sum_{m_a, m_b} \langle j_a m_a j_b m_b \mid JM \rangle$$
$$\times \; [\phi_1(l_a j_a m_a)\phi_2(l_b j_b m_b) - \phi_1(l_b j_b m_b)\phi_2(l_a j_a m_a)] \quad (186a)$$

where, for $a \neq b$, $1/\sqrt{2}$ is the normalization constant so that

$$\int d\mathbf{x}_1 \, d\mathbf{x}_2 \, |\phi_A|^2 = 1.$$

If the quantum numbers $l_a j_a$ are equal to the quantum numbers $l_b j_b$, that is, $(l_a j_a) = (l_b j_b) = (lj)$, the antisymmetric wave function is given by

$$\phi_A[(lj)^2 JM] = \tfrac{1}{2} \sum_{m, m'} \langle jm \, jm' \mid JM \rangle [\phi_1(ljm)\phi_2(ljm') - \phi_1(ljm')\phi_2(ljm)]$$
$$= \tfrac{1}{2} \sum_{m, m'} [\langle jm \, jm' \mid JM \rangle - \langle jm' \, jm \mid JM \rangle] \phi_1(ljm)\phi_2(ljm')$$
$$= \tfrac{1}{2}[1 - (-1)^{2j-J}] \sum_{m, m'} \langle jm \, jm' \mid JM \rangle \phi_1(ljm)\phi_2(ljm')$$
$$= \begin{cases} \sum_{m, m'} \langle jm \, jm' \mid JM \rangle \phi_1(ljm)\phi_2(ljm') & \text{for } J = \text{even} \\ 0 & \text{for } J = \text{odd} \end{cases}$$
$$(186b)$$

where in the last step we have made use of the fact that j is a half-integer. The normalization constant in Eq. (186b) is $\frac{1}{2}$.

The complete wave function including charge states of the two nucleons can be written by combining Eqs. (183) and (184) with Eq. (186a) and the symmetric wave function ϕ_S by making use of the generalized Pauli principle. According to this principle, the two-fermion wave function must be antisymmetric with respect to the exchange of all the coordinates, including the isospin of particles 1 and 2. Thus the antisymmetric ϕ_A is multiplied by the symmetric charge function η_1 and the symmetric ϕ_S is multiplied by the antisymmetric charge function η_0^0. We thus obtain the following totally antisymmetric wave functions:

$$\psi_{pn}^{T=0}(j_a j_b \, JM) = \phi_S \eta_0^0 = \tfrac{1}{2} \sum \langle j_a m_a j_b m_b \mid JM \rangle$$
$$\times \, [\phi_1(a)\phi_2(b) + \phi_1(b)\phi_2(a)][\eta_1(\tfrac{1}{2})\eta_2(-\tfrac{1}{2}) - \eta_1(-\tfrac{1}{2})\eta_2(\tfrac{1}{2})] \quad (187)$$

$$\psi_{pn}^{T=1}(j_a j_a \, JM) = \phi_A \eta_1^0 = \tfrac{1}{2} \sum \langle j_a m_a j_b m_b \mid JM \rangle$$
$$\times \, [\phi_1(a)\phi_2(b) - \phi_1(b)\phi_2(a)][\eta_1(\tfrac{1}{2})\eta_2(-\tfrac{1}{2}) + \eta_1(-\tfrac{1}{2})\eta_2(\tfrac{1}{2})] \quad (188a)$$

$$\psi_{pp}^{T=1}(j_a j_b \, JM) = \phi_A \eta_1^1 = \frac{1}{\sqrt{2}} \sum \langle j_a m_a j_b m_b \mid JM \rangle$$
$$\times \, [\phi_1(a)\phi_2(b) - \phi_1(b)\phi_2(a)]\eta_1(\tfrac{1}{2})\eta_2(\tfrac{1}{2}) \quad (188b)$$

$$\psi_{nn}^{T=1}(j_a j_b \, JM) = \phi_A \eta_1^{-1} = \frac{1}{\sqrt{2}} \sum \langle j_a m_a j_b m_b \mid JM \rangle$$
$$\times \, [\phi_1(a)\phi_2(b) - \phi_1(b)\phi_2(a)]\eta_1(-\tfrac{1}{2})\eta_2(-\tfrac{1}{2}) \quad (188c)$$

The *pp* and *nn* states are pure $T = 1$ state, whereas the *pn* system is a mixture of $T = 1$ and $T = 0$ states.

A.21 Dirac Equation

The Dirac equation describing a free particle of spin $\tfrac{1}{2}$ is given by ($\hbar = c = 1$)

$$\left(\gamma_\mu \frac{\partial}{\partial x_\mu} + m \right) \psi_\alpha(x) = 0 \qquad (189)$$

where m is the mass of the particle and $\psi_\alpha(x)$ is the wave function which has four components labeled by the index α. The γ-matrices are 4×4 matrices satisfying the anticommutation relations

$$\{\gamma_\mu, \gamma_\nu\} = \gamma_\mu \gamma_\nu + \gamma_\nu \gamma_\mu = 2\delta_{\mu\nu} \qquad (190a)$$

(We have the four-dimensional scalar product defined by $A_\mu B_\mu = AB = \mathbf{A} \cdot \mathbf{B} + A_4 B_4$.) The γ matrices are related to the α and β matrices as follows:

$$\gamma_k = i\alpha_k \beta \qquad \gamma_4 = \beta \qquad k = 1, 2, 3 \qquad (190b)$$

The explicit representations usually used for these matrices are

$$\alpha_k = \begin{pmatrix} 0 & \sigma_k \\ \sigma_k & 0 \end{pmatrix} \qquad \beta = \begin{pmatrix} 1 & 0 \\ 0 & -1 \end{pmatrix} \qquad (191a)$$

where 1 and 0 are, respectively, a 2×2 unit matrix and a 2×2 matrix with all elements equal to zero. The σ's are the 2×2 Pauli matrices given by

$$\sigma_x = \sigma_1 = \begin{pmatrix} 0 & 1 \\ 1 & 0 \end{pmatrix} \qquad \sigma_y = \sigma_2 = \begin{pmatrix} 0 & -i \\ i & 0 \end{pmatrix} \qquad \sigma_z = \sigma_3 = \begin{pmatrix} 1 & 0 \\ 0 & -1 \end{pmatrix}$$

(191b)

The matrix representation for the γ matrices is

$$\gamma_k = \begin{pmatrix} 0 & -i\sigma_k \\ i\sigma_k & 0 \end{pmatrix} \qquad \gamma_4 = \begin{pmatrix} 1 & 0 \\ 0 & -1 \end{pmatrix} \tag{191c}$$

Another matrix which will be used is

$$\gamma_5 = \gamma_1\gamma_2\gamma_3\gamma_4 \tag{192a}$$

$$= \begin{pmatrix} 0 & -1 \\ -1 & 0 \end{pmatrix} \tag{192b}$$

It is easy to verify that

$$\{\gamma_\mu, \gamma_5\} = \gamma_\mu\gamma_5 + \gamma_5\gamma_\mu = 0 \tag{192c}$$

The above representation for the matrices is not unique. It is sometimes convenient to take γ_5 diagonal. The following representations also satisfy the commutation relations [Eqs. (190a) and (192c)].

$$\gamma_k = \begin{pmatrix} 0 & -i\sigma_k \\ i\sigma_k & 0 \end{pmatrix} \qquad \gamma_4 = \begin{pmatrix} 0 & 1 \\ 1 & 0 \end{pmatrix} \qquad \gamma_5 = \begin{pmatrix} 1 & 0 \\ 0 & -1 \end{pmatrix} \tag{193}$$

Plane Wave Solution

The plane wave solution for the Dirac equation can be obtained by writing

$$\psi_\alpha(x) = \frac{1}{\sqrt{V}} e^{ipx} u_\alpha(\mathbf{p})$$

$$= \frac{1}{\sqrt{V}} e^{i\mathbf{p}\cdot\mathbf{x} - iEt} u_\alpha(\mathbf{p}) \tag{194a}$$

Substituting Eq. (194a) in Eq. (189), we obtain

$$(i\gamma_\mu p_\mu + m)u(\mathbf{p}) = (i\gamma_k p_k - \gamma_4 E + m)u(\mathbf{p}) = 0 \tag{194b}$$

which is the Dirac equation in the momentum representation.

It is convenient to define the adjoint Dirac operator $\bar{\psi}(x)$ by the relation

$$\bar{\psi}(x) = \psi^*(x)\gamma_4 \tag{195a}$$

where $\psi^*(x)$ is the Hermitian conjugate of $\psi(x)$. The differential equation satisfied by $\bar{\psi}(x)$ is

$$\frac{\partial}{\partial x_\mu} \bar{\psi}(x)\gamma_\mu - m\bar{\psi}(x) = 0 \tag{195b}$$

In the plane wave approximation, Eq. (195b) transforms to

$$\bar{u}(\mathbf{p})(i\gamma_\mu p_\mu + m) = 0 \tag{196a}$$

where

$$\bar{u}(\mathbf{p}) = u^*(\mathbf{p})\gamma_4 \tag{196b}$$

Small and Large Components of the Dirac Spinor u

It is often convenient to write

$$u(\mathbf{p}) = \begin{pmatrix} u_1(\mathbf{p}) \\ u_2(\mathbf{p}) \end{pmatrix} \tag{197}$$

where u_1 and u_2 are 2×1 column matrices. By substituting Eq. (197) in Eq. (194b) it is easy to show that

$$u_1(\mathbf{p}) = \frac{(\boldsymbol{\sigma} \cdot \mathbf{p})}{E - m} u_2(\mathbf{p}) \tag{198a}$$

$$u_2(\mathbf{p}) = \frac{(\boldsymbol{\sigma} \cdot \mathbf{p})}{E + m} u_1(\mathbf{p}) \tag{198b}$$

The requirement that Eqs. (198a) and (198b) be consistent leads to the condition

$$E = \pm\sqrt{\mathbf{p}^2 + m^2} \tag{199}$$

Thus, corresponding to each momentum $\mathbf{p}$, we have solutions which pertain both to positive energy and to negative energy. For each sign of the energy we have two linearly independent solutions corresponding to the choice $u_1 = \begin{pmatrix} 1 \\ 0 \end{pmatrix}$ or $\begin{pmatrix} 0 \\ 1 \end{pmatrix}$. The normalized positive energy solutions are given by

$$u_+^{(1)}(\mathbf{p}) = \sqrt{\frac{E + m}{2E}} \begin{bmatrix} 1 \\ 0 \\ \dfrac{\boldsymbol{\sigma} \cdot \mathbf{p}}{E + m} \begin{pmatrix} 1 \\ 0 \end{pmatrix} \end{bmatrix} \tag{200a}$$

$$u_+^{(2)}(\mathbf{p}) = \sqrt{\frac{E + m}{2E}} \begin{bmatrix} 0 \\ 1 \\ \dfrac{\boldsymbol{\sigma} \cdot \mathbf{p}}{E + m} \begin{pmatrix} 0 \\ 1 \end{pmatrix} \end{bmatrix} \tag{200b}$$

The negative energy solutions are given by

$$u_-^{(1)}(\mathbf{p}) = \sqrt{\frac{E+m}{2E}} \left[\frac{-\boldsymbol{\sigma}\cdot\mathbf{p}}{E+m} \binom{0}{1} \right]$$

(201a)

$$u_-^{(2)}(\mathbf{p}) = \sqrt{\frac{E+m}{2E}} \left[\frac{\boldsymbol{\sigma}\cdot\mathbf{p}}{E+m} \binom{1}{0} \right]$$

(201b)

Equations (200) and (201) form the set of basic solutions. They satisfy the orthogonality relations

$$\left. \begin{aligned} u_+^{(r)*}(\mathbf{p})u_+^{(s)}(\mathbf{p}) &= \sum_{\alpha=1}^{4} u_{+\alpha}^{(r)*}(\mathbf{p})u_{+\alpha}^{(s)}(\mathbf{p}) = \delta_{rs} \\ u_-^{(r)*}(\mathbf{p})u_-^{(s)}(\mathbf{p}) &= \sum_{\alpha=1}^{4} u_{-\alpha}^{(r)*}(\mathbf{p})u_{-\alpha}^{(s)}(\mathbf{p}) = \delta_{rs} \end{aligned} \right\} r, s = 1, 2 \qquad (202\mathrm{a})$$

Other relations satisfied by the u's are

$$\sum_{r=1,2} [u_{+\alpha}^{(r)*}(\mathbf{p})u_{+\beta}^{(r)}(\mathbf{p}) + u_{-\alpha}^{(r)*}(\mathbf{p})u_{-\beta}^{(r)}(\mathbf{p})] = \delta_{\alpha\beta}; \qquad \alpha, \beta = 1 \text{ to } 4 \qquad (202\mathrm{b})$$

$$\sum_{\alpha=1}^{4} u_{+\alpha}^{(r)*}(\mathbf{p})u_{-\alpha}^{(s)}(\mathbf{p}) = 0$$

(202c)

and

$$\sum_{r=1,2} \bar{u}_{+\alpha}^{(r)}(\mathbf{p})u_{+\beta}^{(r)}(\mathbf{p}) = -\frac{1}{2E}(i\gamma p - m)_{\beta\alpha}$$

(203a)

$$\sum_{r=1,2} \bar{u}_{-\alpha}^{(r)}(-\mathbf{p})u_{-\beta}^{(r)}(-\mathbf{p}) = -\frac{1}{2E}(i\gamma p + m)_{\beta\alpha}$$

(203b)

We note that in the nonrelativistic limit the components u_2 of a positive energy solution are of order v/c compared to u_1 and therefore are referred to as small components.

Projection Operators

In the calculation of transition probabilities, it is very often necessary to sum over intermediate spin states corresponding to only positive energy or only negative energy. However, the completeness relation Eq. (202b) involves summation over both signs of energy. It is therefore necessary to introduce projection operators $\Lambda_{\pm}(\mathbf{p})$ which have the following properties:

$$\Lambda_{\pm}(\mathbf{p})u_{\pm}^{(r)}(\mathbf{p}) = u_{\pm}^{(r)}(\mathbf{p}) \tag{204a}$$

$$\Lambda_{\pm}(\mathbf{p})u_{\mp}^{(r)}(\mathbf{p}) = 0 \tag{204b}$$

$$\Lambda_{+} + \Lambda_{-} = 1, \qquad (\Lambda_{\pm})^2 = \Lambda_{\pm}, \qquad \Lambda_{+}\Lambda_{-} = 0 \tag{204c}$$

It is easy to see from Eqs. (204a) to (204c) that the projection operators are given by

$$\Lambda_{\pm}(\mathbf{p}) = \frac{|E| \pm H(\mathbf{p})}{2\,|E|} \tag{205a}$$

where

$$H(\mathbf{p}) = \boldsymbol{\alpha} \cdot \mathbf{p} + \beta m, \qquad H(\mathbf{p})u_{\pm}(\mathbf{p}) = \pm\,|E(\mathbf{p})|\,u_{\pm}(\mathbf{p}) \tag{205b}$$

We consider the evaluation of $\sum\limits_{r=1,2} u_{\pm\alpha}^{(r)}(\pm\mathbf{p})u_{\pm\beta}^{(r)*}(\pm\mathbf{p})$ which involves summation over spin states but only one sign of energy.

$$\sum_{r=1,2} u_{\pm\alpha}^{(r)}(\pm\mathbf{p})u_{\pm\beta}^{(r)*}(\pm\mathbf{p})$$

$$= \sum_{r=1,2} (\Lambda_{\pm}(\pm\mathbf{p}))_{\alpha\gamma}[u_{\pm\gamma}^{(r)}(\pm\mathbf{p})u_{\pm\beta}^{(r)*}(\pm\mathbf{p}) + u_{\mp\gamma}^{(r)}(\pm\mathbf{p})u_{\mp\beta}^{(r)*}(\pm\mathbf{p})]$$

$$= (\Lambda_{\pm}(\pm\mathbf{p}))_{\alpha\gamma}\delta_{\gamma\beta} \qquad \text{(from Eq. 202b)}$$

$$= (\Lambda_{\pm}(\pm\mathbf{p}))_{\alpha\beta} \tag{206a}$$

Similarly,

$$\sum_{r=1,2} u_{\pm\alpha}^{(r)}(\pm\mathbf{p})\bar{u}_{\pm\beta}^{(r)}(\pm\mathbf{p})$$

$$= \sum_{r=1,2} (\Lambda_{\pm}(\pm\mathbf{p}))_{\alpha\gamma}[u_{\pm\gamma}^{(r)}(\pm\mathbf{p})u_{\pm\delta}^{(r)*}(\pm\mathbf{p})(\gamma_4)_{\delta\beta} + u_{\mp\gamma}^{(r)}(\pm\mathbf{p})u_{\mp\delta}^{(r)*}(\pm\mathbf{p})(\gamma_4)_{\delta\beta}]$$

$$= (\Lambda_{\pm}(\pm\mathbf{p}))_{\alpha\gamma}\delta_{\gamma\delta}(\gamma_4)_{\delta\beta}$$

$$= (\Lambda_{\pm}(\pm\mathbf{p})\gamma_4)_{\alpha\beta} = \frac{(|E|\,\gamma_4 + \boldsymbol{\alpha}\cdot\mathbf{p}\gamma_4 \pm m)_{\alpha\beta}}{2\,|E|}$$

$$= \frac{(\pm m - i\gamma_\mu p_\mu)_{\alpha\beta}}{2\,|E|} \tag{206b}$$

which is the same as Eqs. (203a) and (203b).

References

1. Condon, E. U., and G. H. Shortley, *The Theory of Atomic Spectra*, Cambridge University Press, Cambridge, 1935.
2. Watson, G. N., *A Treatise on the Theory of Bessel Functions*, 2nd ed., Cambridge University Press, Cambridge, 1945.
3. Wigner, E. P., Gruppentheorie, Friedrich Vieweg and Sohn, Brunswick, 1931.
4. Racah, G., *Phys. Rev.* **62**, 438, 1942.

5. Wheeler, J. A., *Phys. Rev.* **52,** 1107, 1937.
6. Heisenberg, W., *Z. Physik* **120,** 573 and 673, 1943.
7. Schweber, S., *Introduction to Relativistic Quantum Field Theory*, p. 321, Harper and Row, New York, 1961.
8. Whittaker, E. T., and G. N. Watson, *A Course of Modern Analysis*, 4th ed., Cambridge University Press, Cambridge, 1927.
9. Gordon, W., *Z. Physik* **48,** 180, 1928.
10. Blatt, J. M., and L. C. Biedenharn, *Phys. Rev.* **86,** 399, 1952.
11. Hulthén, L., and M. Sugawara, in *Handbuch der Physik* Vol. 39, p. 1, Springer-Verlag, Berlin, 1957.
12. Rohrlich, F., and J. Eisenstein, *Phys. Rev.* **75,** 705, 1949.
13. Matsumoto, M., *Prog. Theor. Phys. Japan* **13,** 329, 1955.

Additional References

1. Schiff, L. I., *Quantum Mechanics*, 2nd ed., McGraw-Hill, New York, 1955.
2. Mott, N. F., and H. S. W. Massey, *The Theory of Atomic Collisions*, 2nd ed., Clarendon Press, Oxford, 1949.
3. Rose, M. E., *Elementary Theory of Angular Momentum*, John Wiley and Sons, New York, 1957.
4. Wu, T. Y., and T. Ohmura, *Quantum Theory of Scattering*, Prentice-Hall, Englewood Cliffs, N.J. 1962.
5. Morse, P. M., and H. Feshbach, *Methods of Theoretical Physics*, Parts I and II, McGraw-Hill, New York, 1953.

AUTHOR INDEX

591

SUBJECT INDEX

601

Magnetic moment, experimental values, 44
  g-factor (gyromagnetic ratio), 75
  neutrons, 50, 75
  nuclear, 2 f, 456
  protons, 50, 75
  shell model, 244
  single-particle model, 43 f, 244
  spin-flip of dipole, 459
  see also Multipole moments; Radiative transitions
Magnetic multipole moments, 41
Magnetization, density of, 39, 442, 452
Majorana force, 142, 144, 148
Majorana potential, 47
Many-body, dispersion formula, 363
  two-particle wave function, 327, 331
Many-body treatment of the nucleus, 320 ff
Many-particle shell model, *see* Individual particle model
Mass, atomic, 141, 156
  decrement, 159
  defect, 159, 457
  determinations, 157
  distribution in fission, 164
  residual, 159
  see also Binding energy
Mass formulas, *see* Semiempirical mass formulas
Mass spectroscopy, 158 f
Matrix element, *see* Brueckner model; Coefficient of fractional parentage; Collective model; Deuteron; Radiative transitions; Reactions
Matrix, *K*, *see* Reaction matrix
  reaction, *see* Reaction matrix
  scattering, *see* Scattering matrix
Matter, distribution of nuclear, 13
  nuclear, 3, 141, 321, 325
Maxwell's equations, 435, 442
Mean (common) potential, *see* Single-particle model
Mean life, 202
  see also Beta-decay, mean life
Mean square radius, 14, 16, 22, 26, 37, 233, 246
Meson, cloud, around nucleons, 461
  exchange, in nuclear forces, 112, 122
  μ, 2, 14, 533 f, 536
  μ-mesonic atoms, 14 ff
  π-, 2, 136
  other mesons in nuclear potentials, 136

Meson, production in nuclear collisions, 90
  theoretical potential, 134 ff
  virtual, 535
Mesonic current, 50, 76 f, 463
Mirror nuclei, 414
  energy levels of, 12 f
  and nuclear radii, 11
Mirror reactions, 414
Mixing of states, *see* Configuration mixing; Deuteron
Mixing ratio, 8, 276
Models of the nucleus, *see* Individual (independent) particle model; Liquid drop model; Optical model; Single-particle model; Statistical model; Unified (collective) model
Moment of inertia, 264
Mott scattering, 21
Multipole expansion, 434
  alternative procedure, 438
Multipole moments, approximate expressions for electric, 446
  electromagnetic interactions with nuclei, 445
  induced electric, 446
  static electric, 446
  static magnetic, 446
Multipole moment operator, 271
Multipole radiation, 243
  angular correlation, γ-γ, 480, 490
  angular distribution of, 440, 448 ff, 483 f, 494
  approximate expressions, 446
  density matrix, 485
  magnetic dipole spin-flip transition, 459, 469
  monopole radiation, vanishing of, 441
  near zone, 446
  parity of, 440, 450
  polarization of, 448, 487
  selection rules for, 450 f, 453
  sources of, 442 ff
  transition probability, 460, 482, γ-decay, 243 f, 451 ff, 456, 486 f
  wave zone, 447
  see also Radiative transitions
Muon, *see* Meson, μ

Near Zone, multipole radiation in the, 446 f